Mental Retardation

Modern Applications in Psychology

under the editorship of

Joseph D. Matarazzo   Judson S. Brown
UNIVERSITY OF OREGON MEDICAL SCHOOL   UNIVERSITY OF IOWA

Mental Retardation

APPRAISAL, EDUCATION, AND REHABILITATION

edited by

ALFRED A. BAUMEISTER
UNIVERSITY OF ALABAMA

ALDINE PUBLISHING COMPANY / *Chicago*

First published 1967 by
ALDINE Publishing Company
529 South Wabash
Chicago, Illinois 60605

Fourth Printing 1971

Library of Congress Catalog Card Number 66-23158
Designed by Bernard Schleifer
Printed in the United States of America

Preface

DIAGNOSIS of mental retardation has often been confused with prognostic implications. Many people, both professionals and laymen, still believe that it is impossible to produce significant changes in the behavior of the retarded. Many still assume that a diagnosis of retardation invariably implies a prognosis of no improvement, of despair. Thus, when distinct and desirable changes occur in the behavior of a retarded person, it is often concluded that the diagnosis was wrong, that the person was not really retarded in the first place.

This viewpoint, although still prevalent, has been seriously questioned. A renewed and reasoned optimism, founded on scientific and political progress, seems to be emerging. Significant advances have been made in our understanding of the behavioral and biological correlates of mental retardation. In addition to these dramatic accomplishments, basic data are rapidly accumulating showing that appropriate adaptive behaviors can be "shaped" in retarded individuals, including those heretofore regarded as "subtrainable." The increasingly widespread public concern for the social and economic consequences of retardation is reflected in the substantial government appropriations that support research and service activities.

This book grows out of the optimistic view that mental retardation can be treated. It views treatment broadly. While the concept of treatment is usually interpreted in a strictly medical sense, this book is based upon the premise that mental retardation is primarily a behavior problem. It recognizes a child is not diagnosed as retarded simply because he has, say, a chromosomal anomaly, but rather because he behaves in certain maladaptive ways. We view any intervention that is intended to produce adaptive changes in the behavior of the retarded as "treatment." While the emphasis of this book is on behavior, the book is not a psychology text. Its authors come from the fields of medicine, special education, and speech and hearing, as well as from psychology.

The purpose of this book is to help students and workers in the field apply research findings and theoretical formulations to the appraisal and treatment of mental retardation. The primary emphasis of the book is empirical. Discussion of diagnosis and treatment has been couched too frequently in authoritarian terms that have never been put to empirical tests. While many of the suggestions made in this book have not been subjected to rigorous experimental scrutiny, almost all have been derived from a close examination of the research literature. Our view is that such empirically based hypotheses are superior to unbolstered assertions of "authorities."

In preparing this book, we have assumed the reader already has a general acquaintance with the field of mental retardation. Our goal has been to identify and deal with several critical problem areas in a way that will be helpful to those who work with the retarded. Frankly, our interest is in ameliorating the condition of the mental retardate. This book will not likely excite the purist. We have forgone extensive, critical reviews of the literature and emphasized the practical implications of research. We have tried to offer the student an optimistic glimpse of a field in which a technology is rapidly developing from research—a field he may enter convinced that he will be more than a passive observer and custodian of nature's errors. Finally, we have suggested to the researcher some gaps in the current status of information in this field.

A wide diversity of topics has been included in this volume. Two criteria were followed for including a particular topic: (a) the relevance of the topic to the understanding and modification of defective behavior: (b) the subject's popularity or neglect in other sources. Some chapters are considerably longer because more data are available in some areas, some topics are more general, and authors whose subjects had not been recently or adequately reviewed elsewhere were encouraged to develop them fully.

Alfred A. Baumeister

Contents

Mental Retardation

Definition, Diagnosis, and Classification 1

DAVID W. BRISON

WORKERS in the field of mental retardation have been unable to agree how mental retardation should be defined. The problem of definition is by no means superficial. Different definitions have reflected opposing theoretical views of etiology and prognosis, and these views have had definite implications for the management and education of the mentally retarded. The issue of whether irreversibility should be included in the definition of mental retardation reflects the importance of the definition.

Diagnosis is defined as (1) "identification of disease or abnormality from symptoms presented and from a study of its origin and course (2) any classification of an individual on the basis of observed characters" (English and English, 1958). In relation to diagnosis in mental retardation the accepted definition of mental retardation determines the nature of the disease or abnormality that is identified. One must also decide whether diagnosis of mental retardation should be based on origins and course or should emphasize classification of observed characters.

Classification is "the process of grouping objects into mutually exclusive classes, ranks, or categories; or the group so classified" (English and English, 1958). If the second definition of diagnosis is used with respect to mental retardation, diagnosis and classification are synonomous terms. This is the prevailing view of diagnosis in the field of mental retardation. However, in terms of their particular usage in the field, classification usually refers to the assignment of individuals to subgroups within the more inclusive group of mentally retarded individuals. Diagnosis is often reserved for the initial determination of whether an individual is mentally retarded.

The American Association of Mental Deficiency published in 1959 a detailed manual on terminology and classification in mental retardation (Heber, 1959). In many respects, this document coalesces divergent opinions on definition and subsequent diagnosis of mental retardation, although reaction to the manual has not indicated a universal acceptance. In this chapter, we will first review the manual's definition of mental retardation and then briefly consider its salient features in terms of their historical antecedents. This treatment of definition is not intended to be a detailed history of the use of terms and definitions. Reviews of this nature are available elsewhere (Clarke and Clarke, 1958; Robinson and Robinson, 1965; Sarason, 1959). The aim of the first part of this chapter is to acquaint the reader with the currently acceptable definition of mental retardation. The remainder of the chapter discusses the uses and abuses of diagnosis and classification in the field of mental retardation.

DEFINITION

The basic definition of mental retardation adopted by the American Association on Mental Deficiency in May, 1960, is:

Mental retardation refers to sub-average general intellectual functioning which originated during the developmental period and is associated with impairment in adaptive behavior. (Heber, 1961)

The subaverage general intellectual functioning group includes all individuals whose performance on suitable objective tests of general intellectual ability is more than one standard deviation below the population mean. The upper limit of the developmental period is considered to be at approximately sixteen years.

Adaptive behavior is manifested in three principal manners: (1) maturation, (2) learning, and (3) social adjustment. Each of these three factors assumes primary importance during a certain stage of the developmental period. Thus, maturation, which refers to the rate of development of sensory motor skills such as sitting, walking, talking, is the important criterion of adaptive behavior during the pre-school years. Learning, defined as ability to acquire academic skills, is important during the school-age years. Social adjustment assumes primary importance on the adult level. The principal indicators of social adjustment at the adult level are:

the degree to which the individual is able to maintain himself independently in the community and in gainful employment as well as by his ability to meet and to conform to other personal and social responsibilities and standards set by the community. (Heber, 1959, p. 4)

The quality of interpersonal relationships is an important manifestation of adaptive behavior during the pre-school and school periods. However, social adjustment is considered the primary criterion of adaptive behavior only at the adult level.

SALIENT FEATURES OF THE DEFINITION

Perhaps the most important characteristic of this definition is the emphasis on the co-existence of deficits in both adaptive behavior and general intellectual functioning. Historically, reliance has shifted between measured intelligence and adaptive behavior as the basis for determining mental retardation. In one sense the principal indicator of mental retardation is still subaverage intellectual functioning. If an individual is subaverage in general intellectual ability but not impaired in adaptive behavior, the assumption is that his adaptive behavior reflects a higher level of intelligence and casts doubt on tests of the individual's intellectual functioning. If the individual does not demonstrate subaverage gen-

eral intellectual ability but is impaired in adaptive behavior, the assumption is factors other than intellectual ability are responsible for his adaptive impairment. In effect, this definition provides a double check on impaired intellectual functioning.

Another important feature of the definition is its exclusion of both the cause and probable course of the behavioral disorder. The emphasis is on symptoms, not on etiology or prognosis—the diagnostician, at least in theory, relies neither on case history nor his best predictions of the eventual outcome when he decides if an individual is classified in the broad category of the mentally retarded.[1] The diagnosis of mental retardation does not imply the retarded person will always be incapable of either average intellectual functioning or unimpaired adaptive behavior. In other words, the condition is not defined as irreversible.

The establishment of minus-one standard deviation as the point indicating subaverage intellectual performance means that 16 per cent of the total population could be classified as mentally retarded. However, since measured intelligence has to be considered in conjunction with impaired adaptive behavior, the total percentage of the population diagnosed as retarded would never actually reach sixteen per cent. But the percentage is higher than in most other classification systems that have stipulated intelligence quotients for the diagnosis of mental retardation (Gelof, 1963). This attempt to raise the IQ level for indicating suspected retardation has been questioned by some critics (Blatt, 1961; Garfield, 1960).

THE DEFINITION IN HISTORICAL PERSPECTIVE

To appreciate fully the AAMD definition of mental retardation, one must contrast it with its historical antecedents. The important aspects of the definition are: coexistence of subaverage intellectual functioning and impaired adaptive behavior, emphasis on present behavior rather than etiology, and the absence of statements implying mental retardation is irreversible.

1. It is sometimes necessary to rely on the subject's history to determine if the retardation originated during the developmental period. This is only true in those cases where adults are being diagnosed.

Some authorities used to employ the intelligence quotient as the sole criterion of mental retardation. Others relied on adaptive behavior, which has been more broadly defined as social competence. Though Doll (1941) proposed that both social adjustment and mental subnormality be present in what he termed mental deficiency, his criteria included statements about both etiology and prognosis. In this respect, he differed from the present most widely accepted definition of mental retardation.

IQ AS THE SOLE CRITERION OF MENTAL RETARDATION

In 1904 Binet was commissioned by the French Ministry of Public Instruction to devise methods to differentiate between school children who could profit from public school instruction and those who needed special instruction. He published with Simon his first intelligence scale in 1905, revising it in 1908 and 1911. Since that early date, Binet scales and their subsequent revisions and adaptions in both the United States and England have been used periodically by psychologists as the sole criterion for mental retardation. As Clarke and Clarke (1958) and Gelof (1963) point out, different classification systems have established varying intelligence levels as cutoff points for the mentally retarded. Terman's commonly used system classified those who scored below 70 IQ on the Terman revision of the Binet as definitely retarded.

Criticisms of measured intelligence as the sole criterion of mental retardation are:

1. The intelligence test may not give an adequate sample of those problem solving tasks involved in some areas of social competence (Sarason, 1959). Therefore, social competence does not always correspond to the level of measured intelligence (Clarke and Clarke, 1958).

2. Intelligence test scores, though relatively constant, show some fluctuation. This criticism was important for those who thought mental retardation was irreversible. If the condition was defined as irreversible, then IQ, which varied, could not be used as the sole diagnostic criterion.

3. Low scores on intelligence tests can result from such various causes as sensory deprivation, injury to the central nervous system, and emotional problems. Depending on which factor is involved, the prognosis will be different.

Recent research has repudiated IQ as the sole criterion of mental retardation primarily because measured intelligence does not always correspond to social competence or adaptive behavior. Other criticisms are based on the assumption that mental retardation is irreversible or that different causes lead to a different prognosis.

SOCIAL COMPETENCE AS THE SOLE CRITERION

Tredgold (1952) was the chief advocate of using social competency as the sole diagnostic criterion of mental deficiency. His views have had definite impact, particularly in England. He rejected educational and intellectual measures as criteria of arrested mental development and maintained that the inability to adapt to the environment, to live independently, was the best criterion. As Clarke and Clarke (1958) point out, Tredgold realized the failure to maintain independent existence might be due to political and social reasons, rather than psychological causes. He states that such failure must be due to psychological reasons to constitute a mental defect. "He does not, however, give any indication of the criteria to be employed in coming to such a distinction" (Clarke and Clarke, 1958).

The failure to maintain an independent existence could have several causes: (1) inability to delay immediate gratification, (2) failure to accept moral standards, or (3) learned patterns of deviant behavior. In these instances, subaverage intelligence may or may not be the cause of an individual's inability to adapt. Therefore, one needs some means to ascertain whether subaverage intelligence is involved in social incompetence. The dual reliance on measured intelligence and adaptive behavior is an obvious solution.

DEFINITION OF MENTAL DEFICIENCY

E. A. Doll (1941) proposed what he thought were the essentials of an inclusive definition of mental retardation. In many respects this article was a reaction to the notion of measured intelligence as the only criterion of mental deficiency. He pointed out that intelligence tests are an unreliable measure of a maturing subject and that persons who score low in one test may do better on another. He also drew attention to the predominance of verbal tests in intelligence measures. His conclusion was that the degree of social competence was better than measured intelligence—as a single criterion of mental deficiency.

Doll did not, however, mean that a single criterion should be employed. He listed six criteria of an inclusive concept of mental retardation:

1. Social incompetence, designed as "inherent incapacity for managing themselves independently beyond the marginal level of subsistence." Doll attempted to measure this capacity by use of the Vineland Social Maturity Scale, which he developed.

2. Mental subnormality, referring primarily to measured intelligence. Doll expressed doubts about this criterion but indicated he thought its use in conjunction with social incompetence was justified.

3. Developmental arrested mental subnormality, as distinguished from deterioration caused by mental illness or epilepsy.

4. Constitutional origin, either transmitted genetically or acquired through injury or disease.

5. Obtains at maturity, as opposed to a problem that could be outgrown.

6. Essentially incurable, a point on which Doll is rather explicit.

He says:

The condition is essentially incurable through treatment and unremediable through training except as treatment and training instill habits which superficially or temporarily compensate for the limitations of the person so affected while under favorable circumstances and for more or less limited periods of time. (Doll, 1941, p. 217)

In summary, Doll stated that both social incompetence and subaverage intelligence should be used as diagnostic criteria for mental deficiency. Doll's definition differs from the AAMD definition in two major respects: (1) the insistence on constitutional origin, with diagnosis thus based on other than present symptoms and; (2) his position that true mental deficiency is essentially incurable and therefore prevails at maturity. (In other words, from his analysis of the origin of the disorder, Doll made definite statements about probable outcomes. The diagnosis itself was based on other than present symptoms.)

Doll's underlying assumption is that there is a direct relationship between a cause of constitutional origin and present observed behavior. Furthermore, he said this direct relationship will continue in the future life of an individual despite education. A corollary of this assumption is that it is possible to discover a cause from inferences about present behavior or reconstruction of an individual's history.

Doll (1947) maintained there was a distinction between mental deficiency (synonymous with feeblemindedness) and intellectual retardation. Intellectual retardation was not of constitutional origin and eventual social competence was possible. In 1962 E. E. Doll indicated acceptance of the AAMD inclusive definition of mental retardation, but insisted that mental deficiency is a specific type of mental retardation that is, "(1) developmentally manifest, (2) based upon structural defect, and (3) such as to render the individual socially incompetent. Such deficient retardation, being caused by inferiority or maldevelopment of the central nervous system, is irreversible" (Doll, 1962, p. 22).

Sarason (1959) also distinguished between mental deficiency and mental retardation. The mentally retarded are without central nervous system pathology, he said, and their retardation is mainly a reflection of cultural factors rather than an indication of lowered intellectual potential. Mental deficiency is characterized by constitutional abnormalities and is considered irreversible, he concluded.

The AAMD manual did not make this distinction between mental retardation and mental deficiency. The difference between these terms is one of cause, and cause or origin is not taken into account in the definition, as previously noted. Proponents of such a distinction assume that if two individuals show the same patterns of symptoms but have different etiology, the prognosis will be different. Further, they say individuals with structural central nervous system defects (either acquired or inherited) have an irreversible condition, while those with other causes (for example, cultural) have a higher intellectual potential. Obviously, the AAMD committee did not think these assumptions were warranted at the time it published its manual on terminology and classification (Heber, 1959).

DIAGNOSIS AND CLASSIFICATION

In the introduction, two definitions of diagnosis were given. The first was identification of an abnormality on the basis of present symptoms, origin, and course. The second stressed classification from observed characters. Mental retardation has been defined so as to make identification independent of origin and course. Diagnosis therefore must mean classification from observed symptoms.

Though classification and diagnosis are often regarded as synonymous terms, they are used somewhat differently in this article. Diagnosis refers to the classification of individuals as belonging to the broad group of the mentally retarded. Classification is the process of assigning the mentally retarded individuals into subgroups.

ASSUMPTIONS UNDERLYING THE EMPHASIS ON CAUSE IN DIAGNOSIS

A curious parallel exists between the development of diagnosis of mental retardation and psychiatric diagnosis of general mental disorder such as neurosis and psychosis. In both cases emphasis was placed on present behavior versus origin and course. This parallel existed because authorities in both fields made the same assumption about the relationship between genotype "the constellation of genes that an organism receives from its progenitors" (Hunt, 1961), and the phenotype, the observed characteristics of an organism at any point in time. They believed that certain observed behaviors (phenotype) were predetermined by the genotype in an unchanging pattern. A uniform relationship also was assumed to exist between any injury to the central nervous system and observable behavior.

Once this assumption about the direct relationship between cause and effect was made, the general diagnostic strategy in both fields was to find symptoms associated with inherited causes. Then the job was easy because one knew what the outcome had to be. If subsequent observation of the disorder's course did not bear out one's prognosis, then one must have been mistaken about the cause.

Kraepelin illustrates how this process developed. Kraepelin intended to establish a detailed description of the symptoms of his psychiatric patients. Because of his assumptions about cause and effect in behavioral disorders, he thought he ought to be able to correlate certain patterns of symptoms with certain types of causes. The description of present behavior was really only a short cut to the discovery of the etiology. Once this relationship was established, then prediction was guaranteed. Zigler and Phillips (1961) point out that Kraepelin refused to accept the diagnosis of dementia praecox if the patients subsequently recovered because he had already determined that the pattern of dementia praecox symptoms was caused by a neurophysiological disturbance. Behavioral disorders caused by this type of disturbance were irreversible—therefore if the patient recovered the diagnostician must have made a faulty diagnosis in the first place.

In mental retardation, diagnosis has followed a similar pattern. Doll (1941) made the same assumption about the relationship between an inherited cause and the phenotype. The outstanding characteristic of this relationship was irreversibility. Where a diagnosis of mental deficiency was established and the condition showed improvement over time, the term pseudo-feeblemindedness has been employed. The concept of pseudo-feeblemindedness has been debated at length in the literature on mental retardation (Cantor, 1955; Cassel, 1949; Clarke, 1958; Windle, 1962). Much of the confusion about this concept reflects the unwarranted assumption that symptoms equal cause and cause equals outcome.

Other parallel trends have developed in diagnosis of mental retardation and psychiatric disorders. In both fields, diagnosis has been the responsibility of a supposedly skilled, experienced practitioner who subjectively and intuitively combines all the available data into the eventual diagnosis. Many statements have appeared in the literature about the fallibility of objective measures, such as test scores, for diagnostic purposes. This trend has culminated in recent reactions against this type of clinical diagnosis (Meehl, 1954). However, psychiatric diagnosis has also received a tremendous amount of criticism (Bandura and Walters, 1963).

ASSUMPTIONS UNDERLYING THE PRESENT
CONCEPTION OF DIAGNOSIS AND
CLASSIFICATION

The doctrine of predetermination has been largely discredited. Hunt (1961), in his book dealing with the effects of experience on intelligence, concludes that the phenotype of intelligence is a result of the interaction between the genotype and the environment. Ausubel (1958) presents an excellent discussion on the history of predeterminism in child development, outlining reasons for the strength of the doctrine and tracing its diminishing influence. Behavior is certainly determined by many factors, and attempts to ascribe behavior to any single cause are in almost all instances futile.

The trend toward recognition of multidetermination in behavioral disorders has had a similar impact on diagnosis of both mental retardation and psychiatric disorder. Both fields have been dominated in the past by a concept of diagnosis derived from the medical-disease model. Eysenck (1961) has explicitly formulated the distinction between diagnosis based on the medical-disease model and diagnosis more applicable to behavioral disorders. The primary difference is the absence of a single cause in the latter. Although Eysenck's remarks refer to abnormal psychology, the analysis also pertains to mental retardation because both are behavioral disorders caused by multiple factors.

In medical practice, "diagnosis may be made on the basis of either the noxious agent which is designated the 'cause' of the disease, or on the basis of the syndrome which is typical of the disease . . ." (Eysenck, 1961; p. 1). In the latter case, the assumption is that a cause can be accurately inferred from a pattern of symptoms.

In the diagnosis of behavioral disorders, the picture is far more complicated. Some diseases with a demonstrable physical cause have definite behavioral concomitants. General paresis and phenylketonuria (a condition caused by a single gene abnormality resulting in an enzyme deficiency that prevents conversion of the amino acid phenylalanine into tyrosine vital for brain functioning) are examples of behavioral disorders that are primarily medical. However, both inherited and environmental factors contribute to most forms of retardation.

The distinction between a disease (and therefore a medical problem) and behavioral disorders seems acceptable. However, there are instances where a demonstrable medical disease is caused by both psychological and physical factors. As Ausubel (1961) points out, a man may have a heart attack due to a coronary failure that was caused by overeating. Although the ultimate intellectual level of an individual afflicted with phenylketonuria is relatively fixed, differences in the interaction between afflicted individuals and their environments may lead to marked variations in intelligence levels.

The acceptance of multidetermination by almost all workers in the mental retardation field has brought about a new view of diagnosis. No longer do psychologists think classification of present symptoms will result in short cuts to statements about etiology. Instead, the emphasis is on accurate description of behavioral characteristics as a first step. Then the symptoms are classified into groups that in turn are compared with empirically established correlates. Theoretically, the diagnostician can make probability statements about cause, educability, and other existing correlates based on how an individual's symptoms fit into classification.

An infinite number of ways exist for classifying the behavioral symptoms of mentally retarded individuals. As Cantor (1955) points out, such individuals can be grouped based on how far they can throw a baseball or some other seemingly trivial characteristics. Knowing which systems of classification will correlate with meaningful outside criteria is essential.

Diagnosis and classification can be used for two different general reasons. The data derived from classification can be used as one of the first steps in scientific investigation. Basic science generalizations are formulated on hypotheses derived from these data. These generalizations usually do not have any immediate practical application to problems in an area such as mental retardation. The other general use of classification is of direct practical benefit. For instance, existing classifications can be correlated with such socially useful criteria as probable success in school, length of institutionalization, or success in sheltered work programs. The result of such investigation is purely correlational. The nature of the relationship can be studied only by careful scientific manipulation of existing variables. Therefore, if classification is going to be used for basic science purposes, it must go beyond simple correlation.

In summary, diagnosis in the field of mental retardation has been until recently under the influence of unwarranted assumptions about the genotype-phenotype relationship. Psychologists have regarded classification of present symptoms as a short cut to a system based on etiology and have prematurely replaced an accurate description of retarded behavior with statements about causation. Many workers in the field now prefer the notion of multiple causation. The first step is accurate description of behavior, then reliable classification into subgroups followed by the correlation of factors such as cause and prognosis with the classification. The diagnostician theoretically is in a position to make probability statements concerning prognosis or etiology when he can classify an individual into an existing classification. The goal of this method is the determination of the individual's social usefulness. Since the nature of the relationship between criteria and classification is not known, application of the correlation is limited.

THE PROBLEM OF PSEUDO-FEEBLEMINDEDNESS

Psuedo-feeblemindedness is a term that sometimes has been applied in cases of individuals who have been diagnosed as feebleminded but ultimately improve. Since Doll (1941) insisted incurability was a characteristic of feeblemindedness, someone who was cured could not have been truly feebleminded in the first place. As has been pointed out, the notion of incurability was based on an unwarranted genotype-phenotype distinction (Papageorgis, 1963).

Pseudo-feeblemindedness clearly illustrates the distinction between the earlier and the more recent methods of diagnosis and classification in mental retardation. This concept has received much attention in the literature (Cassel, 1949; Clarke and Clarke, 1955; Cantor, 1955; Papageorgis, 1963; Windle, 1962).

Nowadays, incurability is not a criterion of mental retardation but can only exist as a probability in a given instance. The idea of incurability as a criterion obviously is untenable because it is based on the disease model of mental retardation, which ignores effects of interaction between the genotype and the environment. Cantor (1955) states that psuedo-feeblemindedness can be reliably defined utilizing the criterion of incurability but that this definition has limited practical reliability because it is always a post tem diagnosis and is therefore not useful in making predictions.

Cassel (1949) and Clarke and Clarke (1955) suggest the term "pseudo-feeblemindedness" be applied when the reason for the apparent reversal of behavior is an incorrect initial evaluation by the examiner. Differentiating between the cases where false conclusions were made and those where the change resulted from environmental conditions after diagnosis is difficult. Nevertheless, the notion of irreversibility is not involved in either case.

THE AAMD CLASSIFICATION SYSTEMS

Two separate classification systems are presented in the AAMD manual—a medical classification based on etiological rules and the behavioral classification. Under the former system, mental retardation "is regarded as a manifestation of some underlying disease process or medical condition" (Heber, 1959). The behavioral system classifies on the bases of measured intelligence and adaptive behavior and is an extension of the manual's definition of mental retardation. This classification is not based on etiology but on observed characteristics of present behavior.

Eysenck's (1961) distinction between medical and behavioral disorders in general psychiatric diagnosis is evident in the organization of the AAMD manual. Some types of mental retardation are clearly medical in that they are caused by demonstrable physical conditions, for example, phenylketonuria or general paresis. Moreover the degree of mental retardation, as evidenced by measured intelligence and adaptive behavior, is not due to a single causal factor (although the upper limits of intelligence are undoubtedly fixed) but to the interaction of multiple factors. A reliable etiological classification system is of value only if it enables the investigator to do something about the cause and "cure" the retardation, or if to make accurate probability statements about prognosis.

In medical classification of mental retardation, the cause can be arrived at by detection of the noxious agent or from symptoms and syndromes typical of the disease. An example of the first method would be identification of genetic abnormalities in mongolism. Diagnosis of hydrocephalus is an example of inference of cause from the afflicted individual's symptoms. As has been seen, the inference of etiology from present symptoms of behavioral retardation usually is difficult because of the absence of a single cause. In these instances, etiology exists only as a correlate of a classification and does not enable the diagnostician to make very accurate statements about prognosis.

Historically, one of the errors in diagnosis of mental retardation was that etiology was assumed to be a correlate of certain classifications before it was established as such. As a result, efforts to carefully describe present behavior and then classify into syndromes have been abandoned too quickly. To prevent repeating this error, etiology should only supplement behavioral classification when the cause can be definitely ascertained from present behavior. Even then etiological classification can only supplement behavioral classification not replace it because the level of retardation is still due to multiple causes.

In the AAMD classification system, etiological and behavioral classification do supplement each other. There do seem to be instances in the etiological classification where the cause is inferred prematurely. The error seems to be in regarding mental retardation as a disease in cases where it is most adequately described as a behavioral disorder.

Medical Classification Based on Etiological Groupings. The following is a simplified outline of the medical classification from the AAMD manual. Examples are given for each main category.

I. Mental retardation associated with diseases and conditions due to infection: for example, rubella contracted during the first trimester of pregnancy resulting in mental defect.

II. Mental retardation associated with diseases and conditions due to intoxication for example, cerebral pathology caused by maternal intoxications such as carbon monoxide, lead, arsenic, or ergot poisoning.

III. Mental retardation associated with dis-

eases and conditions due to trauma or physical agent; for example, brain injury at birth caused by difficulty of labor, postnatal brain injury.

IV. Mental retardation associated with diseases and conditions due to disorder of metabolism, growth, or nutrition: for example, phenylketonuria, galactosemia, a congenital disorder of carbohydrate metabolism that results in an accumulation of galactose in the bloodstream.

V. Mental retardation associated with diseases and conditions due to new growths: for example, "tuberous sclerosis, a disease transmitted by a dominant gene with reduced penetrance, characterized by multiple gliotic nodules irregularly disposed through the cerebrum and central nervous system."

VI. Mental retardation associated with diseases and condition due to unknown prenatal influence. The distinguishing feature is that the condition although of unknown origin was present at birth.

VII. Mental retardation associated with diseases and condition due to unknown or uncertain cause with the structural reaction manifest. Similar to Category VI but the temporal conditions are not limited to the prenatal period.

VIII. Mental retardation due to uncertain (or presumed psychologic) cause with the functional reaction alone manifest: for example, cultural-familial mental retardation represented by absence of organic disease or pathology and evidence of retarded intellectual functioning in one parent or at least one sibling. Retardation caused by emotional disturbance, environmental deprivation, or psychotic disorders are also included in this category.

In addition to the main categories outlined above, there are six supplementary categories: (1) genetic compliment, (2) secondary cranial anomaly, (3) impairment of special senses, (4) convulsive disorder, (5) psychiatric impairment, and (6) motor impairment.

Each of the supplementary listings represents a descriptive statement of the patient's level of functioning. For example, within subcategory 3, an individual could be described as having no sensory impairment or as having a localized impairment such as blindness, deafness, etc.

In the main categories I-VII, the physician presumably can establish that there is actual disease or pathology of the brain which in turn results in mental retardation. The pathology is the mechanism through which the retardation is expressed behaviorally (Heber, 1962). Actual pathology is established through (1) behavioral symptoms, (2) direct observation of brain lesions from techniques such as pneumoencephalogram or indirect observation such as the electro-encephalograph, (3) patterns of present physical symptoms such as abnormal size and shape of skull, and pigmentation of skin, hair color, etc.

The cause of the pathology or disease is often difficult to establish. The diagnostician depends on (1) developmental history recounted by someone closely involved with the patient or gleaned from available hospital records, (2) patterns of present symptoms, physical or behavioral, or (3) direct observation of a presently operative causal mechanism such as phenylalanine in the blood in the case of phenylketonuria.

The existence of pathology and its presumed cause often are recognized by inferences from the retarded individual's characteristics or behavioral symptoms. The behavior from which pathology is inferred should be carefully described and the correlation empirically established. If both these criteria are not met the result is often that an individual is described as having brain pathology when neither the pathology or the cause has been definitely ascertained. Since a physician's diagnosis usually is not challenged, his classification generally is accepted, and the behavior on which this diagnosis was based is dismissed.

Category VIII is used only after exhaustive medical examination has eliminated the possibility of organic disease or pathology. The distinction between the cultural familial, environmental, emotional disturbance, and psychiatric (or major personality) subgroups is made on the basis of inferences from present behavior. Psychological causes are assumed because they are all that is left after organic disease or pathology has been eliminated. The problem of choosing the appropriate subgroup is one of differential diagnosis. This type of diagnosis, based as it is on inferences from present behavior, runs the same risk as outlined above in reference to diagnosis of pathology and its cause from present behavioral symptoms.

Mental retardation in category VIII is be-

havioral as distinguished from medical. Including category VIII in the etiological or medical classification seems of dubious value because: (1) etiology, in most cases of psychogenic factors, has not yet been established empirically as a correlate of behavioral symptoms, and (2) knowledge of cause is of only limited assistance in prognosis because of multiple determinants of behavior. The present inclusion of this category contributes only to confusion and lends support to premature and unwarranted judgments about psychogenic causality.

Behavioral Classification. Since the behavioral classification system is a direct amplification of the AAMD definition of mental retardation, the discussion does not have to be as extensive. The emphasis is on deficits in both measured intelligence and adaptive behavior. Subgroups in both dimensions are based on degrees of deviation from a population mean expressed in standard deviation units.

Intellectual performance is estimated by an evaluation of current intellectual functioning on standardized individual intelligence tests. The choice of the appropriate test is left to the diagnostician. In cases of conflicting test results, the psychologist determines the weight to be assigned each test. The child should be compared to a sample drawn from a population of children his own age. This recommendation was occasioned by the fluctuating standard deviations at various age levels on the 1939 revision of the Stanford-Binet. However, it is no longer applicable to the 1960 Stanford-Binet, which utilizes a deviation intelligence quotient.

The following table summarizes the levels of measured intelligence. Descriptions of the intellectual retardation are included with corresponding IQs for the two most widely used individual intelligence tests: the 1960 revision of the Stanford-Binet and the Wechsler scales of intelligence (Heber, 1961).

The classification of adaptive behavior is more complex than measured intelligence because of the former's lack of objective measures. The level of retardation in adaptive behavior is also expressed in standard deviation units accompanied by descriptions.

The Vineland Social Maturity Scale—supplemented where necessary by portions of the Gesell Developmental Schedules, the Cattell Infant Intelligence Scale, and the Kuhlmann

TABLE I. Levels of Measured Intelligence

Word description of retardation in measured intelligence	Level of deviation in measured intelligence	Range in Standard Deviation Value	Corresponding IQ range for	
			Stanford–Binet SD-16	Wechsler SD-15
borderline	−1	−1.01 to −2.00	68-83	70-84
mild	−2	−2.01 to −3.00	52-67	55-69
moderate	−3	−3.01 to −4.00	36-51	40-54
severe	−4	−4.01 to −5.00	20-35	25-39
profound	−5	−5.00	below 20	below 25

TABLE II. Levels of Retardation in
Adaptive Behavior

Mild	−1
Moderate	−2
Severe	−3
Profound	−4

Tests of Mental Development—is recommended for use at the pre-school level as a measure of adaptive behavior. During the school-age period, standardized achievement tests will be the primary measure, though the Vineland still will be used to differentiate between the lower levels of retardation. At the adolescent and adult level, adaptive behavior is best seen in social adjustment, but there are few instruments available that assess this behavior. Subsequently the level of social adjustment is determined by the diagnostician's assessment of the individual's social and vocational adjustment.

In addition to classification based on deficits in measured intelligence and adaptive behavior, the AAMD manual provides personal-social and sensory-motor behavioral categories. Heber (1959) provides the following justification for the inclusion of these categories:

An individual's total behavioral adaptation to the environment is influenced by intellectual personal-social and sensory-motor factors . . . impairments in personal-social and sensory-motor skills frequently are concomitants of mental retardation. When specific deficiencies with respect to these aspects of behavior are present they are important considerations in planning for education and habilitation and in prognosis. (p. 65)

Personal-social factors are divided into:
(a) impairment in interpersonal relations: an individual's dealings with peers or authority figures.

(b) impairment in cultural conformity: "behavior that does not conform to social mores, behavior that does not meet standards of dependability, reliability and trustworthiness; behavior that is persistently asocial, antisocial, and/or excessively hostile."

(c) impairment in responsiveness: inability to delay need gratification or to exhibit goal-directed behavior.

Sensory-motor factors are subgrouped into:
(a) impairment in motor skills—gross or fine motor co-ordination
(b) impairment in auditory skills
(c) impairment in visual skills
(d) impairment in speech skills
In the 1959 manual (Heber, 1959), each of the supplementary categories was placed into one of three levels on the basis of degree of deficiency. This method proved to be unworkable and was revised (Heber, 1961) so that the behavior in each category was rated as either impaired or not impaired.

CRITICISMS OF DIAGNOSIS AND CLASSIFICATION

Educators, clinical psychologists, and experimental psychologists have become increasingly critical of diagnosis and classification in mental retardation. In many instances, they have questioned the basic process of diagnosis and classification; in other cases the criticisms have been leveled against abuses of the systems. An analysis of criticisms is helpful at this point, particularly if the AAMD manual on classification can be shown to have remedied these difficulties.

NATURAL SCIENCE APPROACH

This approach to the study of mental retardation is derived from the work of Skinner (1953) in general behavioral psychology. Bijou and Baer (1961) have applied general natural science principles to the field of child development, and Bijou (1963) has also outlined the natural science approach to the study of mental retardation. Bijou's article (1963) is not an analysis of diagnosis and classification in mental retardation, but the general theoretical framework he advocated conflicts with the process of diagnosis and classification outlined in this chapter. Let us review Bijou's developmental theory as it related to mental retardation so that we can see the points of conflict.

Most definitions of mental retardation are behavioral descriptions of what is generally agreed to be unintelligent behavior. For instance, the AAMD definition (Heber, 1959) uses the descriptive categories of current intellectual functioning and adaptive behavior. The study of the causes of unintelligent behavior has, according to Bijou (1963), taken two forms. First, there is the tendency for general descriptive adjectives such as intelligent to become nouns such as intelligence (Skinner in Bijou, 1963). The next step is to attribute the failure to exhibit intelligent behavior to a lack of intelligence. Intelligence, the supposed causal factor, is a hypothetical construct inferred from present behavior. The other general approach has been to infer the existence of a hypothetical construct of intelligence from both present behavior and antecedent conditions. As an example, consider a group of 6-year-old children who are unable to learn in school. They are exhibiting unintelligent behavior. Investigation shows that they were subjected to prolonged periods of sensory deprivation in childhood. The conclusion is then that they have defective intelligence (a hypothetical construct) caused by a lack of sensory stimulation in infancy.

Bijou reacts against the inference of a hypothetical construct irrespective of how it is derived. A basic natural science approach is that only what can be observed is admissable as data. One cannot directly observe intelligence; it has to be inferred from intelligent behavior. Bijou thinks inferences of this type are not advantageous in the study of behavior.

The same argument against the use of traits in personality study has been advanced by the positivist school and has been attacked by Allport (1965).

Bijou states that one must establish functional relationships between observed behavior and the observed events (usually environmental) that have immediately preceded the behavior. In other words, in order to establish a causal relationship, one must show how an observed event produces or is related to observed behavior. To do this one needs to study the continuous interaction between an individual and his environment. Bijou (1963, p. 101) defines a retarded individual as "one who has a limited repertoire of behavior evolving from interactions of the individual with his environmental contacts which constitute his history." He then suggests the limited repertoire is a result of such factors as intermittent reinforcement and extinction, inadequate reinforcement histories, and severe punishment.

Bijou reacts negatively to inferences of hypothetical intellective constructs for three additional reasons. First, emphasis on the hypothetical construct implies that something basically unobservable inside the organism is fundamentally important. This discourages the detailed search "for observable physical and social events that might play a role in retarding psychological growth, especially in the very early phases" (Bijou, 1963, p. 98). Second, interest usually focuses on interactions between intervening variables, and the conditions that might limit behavior are not described. Third, the classes of variables usually looked for as antecedents (congenital, environmental, exogenous, endogenous) are not adequate for predictive purposes because behavior is the result of many causes.

The first step in classification, as described here, is to create accurate and reliable classes. Next, one must find correlates of the existing classes, and once established empirically, these become part of the system. The natural science approach advocated by Bijou differs from this system of classification mainly in the kinds of correlates that have been sought. In general, the traditional (non-natural science) school has not attempted to look for the observable environmental conditions that have influenced behavior. In addition, it has had a tendency to treat intelligence as a hypothetical construct and to search for antecedents of this construct.

The manner in which classification has been used to study mental retardation is not necessarily a product of the process of classification itself. For instance, Bijou maintains that it is behavior which is retarded and looks for correlates of this retarded behavior. The correlates, however, have to be observable events that demonstrably limit or control behavior. After observing correlates, he then attempts to classify antecedent events in classes such as intermittent reinforcement factors, or consequences of severe punishment, etc. Of course, the ultimate criterion of the validity of this system rests on how well its proponents are able to predict behavior and how accurately they can control behavior when they manipulate the environmental conditions.

Note that in the traditional (or non-natural science) system, a clinician can make probability statements about any individuals he classifies in a category. He might say that there is a certain chance that the individual has suffered brain injury and that, furthermore, the latter is unlikely to respond to formal educational methods. The behaviorist, after deciding that behavior is retarded, would have as a guide certain classes of events (intermittent reinforcement, inadequate reinforcement history, etc.) that he would assume to be limiting the individual's behavioral repertoire. Once the relationship is established, the clinician assumes that if he can change the conditions he can control behavior. No probability statements are applied to individual cases.

An evaluation of the two general schools is outside the scope of the present chapter. Those who advocate the use of hypothetical constructs say they are developing basic science generalizations about retarded behavior that will ultimately be of use in individual cases. They also maintain that certain hypothetical constructs such as intelligence have practical utility in individual cases. The behaviorists counter that unobservable entities will never form the basis for a scientific understanding of behavior, and that constructs that have to be inferred cannot be of use in individual cases.

FAILURE TO ESTABLISH PREDICTIVE VALIDITY

One of the most common criticisms of classification systems in mental retardation is that they do not provide the diagnostician with very accurate or helpful statements about the future level of functioning of an individual. If a diagnosis and classification system is to be useful for the worker in mental retardation, it must have predictive validity.

Windle (1962) in his discussion of prognosis in mental retardation concludes "patients with general familial or undifferentiated diagnosis are more likely to be released from institutions than are patients with specific clinical disorders; however, little else (i.e., parole outcome, change in IQ, and response to drug treatment) seems to be clearly predictable from the crude diagnosis used at present" (p. 134). Not enough persons are really concerned about this lack of predictive validity. In many state institutions for the retarded, most of the psychological help are involved in diagnostic appraisal, although results do not justify the effort expended.

Among the possible reasons why classification systems lack predictive validity are: (1) The classification system lacks reliability. (2) The dimensions of behavior included in the classification system are not those that are most potentially useful. (3) Psychologists have expended more effort on rules of classification than they have on investigation of predictive validity—classification has become an end in itself. (4) Once correlations between classifications and predictive criteria have been established, few attempts have been made to study the nature of the relationship. (5) Diagnosticians often order their behavioral observations of children to insure confirmation of their own particular theoretical views. (6) With a passage of time, correlates of a classification are assumed even though they have not been empirically established. (7) Hypothetical constructs have been used, and subsequently the observable interaction between an individual and his environment has not been investigated (essentially the Skinnerian position outlined above).

Reliability is accepted as necessary for obtaining predictive validity. Those who use the system must classify the same behavior in a similar fashion (inter-judge agreement). Orr and Matthews (1961) had four experienced diagnosticians classify case records according to the AAMD behavioral classification system. The two main categories of measured intelligence and adaptive behavior were used in addition to the six supplementary categories. Only two categories, intelligence and speech skills, were used in roughly the same manner by the judges. Orr and Matthews concluded that the scales were not described in enough detail to obtain inter-judge agreement.

The AAMD's adaptive behavior category does not, at the present time, have enough objective measures to insure reliability between judges. This is particularily true at the adult level where the judgment of social competence is a global rating by the diagnostician. The lack of demonstrated reliability points up the need for further investigation in this area and for the development of reliable instruments for measuring adaptive behavior.

Another reason why classification has not resulted in predictive validity may be that the dimensions of behavior that are studied may not be the most potentially useful ones. For instance, we can classify retardates according to body build, hair color, or physical strength but these dimensions would not correlate very highly with predictive criteria such as success in school. In the intellectual domain, Guilford has used factor analytic techniques to investigate specific dimensions of intellectual abilities. This was an attempt to look at other than general intellectual ability, which has been the principle measure of intellectual ability. The predictive validity of Guilford's factor has not as yet been established.

Spivack and Levine (1964) and Spivack and Spotts (1965) also have studied symptoms of emotional behavior by the use of factor analysis. Spivack and Spotts (1965) had house parents or child care workers rate institutionalized children (mean IQ = 71) on 121 behavioral items. The factor analysis of these ratings yielded 15 first order factors. In addition to the prospect of locating factors that would be useful for predictive purposes, this approach is likely to be reliable and can be used to measure change after treatment. However, once again predictive validity has not been established for this method.

The paucity of research on predictive validity reflects diagnosticians' lack of concern for empirical validation of their hypotheses. They tend to think that a diagnosis, once reached, can be validated simply by having someone else agree with their diagnosis. In many settings, physicians, clinical psychologists, or school psychologists have limited opportunity to check even informally on the progress of individuals that they have classified. Diagnosis has been artificially separated from treatment. The separation of diagnosis and treatment is particularly evident in many institutional situations or schools where the psychologists' only contact with children is through an initial intake appraisal. Moreover, practicing clinicians are not prone to conduct formal validation studies. This type of research is not rewarded in the medical settings in which many of them work. Thus classification becomes an end in and of itself with little relationship to its real purpose, predictive validity.

The failure to investigate the nature of the correlation between a classification and predictive criteria also may well represent the most serious shortcoming in the field of mental retardation. Lack of knowledge about the nature of the relationship between a classification and an independent criterion limits the generality of the application of relationship to other cases. McNemar (1964), commenting on precisely this problem, bemoans the lack of studies that investigate the process of intellectual growth. Apparently, psychologists have been content to establish correlations between intelligence and independent criteria but have not attempted to study the necessary and sufficient conditions for the acquisition of problem-solving abilities.

An increasingly popular term in the area of diagnosis of learning disabilities is "diagnostic teaching." Here, diagnosis is formulated on the basis of the observation of a child's reaction to a learning situation. The typical diagnosis is a result of observation of the products of learning (e.g., use of vocabulary words on an intelligence test). Diagnostic teaching avoids the separation of diagnosis from treatment and concentrates on the process of learning and not the products. However, it remains to be seen whether diagnostic teaching can be used for the multitude of predictive purposes for which any diagnostic instrument is needed.

In many situations, a diagnostician is more interested in the confirmation of a hypothesis than the accurate description of observed behavior, which can then be correlated with predictive criteria. One possible explanation is that there is often pressure on the diagnostician to provide immediate answers to questions about cause of retarded behavior and probable outcome. A definite answer to these questions is usually not possible because of absence of single causal factors and also the lack of empirical data.

Whether the AAMD classification systems will be of practical benefit for predictive purposes depends to a large extent on their subsequent development. Presently the adaptive behavior category is too poorly defined to obtain adequate reliability, and this necessarily limits predictive validity. This inadequacy was of course recognized by the committee that designed the manual. Other reasons for the lack of predictive validity are not necessarily a result of the AAMD classification systems. The dimensions of behavior are sufficiently broad to allow for further subdivisions such as Guilford proposes; classification does not have to become an end in itself; and though classification will probably remain primarily correlational there is no reason why it cannot lead to investigation of the nature of its correlations.

KIRK'S CRITICISM OF CLASSIFICATION

Kirk and McCarthy (1961) claim that it is necessary to differentiate between diagnosis and classification. According to these authors, classification "is for the purpose of labeling a child as belonging to a particular group, type, or category" and diagnosis is an assessment of a child that leads directly to a specific type of educational or remedial program. They are critical of present-day classification systems because they do not lead to suggestions for remediation. According to an earlier definition in this chapter (English and English, 1958), classification is the "process of grouping objects into mutually exclusive classes, ranks, or categories, or the group so classified." Kirk and McCarthy, however, ignore the process and concentrate on the product or the "group so classified" part of the definition. They would be more correct to say that the purpose of classification is to assign a child to a certain group on the basis of clearly defined classification rules.

Diagnosis, in mental retardation, is classification of an individual on the basis of observed symptoms. Diagnosis and classification are synonymous in respect to mental retarda-

tion, and differentiating between them does not seem necessary. Classification leads to definite educational or remedial programs when indicators of prognosis have been established as correlates of a classification system.

Unfortunately, Kirk's criticism of classification has been construed as an attack on the basic process of classification itself. But one does not get this impression from an examination of his procedure for diagnosis of learning disabilities. First of all, he classifies verbal behavior. His classification is derived from Osgood's psycholinguistic model (Osgood, 1957). On the basis of this classification, he then predicts that the child's learning disability is caused by a particular deficit around which he plans remedial treatment. Predictive validity is established indirectly by the success or failure of the treatment.

Kirk really seems to be objecting to two other abuses of classification, namely: (1) failure to classify on the basis of clearly defined rules; (2) failure to investigate the necessary dimensions of behavior.

PREDICTIONS BASED ON RESEARCH RESULTS

Diagnosticians often are asked to predict possible outcomes for individuals. These predictions range from questions about whether a child will be able to finish high school to queries about his ultimate level of self-sufficiency. In responding to these practical problems, the diagnostician quite often depends on research that has empirically established relationships between certain classifications and predictive criteria. The research that the diagnostician draws on can itself vary in the degree of its direct relationship to the individual case. It may be a definitely established correlate of a classification; or on the other hand, it may simply pertain to certain variables which the diagnostician observes in an individual. The diagnostician, for instance, may observe that the individual is hyperactive or is very concrete in his thought processes. Assessment of these variables may not yet be incorporated into a classification system, but the diagnostician is familiar with research that relates these variables to predictive criteria.

There are, however, certain precautions that should be observed when attempting to apply research to individual cases. However, these cautions are often not observed by diagnosticians, leading to criticisms of both diagnosis and research. Diagnosis is criticized because predictions based on research results are not confirmed in the case at hand, and research is said to be invalid because it did not lead to an accurate prediction. This is a somewhat different situation than the general failure to obtain predictive validity.

This failure of a prediction to be confirmed may be a result of several factors that should be considered before either research or diagnosis is criticized. First, the diagnostician may have had a poor understanding of the nature of the relationship between research and diagnosis and therefore made poor predictions. Secondly, individual predictions are statements of probability, and lack of confirmation in a single instance does not refute either the underlying research or diagnosis. The first general factor will be considered in more detail. The second is obvious but often ignored by both diagnosticians and by those receiving individual predictions.

Diagnosticians for one reason or another often ignore the following basic conditions when they attempt to apply research to individual predictions:

1. The variables the diagnostician uses in assessing an individual case may not be the only important ones. When several are important, research on the interaction between these variables quite often is not as definitive as the diagnostician thinks it is.

2. In an individual case, the diagnostician may not be reliably assessing the same variables as the ones used in research studies. This discrepancy will usually lead to inaccurate predictions.

The use of more general research on variables to make predictions in an individual case is clearly not in line with classification as outlined in this chapter. In effect, variables of this nature have not been formulated into a classification system and predictive criteria have not been established as correlates. However, making predictions in the absence of empirically founded correlates is often necessary. This type of a prediction is legitimate only when the decisions so formed are not terminal but can be altered easily. In many instances, a diagnostician is asked to come up with predictions concerning the education of a child. If the educational plans can be easily changed in cases when the psychologist is not accurate in his predictions, calculated guesses with a low level of probability are warranted. In making these guesses, a diagnostician can often make judicious use of research related to the variables he observes in the child. He should make every attempt to avoid the pitfalls listed above.

SUMMARY

A general classification system such as the one proposed by the AAMD should be useful for practitioners in the field of mental retardation. It is somewhat discouraging to note that half a century of emphasis in this country on diagnosis and classification has not resulted in a system that presently has any practical utility. The AAMD classification systems need to be further developed within the general framework provided. The emphasis should be on accurate description of symptoms, classification of these symptoms into useful systems, and attempts to establish predictive validity.

REFERENCES

ALLPORT, G. W. Traits revisited. *Amer. Psychologist,* 1966, *21,* 1-10.

ARTHUR, G. Pseudo-feeblemindedness. *Amer. J. ment. Defic.,* 1947, *52,* 137-42.

ARTHUR, GRACE A. Some factors contributing to errors in the diagnosis of feeblemindedness. *Amer. J. ment. Defic.,* 1950, *54,* 495-501.

AUSUBEL, D. P. *Theory and problems of child development.* New York: Grune and Stratton. 1958.

――――. Personality disorder is disease. *Amer. Psychologist.,* 1961, *16,* 69-74.

AXLINE, VIRGINIA M. Mental deficiency—symptom or disease. *J. consult. Psychol.,* 1949, *13,* 313-27.

BAER, P. E. Problems in the differential diagnosis of brain damage and childhood schizophrenia. *Amer. J. Orthopsychiat.*, 1961, *31*, 728-737.

BANDURA, A., and WALTER, R. *Social Learning and Personality Development.* New York: Holt and Rinehart, and Winston, 1963.

BENDA, C. E. Childhood schizophrenia, autism and Heller's disease. In P. W. Bowman and H. V. Mautner (Eds.), *Mental retardation: proceedings of the First International Medical Conference.* New York: Grune and Stratton, 1960, 469-492.

————, FARRELL, M. J., and CHIPMAN, C. E. The inadequacy of present-day concepts of mental deficiency and mental illness in child psychiatry. *Amer. J. Psychiat.*, 1951, *107*, 721-727.

BENOIT, E. P. Toward a new definition of mental retardation. *Amer. J. ment. Defic.*, 1959, *63*, 559-564. Excerpts in Chapter 12 reprinted with the permission of the publisher.

BIJOU, S. W. Theory and research in mental (developmental) retardation. *Psychol. Rec.*, 1963, *13*, 95-110.

————. Experimental studies of child behavior, normal and deviant. In L. Krasner and L. P. Ullman (Eds.), *Research in behavior modification.* New York: Holt, Rinehart, and Winston, 1965. 56-81.

———— and BAER, D. M., *Child Development.* Vol. I. A systematic and empirical theory. New York: Appleton-Century-Crofts, Inc. 1961.

BINET, A., and SIMON T. Upon the necessity of establishing a scientific diagnosis of inferior states of intelligence. In W. Dennis (Ed.), *Readings in the history of psychology.* New York: Appleton-Century-Crofts, 1948, 407-411.

BLATT, B. Towards a more acceptable terminology in mental retardation. *Train. Sch. Bull.*, 1961, *58*, 47-51.

CANTOR, G. A critique of Garfield's and Wittson's reaction to the revised manual on terminology and classification. *Amer. J. ment. Defic.*, 1960, *64*, 954-956.

————. Some issues involved in category VIII of the AAMD Terminology and Classification Manual. *Amer. J. ment. Defic.*, 1961, *65*, 561-566.

CANTOR, G. N. On the incurability of mental deficiency. *Amer. J. ment. Defic.*, 1955, *60*, 362-365.

CASSEL, R. H. Relation of design reproduction to the etiology of mental deficiency. *J. consult. Psychol.*, 1949, *13*, 421-428. (a)

————. Notes on pseudo-feeblemindedness. *Train. Sch. Bull.*, 1949, *46*, 119-127. (b)

CLARKE, A. D. B., and CLARKE, A. M. Pseudo-feeblemindedness—some implications. *Amer. J. ment. Defic.*, 1955, *59*, 507-509.

CLARKE, A. M. Criteria and classification of mental deficiency. In A. M. Clarke and A. D. B. Clarke (Eds.). *Mental deficiency: The changing outlook.* Glencoe, Ill.: Free Press. 1958, 43-64.

CRONBACH, L. J. The two disciplines of scientific psychology. *Amer. Psychologist,* 1957, *12*, 671-684.

————. *Essentials of psychological testing.* (2nd ed.) New York: Harper and Row, 1960.

DOLL, E. A. Feeble-mindedness versus intellectual retardation, *Amer. J. ment. Defic.*, 1947, *51*, 456-459.

DOLL, E. E. A historical survey of research and management of mental retardation in the United States. In E. P. Trapp and P. Himelstein (Eds.), *Readings on the exceptional child.* New York: Appleton-Century-Crofts, 1962, 21-69.

ENGLISH, H. B., and ENGLISH, A. C. *A comprehensive dictionary of psychological and psychoanalytic terms.* New York: David McKay, 1958.

Eysenck, H. J. Classification and the problems of diagnosis. In H. J. Eysenck (Ed.), *Handbook of abnormal psychology.* New York: Basic Books, 1961, 1-32.

FELDMAN, I. S. Psychological differences among moron and borderline mental defectives as a function of etiology. *Amer. J. ment. Defic.,* 1953, *57,* 484-94.

GALLAGHER, J. Measurement of personality development in pre-adolescent mentally retarded children. *Amer. J. ment. Defic.,* 1959, *64,* 296-301.

GARDNER, W. I., and NISONGER, H. W. A manual on program development in mental retardation. Monograph supplement to *Amer. J. ment. Defic.,* 1962, *66,* 1-192.

GARFIELD, S. L. Problems in the psychological evaluation of the subnormal individual. *Amer. J. ment. Defic.,* 1959, *64,* 467-471.

—— and WITTSON, C. Some reactions to the revised manual in terminology and classification in mental retardation. *Amer. J. ment. Defic.,* 1960, *64,* 951-953.

——, WILCOTT, J. B., and MILGRAM, N. A. Emotional disturbance and suspected mental deficiency. *Amer. J. ment. Defic.,* 1961, *66,* 23-29.

GARRISON, M. JR. Classification and research in mental deficiency. *Train. Sch. Bull.,* 1957, *54,* 2-4.

GELOF, M. Comparison of classification relating degree of retardation to measured intelligence. *Amer. J. ment. Defic.,* 1963, *68,* 297-317.

GOLDSCHMID, M. L., and DOMINGO, G. Some para-diagnostic implications of the IQ among mentally retarded patients. *Train. Sch. Bull.,* 1965, *61,* 178-183.

GUERTIN, W. H. Differential characteristics of the pseudo feeble-minded. *Amer. J. ment. Defic.,* 1950, *54,* 394-98.

GUILFORD, T. P. Three faces of intellect. *Amer. Psychologist,* 1959, *14,* 469-479.

GUNZBERG, H. C. Psychological assessment in mental deficiency. Psychotherapy with the feebleminded. In A. M. Clarke and A. D. B. Clarke (Eds.), *Mental deficiency: the changing outlook.* Glencoe, Illinois: Free Press, 1958, 257-291, 365-392.

HEBER, R. Terminology and the classification of mental retardation. *Amer. J. ment. Defic.,* 1958, *63,* 214-219.

——. Modifications in the manual on terminology and classification in mental retardation. *Amer. J. ment. Defic.,* 1961, *65,* 499-500.

HEBER, R. F. A manual on terminology and classification in mental retardation. *Amer. J. ment. Defic.,* 1959, *64.* Monograph supplement.

HUNT, J. McV. *Intelligence and experience.* New York: Ronald Press, 1961.

JACOB, WALTER. A report on the conference on diagnosis in mental retardation. *Train. Sch. Bull.,* 1958, *55,* 17-44.

JASTAK, J. A rigorous critique of feeblemindedness. *J. abnor. soc. Psychol.,* 1949, *44,* 367-78.

KELLY, G. A. The theory and technique of assessment. *Annu. Rev. Psychol.,* 1958, *9,* 323-352.

KIRK, S. A., and BATEMAN, B. Diagnosis and remediation of learning disabilities. *Except. Child.* 1962, *29,* 73-78.

—— and McCARTHY, J. J. The Illinois test of psycholinguistic abilities—an approach to digerential diagnosis. *Amer. J. ment. Defic.,* 1961, *66,* 399-412.

LORR, M. Classification of the behavior disorders, 1961. *Annual Review of Psychology, 12,* 195-216.

MCNEMAR, Q. Lost: our intelligence? Why? *Amer. Psychologist,* 1964, *19,* 871-882.

MEEHL, P. E. *Clinical versus statistical prediction: a theoretical analysis and a review of the evidence.* Minneapolis: University of Minnesota Press, 1954.

MENOLOSCINO, F. J. Psychoses of childhood: experiences of a mental retardation pilot project. *Amer. J. ment. Defic.,* 1965, *70,* 83-92.

MEYERS, C. E., ORPEL, R. E., and ATTWELL, A. H. Psychometric examination as a standardized situation yielding personality data. *Train. Sch. Bull.,* 1964, *61,* 97-102.

MOLISH, H. B. Contributions of projective tests to problems of psychological diagnosis in mental deficiency. *Amer. J. ment. Defic.,* 1958, *63,* 282-93.

NISONGER, H. W. Changing concepts of mental retardation. *Amer. J. ment. Defic.,* 1962, *67,* 4-13.

ORR, T. B., and MATTHEWS, G. G. Inter-judge agreement on the behavioral scales of the new AAMD classification manual. *Amer. J. ment. Defic.,* 1961, *65,* 567-576.

OSGOOD, C. E. *Contemporary approaches to cognition, a behavioristic analysis.* Cambridge: Harvard University Press, 1957.

PAPAGEORGIS. D. Pseudo-feeblemindedness and the concept of mental retardation. *Amer. J. ment. Defic.,* 1963, *68,* 340-344.

POLLACK, M. Brain damage mental retardation and childhood schizophrenia. *Amer. J. Psychiat.,* 1958, *115,* 422-428.

ROBINSON, H. B., and ROBINSON; N. M. *The mentally retarded child: a psychological approach.* New York: McGraw-Hill, 1965.

RUNDLE, A. T. Etiological factors in mental retardation: 1. Biochemical. 2. Endocrinological. *Amer. J. ment. Defic.,* 1962, *67,* 61-78.

SARASON, S. B. *Psychological problems in mental deficiency.* (3rd ed.) New York: Harper and Brothers, 1959.

SCHACHTER, FRANCES F., MEYER, LUCILE R., and LOOMIS, E. A. Childhood schizophrenia and mental retardation: differential diagnosis before and after one year of psychotherapy. *Amer. J. Orthopsychiat.,* 1962, *32,* 584-594.

SHAFTER, A. J. The vocational placement of institutionalized mental defectives in the U.S. *Amer. J. ment. Defic.,* 1954, *59,* 279-307.

SIEVERS, DOROTHY J., MCCARTHY, J. J., OLSON, J. L., BATEMAN, BARBARA D., and KASS, CORRINE E. *Selected studies on the Illinois Test of Psycholinguistic Abilities.* Madison, Wis.: Photo Press, 1963.

SILVERSTEIN, A. B. Note on terminology. *Amer. J. ment. Defic.,* 1962, *67,* 303-305.

SKINNER, B. F. *Science and human behavior.* New York: Macmillan, 1953.

SLOAN, W., and BIRCH, J. W. A rationale for degrees of retardation. *Amer. J. ment. Defic.,* 1955, *60,* 258-264.

SPIKER, C. C., and MCCANDLESS, B. R. The concept of intelligence and the philosophy of science. *Psychol., Rev.,* 1954, *61,* 255-266.

SPIVACK, G., and LEVINE, M. The Devereux child behavior rating scales: A study of symptom behaviors in latency age atypical children. *Amer. J. ment. Defic.,* 1964, *68,* 700-717.

——— and SPOTTS, J. The Devereux child behavior scale: symptom behaviors in latency age children. *Amer. J. ment. Defic.,* 1965, *69,* 839-853.

STULL, C. E. Psychological diagnosis. In Program planning for the moderately and severely retarded child: a symposium. *Amer. J. ment. Defic.*, 1961, *65*, 696-698.

————. Southbury classification plan. *Amer. J. ment. Defic.*, 1959, *63*, 1022-1027.

WIENER, G., RIDER, R. V., and OPPEL, W. Some correlates of IQ changes in children. *Child Developm.* 1963, *34*, 61-68.

WINDEL, C. D. Prognosis of mental subnormals. *Amer. J. ment. Defic.*, 1962, *66*, (2) (5, monogr. suppl.), 180.

WOLFENSBERGER, W. Age variation in Vineland SQ scores for the four levels of adaptive behavior of the 1959 AAMD behavioral classification. *Amer. J. ment. Defic.*, 1962, *67*, 452-454.

YANNET, H. Classification and etiological factors in mental retardation. *J. Pediatr.*, 1957, *50*, 226-230.

ZIGLER, E., and PHILLIPS, L. Psychiatric diagnosis: A critique. *J. abn. soc. Psychol.*, 1961, *63*, 607-618.

The Multidisciplinary Approach to Mental Retardation

RICHARD KOCH[1]

THE physician is often the first professional person to suspect the presence of mental retardation in a young child (Illingworth, 1960; Levinson and Bigler, 1960). His initial approach to diagnosis is often crucial in initiating treatment, early parent counseling, and the use of proper community resources. But too often the physician is unaware of the cause of the mental retardation, too often has little if any specific therapy for the particular problem, and does not have tools available that will adequately forecast future development. Under such circumstances, it is natural for parents to seek further diagnostic help and counsel. The two major causes for "shopping" for additional diagnostic help are the dissatisfaction of the parents with the physician's initial appraisal of their child and the impact of mental retardation in a child in our society (Kirk, Karnes, and Kirk, 1958).

Parents often are dissatisfied with the initial appraisal of their child. The physician's confirmation of mental retardation likely may cause intense subconscious anger on the part of the parents and development of an innate pattern of parental rejection of the child. Parents often have difficulty coping with these feelings. Even the most mature parents find these subconscious reactions troublesome. Anger may manifest itself in various ways, but often is directed toward the doctor who first suspected the presence of mental retardation. Rejection of the child often causes guilt feel-

ings that result in an oversolicitous attitude toward the child with subsequent lack of discipline, a search for additional diagnostic help, and expenditures of money for questionable forms of medical therapy.

Diagnosis, while not an end in itself, is the beginning of reality and planning by both parents and professionals. In order to plan in a comprehensive way for a handicapped child, the skills of many disciplines are required. A multidisciplinary approach (Gardner and Nisonger, 1962) to the problems posed by handicapped children (especially the mentally retarded) can offer integrated help to the parents at the community level. The "core" team needed for such an evaluation of a preschool child is composed of the pediatrician, psychologist, social worker, speech and hearing consultant, and public health nurse.

Though most types of retardation are of a lasting nature, a few preventable forms do exist and respond to medical measures, providing treatment is begun early in infancy (Hsia, 1959). For this reason, a thorough medical evaluation performed by an experienced physician is of utmost importance. A careful medical history, physical examination, and certain laboratory procedures are essential. In many clinics a routine blood count, urinalysis, urine for phenylpyruvic acid, electroencephalogram, and skull X rays are performed. In addition to these studies, we perform a tuberculin skin test, urine amino-acid study, and an X ray of the wrist for skeletal bone age determination. If the bone age is retarded, a blood protein-bound iodine is performed frequently to check for the presence of hypothyroidism. Buccal smear and chromosomal anal-

1. The author wishes to acknowledge the assistance of the following individuals in the development of the material in this chapter: Karol Fishler, Sylvia Schild, Betty Graliker, Nancy Ragsdale, David Chadwick, and Richard Straw.

TABLE I. Relationship of Specific Laboratory Tests, Results, and Type of
Disease Exhibiting such an Abnormality

Specific Lab. Study	*Abnormalities*	*Disease Associated with Retardation of Growth or Development*
Routine blood count	Severe anemia	(1) Iron deficiency (2) Lead poisoning
Fasting blood sugar	Low (30 mg. %)	(1) Hypoglycemia (2) Leucine-sens. Hypoglycemia
Serum Calcium and Phosphorus	Elevated calcium Elevated phosphorous Low calcium	(1) Idiopathic Hyper-calcemia (1) Renal insufficiency (1) Tetany (2) Pseudo-Hypopara-thyroidism
Non-protein nitrogen	Elevated	(1) Renal insufficiency
Blood protein iodine	Elevated (over 9 μg.) Low (less than 4 μg.)	(1) Hyperthyroidism (2) Hypothyroidism
Serum phenylalanine	Elevated (over 15 mg. %).	(1) Phenylketonuria
Red-cell galactose —1-phosphate	Normal tyrosine Elevated	(1) Galactosemia
Urinalysis	Galactosuria Albuminuria	(1) Galactosemia (1) Lowe's syndrome
Urine phenylpyruvic acid	Phenylpyruvic acid	(1) Phenylketonuria
Aminoaciduria	Gross	(1) Phenylketonuria (2) Galactosemia (3) Lowe's syndrome (4) Lead poisoning (5) Wilson's disease (6) Hartnup's disease
	Specific amino-acid abnormality	(1) Maple Syrup disease (2) Other rare diseases such as Histidinemia, etc.
Urine polysaccharide	Positive	(1) Gargoylism (Hurler's disease)
Urine for virus culture	Presence of specific virus	(1) Cytomegalic disease
Electroencephalogram	Convulsive pattern	(1) Convulsive disorder, Grand mal, Petit mal, Psychomotor, Myoclonic
Skull X rays	Large Small	(1) Hydrocephalus (1) Microcephaly

Specific Lab. Study	*Abnormalities*	*Disease Associated with Retardation of Growth or Development*
Skull X rays	Calcifications	(1) Toxoplasmosis (2) Cytomegalic disease (3) Craniopharyngioma (4) Tuberous sclerosis (5) Parasitic infestation
Skull X rays	Suture separation due to increased pressure	(1) Brain tumor (2) Subdural hematoma
Skull X rays	Suture abnormality	(1) Craniostenosis
Skull X rays	Retarded bone age Cortical structure of bone	(1) Hypothyroidism (1) Hurler's disease
Skeletal bone X ray (wrist)	Lead lines Increased density	(1) Lead poisoning (1) Hypercalcemia
Skeletal bone X ray (wrist)	Absent 5th metacarpal	(1) Down's syndrome
X ray of pelvis	Flaring of ilium	(1) Down's syndrome
Routine tuberculin skin	Positive	(1) Look for tuberculous focus. Rule out early meningitis
Electromyogram	Abnormality	(1) Myopathy such as Glycogen Storage disease
Spinal puncture	Increased cells Increased protein Decreased sugar	(1) Occult infection (1) Degenerative disease (1) Hypoglycemia
Pneumoencephalogram	Cerebral anomaly	(1) Congenital defect
Cerebral angiogram	Cerebral anomaly	(1) Vascular anomaly
Ventriculogram	Cerebral anomaly	(1) Brain tumor or Congenital anomaly
Chromosome analysis Trisomy 21 Trisomy 16-18 Trisomy 13-15 Deletion of 5	 Down's syndrome Multiple congenital anomalies Multiple anomalies "Cri du Chat"	 (1) Down's syndrome
Buccal smear	Additional or deletion of X chromosome	(1) Klinefelter's syndrome (XXY) (2) Triple X syndrome (XXX) (3) Turner's syndrome (XO)

ysis are not done routinely. Further diagnostic studies such as spinal puncture, pneumoencephalogram, or ventriculogram are rarely required. Urine for cytomegalic inclusion virus culture also is obtained from young children with multiple defects.

The routine use of laboratory studies is criticized by some but is essential to a complete evaluation of each patient. Table I outlines the relationship of the commonly used tests with specific abnormalities and certain disease states.

Another team member who participates in the child's initial evaluation is the clinical psychologist. His chief role is to assess the mental capacity of the child ·by means of appropriate psychological tests and to appraise the personality factors that are so crucial in planning for a child's future habilitative program.

The social worker helps the parents to find ways of solving problems of adjustment that they may not be able to solve themselves. His role is a very delicate one, for acceptance of the child's real condition often comes with patience, sustained interest, and skill in enabling the parents to gain greater insight and understanding. In the initial evaluation of the knowledge of the functioning of the child's family and an assessment of the family's ability to carry out the recommendations of the team, his advice may be crucial.

Invaluable to the family's morale are the visits of the public health nurse, whose contact with the parents of the mentally retarded child will encourage his best possible care and management at home. She also brings to the team an assessment of the home management of the child and assists the parents in carrying through with team recommendations.

Speech and hearing clinicians, nutritionists, teachers, physical therapists, laboratory technicians, and various medical specialists all add their skills and knowledge to the problem.

Though parents must be encouraged to accept all of the responsibility they can, the various professional disciplines must furnish their integrated support to help the child develop to his fullest.

An accurate evaluation not only incorporates purely medical findings, but also psychological, educational, and social factors as well, thus enabling all concerned to view the patient and his family as a total problem. This alone makes the team approach more useful than a single disciplinary approach. This is true particularly in the field of handicapped individuals, which inherently involves many community, social, and health facilities.

Since retarded children usually require care for many more years than normal children, parents who inform themselves as well as they can and attain objectivity about their. children are in a better position to coordinate and apply all of the facts to the best advantage of the child (Buck, 1950).

Physicians, educators, psychologists, and other professionals have embarked upon research projects and have begun to pool their findings. Studies of mentally retarded children in institutions for the mentally retarded have been valuable in assembling much of the present knowledge about the etiology of mental retardation (Heber, 1959; Masland, Sarason, and Gladwin, 1958; Yannet, 1956). The present collaborative study of 40,000 pregnancies by the National Institute of Neurological Diseases and Blindness will be of great value in pinpointing important areas for future research. Only in this manner can proper effort be made in the important areas of the basic sciences that hopefully will prevent the occurrence of various types of mental retardation in the future. Once such factors are known, other methods for instituting proper procedures for utilizing such knowledge must be developed. But even today we are not applying and reaping the benefits of knowledge discovered some years ago.

GENETIC FACTORS

Chromosomal causes. Since knowledge of gene structure in human beings is limited and not derived from one man's direct observation of several generations, many statements about heredity are based upon experiments with plants, insects, and animals (Knudson, 1965).

The rapid advances made during the last few years are dramatic. The biochemical makeup of the gene has been elucidated and chromosomal knowledge has been expanding. For example, in 1959 the etiology of mongolism was obscure. Through the pioneering work of Lejeune, we know this syndrome is associated with an extra chromosome resulting in 47 chromosomes for each cell of a child with mongolism, in comparison to 46 which is the proper number. This finding occurred at a time when only a small number of people, primarily geneticists working in the field of botany, were familiar with the techniques for working with chromosomes.

We know that there are several different kinds of chromosome abnormalities found in man; (a) the trisome, the presence of a single additional chromosome; (b) the monosome, the absence of a chromosome that should be there; (c) deletion, the absence of a part of a chromosome; (d) translocation, the moving of a piece of one chromosome from where it ought to be to another chromosome where it perhaps ought not to be, and (e) triploidy, a condition in which an individual has half again as many chromosomes as he ought to have. A distinct proportion of the cases so far described have had abnormal segregation of the sex de-termining chromosomes. Some of these are gonadal dysgenesis: Turner's syndrome and Klinefelter's syndrome or testicular fibrosis. Animals that have the same kind of a sex-de-termining mechanism as man seem to tolerate abnormalities in distribution of sex chromo-somes much better than they do abnormalities of other kinds of chromosomes.

Man has 22 pairs of chromosomes that are called autosomes, and in normal individuals there are two additional sex chromosomes labeled XX in the female and XY in the male for a total of 23 pairs or 46 chromosomes. The configuration of chromosomes is similar. They are identified by their relative length, by the position of a little constriction called a centromere, and in some cases by the pres-ence of a little appendage called a satellite, which is present in some but not all of the chromosomes. The main reason human chro-mosomes were not counted properly before was due to inadequate techniques.

With the development of cancer and virus research and tissue culture techniques for growing cells in vitro, a system became available in which cells could divide much more rap-idly than they do in the human body and thus be studied. Under these conditions, a relatively large number of cells can be obtained. To make an analysis, it is necessary to take a picture of a dividing cell in metaphase, en-large that picture considerably, cut out all of the chromosomes with scissors, measure them, match them up in the right pairs, and then mount them in a group called a karyotype or

idiogram. Sometimes, one chromosome, or perhaps even more than one chromosome, is present too many times. If a single extra chro-mosome is present, this is called trisomy. Several trisomic types already have been described: trisomy for numbers 15, 18, and 21 as well as abnormalities of the X chromosome. Tri-somy 21 is the abnormality associated with Down's syndrome (mongolism). So Trisomy 21 is another new name for Down's syndrome.

The other chromosomal disorders that were mentioned singly or in multiple situations are associated with cases of multiple congenital anomalies. A great deal of evidence exists on how trisomies behave. Chromosomal aberra-tion is apparently tolerated much more readily by plants than animals. In plants, every indi-vidual chromosome in the trisomic state has a different syndrome of abnormality associated with it. We see the same thing in man. Perhaps trisomy for every one of man's chromosomes will be discovered eventually. Nullisomic, the absence of a chromosome, probably produces severe difficulty; none have been found, except for the absence of an X chromosome—the XO syndrome in Turner's.

Two questions are raised by the discovery of a chromosomal cause for Down's syn-drome. The first one is, what causes it? Nor-mal development, which is gene-controlled in every plant and animal, depends not only on the genes being of the right kind, but also to a large extent upon balance between the genes, so that two chromosomes of every kind are required for normal development. An upset of this genetic balance results, in turn, in an up-set of metabolism of the cells. The fact that children with Down's syndrome are retarded in physical and mental growth is undoubtedly related to the presence of the extra chromo-some.

How the extra chromosome is created is of great interest. In order to discuss this, we should review the events that occur in gamete production. During meiosis, the chromosomes replicate and then separate by migrating to opposite poles as cell division occurs. This results in two cells with 23 chromosomes each, whereas the cell we began with had 46. This is the reduction division that leads to the formation of all gametes (meiosis). In nondis-junction, the chromosomes may pair normally and line up on the metaphase plate normally, but if for some reason they fail to disjoin normally, both or one of the chromosomes may go to one pole and neither of that pair to the other pole. This will result in two cells, one having 24 chromosomes and the other having 22, the cell with 24 receiving the extra one donated by the pair that failed to disjoin. A gamete (an egg or sperm) that has such an extra chromosome may be fertilized by one that has the normal number of chromosomes from the other parent. This fertilized egg then develops into an embryo that has an extra chromosome. In the case of man, this results in the presence of 47 chromosomes, with the result that the physical and mental disturbances mentioned earlier ensue. Apparently the gamete with only 22 chromosomes dies, since none as yet have been described.

What factors influence this nondisjunctional event? In plants, and possibly also in man, the size of the chromosome is a factor. When the chromosomes are pairing, they are held together by exchanges of material between the homologous chromosome. These exchanges are visible in a structure called a chiasma, a cross. The number of chiasmata that a pair of chromosomes has is related to the length of the chromosomes—at least in a general way, so that one might expect, for instance, that smaller chromosomes accidentally might not have any. This might cause them to not stay together, and thus line up independently on the metaphase plate and go accidentally to the same pole. Perhaps there are specific genes that control this pairing together or synapses. We know there are such genes affecting the degree of synapses in plants. Gene abnormalities in man possibly may affect the way the chromosomes pair and the way they come apart.

Gene inheritance patterns. Many human anomalies are unexplained. In certain well-established hereditary diseases, the cause is related to the presence of recessive or dominant genes that are located in the various chromosomes. In these diseases, the presence of the gene not only seems to explain the facts, but it predicts quite accurately the conditions under which the symptoms will reappear in the offspring.

For example, let us consider galactosemia (Donnell, Bergren, and Cleland, 1960), a condition due to an inherited disorder caused by a recessive gene present in both parents.

Both are normal, because the recessive gene cannot gain expression unless it pairs up with another similar gene to form the homozygote recessive state. In the parent, the presence of a normal gene suppresses the one recessive galactosemic gene. This condition is called a heterozygote. When two parents mate, each of whom having a recessive gene for galactosemia, then offspring with the disease are produced (see Fig. 1). From the diagram it is

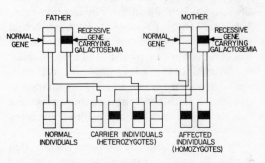

FIG. 1. Schematic presentation of genic inheritance in Galactosemia.

apparent that the chances of producing a galactosemic child are one in four. Notice that, of the possible combinations, one is normal, two are heterozygotes (carriers of the gene, but normal), and one is homozygote (carrier of two recessive genes) and has the disease known as galactosemia. This disorder is characterized by mental defect, ocular cataracts, and liver disease and is due to a genetically produced enzyme defect that prevents the conversion of galactose to glucose. Proper treatment consists of dietary management in which the sugar galactose is deleted from all ingested foods. If the diagnosis is established in early infancy, mental retardation can be prevented or ameliorated by judicious dietary management.

Several other recessively inherited diseases cause mental retardation. Phenylketonuria (Kretchmer and Etzwiler, 1958) is an amino-acid disorder in which an inherited defective enzyme system results in failure of conversion of one amino acid (phenylalanine) to another amino acid (tyrosine). The phenylalanine is constantly absorbed from protein nutrients ingested in the diet into the bloodstream and then to other body tissues. Since it is not being utilized normally, it is finally excreted as phenylpyruvic acid by the kidney and is released into the urine. Even so, patients with the disease have a markedly high level of phenylalanine in the blood. Some phenylalanine is even excreted in sweat. Untreated children are usually blond, blue-eyed, and severely mentally retarded. Treatment consists of removing phenylalanine from the diet. If it is diagnosed during early infancy and if proper treatment is instituted, the mental defect can be prevented or significantly ameliorated. Children over age 5 at the time of diagnosis usually do not benefit significantly by diet treatment. The cause of brain damage in the untreated child is not known. Tay Sachs (Abt, 1911) disease and Hurler's disease (gargoylism) (Lahey, Lomas, and Worth, 1947) are examples of two metabolic diseases for which we still have no specific treatment. Both are inherited in a recessive manner. More diseases such as these are being described.

A dominant gene transmission is one that is able to gain expression even when paired with a normal gene: the heterozygote state. Few such diseases are associated with mental retardation. Some authorities suggest that tuberous sclerosis (Chao, 1959) is transmitted in a dominant pattern. The disease manifests itself by convulsions, mental retardation, and tuberous formations on the face. Intracranial calcifications are often seen on skull X rays in this disease. The variability of expression of the symptoms has made it difficult to be certain of the dominant mode of inheritance. Statistics show that 50 per cent of the children of a parent with such a dominant trait will be affected (see Fig. 2).

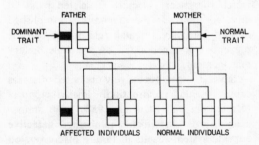

FIG 2. An example of a dominant-trait inheritance.

Still some other genetic diseases are said to be sex-linked. This means only the male is affected by such diseases as hemophilia or color blindness. The oculo-cerebral-renal (Lowe, Terrey, and MacLachlan, 1952) disease is caused by a defective gene on the X chromosome. By examining Figure 3, one sees that only sons would be affected by such a mating in which the heterozygote normal mother (carrying this gene) marries a normal father. Males carrying this gene on their only X chromosome are severely mentally retarded. The diagnosis is made by the presence of cataracts, renal aminoaciduria, and mental defect in a male occurring in the inheritance pattern as shown (see Fig. 3). Because of the

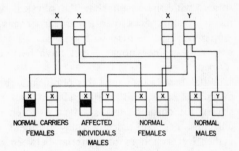

FIG. 3. Schematic presentation of a sex-linked pattern of inheritance.

high rate of occurrence (50 per cent of males born in families) and the profound degree of mental defect, parents producing children with this disease are advised not to have more children.

Heredity and environment. Most authorities agree that certain types of mental retardation have a genetic origin, in which we are unaware of the number of genes involved or of the mode of transmission. Most workers feel that the majority of such individuals are but mildly affected mentally. At the other extreme, however, are the families in which three to five children are microcephalic and obviously severely retarded. In the latter case, the inheritance pattern may be due to a single gene in his search for scientific answers in the area inheritance.

The problem revolves about the interaction of heredity and environment. Intelligence undoubtedly is the result of multiple gene inheritance interacting with environment. The metabolic diseases such as phenylketonuria are typical examples in which dietary changes allow the affected individuals to develop their intelligence capacities to the fullest.

The difficulties that have faced the geneticist

in mental retardation are well known. One must conclude that most of the work done in previous years is unacceptable in view of modern knowledge. Many of the early studies simply are not valid because mental retardation is a symptom of over 100 different disease processes, only a few of which could be analyzed by genetic methods such as additive gene hypothesis. Most of the studies in the literature suffer from this difficulty. One cannot analyze the meaning of IQ data obtained from parents and siblings of individuals who are retarded for many different reasons. Therefore, until we find some method of accurately identifying individuals who are mentally retarded due to solely genetic means, scientific conclusions must be held in abeyance. It is not too optimistic to think that accurate conclusions can be made within the foreseeable future. The discovery of methods of chromosome analysis has already led to greater validity in our thinking about the cause of mental defect. Gross chromosomal aberrations such as in Down's syndrome are merely the first obvious pathologic states to be identified. When newer techniques are developed to identify less obvious chromosome disorders, our knowledge of etiology again will be increased greatly.

This, of course, does not mean we should all stop, look, and wait for such events, but we must temper our conclusions in terms of social action. For a moment, let us discuss the hypothesis that at the time of conception all fertilized ovum have the potential for superior intelligence just as they do for two hands, two eyes, etc. If this were true, then society would wish to provide the best of everything for the expectant mother in the way of nutrition, health habits, obstetrical facilities, etc., in order for each product of conception to achieve its maximum potential. Even though this hypothesis seems unlikely from the genetic point of view, it is preferable from the social point of view.

The most useful predictors of intelligence of offspring are the social status of the parents (Doll, 1937) and the average IQ of both parents (Penrose, 1963), although both methods have their shortcomings.

The regression of intelligence toward the mean now seems a well-accepted conclusion (Penrose, 1963; Pevzner, 1961). This means that the children of superiorly endowed parents probably will have intelligence quotients midway between superior to normal levels, whereas the intelligence of children of dull to feeble-minded parents will usually fall midway between dull to normal.

The discussion of the importance of heredity and environment in procreation is far from settled (Pevzner, 1961; Reed and Reed, 1965). A middle ground is probably the best place for most of us. Since we can influence environment more easily than heredity, we should concentrate our efforts to improve this aspect of the problem as much as humanly possible.

PRENATAL FACTORS

The intrauterine growth period is an important time for study and research (Bowman and Mautner, 1960; Crothers and Paine, 1959; Montagu, 1962). Contrary to what one might expect, little is known about the causative factors of mental retardation. The study of human reproduction has lagged due to cultural and religious influence. As an example of this, the last division of the Institute of Health to be formed was the one on child health and human development in 1963. This new division is expected to stimulate research in this vital area of concern.

As early as the eighteenth day of pregnancy, the cells of the embryo are being arranged in three germinal layers: ectoderm, mesoderm, and endoderm. The ectoderm provides the structural basis of the central nervous system, skin, hair, and nails. Some of the known adverse factors that affect the unborn child are maternal: infection, nutrition, chronic illness, drug ingestion, radiation, trauma, anoxia, and possibly emotional distress. The evidence for the latter is scanty. Prematurity, toxemia of pregnancy, and blood incompatibility are other important influences. In short, any factor causing maternal ill health may affect the unborn child.

Our best information concerns the role of maternal infection. Since viruses play such an important role, they will be discussed in a later section. Syphilis, before the advent of antibiotics, was a common form of congenital disease, causing prematurity, keratitis, rhagades, mental defect, and bony changes (Benda, 1942). Spirochaetal invasion of the nervous system causes the mental defect.

Nowadays, with compulsory premarital and prenatal tests for syphilis and adequate penicillin therapy, this form of mental defect is uncommon.

Toxoplasmosis is a protozoan disease that usually is undiagnosed in the general population. However, when a mother contracts the disease early in pregnancy, congenital anomalies involving the central nervous system occur. Toxoplasmosis is a common disease. Nearly one-third of the population carry antibodies to this organism. Manner of infection is not definitively known, but raw meat (sheep) is known to be a vector. Presumably there are other important methods of spread; for toxoplasmosis is widespread in the United States. An infant infected by toxoplasma may exhibit serious anomalies of the central nervous system of choroiditis. Intracranial calcifications are commonly noted in skull X rays. Mental defect and convulsions usually occur (Feldman and Miller, 1956). No therapy is of proven value yet. It may account for one-half per cent of the mentally retarded. The clinical diagnosis can be confirmed by antibody studies on the mother and a positive skin test on the affected child.

Cytomegalic virus inclusion disease (salivary gland virus infection) is a recently described maternal infection causing "flu" (Weller and Hanshaw, 1962). Yet the infant can be severely affected ranging from microcephaly to normal intelligence with mild spastic diplegia. Treatment is not available yet. Signs of the disease are mental defect, choroiditis, and intracranial calcifications on X ray of the skull. The virus can be grown easily from the urine of the affected infant.

Any chronic maternal illness such as hypertension, renal disease, or diabetes increases the risk to the unborn child. One such example is maternal phenylketonuria (Forbes, 1965). In this disease, the serum phenylalanine is elevated in the mother, possibly causing in utero damage to the infant's developing brain. The fetus of a galactosemic mother may suffer brain damage if the mother does not observe dietary restriction of galactose during her pregnancy. The latter situation has not been described; however, there have been several cases of maternal phenylketonuria in which offspring were defective.

The hypothesis that severe maternal malnutrition causes an increased prevalence of congenital defect in offspring has not yet been proven clearly, although the evidence is suggestive (Antonov, 1947). I have observed mental retardation in children of mothers who develop pernicious anemia during the pregnancy. It seems conceivable that a deficiency of vitamin B-12 in utero is damaging to the central nervous system. Studies in experimental animals have shown increased occurrence of anomalies with various maternal vitamin deficiencies (Warkany, 1947).

Drug ingestion of various kinds have been shown to cause a variety of malformations. The drug thalidomide is the most recent example of the danger of maternal ingestion of drugs during pregnancy. Thalidomide taken during the first trimester causes limb malformations of a severe degree. Various antimetabolic drugs such as folic acid antagonists or mercaptopurine induce miscarriage. Antidiabetic drugs may be dangerous. Cortisone has been shown to increase the rate of congenital defects in experimental animals. Excessive cigarette smoking by the mother has been incriminated recently as a cause for an increased rate of prematurity. Quinine taken to induce abortion may cause deafness in the newborn if the attempt is unsuccessful.

Radiation is harmful when the fetus is less than three months old. This was discovered in the 1930s when radiation treatment for cancer of the uterus in pregnant mothers caused microcephaly and other anomalies in their offspring. Nowadays dilatation and curettage of the womb is performed prior to radiation therapy for cancer of the uterus. Other evidence that exposure of the pregnant mother to radiation is harmful was obtained by studying Japanese mothers who survived the atomic bombings of Hiroshima and Nagasaki. Microcephaly was observed in the offspring of mothers who were in the early period of pregnancy and located close to the epicenter. Similar evidence has been gathered by study of experimental animals exposed to radiation during pregnancy and examination of the offspring.

Maternal anoxia due to near-drowning, accidental suffocation, or carbon monoxide poisoning can affect the unborn child. The evidence that maternal trauma can cause damage to the unborn baby is unclear, but logic dictates that it is reasonable to assume trauma of any kind to the abdomen might cause premature separation of the placenta and thus secondary anoxia and premature delivery. Attempted abortion by introduction of foreign objects into the uterus of course can injure the fetus.

The role of emotional stress during the pregnancy is unclear, but here again it is reasonable to assume that any severe stress, either mental or physical, can affect an unborn child. Scientific data on this problem is difficult to obtain. Suffice it to say that the healthier the pregnancy from all aspects, the better the chance there is for the newborn baby to be normal.

A major contributor to mental retardation is prematurity, which alone accounts for 24.5 per cent of all neonatal deaths (Gold, 1962). It is associated with 15 to 20 per cent of all cases of mental retardation. An infant is classified as premature if his birth weight is less than 2500 grams (5 pounds and 8 ounces). In some South American countries where maternal nutrition is inadequate, this empirical figure is estimated to range between 2200 and 2300 grams. Mortality and morbidity are directly related to birth weight. Survival chances are excellent for infants weighing over 2000 grams but drop to as low as 10 per cent when less than 1000 grams in weight. This relationship of mortality to birth weight is not completely understood. It is thought that the more premature the fetus, the greater mortality is related to the immaturity of certain body tissues. This is probably the correct answer, but when one remembers the unhappy consequences from overzealous administration of oxygen in the infants with retrolental fibroplasia, one cannot be sure. I stress again that iatrogenic factors may be playing a role in the high mortality and morbidity in very small babies.

Several factors account for the high prevalence of cerebral damage in the premature baby:

1. Fetal position is important because the premature infant's small size predisposes him to abnormal position within the womb. The occurrence of breech, transverse, or some other abnormal presentation is higher with the premature. Since increased mortality and morbidity are associated with abnormal presenta-

tion, it is understandable that the premature infant is at greater risk.

2. The immaturity of certain organ systems obviously can lead to difficulties. The infant is a delicate "unfinished" creature. Neonatal lung collapse is more common in the premature. The problem of hyaline membrane disease is peculiarly related to premature birth. Liver immaturity is a serious problem. The liver may be unable to adequately handle the many metabolic tasks that it must to carry on extrauterine existence. Hyperbilirubinemia, common in the newborn, is related to deficient transference activity in the liver, which results in the baby being unable to properly metabolize bilirubin, a bile pigment. The retained pigment accumulates in the blood stream causing the infant to become jaundiced (yellow). When the level of bilirubin exceeds 20 mg. per cent, damage may result as manifested by deafness, athetosis, and mental retardation. The kidneys are also known to be immature. Accordingly, formula requiring less renal function usually is prescribed for the premature baby.

3. Twinning often causes prematurity, but the reason for this is not yet clear. The second twin is born at greater risk because of the problems of longer labor, premature separation of the placenta, anoxia, and sometimes the failure to diagnose twin birth.

4. Premature births are at greater risk because they are more often associated with significant maternal illness such as the Rh incompatibility, toxemia of pregnancy, maternal diabetes, etc. Frequent pregnancies may lead to prematurity.

Maternal toxemia is a severe condition of pregnancy that can be eliminated almost completely by good prenatal care. The cause of toxemia is not yet known. Almost always associated with the third trimester of pregnancy, it manifests itself by hypertension, headache, edema, and albuminuria. If untreated, convulsions, coma, and death may result. It accounts for one-third of maternal deaths.

Treatment consists of salt restriction, rest, and sedation. The condition is identified easily by blood pressure determination and frequent urinalysis for albumin. Some authorities suggest that infants born of mothers with unrecognized toxemia are at greater risk. This is certainly true in severe cases of convulsions and coma. If toxemia results in premature delivery, then of course morbidity is related to the degree of prematurity as well. A longitudinal study of babies born to toxemic mothers is needed urgently.

In summary, many prenatal factors are of grave importance (Drillien, 1964; Lesser, 1964). Maternal factors may be the most important events leading to mental retardation. Several important factors have not been discussed here. These are the curious relationships of maternal age to several types of congenital abnormalities such as Down's syndrome. Young and older mothers run greater risks in both neonatal mortality and morbidity. The significant increase in mortality and morbidity in the unwed mother also needs greater study. In my opinion, we are just beginning to pay greater heed to this very important period of fetal life. The maternal infant care projects of the Children's Bureau and the Collaborative Cerebral Palsy project of the National Institute of Neurological Diseases and Blindness will do much to shed light on this much neglected period of life.

THE ROLE OF VIRUSES AS PRENATAL ETIOLOGICAL AGENTS

The first real breakthrough in this area came just a little more than a decade ago when an Australian opthalmologist discovered that many children with cataracts had mothers who had had rubella (German measles) during their first trimester of pregnancy. Congenital anomalies produced by any kind of intrauterine event usually result from events during the first trimester of pregnancy. Infections after the first trimester are more likely to produce only superficial damage.

Well over 150 viruses have been isolated from human beings, and a certain number of these have been related to specific disease syndromes, and a great number still have not. Many viral infections are difficult to recognize. We all can recognize measles, rubella, chicken pox—the old-fashioned contagious diseases that produce rather definite and clear-cut clinical syndromes. Other viruses, and particularly the enteroviruses, which are invaders of the intestinal tract and to some extent the bloodstreams at times, causing a large variety of minor illness, are very difficult to differentiate. Only by doing specific laboratory studies

is it possible to define these rather minor and overlapping clinical syndromes.

What happens when a virus invades a human being? The body's method of identifying this invader as something foreign and of forming antibodies has survival value for the host, and is usually to the detriment of the parasite. These things occur regularly, and we all have these mechanisms in us, which are summed up under the term "immunology."

The developing embryo lacks such a mechanism. So when a virus enters the placenta and penetrates to the embryo, events are likely to be considerably different. The mother has the immune response, but the intrauterine embryo does not, and the result probably is that most viral infections that invade the embryo or fetus result in death and subsequent abortion. This seems to apply in poliomyelitis, in which there is a marked increase in the number of fetal deaths after infection of pregnant mothers. However, in babies who survive, major anomalies are infrequent. The same applies in mumps and infectious hepatitis, viral diseases that have been studied carefully in this regard. Obviously, not all women who have infections have fetal death and abort. Some of them do not, and it may be that the critical event is whether the virus entering the bloodstream of the mother penetrates the placenta to the fetus.

Influenza, a well-known virus disease that produces respiratory illness with aches and pains, does not produce fetal death and does not seem to produce anomalies. A follow-up study of mothers who were pregnant during the 1957–1958 influenza outbreak did not reveal an increased occurrence of anomalies in their offspring—probably because influenza virus does not regularly invade the blood stream but remains in the respiratory tract.

The only known virus that frequently produces anomalies in newborn babies is rubella, the three-day measles, or German measles. The syndrome is fairly well-defined. If rubella occurs in the first four weeks of pregnancy, about half of the embryos will be killed by the virus, another 25 per cent will have major congenital anomalies, and about 25 per cent will be entirely normal. If rubella occurs during the second four weeks, fetal death remains at about 50 per cent, but the incidence of anomalies falls to about 10 per cent. During the third four weeks, fetal death does not seem to occur from rubella, but there still is a persistent occurrence of major congenital anomalies in the order of 5 to 7 per cent. In addition, the babies who have no anomalies, and who survive, are apt to be premature and will have birth weights below normal.

A little applied embryology in this situation will give us an idea of what anomalies to expect. For each organ there is a critical period of development when the primordium of this organ first appears in the embryo. For the eye, which is the commonest affected organ in the rubella syndrome, the critical period is probably from the fourth to the tenth week. Cataract, a lenticular opacity, results from interference of development of the lens, usually around the fourth week. Retinal problems in the eye and other eye disturbances result from rubella in the second four weeks.

The heart is in a fairly critical stage of development throughout the entire first trimester. The valves and septa, which divide the heart into its various chambers and secure the proper flow of blood through it, are affected most during the first five weeks of gestation of the embryo. The ductus arteriosus is a shunt between the aorta and the pulmonary artery that closes normally at birth. It appears that infection with rubella any time during the first trimester at least can result in an abnormal ductus arteriosus that remains open.

The teeth are affected in the rubella syndrome, and these are at a critical stage from the sixth to the ninth week. The anomalies that result from rubella at this stage are pointed incisors and hypoplasia of the enamel, which causes a marked increase of dental caries later on.

The development of the brain is still not complete at birth. A critical period cannot be assigned accurately, embryologically speaking, but it appears to be throughout the first trimester. Microcephaly may occur from rubella infection any time during the first three months of pregnancy. After the first three months, despite the fact that the brain is far from completely developed, this does not seem to be a problem.

Deafness is a common problem in post-maternal rubella babies. Curiously, this defect may be either bilateral, or unilateral. The unilateral cases are much more difficult to diagnose, and are not picked up until the child is usually considerably older.

All of these problems—the eyes, the heart, the teeth, the brain, and hearing—may occur in various combinations, but mental retardation is probably involved in about one-half of the children who have the so-called rubella syndrome. How can we prevent this? Because the rubella virus has been isolated just recently in the laboratory, adequate vaccination procedures are still in the experimental stages. Widespread immunization will undoubtedly become available soon. Obviously prevention by compulsory immunization will be the most efficacious. At present human volunteers can be infected easily since rubella is a very benign disease with few complications. A young girl ought to contract it before she grows up and becomes a mother. However, it is not absolutely certain that exposure to and subsequent production of rubella in a little girl will protect her completely from a recurrence of rubella.

Another procedure that has been used is passive immunization. This involves taking serum from children who have had rubella recently and whose blood, therefore, contains a fairly large amount of antibodies to rubella and giving the serum to the exposed pregnant mother in order to prevent the disease from occurring. This is partially effective, but by no means completely so, because it is difficult to obtain enough rubella serum from the blood of children who recently had the disease. This is because any serum that is transmitted from one person to another may carry that virus from the inapparent carrier to the person who receives it. Pooled gamma globulin, which is really the antibody protein from a large amount of adult blood collected by pharmaceutical houses in their blood banks and fractionated to obtain a concentration of the antibody protein, has been used as well. This preparation does not have much rubella antibody in it; so a large dose has to be given, and effectiveness is still limited. However, if a dose of 2/10 c.c. per pound of body weight is given to an exposed pregnant mother, some reduction in the incidence of sequellae can be expected.

The third and most drastic approach has been that of therapeutic abortion of mothers who have had rubella during the first trimester of their pregnancy. This approach raises very difficult and complex questions, and no rule whatsoever can be made about it. One must evaluate it in relationship to the individual who is involved. Obviously, the situation of a mother who has six normal children is different from one involving a first pregnancy in an older mother.

To summarize, there is about a one-in-six risk of major anomalies occurring from rubella infection in the first trimester. With other virus infections, this effect has not been studied intensively due to a marked increase in fetal death. The relationship of many viruses to this problem still remains to be studied.

NEONATAL FACTORS

The important elements in the neonatal period are the mother's health, the process of labor and delivery, and the infant's condition at birth. The mother's health was discussed earlier. Maternal diabetes and toxemia are the two most important conditions affecting the newborn, in addition to the problem of blood incompatibility due to the Rh factor. Maternal diabetes predisposes the infant to greater variations of blood sugar; neonatal respiratory ailments are more common. Prematurity is also related to maternal diabetes as is a slightly higher occurrence of congenital anomalies. Maternal toxemia sometimes manifests itself during the process of labor by onset of convulsions. This can, of course, complicate delivery, and is accompanied by increased infant and maternal mortality. A mother who is delivering her first child is a primipara. Her labor will be longer and harder than that of the mother who is delivering her third or fourth baby (a multipara). The length of labor for a primiparous mother is about eighteen hours.

The process of labor is not understood completely yet. The factors that initiate the onset of labor need more study. Labor is divided arbitrarily into two stages. Uterine contractions with rupture of the "bag of waters" (amniotic fluid escape) usually are the first signs of the first stage of active labor. Here the control mechanisms of the speed of labor are not understood clearly. Labor may proceed too rapidly and result in a precipitate delivery, usually a matter of several minutes. This is undesirable because the fetal head molds too rapidly and then with actual delivery re-expands too rapidly, predisposing to rupture of capillary vessels resulting in intracranial hemorrhage. On the other hand, prolonged labor due to a variety of factors may be harmful, too. Uterine inertia, contracted pelvis, excessive head size, an exceedingly large baby, or an abnormal position of the baby in utero can cause prolonged labor resulting in maternal exhaustion or neonatal anoxia. Decrease in fetal heart rate or elimination of meconium by the fetus are the common signs of fetal distress.

The second stage of labor begins with completion of cervical dilation and is complete with delivery. Usually this stage is the most difficult and the physician is apt to prescribe anesthesia. Morphine and other anesthesia seldom are used anymore. Carbon tetrachloride usage has also been abandoned in the United States. Carbon dioxide ("laughing gas") and oxygen, spinal anesthesia, saddleblock, and caudle anesthesia are some of the common procedures utilized. Natural delivery without medication ("The Read Method") is, of course, the safest for the baby. It is said to be used in Russia and has been used here.

The position of the baby in utero obviously influences the course of labor. The cephalic delivery (head first) is more easily delivered than a breech birth. A transverse position is the most serious. Sometimes an infant in the latter position will present with an arm or shoulder. This makes delivery impossible. Before modern obstetrics, such presentation usually resulted in arrested labor and maternal death. Today an emergency Caesarean section or an actual turning of the baby can be performed. It seems evident that brain damage occurs more frequently in breech and transverse deliveries. About 3 per cent of babies are born from these two positions. Presentation of the baby is also defined by the position of the occiput of the head with reference to the pelvis. The commonest is the left occiput anterior (LOA). Face presentations are more difficult to deliver, but should pose no major problems to the skilled obstetrician.

Sometimes the birth process is complicated by anomalies of the uterus. These are rare, but rupture of the uterus due to prior surgical procedures such as a section must always be kept in mind. The location of placental implantation is important. The placenta nearly always is located in the fundus of the uterus. On occasion, though, it may implant over the cervical opening. This condition is called placenta previa. This is a dangerous condition to both mother and child because the infant cannot be delivered without removal of the placenta first. When this happens, neonatal anoxia results due to interference with oxygen supply from the maternal circulation. When this condition is diagnosed, Caesarean section is usually performed.

In rare cases, the placenta separates from the uterus prematurely. This condition (placenta abruptcio) is highly dangerous because intrauterine bleeding may occur without detection. In such cases, the baby often succumbs and, if the bleeding is not discovered, the mother may be endangered by loss of blood and shock.

The cord may be too short or too long. When too short, rupture may occur with hemorrhage. When too long, the cord may prolapse and present at the cervical opening before the head is delivered. This, of course, causes compression of the cord between the head and pelvis causing anoxia. Fortunately, this is a rare occurrence.

Years ago pelvic deformity in cases of maternal rickets was fairly common. Nowadays, automobile accidents resulting in pelvic fractures can cause similar problems. Any mother who delivers a baby after a pelvic injury should be cared for by a skilled obstetrician in case the deformity is great enough to interfere with normal labor.

Birth injury with intracranial hemorrhage or neonatal anoxia used to be considered a common cause of mental retardation. With the advances of modern obstetrics, this is unusual.

Forceps deliveries once were thought to be the cause of many birth injuries resulting in neurological disturbances in the newborn, but now it is felt that the more likely causative factors are the effects of either too prolonged or too precipitate a delivery. Low forceps deliveries minimize the chance of birth injury. High or mid-forceps delieveries should be performed only by a skilled obstetrician.

The baby's status at birth may be affected by congenital anomalies of the brain, convulsions, metabolic disorders, and respiratory depression. If the baby has a developmental abnormality of the brain, he may be apneic or lethargic with poor sucking and cough reflexes. Convulsions during the newborn period are not an uncommon problem. They are due to a variety of causes, but it is thought that intracranial hemorrhage is the most frequent reason. Tetany of the newborn is due to a disorder of calcium and phosphorus metabolism caused by immature kidneys. The convulsions due to tetany rarely cause brain damage. However, those associated with intracranial hemorrhage often are related to various degrees of brain injury. Sometimes convulsions are associated with infections of the brain, in which case mortality is high (Levinson and Bigler, 1960). Another cause for convulsions is hypoglycemia. This disease is manifested by a low blood sugar resulting in convulsions and brain damage. Respiratory depression is treated by a variety of stimulants and resuscitatory measures.

The problem of Rh incompatibility must be recognized and treated appropriately during the newborn period. The Rhesus factor is present in 85 per cent of our population, that is, they are Rh positive. Rh negative (absence of Rhesus factor) causes difficulty only if the mother is Rh negative and the father Rh positive. Since Rh positive is dominant in such a mating, usually only Rh positive offspring occur. Thus, the Rh negative mother carries an Rh positive fetus. The Rh positive fetus immunizes the mother slowly during pregnancy. This occurs by traces of the fetal blood entering the maternal circulation. The mother then begins to build up antibody defenses against the Rh positive factor. Small amounts of the antibody get into the fetal circulation, and then an antigen antibody reaction occurs that destroys the baby's red cells, on which the Rh factor is located. The Coombs test can be performed at the time of birth in suspected cases to determine if maternal antibody has been produced against the Rh factor. If the Coombs test is positive, an exchange transfusion may be indicated, because maternal antibody can destroy most of the red cells in the newborn baby's blood. If untreated, the breakdown products of red cell destruction can cause brain damage by interfering with oxygen uptake by nervous tissue. For this reason, exchange transfusion may need to be done one, two, or three times to remove recurring quantities of bilirubin, which is the toxic substance released by the red cell destruction. The bilirubin can be measured chemically in the baby's blood and a level of over 20 mg. per cent is considered unsafe.

Other blood problems, such as major blood group (AB-O) incompatibility, can cause neonatal difficulty too, but these are less common.

Many children who show abnormal neurological symptoms at birth do not necessarily have trouble in later life; the outcome of such manifestations cannot be predicted with accuracy during the neonatal period. The best treatment should be given and the child carefully checked over a period of time for signs of brain damage during routine pediatric examinations.

POSTNATAL FACTORS

Brain damage producing mental retardation may be caused by a variety of factors. The commonest are infections of the central nervous system, trauma, poisons, anoxia, and endocrine disorders. Other less common causes are neoplasia, uncontrolled convulsive disorders, and allergic reactions (Tarjan, Wright, Dingman, and Sabagh, 1959). The problem is somewhat complicated because several types of physical handicaps, emotional problems, and cultural and maternal deprivation may cause a child with normal intellect to function at a retarded level (Koch, Graliker, Bronston, and Fishler, 1965).

Whether severe nutritional deprivation in itself causes mental retardation is not yet clear. Several experts do feel that nutritional depletion during infancy causes mental retardation. Evidence has accumulated that older children seem to withstand calorie deprivation without mental retardation. Specific vitamin deficiency, however, does cause mental defect. Pellagra is the most common and is due to deficiency of nicotinamide (B-5). Deficiency of pyridoxine (B-6) causes convulsions in infancy, but it is not clear whether mental retardation occurs. Of course, lack of iodine in the diet has been known to cause goiter and secondary hypothyroidism and mental retardation for many years. This condition at one time was very common in the Great Lakes region of the United States and the Alps in Europe. Iodized salt has solved the problem in many countries, but several South American nations still do not utilize this simple method of prevention of mental retardation. Iron deficiency does not itself cause mental retardation. However, secondary anemia resulting from it certainly causes slow development.

Infections may be due to either viruses, bacteria, protozoans, fungi, or other parasites. The term encephalitis is applied to infection of the central nervous system due to a virus. The viruses responsible for such illnesses are difficult to identify and progress has been slow. The Eastern equine, Western equine, and Japanese B viruses all causes encephalitis. Occasionally, even the poliomyelitis virus can cause polioencephalitis. Other viruses—such as echo, coxsackie, measles, chicken pox, and mumps —also may invade the central nervous system but do not ordinarily cause severe brain damage similar to that produced by the previously mentioned viruses.

Infection of the brain due to bacteria is termed meningitis (Koch, Kogut, and Asay, 1961). Any of the common bacterial agents can cause meningitis. The most common forms in children are due to Hemophilus influenzae Type B, pneumococcus, and meningococcus. Children with meningitis are acutely and seriously ill and are always considered medical emergencies. Fever, headache, and a stiff neck and back are common early symptoms. Convulsions occurring during meningitis are a serious sign. With adequate therapy most children survive, although 10 to 20 per cent may exhibit residual brain damage resulting in mental retardation, convulsions, behavior disorders, or deafness. Fungi, protozoans, and other parasites occasionally invade the brain and cause damage, but cases of this kind are relatively rare in our country.

Tuberculosis is not a serious problem in our country. The organism responsible for this disease does invade the central nervous system in children, however, and can cause serious damage. Tuberculous meningitis invariably is secondary to a primary pulmonary infection that is generally contracted from one of the parents or grandparents. When infection of the brain occurs, fever, headache, vomiting, and convulsions develop.

Prompt diagnosis by examination of the cerebrospinal fluid can easily be made by finding white cells and staining the fluid for the acid-fast bacillus. Treatment consists of isoniazid, streptomycin, and para-aminosalicylic acid. Recovery is dependent upon the degree of tuberculous invasion present at the time of initiation of therapy. Early diagnosis favors complete recovery.

Trauma (injury) is an increasing problem in our country, especially with the high automobile accident rate. Of course, any serious injury to the skull can cause brain damage. Trauma to the brain is usually accompanied by unconsciousness. Nausea, vomiting, and incoherency are noted when the subject begins to recover. In a minor injury with or without skull fracture, recovery is rapid and complete within a week or two. In serious cerebral injury, the patient may remain unconscious for weeks and still recover. Where actual destruction of brain tissue occurs, such as in the case of a depressed skull fracture, recovery is determined by the extent of injury. If persistent vomiting follows cerebral injury, subdural hematoma should be suspected. In acute subdural hematoma, a major artery of the brain is usually injured, releasing blood into the subdural space between the dura and the brain. The accumulation of blood compresses the brain and must be treated promptly by surgical removal. The child with chronic subdural hematoma usually has a history of vomiting, enlarging head, failing vision, and convulsions. Diagnosis is generally easy since the above symptoms are recognized readily. Treatment again consists of surgical removal of the blood clots over the brain.

The "battered child" syndrome is always suspected clinically when a parent does not volunteer a history of injury for an infant with skull fracture or subdural hematoma. I have seen several such children who are mentally retarded due to repetitive cerebral injury.

Among the various poisons that can cause brain damage, lead (Cohen and Ahrens, 1959) is a major offender, particularly in the eastern states. If lead ingestion is chronic, deposits in various tissues occur and there is interference with brain cell metabolism. The retardation is generally severe. The common source of lead intoxication is old paint ingestion or battery fume inhalation.

Anoxia can be a secondary occurrence to any suffocating episode. Accidental drowning is not an uncommon cause. Cardiac arrest may produce severe brain damage because of lack of oxygenated blood circulating through the brain. Accidental suffocation in plastic bags or by cord strangling following the same principle of oxygen deprivation may result ultimately in death. Another example of oxygen deprivation is carbon monoxide poisoning, which causes anoxia by preventing hemoglobin from carrying oxygen to the brain. Severe anemia can act in a similar manner, but symptoms like lethargy and pallor lead to diagnosis and therapeutic intervention.

The only major endocrine disease associated with mental retardation is hypothyroidism. Retardation results from a deficiency in the thyroid hormone function, which is necessary for proper brain cell metabolism. The early symptoms are lethargy, weight gain in spite of poor appetite, personality changes, stunted growth, pudgy facial features, sparse hair, dry skin, constipation, anemia, and mental retardation. A diagnosis is verified by finding elevated blood cholesterol levels, reduced circulating protein-bound iodine in the blood, and by measuring skeletal growth by X rays of the wrist. The protein-bound iodine test is usually below 4.8 micrograms and the skeletal age retarded to a significant degree. Early diagnosis is paramount for optimal therapeutic results. Treatment is effective and consists of merely prescribing thyroid extract.

Metabolic diseases account for about 5 per cent of all retardation (Koch, Graliker, Fishler, and Parmelee, 1962). These are usually genetically determined diseases that make their presence known only after birth. For instance, the phenylketonuric child is usually not recognized clinically until 3 to 12 months of age when retardation becomes apparent (Slack, Simpson, and Hsia, 1960).

Hypoglycemia, another metabolic disease causing mental retardation, is characterized by a low, uncontrollable blood sugar level, which is thought to deprive the brain of energy. The low blood sugar level induces convulsions that ordinarily permit a physician to make the proper diagnosis. Steroid drugs and dietary measures are used for treatment.

Severe uncontrolled convulsive disorders can also cause mental retardation, but these are uncommon in our experience.

Neoplasms or cancer can cause retardation because of the progressive expansion of the diseased cell growth. This is not a common problem, and with improved surgical techniques, there are at least means of fighting it.

The various degenerative diseases of the

central nervous system are not well classified yet and even less well understood. Schilder's disease is an example.

Allergic reactions sometimes are responsible for brain damage. Examples of such reactions are the postvaccinal encephalitis cases after smallpox, or rabies post-immunization reactions.

It is not uncommon for a severely disturbed child to be seen in a mental retardation clinic. Five per cent of the children seen in the clinic at the Childrens Hospital of Los Angeles are variously diagnosed as autistic, schizophrenic, or atypical. They are usually males 3 to 6 years old whose parents describe them as "different" from early infancy. They tend to twirl and play with spinning objects. Toe walking is sometimes seen. These children often are mute, play for long periods alone, and are seldom affectionate. Whether this condition is purely environmental has been hotly disputed. Some authorities think this condition can be brought on by both physical and environmental factors together or either alone. Regardless of etiology, prognosis is poor even with treatment. Behavior disorders accompanying mental retardation are common.

Occasionally a normal child with a speech or hearing defect is mistakenly thought to be retarded. Familial-cultural factors (Coleman and Provence, 1957) may further confuse the issue. Sometimes a clear-cut diagnosis cannot be made until the child has been seen several times over a period of several months or even years.

Craniosynostosis. A normal skull X ray of the newborn reveals open coronal, sagittal, lambdoid, metopic, and temporal sutures. These sutures, or joints, are available for expansion. In the newborn, the cranial bones can be separated very easily, and, as the brain grows, the skull stretches. In the adult skull, the sutures are solid and fused together securely. The term, craniosynostosis, means fused cranium, fusion of the various cranial bones. The most common form of craniosynostosis involves the sagittal or central suture running down the crown of the head from front to back. Sagittal synostosis accounted for about 63 per cent of the cases seen at the Childrens Hospital of Los Angeles. This suture normally should be open and the brain allowed to grow for at least twelve years. In babies

with craniosynostosis, however, it is fused at birth. In these children, the head is dolichocephalic because the head cannot broaden. It is proportionately longer than wide and consequently appears narrow. In babies with coronal synostosis, the shape of the head is broad and high, but short. Occasionally only one side of the coronal suture is fused early. In such cases asymmetry of the skull results. Left coronal fusion results in the left parietal-frontal cranial bones being smaller than those on the right. There is elevation of the right eyebrow, some recession of the left eye, flattening of the left forehead on the one side only. If the metopic suture is fused at birth, the head anteriorly becomes rather triangular in appearance (trigonocephaly). In rare cases, all the joints in the skull are fused prematurely, a serious problem that usually is associated with brain anomaly.

Operative techniques have been devised to deal with these problems. Channels are cut into the skull to substitute false joints for the prematurely fused sutures. These are made parallel to or in the line of the fused joints. This provides a means for the cranial bones to separate and allow the brain to grow. This method has been evolved over a good many years and is entirely satisfactory.

This is a relatively common disorder. Before 1944, there were only eight cases of this disorder reported at the Childrens Hospital. Between 1954 and 1960, there were at least 100.

Hydrocephalus. Hydrocephalus means water-head. Not all children with a large head have hydrocephalus. The head may be large for a considerable number of reasons. Some people just have unusually large heads. This may be a familial characteristic. Subdural hematoma and brain tumor also may cause enlargement of the cranium.

In hydrocephalus, the cerebrospinal fluid is obstructed in its normal flow in the ventricles of the brain or the fluid is not properly absorbed back into the blood stream. The cause is usually congenital but can follow conditions such as meningitis, brain tumor, and subdural hematoma. The former type is called an obstructive hydrocephalus; the latter is termed a communicating type. In hydrocephalus, the ventricles become large due to retained fluid. The fluid causes pressure atrophy of the cortex. Early operation is mandatory for satisfactory results. The excess fluid is drained from the ventricle by a tube via the superior vena cava into the heart.

Another cause of hydrocephalus is congenital deformity of the spine. The so-called meningocele or myelomeningocele is accompanied by distortion or derangement of the spinal cord, cerebellum, and base of the brain. When these occur, the head may enlarge; however, the spinal deformity is the major problem. Interruption of spinal nerve pathways occur, and diplegia, loss of bladder and rectal control, and loss of sensation of the lower extremities are common. When hydrocephalus complicates the problem, neurological intervention may not be feasible. The prognosis is poor in such cases.

The postnatal causes of mental retardation are so numerous and varied that it is difficult to categorize them adequately. Many of them are controllable, but society has not developed to the point where constructive action is possible. This is particularly true of under-developed nations in Africa, Asia, and Latin America. In the United States the prevention of mental retardation is finally receiving increasing attention. This move will be strengthened further by an enlightened citizenry during the next decades.

REFERENCES

ABT, I. A. Amaurotic family idiocy. *Amer. J. Dis. Child.*, 1911, *1*, 59.

ANTONOV, A. N. Children born during the siege of Leningrad in 1942. *J. Pediat.*, 1947, *30*, 250.

BENDA, C. E. Congenital syphilis in mental deficiency. *Amer. J. ment. Defic.*, 1942, *47*, 40–48.

BOWMAN, P. W., and MAUTNER, H. V. *Proceedings of the first international medical conference on mental retardation.* New York: Grune and Stratton, 1960.

BUCK, P. *The child who never grew.* New York: John Day, 1950.

CHAO, DORA. Congenital neurocutaneous syndromes in childhood: II. Tuberous sclerosis. *J. Pediat.*, 1959, *55*, 447–459.

COHEN, G. J., and AHRENS, W. E. Chronic lead poisoning. *J. Pediat.*, 1959, *54*, 271–284.

COLEMAN, R. W., and PROVENCE, S. Environmental retardation (hospitalism) in infants living in families. *Pediatrics*, 1957, *19*, 285.

CROTHERS, B., and PAINE, R. S. *The natural history of cerebral palsy.* Cambridge, Mass.: Harvard University Press, 1959.

DOLL, E. A. The inheritance of social competence. *J. Hered.*, 1937, *28*, 153.

DONNELL, G. N., BERGREN, W. R., and CLELAND, R. S. Galactosemia. *Pediat. Clin. N. America*, 1960, *7*, 315.

DRILLIEN, CECIL M. *The growth and development of the prematurily born infant.* Baltimore: Williams and Wilkins, 1964.

FELDMAN, H. A., and MILLER, L. T. Congenital human toxoplasmosis. *Ann. N. Y. Acad. Sci.*, 1956, *64*, 180.

FORBES, N., *et al.* Maternal phenylketonuria. *Nursing Outlook*, in press.

GARDNER, W. I., and NISONGER, H. W. A manual on program development in mental retardation. *Amer. J. ment. Defic., Monogr. Suppl.*, 1962, *66* (4), 25.

GOLD, E. M. A broad view of maternity care. *Children*, 1962, *9* (8), 52–58.

HEBER, R. Manual on terminology and classification in mental retardation. *Amer. J. ment. Defic., Monogr. Suppl.*, 1959, *64* (2).

HSIA, D. Y. *Inborn errors of metabolism.* Chicago: Year Book Medical Publishers, 1959, 107–112, 132–137.

ILLINGWORTH, R. S. *The development of the infant and young child, normal and abnormal.* London: E. and S. Livingstone, 1960.

Josiah Macy Jr. Foundation. *New directions in community planning for mentally retarded children.* New York: Author, 1956.

KIRK, S. A., KARNES, M. D., and KIRK, W. D. *You and your retarded child.* (5th ed.) New York: Macmillan, 1958, 1–2.

KNUDSON, A. *Genetics and disease.* New York: McGraw-Hill, 1965.

KOCH, R., GRALIKER, BETTY V., BRONSTON, W., and FISHLER, K. Mental retardation in early childhood. *Amer. J. Dis. Child.,* 1965, *109,* 243.

———, ———, FISHLER, K., and PARMELEE, A. H. Mental retardation in early childhood. *Postgrad.* Med., 1962, *31,* 169–177.

———, KOGUT, M., and ASAY, L. Management of bacterial meningitis in children. *Pediat. Clin. N. America,* 1961, *8,* 1177.

KRETCHMER, N., and ETZWILER, D. D. Disorders associated with the metabolism of phenylalanine and tyrosine. *Pediatrics,* 1958, *21,* 445–475.

LAHEY N. E., LOMAS, R. D., and WORTH, T. C. Gargoylism. *J. Pediat.,* 1947, *31,* 220.

LESSER, A. J. Accent on prevention through improved service. *Children,* 1964, *11,* 13–18.

LEVINSON, A., and BIGLER, J. A. *Mental retardation in infants and children.* Year Book Medical Publishers, 1960, 11–13.

LOWE, C. U., TERREY, M., and MACLACHLAN, E. A. Organic-aciduria, decreased renal ammonia production, hydrophthalmus and mental retardation. *Amer. J. Dis. Child.,* 1952, *83,* 164–184.

MASLAND, R. L., SARASON, S. B., and GLADWIN, T. *Mental subnormality.* New York: Basic Books, 1958.

MONTAGU, M. F. A. *Prenatal influences.* Springfield, Ill.: Charles C Thomas, 1962.

PENROSE, L. S. *The biology of mental defect.* (3rd ed.) New York: Grune and Stratton, 1963.

PEVZNER, M. S. *Oligophrenia: Mental deficiency in children.* New York: Consultants Bureau, 1961.

REED, E. W., and REED, S. C. *Mental retardation: A family study.* Philadelphia: W. B. Saunders, 1965.

SLACK, J., SIMPSON, K., and HSIA, D. H. Hereditary metabolic disorders involving the nervous system. *Pediat. Clin. N. America,* 1960, *7,* 627.

STERN, C. *Principles of human genetics.* (2nd ed.) San Francisco: W. H. Freeman, 1960.

TARJAN, G., WRIGHT, S. W., DINGMAN, H. F., and SABAGH, G. The natural history of mental deficiency in a state hospital: II. Mentally deficient children admitted to a state hospital prior to their sixth birthday. *Amer. J. Dis. Child.,* 1959, *98,* 370–378.

WARKANY, J. Etiology of congenital malformations. *Advances Pediat.,* (N.Y.), 1947, *2,* 1.

WELLER, T. H., and HANSHAW, J. B. Virologic and clinical observations on cytomegalic inclusion disease. *New Eng. J. Med.,* 1962, *266,* 1233.

YANNET, H. Mental deficiency. *Advances Pediat.* (N.Y.), 1956, *8,* 217–257.

Perceptual, Conceptual, and Psycholinguistic Evaluation of the Mentally Retarded Child

ROBERT M. ALLEN and R. WAYNE JONES

3

OUR primary concern in the tests discussed in this chapter is with function rather than with classification alone. According to Gelof (1963), mental retardation is a "deficit in functioning which handicaps certain people in our verbal, technological society" (p. 298). This is the deficit, or more likely deficits, that the psychologist should evaluate.

Benton (1964) defines psychological evaluation as "primarily objective procedures (usually, but not always, standardized) for the assessment of intellectual functioning (e.g., memory, conceptual thinking), language functions, personality, psychomotor skills, and sensory, discrimination capacity" (p. 17). This view of assessment goes beyond a quantitative expression of a measurement. Selected tests that are meant to elicit varying degrees of perceptual, conceptual and psycholinguistic abilities are presented in this chapter. The sole use of the routine standard intelligence tests emphasizes the drawbacks of equating the intelligence test score with "classified" intelligence. This practice tends to overlook the variations in functions of which any one or combination of tests could present a depressed picture of over-all efficiency.

In the evaluation procedure, the testee's responses reveal the psychological bases for behavior. The individual's abilities can be observed but only as they are manifested in an artificial setting, i.e., controlled stimuli and recordable responses. Many such stimulus-response situations, in diversified contexts, furnish descriptions that yield meanings and inferences about the psychological (and for some investigators, neurophysiological) processes intervening between stimulus and response. Furthermore, the profiling of tests in a battery (or subtest findings) contributes to the understanding of the relationships among important facets of behavior. The validity of the test battery is all the more useful if it enhances the prediction of non-test behavior.

Each child should be respected for his uniqueness regardless of the position he may occupy in a classification system. The test referral, the selected tests, and the final report should be in terms of the specific problem or questions presented by the child to the referral source. The latter should ask relevant questions so that the psychologist may review his repertoire of testing procedures with these in mind. The contents of the psychologist's report should communicate clearly the meaning and implications of the findings to the best advantage of the testee. This requires answers for the specific questions posed and perhaps suggestions for remediation based upon the testee's strengths and weaknesses.

The more frequently asked questions concerning the mentally retarded are: (1) the intellectual status and efficiency of the child; (2) areas of assets and deficits for education in specific settings, that is, regular or ungraded class; (3) potential for success in an "educable" or "trainable" curriculum; (4) conjectural limits for training in academic subjects, pre-vocational potential, and self-help development for the activities of daily living. Much useful information deciding the extent of the testee's involvement in these training experiences will be in terms of perceptual, conceptual, and communication efficiency and expectancy. While standard intelligence tests do produce some of these data, this chapter will focus on the specific tests for evaluation in these three major areas.

The tests are divided into four general categories: (1) picture vocabulary tests, (2) drawing tests, (3) verbal and nonverbal intelligence tests, and (4) tests of perceptual, conceptual and psycholinguistic abilities. These categories are not mutually exclusive since all require varying degrees of perceptual, conceptual, and linguistic skills.

PICTURE VOCABULARY TESTS

The three tests in this section are: the Full-Range Picture Vocabulary Test, the Peabody Picture Vocabulary Test, and the Pictorial Test of Intelligence. All have several common attributes:

1. They require adequate vision and hearing.

2. Oral comprehension of directions is necessary.

3. These tests are feasible with handicapped children, especially those who are unable to reply orally to the test items. For the speech-impaired child, pointing to the selected picture is a response. And if a child is unable to do this, he may respond by a nod of the head, a grunt, or an eye blink when the examiner points to the child's chosen alternative on each plate (see Allen and Jefferson, 1962, for suggested procedures).

4. Testing time is brief.

5. Scoring procedures are simple. These point scales have mental age (MA), percentile, and intelligence quotient (IQ) norms.

FULL-RANGE PICTURE VOCABULARY TEST

The Full-Range Picture Vocabulary Test (Ammons and Ammons, 1948) (FRPVT) is a highly reliable and valid individual intelligence measure based on visual recognition of vocabulary comprehension. There are MA norms for children from 2.5 to 16 years old and percentile norms for adults. The two forms of the test have separate word lists for the same sixteen plates containing four line drawings each.

The reliability of the FRPVT is consistently high, ranging from .86 to .99 for different

groups, for example, .87 for mildly to severely emotionally disturbed children (Schramm, 1954), .99 for normal school children (Ammons, Arnold and Herrmann, 1950). No reliability data have been reported for the mentally retarded child.

The validity of the FRPVT has been reported by Ammons and Ammons (1948) to be satisfactorily high. However, the validity of any instrument should not be generalized. The reported validity with standard intellectual measures varies from .81 with the Wechsler Adult Intelligence Scale (WAIS) IQ for 100 adults (Allen, Thornton and Stenger, 1954) to .69 with the Revised Stanford-Binet Scale (Revised S-B) vocabulary score for 360 school children (Ammons, Arnold and Herrmann, 1950).

Only four reports in the last 15 years have specifically evaluated the effectiveness of the FRPVT with the mentally defective child. In an exploratory study with 60 institutionalized male retardates, Sloan and Bensberg (1954) obtained a correlation of .76 between the FRPVT and the Revised S-B Scale. A significant difference of 6.9 points in favor of the FRPVT was found, suggesting that retardates are more proficient at visual recognition than at recall and manipulation of verbal concepts. Cordell (1959) tested 22 retarded Chippewa Indian children with a mean chronological age (CA) of 10.28 years. He reported two correlations, one of .73 between the FRPVT and an abbreviated form of the Revised S-B Scale, and a second correlation of .04 for the FRPVT and Wechsler Intelligence Scale for Children (WISC) performance achievement. He concluded that the FRPVT and the Revised S-B Scale tapped similar mental capacities that differed, in turn, from those evaluated by the WISC performance subtests. These studies suggest that the FRPVT has acceptable concurrent validity but more systematic comparisons of the FRPVT with standard intelligence tests are needed, particularly at different age levels. Research on the predictive validity of the FRPVT with retardates is lacking.

The influence of increase in CA on FRPVT scores was evaluated in a study by Fisher, Shotwell, and York (1960) in which 66 institutionalized retardates were divided into two age groups, one ranging from 18 to 34 years and those above 35 years. The means and standard deviations for the younger retarded group were similar for both tests, the FRPVT and the WAIS IQs. However, the mean FRPVT IQ of the second group of retardates was a significant 7 points lower than the mean WAIS IQ. These investigators feel that the FRPVT underestimates the intellectual level of individuals over 35 years due to a memory loss in vocabulary.

Ho and White (1963) evaluated the influence of home environment on the relationship between the FRPVT and the Revised S-B scores for 100 retarded white children CA 4 to 18 with a median age of 11 years. All children lived at home with their parents or legal guardians. Half of the subjects were in the younger age group, 4 to 11 years, and half were in the older age group, 11 to 18 years. The mean Revised S-B IQ of the younger CA group exceeded that for the older group, 58 to 47. The mean FRPVT IQs were significantly higher than the mean Revised S-B IQs by 16.2 for the younger and 12 IQ points for the older CA group. The authors attribute this efficiency in verbal comprehension to the increased language stimulation the retarded child receives in a home environment.

These studies indicate that the FRPVT correlates significantly with standard intelligence tests. Although the number of studies with retarded children is still quite small, the results show the FRPVT to have concurrent validity. FRPVT attainment, influenced by home and institutional environments and by the CA of the retardate, is sensitive to the kind and frequency of the retardate's visual perceptual experiences, which are not detected as readily by the more academically oriented tests such as the Binet and Wechsler scales.

Several questions remain to be studied. The reliability of the FRPVT particularly over long periods has yet to be reported. Picture vocabulary efficiency in normal children is a useful indication of preparedness for certain types of academic activity, such as reading and spelling (Smith and Filmore, 1954). Does this relationship hold for retardates? Does picture vocabulary skill differentiate those children who could benefit from educable classes from those best placed in a training program?

PEABODY PICTURE VOCABULARY TEST

The Peabody Picture Vocabulary Test (PPVT) (Dunn, 1959) consists of 150 picture plates designed to measure "a subject's verbal intelligence through his hearing vocabulary" (p. 25). MA equivalents are available from 1 year, 9 months, to 18 years, 5 months; also percentile ratings between 2 years, 5 months, and 18 years, 5 months, are provided.

Test-retest reliability coefficients range from .75 with seventh-grade pupils (Tempero and Ivanoff, 1960) to .97 with a small sample of cerebral palsied children (Dunn and Harley, 1959). With educable mental retardates, CA of 6 to 18 years, Dunn and Brooks (1960) obtained a reliability coefficient of .83 for age-equivalent scores between the two forms of this test. The same reliability with trainable retarded subjects from 6 to 16 years old was found by Dunn and Hottel (1961).

Findings by Budoff and Purseglove (1963) support the notion that the correlation between the PPVT and an academically oriented intelligence test, such as the Revised S-B Scale, is an inverse function of developmental level. In their investigation, Budoff and Purseglove obtained a correlation of .68 for retardates with MAs of 8 years and below. Above this MA level, the correlation between the PPVT and the Revised S-B Scale was .38—because of the emphasis on symbolic conceptualization required for the solution of upper age test items. The older and presumably less intellectually efficient and conceptually mature retardates are simply unable to recall and produce at the same level as their ability to recognize experiential phenomena. Budoff and Purseglove also conclude that the PPVT is a fairly accurate estimate of intelligence for mentally retarded adolescents who are functioning in the mild to moderate range of mental retardation. On the other hand, the PPVT is a relatively poor estimate of intelligence in those institutionalized retarded adolescents who function near the borderline range (utilizing the Revised S-B Scale as the criterion). The poor PPVT achievement by the brighter retardates is attributed to the effects of institutionalization and its reduced stimulating climate.

Somewhat different results were obtained by Tobias and Gorelick (1961), who evaluated the validity of the PPVT as a measure of the intelligence of retarded adults using the WAIS as the validity criterion. The PPVT IQ was consistently higher than the WAIS IQ. Furthermore, the PPVT overestimated the MA levels of 38 per cent of these adult retardates when compared with their WAIS MAs. Tobias and Gorelick's hypothesis ". . . that the vocabulary skills of retardates may continue to mature beyond that of the intellectual factors measured by existing instruments" does not seem to be reasonable since the vocabulary "recall" items of the WAIS and Revised S-B Scale go beyond the MA limits of adult retardates. The explanation must be sought in the "recall" versus "recognition" skills. Moreover, the social surrounding of the noninstitutionalized adult retardate is bound to be more effective as teaching and learning sources than the usually more limited atmosphere of the institution. This is especially significant for adult retardates in relation to the duration of their residence at an institution.

Dunn and Brooks (1960) studied the relationship between both forms of the PPVT and Revised S-B Scale and WISC scores. The correlations were .61 (WISC and PPVT IQs) and .76 (PPVT and Revised S-B MAs). The PPVT IQs were consistently above Revised S-B IQs. However, PPVT MAs were lower than the Revised S-B MAs by approximately four months. This apparent discrepancy is a function of the deviation rather than the mathematical modes of deriving the IQ for each test; the deviation in turn affects the respective MA equivalents.

The level of perceptual development, according to Allen, Haupt and Jones (1964), has a significant effect on the accuracy of the PPVT as contrasted with the WISC IQ of the retardate. In a recent paper, they reported that the PPVT gave a satisfactory estimate of intellectual efficiency for retarded children whose perceptual development was appropriate for their mental ages. Among retarded children whose visual perceptual development was impaired severely, the PPVT significantly overestimated the children's intellectual efficiency.

Dunn (1959) states that the PPVT measures "verbal rather than quantitative, social-practical, or mechanical intelligence. It is believed the test will predict language development better than achievement in science and mathematics, though this remains to be demonstrated" (p. 31). This relationship appears to hold with normal children. Tempero and Ivanoff (1960) obtained correlations between .45 and .63 for PPVT scores and subtests in the California Achievement battery. As Dunn predicted, significantly higher relationships were found in the reading areas than in the arithmetic and language mechanics area. Tobias and Gorelick (1961) obtained a similar relationship (.52) between the PPVT and the reading section of the Wide Range Achievement Test for retarded adults living in the community. However, the relationship between PPVT MA scores and teacher's ratings of reading achievement in a large sample of 220 institutionalized trainable retardates was found to be only .39 (Dunn and Hottel, 1961). This suggests that the vocabulary skill of institutionalized retardates is not related closely to the reading skill of the normal child or of the retardate living in the community.

PICTORAL TEST OF INTELLIGENCE

French (1964) devised the Pictorial Test of Intelligence (PTI) ". . . to provide an easily administered, objectively scored individual testing instrument to be used in assessing the general intellectual level of both normal and handicapped children between the ages of 3 and 8" (p. 1).

This test is similar in design to the other picture vocabulary tests. The test cards, with four pictures on each, are kept in a large metal box. The lid of this container may be used as a stand for holding the response and stimulus cards in an upright position for the testee's viewing. This produces a degree of physical standardization in administration that is lacking in other picture vocabulary tests. For the handicapped child having difficulty verbalizing or pointing to the selected picture on the card, the upright position of the response and stimulus cards gives him an easy response cue such as staring fixedly at his choice to indicate its top, bottom, right or left location.

The PTI subtests are: (1) picture vocabulary, (2) form discrimination, (3) information and comprehension, (4) similarities, (5) size and number, and (6) immediate recall. The standardization population consisted of 1,830 children from 3 to 8 years old distributed among four geographic areas of this country. Community size, sex, and occupational level of father also enter into the sampling population selection.

While each subtest correlates significantly with the total test score, there are also significant intersubtest correlations, which, on the surface, may be one weakness of this test. However, this is mitigated by additional perceptual and conceptual information about the testee that makes the PTI a bit different from, and perhaps preferable to, the other picture vocabulary tests.

Test-retest reliability studies yielded stability coefficients varying from .87 to .93 for the long form (all items) and .86 to .88 for the short form (selected items). Jensen's (Bateman, 1964a) thesis was concerned with a two-year test-retest reliability study of the PTI for 36 second-, third-, and fourth-graders. The stability coefficient was .50 as compared with .68 for the Revised S-B Scale, Form LM. The concurrent validity was .70 at CA 6 years, 10 months, and .58 at 8 years, 1 month, between these two tests. Concurrent validity, using the Columbia Mental Maturity Scale (CMMS) as the criterion, produced a coefficient of .65 and .72 respectively. Apparently the PTI comes closer to tapping the ability to deal with concepts based upon verbal symbolization than with the non-verbal concepts assessed by the CMMS. This is in keeping with French's definition of intelligence as the rationale for his test. His definition, the theoretical basis for his test, is ". . . the use of mental ability to function efficiently in the environment. Mental abilities are functioning efficiently when they are used to: (a) perceive verbal and numerical symbols and spatial relationships, (b) acquire and retain general and specific information in common symbol form for reuse at later times, and (c) relate the symbols to each other and manipulate them in the solution of problem situations" (French, 1964, pp. 1-2).

These, not unexpectedly, are the contents of the six subtests of the PTI. French points out that construct validity is still unsatisfactory, but he feels that content and concurrent validities have been established by: (1) linear increase in mean scores for the six subtests with increase in the CA of the population sample, (2) significant and positive correlations with standard intelligence tests, and (3) significant and positive correlations between PTI scores and teachers' judgments of the childrens' intellectual ability. Predictive validity must await the passage of time to permit longitudinal testing.

There is no published research with this test, but Dr. French has informed us that he is involved in a two-year predictive validity study. Abstracts of masters' theses research furnished by Dr. French indicate adequate positive correlations between the PTI and the Revised S-B Scale.

More important, though, was the fact that the PTI IQs were obtained with handicapped children who could not be tested with the standard intelligence tests. The authors adduce from experience with sensory-motor handicapped children that the PTI is a useful test with this particular population.

DRAWING TESTS

These tests require the reproduction of designs from models as in the Visual Motor Gestalt Test (Bender, 1938) (BG) and the Rutgers Drawing Test (Starr, 1952, 1961) (RDT), or the drawing a person with no visual model, Draw-A-Man Test (Goodenough, 1926) (DMT). The latter two are considered by their authors to be tests of intelligence while the first technique focuses on the perceptual-motor aspects of the completed task.

In the BG and RDT, the child is given a pencil and either some blank sheets of paper (BG) or the test sheet with the models to be reproduced thereon (RDT). In each the testee is asked to draw the figures shown. The DMT subject must draw a person, then one of the opposite sex, and finally a figure of himself or herself (Harris, 1963). The level of perceptual maturation, beyond the requisites of adequate vision and hand-eye motor coordination,[1] are reflected in the quality of the drawings. In addition, the DMT involves the testee's conception of his own body. From the products are derived inferences regarding the perceptual level, configurational skill, and degree of motor co-ordination. The motor-executive aspect is less important than the perceptual and conceptual implications about the testee. The DMT does not have the outside criterion of the adequacy of the drawn

1. It must be assumed that the tester's evaluation of sensory and motor modalities will enter into the selection or non-selection of these tests.

figures as do the BG and RDT. The quality and presence of details of the drawn persons are raw data for estimating mental maturation and the subject's image of his body.

These tests cannot be used with motor-impaired and blind individuals. A general review of visual-motor and perceptual-motor capacities is contained in Leton's (1962) monograph. He makes the point that inadequate reproductions may mean visual or motor impairment or a central dysfunction involving poor "receiving and encoding [of] visual stimuli, perceiving, and discriminating visual perceptions . . ." (p. 408). A minimal requisite is the comprehension of test instructions.

VISUAL MOTOR GESTALT TEST

Silverstein's (1963) survey of psychological tests used with the mentally retarded in state institutions accords the Visual Motor Gestalt Test (Bender, 1938) fourth rank for total mentions and frequency of usage. The research literature is prolific and includes studies with a broad spectrum of pathologies, including mental retardation.

The validity of the test as an index of mental maturation has been well established (Aylaian and Meltzer, 1962; Tolor and Schulberg, 1963; Billingslea, 1964). Condell (1963) provides normative data for the Koppitz (1958b, 1960) scoring system, which is based on a high positive correlation with the WISC. The scores on the reproduced BG figures show a rise from the trainable to the educable and borderline groups of children—but do not differentiate the borderline from the dull normal testee. Tolor and Schulberg present a comprehensive review of the research with the BG test through 1960. They believe that the majority of the studies in the literature establish the test's concurrent validity for defined groups of organically impaired, mentally ill, retarded, and normal persons. Thweatt (1963) offers evidence of predictive validity with specific reference to "school learning disabilities." Employing Koppitz' scoring system, Thweatt selected those who would have reading difficulty. A follow-up evaluation two years after original testing with the BG Test indicated that 77 per cent in the validation group and 55 per cent in the cross-validation group showed previously predicted reading difficulty.

With the mentally retarded, the differential power of the BG Test depends upon the ceiling of the test figures and the scoring methods. Bender (1938), Pascal and Suttell (1951), Clawson (1962), Tolor and Schulberg (1963) and Billingslea (1964) have indicated that neurologically intact children, approaching average intelligence and above CA 11 years, score or reproduce maximally for all scoring criteria. However, the BG Test is a clinically useful tool where brain damage and emotional disturbance are involved.

Once the figures have been reproduced, the tester scores the protocol for a number of variables. There are at least seven manuals devoted to scoring system, ranging from an inspection of the reproduced figures to detailed measurements of lines, angles, degrees of rotation and reversal, and spatial arrangement of each design (Billingslea, 1948; Hutt, 1945; Hutt and Briskin, 1960; Pascal and Suttell, 1951; Peek and Quast, 1951; Koppitz, 1960; Kitay, 1950; Clawson, 1962). The scoring systems use the reproductions of the normal child or adult as the referent for assessing the inaccuracies and deviations present, in varying degrees and combinations, in the records of the non-normal child or adult. The performance of the mentally retarded person usually is not treated as a unified separate topic in these manuals.

A review of the extensive research literature on the BG Test underscores the repetitive presence of brain-damaged subjects as either control or experimental populations. These and mentally retarded children usually are in opposition to each other and give the impression that the distinctions between them are clear-cut.

Variables are further confounded in these investigations by the diversity of criteria for definiing the study populations. More specifically, the brain-damaged group is selected as if encephalopathy were a unitary entity. In Bensberg's (1952) report of the performance of brain-damaged and familial retardates on the BG Test, the former group included subjects diagnosed as cerebral palsied, post-encephalitic, and congenital syphilitic. Other studies merely label one group as "organic," or "brain damaged," or "brain injured" with no further details.

The results of these investigations are contradictory. Bensberg (1949) found that his exogenous groups had far more reversals in the copied figures than the endogenous retardates. This was supported by a second study (1952) in which group differences on reversals were significant at the .05 level. Halpin (1955), on the other hand, found no significant differences in figural rotations between his brain-damaged and familial retardates. A more careful delineation within the former category, using homogenous diagnostic grouping, would probably yield more valid results applicable between and within sample populations.

In the familial category, there is inadequate adherence to definite criteria for the selection of subjects. The standards range from "no history of neurological involvement" on the one hand to the two-fold criterion of the presence of a mentally retarded sibling, parent, or both *and* the absence of overt sensory and motor disability on the other. The difficulty with even this cautious approach is that the absence of overt signs of brain damage may or may not be equivalent to the absence of brain pathology.

Another source of error variance may be found in the studies that compare contrasting groups with too wide age ranges. Bensberg (1952) used 161 matched pairs of subjects ranging from 7 to 61 years with approximate mean CA and MA of 30 years and 6 years respectively. It must be recognized that there is quite a qualitative difference between chronologically younger and older subjects despite their similar MA level.

In review, the research with the BG Test indicates that brain-damaged retardates perform at lower quantitative and poorer qualitative levels than do their familial or endogenous intellectual peers. Some of the more common reproduction inaccuracies used as scoring variables are: reversal, parts repeated, use of lines instead of dots, distortion of shape, rotation, failure of integration, perseveration, parts of figures missing, and difficulty with intersections. A frequent theme in research with the BG Test is the identification of the brain-damaged child (Hain, 1964; Koppitz, 1962; Goldberg, 1957; Goldberg, 1959; Oki, Sakai, Kizu, Hagashi, 1960). The usual experimental design includes normal, psychiatric, brain-damaged, and mentally retarded subjects, who are assigned to one of the categories on the basis of test figure scores or by judges. The results are somewhat as expected, the brain-damaged

and the mentally retarded are most readily identified by the criteria selected by the individual investigators.

Keller (1955) suggests a change of focus in the use of this test. He urges the development of a scoring system that would emphasize the description of the child's visual-motor maturational level rather than an over-all score yielding somewhat dubious classifications. Diller and Birch's (1964) review of the BG Test literature calls attention to the contributions of sensory intactness and variations to the figure-reproduction ability of the normal, brain-damaged, and retarded child. Moreover, diagnosis is not the major concern. Like Keller, these investigators emphasize the identification of "particular patterns of cognitive and conative functioning." They shift the identification from labeling to the functional foundation for educational planning and habilitation.

Research with the widely used BG Test has gone in every direction. Most of the effort in the area of mental retardation has been channeled into the discrimination among previously defined neurological and intelligence groups. Now research must take on the additional task of evaluating sensory, motor, perceptual, and conceptual strengths and weaknesses of the perceptually impaired, intellectually inefficient and conceptually retarded child.

Moreover, further information is needed about how these processes develop in the growing child. Educational and vocational curricula are geared to the time schedule of the maturing physiological bases for learning and responding. Much is known about the normal child. Little is known about the developmental schedule of the retarded child. The perceptual processes involved in the reproduction of the BG Test figures could add to these necessary data.

RUTGERS DRAWING TEST

The Rutgers Drawing Test (Starr, 1952, 1961), similar to the BG, requires the testee to copy a series of geometric designs. Unlike the BG, the RDT provides space for figural reproduction below each design, emphasizing the execution and accuracy of drawing at the expense of observing the child's planning behavior, as in the BG Test.

Two forms of the RDT are available: form A designs, two-dimensional and symmetrical, are for ages 4 through 6 years. The figures of form B, which are fluid, not symmetrical, more difficult and involved, are for years 6 through 9. The RDT is related linearly to the level of intellectual functioning of the testee. Starr (1952) reports a correlation of .72 between the Revised S-B MA and RDT MA for normal children. On a small sample of retardates below CA 12 this relationship was .61.

Test-retest studies are not available. Interjudge reliability of .96 was reported by Jones (1964) for groups of normal and retarded children. Starr does not report reliability data for both forms of the RDT. The RDT, a highly structured method for examining developing perceptual-motor processes, covers the MA range appropriate for the evaluation of most retardates. Concurrent validity studies indicate that the test is related to intellectual efficiency (Jones, 1964). The predictive validity has not been tested; reliability and validity data are needed.

This instrument deserves further attention for two reasons: first, its aim is to evaluate perceptual-motor skills beginning with MA 4 years, a developmental age level sorely in need of further study; and second, the format of the RDT is similar to the type of educational presentation a child meets in his early academic career. Success on the RDT may be a good predictor of readiness for educable class placement for the retardate, but this has not yet been demonstrated.

DRAW-A-MAN TEST

Almost all children enjoy drawing, which makes less formal psychological evaluation possible. The literature shows that children draw the human figure by preference (Ballard, 1912; McCarthy, 1924). Children's drawings of a man have been quantitatively scored according to the procedures enumerated by Goodenough (1926) and recently revised and extended by Harris (1963). The reliability of the scoring procedure has been uniformly high, for example, .90 for normal children (McCarthy, 1944) and .93 for a two-year test-retest evaluation of adolescent retardates (Tobias and Gorelick, 1960).

The validity of the DMT has been established as an index of intellectual development in normal children up to approximately 12 years old (Goodenough, 1926; Harris, 1963). The relationship between standard intellectual measures and DMT IQ for normal adults is quite low (Murphy, 1956). However, the DMT IQs of defectives correlate .78 with the Revised S-B IQs (Murphy, 1956). Birch (1949) obtained similar results for retarded adolescents 10 to 16 years old. He reported a correlation of .69 between Revised S-B and DMT MAs. Holding CA constant by means of partial correlation lowered the relationship to .64. Validity studies with both adults and adolescent retardates indicate the DMT IQ to be a more nearly adequate predictor of the testee's achievement on the performance items of standard intelligence tests than on the verbal or academic subtests. Tobias and Gorelick (1960) report a correlation of only .31 for full scale WAIS IQ and DMT scores. The verbal and performance IQs correlated .16 and .51 respectively with the DMT. The closer relationship of the performance achievement over the verbal attainment with the DMT also was supported by Rohrs and Haworth (1962).

The presence of pathological signs in the retardate's drawings has been shown by Gunzburg (1955) to lower the relationship between Wechsler performance IQs and DMT IQs from .76, when no pathology is present, to .36 in the presence of definite pathology. In summary, the DMT as scored by Goodenough has at least moderate concurrent validity with standard tests of intelligence, particularly nonverbal tests. Reliability is consistently high, even over extended periods of time.

Harris' (1963) book should stimulate further research into the usefulness of this simple evaluative procedure. He presents a more systematic and clear scoring system for the man as well as an alternative scoring scale for the woman and self figures.

While the tests in this section may give some indication of intellectual maturation, their contribution is information regarding visual perception and the motor-executive aspect—how the testee copes with problems. The BG and DMT have sufficient research literature to merit their continued use with confidence. But the RTD requires further investigation, especially with retardates, in order to assess its predictive validity and the inferences that may be made from the results.

VERBAL AND PERFORMANCE TESTS OF INTELLIGENCE

The three tests discussed below are considered to be tests of intelligence, *qua* intelligence. In addition to IQ and MA scores, these tests yield more information regarding the conceptual maturational level than do techniques presented in the first two sections of this chapter. Furthermore, they owe their unique place in the repertoire of tests to their feasibility with retarded and handicapped children.

The Columbia Mental Maturity Scale and the Leiter International Performance Scale find their widest application as tests of intelligence with children who have sensory and/or motor deficits or who are unable to read or speak English. These two tests usually substitute for the standard intelligence tests, which are not always possible with some retarded and handicapped children.

The Slosson Intelligence Test does not share this attribute of ready adaptation for use with the auditory- and/or speech-impaired child. It is more suitable with the non-sensory- or speech-involved retarded child. With very young children, this test may be completed by obtaining information from a parent or other knowledgeable person. However, beyond CA two years the child must understand English and be able to respond orally.

The Columbia Mental Maturity Scale and the Leiter International Performance Scale, on the other hand, are free from language ties since the instructions may be pantomimed and demonstrated until the tester is certain that the child does or does not comprehend the tasks. There are more avenues for reaching the child to evaluate the level and rate of intellectual maturation with these three tests than with other group or individual tests of intelligence. These tests correlate significantly with the Revised S-B and Wechsler Scales so that the over-all estimate of intelligence, in terms of IQ or MA, will be as satisfactory as the standard test where such information is required.

SLOSSON INTELLIGENCE TEST FOR CHILDREN AND ADULTS

The Slosson (1963) Intelligence Test (SIT) is very recent and has no research literature beyond that in the manual. The SIT is an age scale ranging from 0-0.5 months to 27 years. Slosson acknowledges the Revised S-B Scale, Form LM, and the Gesell Institute of Child Development behavior inventory as sources for many items included in this test.

For 0.5 month to 1 year, 11.5 months, there is one item for each .5 month-interval. Up to one year of age the items focus on neurological functions, as in most baby tests. Vocabulary, locomotion, and self-care items are introduced at 1 year. Between 2 years and 4 years, 11 months, there is only one item at each month level. The Revised S-B items serve as models, for example, copying geometric designs, repeating short sentences, using analogy, showing parts of the body, etc. From 5 years to 15 years, 10 months, there is one item at each two-month interval. This results in reduced sampling of processes tapped, which means a less adequate evaluation of the depth and variety of intellective functions than that obtained from the models of this test. The final set of items spreads from 16 to 27 years in three-month steps and are essentially arithmetic and vocabulary questions.

The SIT is designed for individual administration, which is unusual for a screening test. MA and IQ ratings are available. The standardization population of children and adults resided in New York State. The manual gives the impression that this population, whose size is not stated specifically, was the result of referrals from a wide variety of sources, including retardates, the gifted, institutionalized children, graduate students, handicapped, disturbed, and normal people. More information is needed about the method of selecting the normative sample. If this group is as stated in the manual, then doubt surrounds the value of the norms.

Reliability data consist of a two-month test-retest correlation of .97 for 139 subjects between 4 and 50 years old. The mean test-retest IQs for this group were 99 and 103 respectively—a far cry from adequate evidence of test stability.

Concurrent validity of the SIT with the

Revised S-B Scale, form LM, IQs is reported for 701 subjects ranging from 4 to 18 years and above. The correlations at one-year intervals cluster around .96 with average differences for the two tests between 4.4 and 6.7 IQ points. Slosson also cites the Revised S-B Scale and SIT IQs for different groups, namely gifted children and adults, retarded women, and normal persons, as well as SIT correlations with the WISC and the Cattell Infant Intelligence Scale as validity evidence. The coefficients are high and positive, but this sort of criterion is acceptable only for concurrent validity. No evidence is presented that the average differences between SIT IQs and those for the other tests serving as the external validity criteria are statistically significant. Neither reliability nor validity has been established satisfactorily. There seems to be too much validity by prestige and usage and not enough statistical validity.

The most compelling recommendations for the SIT are its rapid screening potential and the feasibility of using this age scale in same manner as the Vineland Social Maturity Scale or the Gesell Developmental Schedule with children up to 2 years old. The items above this level should be administered directly to the child since scoring is dependent upon verbal and motor responsivity. Although this is beyond the recommendations and purpose of the test, psychologists needing a test to use on young children may consider the idea worthwhile. While the grossness of the evaluation may be exaggerated by this suggested procedure, the test can be helpful in those instances in which the very young testee does not or cannot perform "on demand" in the presence of the tester.

No published research literature exists for this new test. Mental retardates have been included in the standardization population. A sample of 11 institutionalized retarded women, 18 to 54 years old, achieved scores showing an average difference of 3.6 IQ points between the SIT and the Revised S-B Scale, Form LM. The former test IQs spread from 32 to 95 while the range for the latter test was 33 to 87. The usefulness of this test, in standard or modified administration procedures, will have to await judgment based on further usage and controlled study. The SIT does give the psychologist another tool to be employed in the evaluation of the retarded or motor-handicapped child.

COLUMBIA MENTAL MATURITY SCALE

The Columbia Mental Maturity Scale (CMMS) was constructed by Burgemeister, Blum and Lorge (1959) as an intelligence test for children with MA 3 to 10 years and requires very little in the way of a motor response and no speech. The CMMS consists of 100 cards administered individually. The testee responds by selecting one of the several pictures or drawings on each card that is "different from" the others or "does not belong there."

The original version of the CMMS, constructed in 1954, was standardized on 957 normal children 3 to 12 years, 11 months old. Research indicated the need for changes in the contents of several plates (Allen and Sandler, 1956; Canter, 1956). These studies established the concurrent validity of the test on a variety of samples including normal, cerebral palsied, physically handicapped, and retarded children and children with speech difficulties. While the results were satisfactory, with most of the individual tests of intelligence as the external criteria, the CMMS scores were usually higher than those of the intelligence tests (Canter, 1956; French and Worcester, 1956; Witsaman and Jones, 1959; Gallagher, Benoit, and Boyd, 1956).

The revised 1959 edition was standardized separately on 1,352 preschool and first-, second-, third-, and fourth-grade school children between 4 and 12 years old. The revised norms lower the IQs of high-scoring children (from the norms of the original edition) to meet one of the major objections to the earlier CMMS. However, increased homogeneity, as both testees and test items approach the MA ceiling, could reduce the reliability of the CMMS.

Concurrent validity with several groups and individual intelligence tests is shown in correlations ranging from .39 to .70, with ten of the fourteen correlations reported by the publisher at .52 and above. Smith (1961) and Bligh (1959) add to the concurrent validity data of the 1959 CMMS. The former reports a correlation of .52 between this test and the full scale WISC IQs. Bligh correlated CMMS scores with the Van Alstyne Picture Vocabulary and the Revised S-B, form L. The children were similarly ranked for intelligence by the CMMS and the Revised S-B Scale. The scores for the younger group of children, 4 years old to 4 years, 11 months, correlated .70. The same data for the 5 to 5 years, 11 months, group was .59.

Investigators have characterized the CMMS as a non-academic, non-verbal test of perceptual and conceptual skills that can be administered to a wide variety of handicapped individuals not testable with the standard tests. Berko (1955), writing on the earlier edition, indicated that the CMMS required visual perception and the ability to abstract and categorize. To this Barratt (1956) added that number concepts are involved. Since the 1959 version has changed only in terms of seventeen new cards, these processes still may be tapped by the test and may well form the bases for construct validity or content validity studies.

Some of the special populations to whom the test had been administered include the cerebral palsied (Dunn and Harley, 1959), the speech disordered (Hirschenfang, 1961) and the mentally retarded (Warren and Collier, 1960). A study with 100 children in retarded classes reported by the publisher discloses correlations of .65 and .56 for MA and IQ scores respectively between the CMMS and the Revised S-B Scale, LM. The mean Binet and CMMS MAs were 86.6 and 79.5 months with IQs of 66 and 61.6 respectively. Warren and Collier administered the CMMS and two other intelligence tests to 49 females in a state institution for the mentally retarded. The mean CMMS and WAIS IQs were close to each other, especially for retardates 12 years old and over. Dunn and Harley reported that the CMMS scores correlated .89 and .93 with teacher rankings of cerebral palsied children for reading and arithmetic achievement.

The predictive validity needs to be established with normal children. Item and process analyses would be more relevant to the value of the CMMS with retardates than continued reports of inter-test correlations. It would be particularly helpful to relate the processes of intellectual functioning with the strengths, weaknesses, and even response to remediation based on test evaluation of the child. Finally, the most significant usefulness of the CMMS is with the physically handicapped and speech-involved child (Allen and Jefferson, 1962).

LEITER INTERNATIONAL PERFORMANCE SCALE

The Leiter (1959) International Performance Scale (LIPS) was revised several times before the current, 1948 edition. Considered a non-verbal test, it has 54 items arranged in age scale format from Year II to Year XVIII.

Items through Year IV depend more upon perceptual ability and less on conceptual skill since the tasks may be completed successfully by visual matching without an over-all guiding principle. At Year V and above, visual perception alone is not sufficent. The child needs to appreciate the relationships between the model designs and the response materials for credit. The principles derive from problems involving matching, analogy, classification, and the detection of similarities and differences.

An important feature of this test is the feasibility of administration without the use of speech. Furthermore, the items at Years II and III permit as much help, demonstration, and correction by the tester as necessary to determine whether the child understands the task. In the instance of a deaf child or one illiterate in English or a child with a word-deafness type of sensory aphasia, the pantomiming of directions and help with the solution makes testing possible where previously the child usually was labeled "untestable." This test also lends itself to assessment of motor-impaired children. The responses require placing individual blocks in appropriate recesses in a wooden frame, but since selection of the proper blocks is the test object, the tester may assist the subject in their placement. (Allen, 1958; Allen and Collins, 1955; Allen and Jefferson, 1962; Maisel, Allen, and Tallarico, 1962).

The validity of the 1948 revision of the LIPS is not indicated clearly. Leiter (1959) writes: "After the physical changes were made, the 1948 scale was compared with the 1940 scale by applying the two scales to a series of 180 unselected subjects equally distributed between the ages of 8 years, 0 months, and 16 years, 11 months. The correlation between the two scales was found to be .92, which was high enough to indicate that the 1948 revision could be used with the same confidence that the 1940 scale was used" (p. 57). This may be so, but the question remains: What were either or both evaluating?

Leiter also points out that his standardization of the present scale did not include children below 8 years old "because Arthur (1949, 1952) had already applied the new arrangement of tests, as far as the 12-year level, to younger children. Her results indicated that none of the younger children would be affected by changes in the scale beyond the 12-year level" (p. 58). Validity based on a satisfactory population sample to whom the entire 1948 revision had been administered would be more nearly acceptable as validity evidence.

Since most of the validity reports are concerned with the 1940 edition, the validity of the current edition is not established. The 1948 LIPS includes the Arthur Adaptation test items through the 12-year level; approximately half of the items above Year XII are new. The correlation between the 1940 and 1948 versions for 180 "unselected" subjects between 8 and 16 years, 11 months, was .92. Leiter found the total IQ scores were usually five points lower than those obtained from other intelligence tests. He suggests that five points be added to the LIPS IQ for comparative purposes. Quoting from Tate (1950, 1952), Leiter cites the Revised S-B and MA and IQ correlations to be .77 and .81 respectively. Leiter interprets these data as supporting the validity of the LIPS. The high correlations indicate some commonality of measurement but the reported differences in mean IQ and MA ratings do not support the conclusion of acceptable validity.

Gallagher, Benoit, and Boyd (1956) question the validity of the LIPS. They point out that the concurrent validity of the non-academic, non-verbal LIPS is based on its correlation with verbal group tests. The issue is: how appropriate is it to use intelligence tests (each with its own validity and reliability status) as the external criteria for a non-verbal test? The two types of tests are not likely to involve similar, let alone identical, intellective processes.

Beverly and Bensberg (1952) correlated the 1948 LIPS with the Revised S-B, form L, and reported a coefficient of .62. Bensberg and Sloan (1951) tested 55 brain-damaged and

55 familial retardates, 11 to 30 years old, with the Revised S-B form L, and the Arthur Adaptation of the LIPS. The correlations for the two tests were .73 and .77 for each group. Most of the validity studies of the LIPS and other tests of intelligence generally do not support the concurrent validity of the LIPS. The reader of Part I of the Manual (Leiter, 1959) encounters difficulty obtaining validity data beyond a series of MA and IQ ratings listed for various groups, and correlations between the LIPS and other tests of intelligence. One must conclude that definitive evidence of the validity of the 1948 LIPS is still wanting.

The findings concerning the mentally retarded vary from high positive relationships for MA and IQ scores to a lack of significance between the LIPS and other intelligence tests. Gallagher, Benoit, and Boyd (1956) compared the LIPS with the Revised S-B Scale and the CMMS for IQ and MA achievement of 40 brain-damaged boys and girls aged 7 years, 4 months, to 13 years, 10 months. The mean IQ scores for the Revised S-B and the LIPS were significantly different at the .05 level. The CMMS mean IQ varied from the other two test scores at the .01 level. These authors concluded that the CMMS and LIPS test results were not comparable and that both of these scales need to be validated independently.

Sharp (1957) administered the WISC, LIPS, and Revised S-B, form L, to 50 slow learners 8 to 16.5 years old. The IQ means varied less than one IQ point. The ranges of these scores were identical for the Revised S-B and the WISC, but the LIPS yielded a six-point greater spread. The correlations were: LIPS-WISC, full scale IQ, .83; LIPS-Revised S-B IQ, .56.

The LIPS and the WISC were closer to each other probably because the performance items of the latter resemble the LIPS to a greater extent than the Revised S-B Scale items do. Both the LIPS and the WISC are non-verbal tests. Furthermore, the homogeneity of items in both tests enhances intercorrelations because of the similarity of the processes being tapped so long as the levels of abilities tested are heterogeneous.

The Revised S-B Scale is more verbal than the LIPS—therefore the lower correlation between the two tests. This is one of the major stumbling blocks in using the Revised S-B

Scale as a validity criterion for the LIPS, an all-too-common occurrence in research with the LIPS. Sharp (1957) further reported that while the mean IQ achievement for the three tests was not statistically significant, the interest variations in IQ ranges were significantly high. CA influenced this variability especially for the retarded children below five years of age. It was also felt that the LIPS should not be used to evaluate the older retardates because the scores varied extensively with increase in CA.

Sharp (1957) offered six-month interval test-retest reliability data for three groups of retarded children in special and regular classes. While the temporal reliability coefficient was .91, the difference between the mean test and retest IQs was significant beyond the .01 level. Sharp suggested that the higher retest mean IQ was influenced by a memory "carryover" from test to retest. Two-thirds of the subjects in this study showed a retest increase from 1 to 14 IQ points. The susceptibility of this test to practice effects decreases its reliability. Part I of the manual (Leiter, 1959) offers no tangible evidence for Leiter's claim of acceptable reliability of the 1948 LIPS. In fact, the terms "reliability" and "validity" seem to be used interchangeably in the manual. Evidence for reliability is essential.

Hunt (1961), Brengelmann and Kenny (1961), and Gallagher (1962) have produced significant studies employing the LIPS with mentally retarded individuals. Hunt tested three groups of retarded subjects—30 familials, 30 brain-damaged subjects without visual disabilities (BD-NVD), and 30 brain-damaged retardates with visual disabilities (BD-VD). The performance of the BDVD group was significantly poorer than the BDNVD group. The familial retarded group scored between the two brain-damaged groups and therefore was not significantly different from either one.

Data supporting the validity of the LIPS was correlated with the Revised S-B Scale and the WAIS, from the gist of the report by Brengelmann and Kenny. Using 75 adult retardates with a mean CA of approximately 36 years, these investigators found an increase in IQs for each of the three tests with a rise in MA levels. The correlation for the LIPS and WAIS performance subtest scales was higher than that between the LIPS and the WAIS verbal subtests, .75 and .59 respectively. The

mean LIPS IQ was three points below the Revised S-B Scale and eleven points below the WAIS full scale score.

The Gallagher study was designed to evaluate changes in verbal and non-verbal abilities of mentally retarded brain-damaged children following cessation of special stimulation. The experimental design included two years of tutoring followed by two years of no training for the experimental group. After two years of no training, the control group was given one year of special stimulation and then tested one year later. There was a total of 42 brain-damaged mentally deficient children aged 7 years, 4 months, to 13 years, 9 months, matched for MA. The IQs varied from 33 to 63. The special tutoring emphasized individual programs based on each child's weaknesses. In general, children benefited from a training program of special stimulation especially in the area of verbal skills. Younger children improved more than the older ones. One of the gains was in attention span. However, the cessation of tutoring resulted in a tendency for the child's development "to regress to lower levels or become arrested." Interestingly enough, verbal abilities suffered and not the non-verbal skills as measured by the LIPS.

Despite the need for more validity and reliability evidence, the LIPS has a definite place in the psychologist's test battery. Many physically, neurologically, and intellectually impaired children may be evaluated more realistically with the LIPS than with some of the standard tests of intelligence—particularly the cerebral palsied and the illiterate child. For the culturally deprived, the LIPS offers fewer academically oriented tasks and therefore is culturally fairer. Many children who previously were considered untestable or were evaluated in a manner that yielded an unrepresentative picture of intellectual functioning may now be assessed realistically.

SPECIAL TESTS OF PERCEPTUAL, CONCEPTUAL, AND LINGUISTIC ABILITIES

In order to gain from learning experiences, a child must receive stimuli, assimilate them and then abstract principles that will be applicable to future events. Finally, the child must have the ability to function adequately through the entire communicative process and use verbal symbols at the receptive, association, and expressive stages.

The three psychological areas covered in this section are perceptual development, conceptual ability, and psycholinguistic functioning. Perception means those processes by which the child receives, organizes, and responds to stimuli. Conceptual ability goes beyond perception to include the notion of dealing with perceived data at levels varying from the minutely concretistic to the highest order of abstraction as exemplified by a classificatory response or enunciating a principle.

The brain-damaged child usually is unable to attain consistent stability in his visual perception of his surroundings, and his response to the visual world is inadequate. The mentally retarded child who is not obviously encephalopathic also has a similar difficulty, perhaps to a lesser degree. The reasons for this may be more than neurophysiologically anchored but the results are somewhat similar and reflect impairment of visual perceptual performance. To evaluate these functions, let us consider three tests: Raven's (1960) Progressive Matrices, the Developmental Test of Visual Perception (Frostig, Lefever, and Whittlesey, 1961b), and the Illinois Test of Psycholinguistic Abilities (McCarthy and Kirk, 1961).

Kephart (1963) points out that the normally developing child first integrates tactual and kinesthetic perception. With perceptual ability at the "ready" level, concept formation comes to the fore. This involves the apprehension of the relationships among percepts and the emergence of a unique combination of these percepts as the response to problems. The sequence develops from perceptual organization to concept formation. Impairment of the former affects the development of the latter. Because education is a product of the developmental sequence and degree of impairment, knowing where the weak link may be in the developmental chain is important. Finding the defects sets the nature of the tasks that the special education teacher and other remedial experts must undertake for education up to potential.

Luria and Yudovich (1959) have emphasized the importance of speech in the development of mental activities and behavior in their study of identical twins. As speech skills progressed, ideation and behavior was enhanced. Turning to the mentally retarded, Luria (1961)

points out the advancement of "differential systems of connections" resulting from training in speech. Assuming the speech system of mental retardates is not as active in the formation of new connections as normal children's, Luria concludes that if changes are to be made from motor to ideational signals in the mentally retarded, the transformation requires slow and repetitive focus on verbal learning.

A language achievement and aptitude test is available in the procedure devised by Kirk and McCarthy (1961). Surveying the work and ideas of Luria (1963), Kirk (1964) and McCarthy (1960, 1964), one gets the definite impression that the linguistic ability of the retarded child is much more than a speech problem—it may hold the key to possible improvement in psychological functioning. The three tests in this section could furnish the special education teacher, speech therapist, and other training personnel tangible evidence of perceptual, conceptual and language skills already available on the one hand, and with bases for predicting potential improvement of these abilities on the other.

STANDARD PROGRESSIVE MATRICES

The Standard Progressive Matrices (Raven, 1960) (SPM), Sets A, B, C, D, and E, and the Colored Progressive Matrices (CPM), Sets A, AB, and B, assess the comprehension of relationships among geometric designs—actually a test of reasoning or concept formation that is not culture free but culture fair. Each set consists of 12 plates covering a limited range of mental development. The tests have percentile norms for children 6 through 14 years and for adults 20 through 65 years old. Young children and mentally defective individuals are expected to solve only the problems in Sets A and B and the easier problems of Sets C and D of the SPM. These items do not require reasoning by analogy or concept problem-solving ability. The CPM, on the other hand, is designed to assess the cognitive processes of children up to 11 years old. Because of vividness of color and simplicity of format, the CPM should be the test choice for assessing the reasoning ability or concept formation in the mentally retarded child.

With normal children and adults, the scale has a test-retest reliability varying with age from .83 to .93. Pinkerton and Kelly (1952) point out that the temporal stability of the matrices test tends to be lowest with very young children and with very old persons. No reports of test-retest reliability with retarded subjects have been made yet.

Raven describes his test as appropriate for "observation and clear thinking" and not an intelligence device. For non-involved and non-handicapped subjects, the 1938 revision of the PM correlated .75 with WISC full-scale IQ, and only slightly lower, .69 and .70, with the Verbal and Performance IQs respectively (Barratt, 1956). Green and Ewert (1955) studied a sample of 1,214 children aged 6 years, 6 months, to 12 years, 5 months. Their findings are particularly interesting for ascertaining the influence of CA on test performance. A significant variance in correlation was obtained between PM achievement and Otis IQ as a function of CA. Between the ages of 6 years, 6 months, through 9 years, 5 months, the correlations ranged from .62 to .71. From CA 9 years, 6 months, to 12 years, 5 months, the correlations dropped significantly to between .19 and .38. No apparent explanation is offered for this change in relationship. The authors did not obtain a similar variation as a function of CA with a non-verbal test, the CMMS. Instead they found consistently lower correlations across all ages ranging from .37 to .47 with the PM. The available evidence indicates that the PM taps perceptual ability not closely related to verbal concept formation and that this phenomenon is more marked in older children. The older retardates disclose more dramatically the decrease in verbal conceptualizing ability as contrasted with somewhat more stable visual perceptual ability—more stable, that is, in the sese that it deteriorates less rapidly than symbolic problem-solving ability.

Although Raven did not develop the PM to be a test of intelligence, a series of concurrent validity studies has been conducted with retardates. Working with a group of adult defective subjects, Stacey and Gill (1955) reported that the 1947 version of the SPM correlated .86 with the Revised S-B IQ. This fell to .68 with the Wechsler-Bellevue Adult Intelligence Scale IQ. Consistent with Barratt's (1956) findings with normal children, the block design subtest produced the highest correlation (.60) with the PM. The lowest subtest correlation was .29 with the arithmetic items.

These results again emphasize that the PM taps cognitive capacity but primarily on a perceptual rather than a verbal-symbolic level.

The concurrent validity of the PM as a measure of general intellectual functioning in mildly retarded children has been shown by Stacey and Carlton (1955) to be lower than that reported for adults. Malpass, Brown, and Hoke (1960) contrasted 104 retarded children with a population of normal children of approximately similar CA to ascertain the influence of CA. Holding CA constant, a partial correlation of .56 was obtained between the PM and WISC full-scale IQ. The partial inter-test correlation for normal children was .54. The authors say the PM and the WISC overlap so far as scores are concerned, but they tap different intellectual processes.

The literature seems to emphasize repeatedly that the PM does not measure the identical processes that are tapped by standard intelligence tests. Little attention is directed toward determining the importance of non-verbal symbolic reasoning in the training and education of the retarded child. Yet the retardate is, by definition, limited in verbal fluency. The PM is designed to offer the diagnostician a special tool for both understanding and predicting the retardate's ability to manipulate his environment, but has not been utilized as such.

The CPM has been shown by Orme (1961) to be more closely related to WAIS IQ scores for subnormal English adults than the SPM. While Orme's findings indicate that the CPM is a more valid estimate of intelligence in retardates than the SPM, his results provide no information as to the validity of the CPM as a test of concept formation for this type of population. His findings suggest that retardates score significantly better with color stimulation than they would with non-color plates (SPM).

Several investigators have employed the PM as an indicator of brain damage in non-retarded populations. Dils (1960) proposed a "scatter-scoring" technique that is effective in differentiating organic from non-organic long-term hospitalized patients. Knehr (1956) tested the hypothesis that severity of cerebral pathology alters the progression of accuracy on the PM. His results indicate that the PM might prove effective as a guide for planning classroom activities for the retardate.

The question facing the special education teacher is often not "What is this child's IQ?" but rather "What can he do with his capacity?" and "Which instructional technique will be most effective?" The PM should not be considered a brief intelligence test; it is only moderately valid for this purpose. The validity of the PM as a measure of reasoning capacity has hardly been explored. The reliability of this instrument is fully adequate to proceed with some imaginative investigations into the world of the retardate. An IQ will never provide complete understanding of how a specific child learns. The PM is an available tool to analyze conceptual processes and deserves more experimental attention.

DEVELOPMENTAL TEST OF VISUAL PERCEPTION

This relatively new, empirically based test was developed by Frostig (1963) and Frostig, Lefever, and Whittlesey (1961a, 1961b, 1963). The most recent manual was published by Maslow, Frostig, Lefever, and Whittlesey (1964). The test developed from their experiences with children enrolled at an "educational therapy" school for children with learning difficulties. A common condition noted was the presence of visual or auditory perceptual disturbances that contributed to the children's learning problems and to their low achievement on standard intelligence tests. The children performed as if they were retarded. Previous research, coupled with the school experiences, led the test authors to evaluate visual perception in five areas: (1) eye-motor co-ordination, (2) figure-ground discrimination, (3) form constancy, (4) perception of position in space, and (5) spatial relations. Difficulties in these visual perceptual areas usually accompanied reading and writing deficiencies, inability to pay attention for sustained periods, and the display of marked behavioral deviations.

The present form of the Developmental Test of Visual Perception (Frostig Test) consists of the five subtests, one for each area listed above. The 1963 standardization population included 2,116 nursery and elementary school children from 3 to 9 years old divided into six-month group intervals (3 to 3 years, 6 months, 3 years, 6 months to 4 years, etc.) Since normative and developmental curves for each of the processes tapped by the five sub-tests disclosed individual maximal maturation between 4 and 7.5 years, the test was limited for use with young children, with norms for ages 3 to 9 years, 6 months. The most recent manual (Maslow, *et al.*, 1964) has norms up to 7 years, 11 months (CA).

Maslow *et al.* (1964) describe the purpose of this test as a screening device to detect preschool and first-grade children's need for perceptual training. In broader terms, the test may help determine the status of the several visual perceptual functions of children with learning difficulties. Test findings are expressed in perceptual age equivalents and scale-scores for each of the five subtests separately. The norms for the whole test provide total scale scores, percentile ranks and perceptual quotients (PQ).

Validity studies, reported by Maslow *et al.* (1964) and Frostig *et al.* (1961, 1961b) are based on the criteria of teachers' ratings of the children's classroom adjustment, motor co-ordination and intellectual functioning. The correlations between the teachers' ratings on these variables and the Frostig Test scale scores are significantly positive: .44, .50 and .49 between each of the three variables (adjustment, co-ordination and intelligence) and the total test scale scores respectively. The test authors report correlations of .46, .31 and .36 respectively for kindergarten, and first- and second-grade children between the Frostig Test PQs and Goodenough Draw-A-Man IQs. The poor to moderate relationships between these two tests are expected since the Frostig Test was not designed to assess intellectual ability directly nor was it standardized with this in view. These correlations indicate that the processes evaluated by the DMT and the Frostig Test have little in common. A relevant predictive validity was accomplished by Frostig and her collaborators with 25 children in a university elementary school. The low scorers, less than 90 PQ on the Frostig Test, were predicted to be potentially poor readers. In the follow-up reading evaluation, all but one of the low scorers achieved below-grade level in reading ability.

Frostig *et al.* (1961a, 1961b, 1963) evaluated neurologically involved children and found "an impressive correlation between perceptual disabilities and neurological handicaps." The variation in age-equivalent subtest scores was greater and total scores on the Frostig Test were much lower for the neurologically handicapped than for the normal children. The validity of the test seems to be better established for functioning variables as derived from validity criteria than for general intelligence. Silverstein (in press) reports that his research with this test supports the delineation of relatively distinct areas of perception.

Maslow *et al.* (1964) found a correlation of .98 for a three-week interval test-retest reliability study with 50 children diagnosed as having learning disabilities. A second sample of 35 first- and 37 second-grade children yielded a temporal stability reliability coefficient of .80. The test-retest correlations of the individual subtests ranged from .42 to .80. A much larger sampling of school children with 14 days between test and retest revealed a product moment correlation of .69 for the total test score. The authors say the somewhat lower test-retest correlation with normal children is due to the rapidity with which visual perception develops as a function of special training and the accumulation of experiences. An analysis of the time-score growth curves (Maslow *et al.*, 1964) for each of the five subtests supports this concept. Since these curves flatten as a subject approaches 7 years, score variances and the size of the correlation coefficients are reduced.

Split-half reliabilities for total score and for each of the five subtests produced satisfactory correlations at four age levels, based on a population of 1,459 children between five and nine years of age. The reliability coefficients decreased slightly with age due to the flattening effect of perceptual maturation as measured by this test with increase in CA.

Research reports by investigators other than the test constructors are quite sparse. Corah and Powell (1963) analyzed the Frostig Test scores of 40 normal children in the 50 to 60 months age range. Two factors emerged: (1) general intelligence, involving the recognition of external stimuli as unique events, the detection of cues leading to similarities and differences among stimuli, and the analysis and synthesis of complex stimuli; and (2) developmental changes due to age, including hand-eye motor co-ordination, resistance to distractions, and the comprehension of size, form, and spatial orientation of stimuli. Subtests IV (position in space) and V (space relation-

ships) should be lengthened so as to offer finer age-equivalent discriminations. A score difference of one point is translated into age-equivalent variations ranging from as little as three months to as much as 21 months (see Table 2, Subtests IV and V, in Maslow *et al.*, 1964, p. 469).

Allen, Haupt, and Jones (1964a, 1964b) reported on the use of the Frostig Test as part of a battery administered to educable mentally retarded children in public school special education classes. The retardates were divided into two groups, high and low perceivers in accordance with Frostig Test PQ scores. The achievement of each group on the WISC, the PPVT and the RDT, forms A and B, were analyzed. The importance of the level of perceptual development was strongly indicated by the significant differences in the test performances of the high and low perception groups. In short, the subtests produced objective information about the perceptual development of the retarded child. The findings highlighted those perceptual deficiences that differentiated the low from the high perception group and both from the non-retarded population.

The use of the Frostig Test should be limited to the purposes stated by the authors. Allen, Haupt, and Jones (1964b, 1965) have indicated that while the test differentiated levels of visual perceptual development among retardates, it should not be employed to assess intelligence. Clearly, further research with this instrument is needed. In the year or so before entering elementary school and in the first, second, or third year immediately thereafter, the classroom teacher most likely will be the first to detect the child's learning difficulties. A standard intelligence test can be very helpful in checking the teacher's estimate. The Frostig Test can aid in locating those processes that may be contributing to the learning problem and make possible the initiation of remedial measures. This is the promise of the Frostig Test that needs to be investigated.

ILLINOIS TEST OF PSYCHOLINGUISTIC ABILITIES

The Illinois Test of Psycholinguistic Abilities (ITPA) was constructed by McCarthy and Kirk (1961, 1963; McCarthy, 1964; Kirk and McCarthy, 1961). The present form of the ITPA is an outgrowth of Sievers' (1955) interpretation of Osgood's (1957) model of communication processes. Schiefelbusch (1965) succinctly labels this "communication behavior," an ability that characteristically is retarded in "low IQ children" (Bateman and Wetherell, 1965).

The ITPA, a relatively new test, is made up of nine subtests which measure the auditory and visual decoding, the auditory-vocal, and visual-motor association, the vocal and motor encoding, the auditory-vocal automatic, and the auditory-vocal and visual-motor sequential aspects of psycholinguistic maturation. These subtests provide information regarding the testee's facility with auditory and visual stimuli on the one hand and efficiency of vocal and motor responsivity on the other. Decoding (receptive), encoding (expressive) and associating (association or internal manipulation of symbols) processes also are assessed. Finally, "the level of symbolic meaning in the language symbols" are evaluated on two stages: the "representational" or "meaningful" and the "automatic-sequential" or "rote, automatic, less meaningful" phases (Bateman, and Wetherell, 1965, p. 8).

McCarthy's (1964, 1965) rationale for this test implies a high degree of communality and perhaps even a causal relationship between intelligence and linguistic abilities. The studies of Stippich (1940) and Skodak and Skeels (1949) based on follow-up investigations with retarded children support this. More direct evidence for this rationale is offered by Luria (1961) and Clarke and Clarke (1960). If this assumption continues to be valid, then intellectual functioning may be enhanced by improving linguistic abilities. However, the strengths and weaknesses in communication behavior should be known prior to planning a linguistic remediation program. The ITPA fulfills this need by stressing evaluative information derived from individual subtests tapping the above-mentioned nine areas of communication skills.

McCarthy and Kirk (1963), McCarthy and Olson (1964), and McCarthy (1965) present validity and reliability data. Using increase in raw scores as one validity criterion, they show an irregular pattern of significant subtest score increases for a group of 700 normal children from 2 years, 6 months, to 9 years old. The Revised S-B Scale IQs for 50 subjects tested at each six-month interval ranged between 80 and 120. While the ITPA total scores were significantly higher for each succeeding age-step up to the 8-year to 8-year, 6-month interval, the subtests became less discriminating beyond 7 years, 6 months. The concomitantly linear increase in CA and raw score is inadequate as a validity criterion. The nature of the relationship between the temporal and psychological events is not disclosed beyond the completion of more items as a function of age.

Other approaches to validity find Kirk and McCarthy (1961), McCarthy and Olson (1964), and McCarthy (1965) concerned with the diagnosis of linguistic problems and the assessment of treatment over a period of time. These involve concurrent, predictive, content, constructive, and diagnostic validities. Concurrent and predictive validities are not equally satisfactory for the nine subtests individually but are satisfactory for the total test score. Based on McCarthy's findings (McCarthy and Kirk, 1963), that MA is positively related to linguistic ability, the authors report significant correlations between Revised S-B Scale MAs and ITPA raw scores.

Does the ITPA cover all aspects of psycholinguistic ability and how representative are the selected items? These questions of content validity are answered indirectly by pointing to the internal consistency of the items to establish their homogeneity within each subtest and by extracting general and specific factors at each age level (related to construct validity, too). McCarthy (1965) describes the content validity of the ITPA as less satisfactory than its concurrent and predictive validities. Construct validity seeks to determine whether the test supports its fundamental psychological concepts. In their factor analysis of the ITPA, the authors have succeeded in extracting only what they put into the test. We are not so much criticizing the test as we are calling attention to the pitfall of redundancy of this type of validity evidence. The inter-subtest correlations are low and each subtest correlates significantly with the total ITPA score. Beyond this, no validation of the ITPA is presented in terms of Osgood's communication model. Discussing the test's construct validity, McCarthy (1965) states quite definitely that this characteristic of the test is based on a "factor of importance" selected for each subtest (p. 77), and then he makes a prediction concerning "the magnitude and direction of its relationship with the given ITPA subtest." The basic rationale has not been tested and needs to be.

The "diagnostic" validity postulated by McCarthy consists of the "well beyond chance" successful matching of ITPA profiles with clinical diagnoses by "experts." Cronbach's (1948) paper points out the weakness of this approach.

Reliability in terms of the internal consistency within each subtest, or item homogeneity, is best for the middle age groups of the standardization population. The age interval of 6 years to 6 years, 6 months, yielded product moment correlations for test-retest ranging from .18 to .86, with only four at .70 or higher—a definite weakness readily conceded by the test authors. Rather than estimating the range correlations (which are higher than the restricted range correlations), the entire range should be explored with the test-retest intervals stated explicitly.

Two years after the publication of the Manual by McCarthy and Kirk (1961), Bateman (1963c) wrote a supplement based on experience with the administration of the ITPA. A definite help to the psychologist unfamiliar with the ITPA, it is a compilation of "helpful hints for administration and scoring" of the subtests and includes germane comments about the subtests. In order to improve and perhaps objectify the ITPA, Bateman (1963a, 1963b) suggests a "reference line" for the interpretation of the profile of psycholinguistic scores obtained by a child, an approach that is similar to the pattern or scatter analysis concept formerly popular with the Wechsler Scales. Bateman uses the child's mean language age (LA) as the reference or base line because it is "independent of both mental age and chronological age and is assumed to fairly represent over-all psycholinguistic functioning level" (p. 5). More important for the psychologist and educator would be the pattern of disabilities. In a later paper, Bateman (1963b) introduces the notion of the coded deviation profile not unlike the coding technique of the MMPI. This notion may be helpful provided patterns do not substitute for understanding the individual in terms of his demonstrated strengths and weaknesses.

Most of the reported research with the ITPA consists of doctoral dissertations, mimeographed articles, and paper presentations, which have been summarized by Bateman (1964a) and McCarthy and Olson (1964). Six of the studies deal specifically with mentally retarded children. Semmel and Mueller factor analyzed the ITPA scores of 118 retarded subjects to obtain nine factors identical to the nine subtests defined by McCarthy and Kirk, and they offered this as factorial validation of the ITPA. They also found high positive correlations, .52 to .81, between total LA and each of the subtests. Slightly lower but positive correlations were shown between MA and the nine subtests, .33 to .62.

Loeffler administered the ITPA and other tests to 100 retardates whose mean MA was 6 years, 7 months. Five factors emerged: (1) verbal comprehension, (2) visual memory, (3) figural reasoning, (4) auditory memory, and (5) fluency. Since other tests were included in the battery along with the ITPA, assessment of the congruence with the Semmel and Mueller factors is difficult. The names do give the impression of factorial similarity in both studies.

A master's thesis by Hermann (Bateman, 1964a) presents a psycholinguistic analysis of three retarded siblings with a history of familial deficiency. The three profiles for the ITPA were similar "with assets centered in the visual-motor area and deficits in the auditory-vocal areas" (p. 8). This study also focused on the training of and improvement by two of the retardates in their auditory-vocal automatic functioning. This opens an area of investigation that could test McCarthy's contention that intellectual ability may be enhanced by improving linguistic ability through remedial training.

Smith (1962), Hart (Bateman, 1964a), Blue (Bateman, 1964a), and Hasterok (Bateman, 1964a), investigating the effects of remedial training with retarded children, reported varying gains in mean LA by the trainable and educable retardates. While these subjects benefited from special learning experiences, the important question is the duration of the increase in LA. Mueller and Smith (1964) followed up thirteen matched pairs of educable mentally deficient children reported previously by Smith (1962). The experimental group (one of each matched pair) had received three months training in language reception, association, and expression. The change in LA scores from pre- to post-training testing showed a mean improvement of 6.75 months compared with the control group (no training) average gain of only .4 month, a rather significant gain for the trained group, $p < .05$. Approximately thirteen months after original training had begun, these paired subjects were retested with the ITPA. The experimental group still retained a higher mean LA than the control group, but this difference was not statistically significant. An incidental contribution of this study to reliability data of the ITPA is the test-retest correlation of .94.

The ITPA can be very helpful for the evaluation of the slow learner and the retarded child regarding the specific communication skills already available or potentially so with training. But it is not a test of intelligence or a tool for detecting encephalopathy. The ITPA should lay the basis for a stimulation program in special education classes or for remedial tutoring. The information gleaned from the quality and manner of responding to the individual subtest items is useful to the special education teacher, the speech and hearing therapist, and other members of the remediation team who need to know the specific areas of competency and inadequacy of the child.

The ITPA's detection of specific areas of potential improvement in language skills development for communication adequacy adds to the trainability and educability of the mentally retarded child. But knowledge of the sensory or motor modalities available for learning and for responding is related intimately to the nature of the remediation program. Another possible application of this test would be to confirm Birch and Belmont's (1965) concept of "auditory-visual integrative functioning." The subtests involve auditory and visual perception as well as concept formation so that some of Birch and Belmont's experimental techniques could be varied and extended to test their hypotheses.

The authors of this test, research collaborators, and other investigators have contributed materially to the various types of validities of the ITPA. The numbers and types of subjects have gone beyond the standardization population. Whereas construct and concurrent validities appear to be somewhat satisfactory, more research needs to be done to establish the diagnostic feasibility of this test with different kinds of retarded children. Longitudinal studies of predictive and content validities also are necessary to enhance the usefulness of the ITPA.

SUMMARY AND CONCLUSIONS

If the major concern with mental retardation is classification, the issues involved are limited by the basic definition of mental retardation and the categories subsumed. Beyond administrative and fiscal convenience, this concern serves little other purpose. From the point of view of the retardate, the parents, and society, the human problems remain to be solved.

If, however, the concern is the recognition of the uniqueness of the individual retardate, the length to which the phenotype may be pushed to fulfill the favorable potential of the genotype and the environment, the issues become complex. This chapter attempts to deal with the preliminaries to the training or education of the retarded child, that is, the efforts to evaluate the psychological assets and deficits as reflected in testing procedures.

Four categories of tests were described, each designed for the observation and assessment of different sensory-motor capabilities on one hand, and psychological functions manifested in perceptual, conceptual, and communication skills on the other. The processes tapped by these tests overlap considerably, and not all of the tests have equal validity and reliability attributes. Therefore, the psychologist needs to determine the questions to be answered before he administers a test. The routine use of several of these test techniques may not merit the time and effort put into it.

"Testing for what?" becomes the key to test selection. The usefulness of the tests in this chapter lies more in helping the special education and habilation personnel than in determining intellectual status.

Benton (1964) makes the point that the organization of abilities is important but that the differences between the normal and the retarded child's functioning is still obscure.

The standard tests of intelligence, for instance, the Revised S-B and Wechsler Scales, are not designed primarily to assess in depth the variables that are built into the special tests discussed in this chapter.

We wish to emphasize that these special tests are not to be used alone to estimate the intelligence level unless standard tests are not feasible for the particular testee. Nor should the standard tests of intelligence be employed alone to ascertain areas of strengths and weaknesses for special education evaluation and planning.

REFERENCES

ALLEN, R. M. Suggestions for the adaptive administration of intelligence tests for those with cerebral palsy. Part 2. *Cerebral Palsy Rev.*, 1958, *19* (2), 6–7.

―――. *Variables in personality theory and personality testing: An interpretation.* Springfield, Ill.: Charles C Thomas, 1965.

―――. The appraisal of social and perceptual competence of school children. In J. F. Magary (Ed.), *School psychology.* Englewood Cliffs, N.J.: Prentice-Hall, in press.

――― and ALLEN, S. P. *Intellectual evaluation of the mentally retarded: a handbook.* Los Angeles: Western Psychological Services, in press.

――― and COLLINS, M. G. Suggestions for the adaptive administration of intelligence tests for those with cerebral palsy. Part 1. *Cerebral Palsy Rev.*, 1955, *16* (3), 11–14, 25.

――― and FRANK, G. H. Experimental variation of the mode of reproduction of the Bender Gestalt stimuli. *J. clin. Psychol.*, 1963, *19*, 212–214.

―――, HAUPT, T. D., and JONES, R. W. The relationship between the development test of visual perception and the WISC factors in mentally retarded children. Paper read at American Psychological Association, Los Angeles, September, 1964(a).

―――, ―――, ―――. A suggested use and non-use for the Peabody picture vocabulary test with the retarded child. *Psychol. Rep.*, 1964b, *15*, 421–422.

―――, ―――, ―――. Visual perceptual abilities and intelligence in mental retardates. *J. clin. Psychol.*, 1965, *21*, 299–300.

――― and JEFFERSON, T. W. *Psychological evaluation of the cerebral palsied person.* Springfield, Ill.: Charles C Thomas, 1962.

―――, JONES, R. W., and HAUPT, T. D. Note of caution for the research use of the Frostig test with mentally retarded children. *Percept. mot. Skills*, 1965, *21*, 237–238.

―――, and SANDLER, J. Concerning the variation of responses on the Columbia mental maturity scale. *Cerebral Palsy Rev.*, 1956, *17*, 38, 49.

―――, THORNTON, T. E., and STENGER, C. A. Ammons and Wechsler test performance of college and psychiatric subjects. *J. Clin. Psychol.*, 1954, *10*, 378–381.

AMMONS, R. B., and AMMONS, H. S. *The full-range picture vocabulary test.* New Orleans: R. B. Ammons, 1948.

―――, ARNOLD, P. R., and HERRMANN, R. S. The full-range picture vocabulary test: IV. Results for a white school population. *J. clin. Psychol.*, 1950, *6*, 164–169.

ARTHUR, G. The Arthur adaptation of the Leiter international performance scale. *J. clin. Psychol.*, 1949, *5*, 345–349.

―――. *The Arthur Adaptation of the Leiter International Performance Scale.* Washington, D.C.: Psychological Service Center, 1952.

AYLAIAN, A., and MELTZER, M. L. The Bender Gestalt test and intelligence. *J. consult. Psychol.*, 1962, *26*, 483.

BALLARD, P. B. What London children like to draw. *J. exp. Pedag.*, 1912, *1*, 185–197.

BARRATT, E. S. The relationship of the progressive matrices (1938) to the Columbia mental maturity scale and the WISC. *J. consult. Psychol.* 1956, *20*, 294–296.

BATEMAN, B. A reference line for use with the ITPA. Unpublished paper, *Inst. Res. except. Child.*, University of Illinois. 1963. (a)

———. The coded deviation profile (ITPA)—an application of mean language age to profile analysis. Unpublished manuscript, *Inst. Res. excep. Child.*, University of Illinois, 1963. (b)

———. *Two years after the manual.* Urbana, Ill.: University of Illinois Press, 1963. (c)

———.*The Illinois test of psycholinguistic abilities in current research: summaries of studies.* Urbana, Ill.: University of Illinois Press, 1964. (a)

———. *Illinois test of psycholinguistic abilities references.* Urbana, Ill.: University of Illinois Press, 1964. (b)

——— and WETHERELL, J. Psycholinguistic aspects of mental retardation. *Ment. Retard.*, 1965, *3* (2), 8–13.

BENDER, L. A visual motor Gestalt test and its clinical use. *Res. Monogr. Amer. Orthopsychiat. Assn.*, 1938, No. 3.

BENSBERG, G. J. A test differentiating endogenous and exogenous mental defectives. *Amer. J. ment. Def.*, 1949, *54*, 502–506.

———. Performance of brain-injured and familial mental defectives on Bender Gestalt test. *J. consult. Psychol.*, 1952, *16*, 61–64.

——— and SLOAN, W. Performance of brain-injured defectives on the Arthur adaptation of the Leiter. *Psychol. Serv. Center*, 1951, *3*, 181–184.

BENTON, A. L. Psychological evaluation and differential diagnosis. In H. A. Stevens and R. Heber (Eds.) *Mental retardation*. Chicago: University of Chicago Press, 1964, 16–56.

BERKO, M. J. The measurement in intelligence of children with cerebral palsy: The Columbia mental maturity scale. *J. Pediat.*, 1955, *47*, 253–260.

BEVERLY, L., and BENSBERG, G. J. A comparison of the Leiter, the Cornell-Coxe and Stanford-Binet with mental defectives. *Amer. J. ment. Def.*, 1952, *57*, 89–91.

BILLINGSLEA, F. Y. The Bender-Gestalt: an objective scoring method and validating data. *J. clin. Psychol.*, 1948, *4*, 1–27.

———. The Bender-Gestalt: A review and a perspective. *Psychol. Bull.*, 1964, *60*, 233–251.

BIRCH, H. G., and BELMONT, L. Auditory-visual integration in brain-damaged and normal children. *Develpm. Med. Child Neurol.*, 1965, *7*, (2), 135–144.

——— and LEFFORD, A. Two strategies for studying perception in "brain-damaged" children. In H. G. Birch (Ed.), *Brain damage in children*. Baltimore: Williams and Wilkins, 1964, 46–60.

BIRCH, J. W. The Goodenough drawing test and other mentally retarded children. *Amer. J. ment. Def.*, 1949, *54*, 218–224.

BLIGH, H. F. Concurrent validity evidence on two intelligence measures for young children. In E. M. Huddleston (Ed.), *The 16th Yearbook of the National Council on Measurement Used in Education*. New York: National Council on Measurement, 1959, 56–66.

BRENGELMANN, J. C., and KENNY, J. T. Comparison of Leiter, WAIS and Stanford-Binet IQs in retardates. *J. clin. Psychol.,* 1961, *17,* 235–238.

BUDOFF, M., and PURSEGLOVE, E. M. Peabody picture vocabulary test performances of institutionalized retarded adolescents. *Amer. J. ment. Def.,* 1963, *67,* 756–760.

BURGEMEISTER, B. B., BLUM, L. H., and LORGE, I. *Columbia mental maturity scale* (rev. ed.). New York: Harcourt, Brace, and World, 1959.

CANTER, A. The use of the Columbia mental maturity scale with cerebral palsied children. *Amer. J. ment. Def.,* 1956, *60,* 843–851.

CLARKE, A. D. B., and CLARKE, A. M. Some recent advances in the study of early deprivation. *J. child Psychol. Psychiat.,* 1960, *1,* 26–36.

CLAWSON, A. *The Bender visual motor Gestalt Test for children.* Beverly Hills, Calif.: Western Psychological Services, 1962.

CONDELL, J. F. The Bender Gestalt test with mentally retarded children using the Koppitz revised scoring system. *J. clin. Psychol.,* 1963, *19,* 430–431.

CORAH, N. L., and POWELL, B. J. A factor analysis of the Frostig developmental test of visual perception. *Percept. mot. Skills,* 1963, *16,* 59–63.

CORDELL, J. F. Note on the use of the Ammons full-range picture vocabulary test with retarded children. *Psychol. Rep.,* 1959, *5,* 150.

CRONBACH, L. J. A validation design for qualitative studies of personality. *J. consult. Psychol.,* 1948, *12,* 363–374.

DILLER, L., and BIRCH, H. G. Psychological evaluation of children with cerebral damage. In H. G. Birch (Ed.) *Brain damage in children.* Baltimore: Williams and Wilkins, 1964, 27–45.

DILS, C. W. The colored progressive matrices as an indicator of brain damage. *J. clin. Psychol.,* 1960, *16,* 414–416.

DUNN, L. M. *Peabody picture vocabulary test: Manual.* Minneapolis: American Guidance Service, 1959.

———— and BROOKS, S. Peabody picture vocabulary test performance of educable mentally retarded. *Train. Sch. Bull.,* 1960, *57,* 35–49.

———— and HARLEY, R. K. Comparability of Peabody, Ammons, Van Alstyne, and Columbia test scores with cerebral palsied children. *Except. Child.,* 1959, *26,* 70–74.

———— and HOTTEL, J. V. Peabody picture vocabulary test performance of trainable mentally retarded children. *Amer. J. ment. Def.,* 1961, *65,* 448–452.

FELDMAN, J. S. Psychological differences among moron and borderline mental defectives as a function of etiology. *Amer. J. ment. Def.,* 1953, *57,* 484–494.

FISHER, G. M., SHOTWELL, A. M., and YORK, O. H. Comparability of the Ammons full-range picture vocabulary test with the WAIS in the assessment of intelligence of mental retardates. *Amer. J. ment. Def.,* 1960, *64,* 995–999.

FRENCH, J. L. *Manual: pictorial test of intelligence.* New York: Houghton Mifflin, 1964.

———— and WORCHESTER, D. A. A critical study of the Columbia mental maturity scale. *Except. Child.,* 1956, *23,* 111–113, 132–133.

FROSTIG, M. Visual perception in the brain-damaged child. *Amer. J. Orthopsychiat.,* 1963, *33,* 665–671.

————, LEFEVER, D. W., and WHITTLESEY, J. R. B. A developmental test of visual perception for evaluating normal and neurologically handicapped children. *Percept. mot. Skills,* 1961, *12,* 383–394. (a)

———, ———, ———. *Developmental test of visual perception.* (3rd ed.)
Palo Alto, Calif.: Consulting Psychologists Press, 1961. (b)

———, ———, ———. *Visual perception in the brain-injured child. Amer.
J. Orthopsychiat.,* 1963, *33,* 665–671.

GALLAGHER, J. J. Changes in verbal and non-verbal ability of brain-injured
mentally retarded children following removal of special stimulation.
Amer. J. ment. Def., 1962, *66,* 774-778.

———, BENOIT, E. P., and BOYD, N. F. Measures in intelligence in brain-
damaged children. *J. Clin. Psychol.,* 1956, *12,* 69–72.

GELOF, M. Comparison of systems of classification relating to degree of
retardation to measured intelligence. *Amer. J. ment. Def.,* 1963, *68,*
297–317.

GOLDBERG, F. H. The performance of schizophrenic, retarded and normal
children on the Bender-Gestalt test. *Amer. J. ment. Def.,* 1957, *61,*
548–555.

GOLDBERG, L. R. The diagnosis of organic brain damage from the Bender-
Gestalt test. *J. consult. Psychol.,* 1959, *23,* 25–33.

GOODENOUGH, F. L. *Measurement of intelligence by drawings.* New York:
Harcourt, Brace, and World, 1926.

GREEN, M. W., and EWART, J. C. Normative data on progressive matrices.
J. consult. Psychol., 1955, *19,* 139–142.

GUNZBERG, H. C. Scope and limitations of the Goodenough drawing test
method in clinical work with mental defectives. *J. clin. Psychol.,* 1955,
11, 8–15.

HAIN, J. D. The Bender Gestalt test: a scoring method for identification of
brain damage. *J. consult. Psychol.,* 1964, *28,* 34–40.

HALPIN, V. C. Rotation errors made by brain-injured familial children on
two visual-motor tests. *Amer. J. ment. Def.,* 1955, *59,* 485.

HARRIS, D. B. *Children's drawings as measures of intellectual maturity.* New
York: Harcourt, Brace, and World, 1963.

HIRSCHENFANG, S. Further studies on the Columbia mental maturity scale
and revised Stanford-Binet (L) in children with speech disorders. *J.
clin. Psychol.,* 1961, *17,* 171.

HO, D., and WHITE, D. T. Use of the full-range picture vocabulary test and
mentally retarded. *Amer. J. ment. Def.,* 1963, *67,* 761–764.

HUNT, B. M. Differential responses of mentally retarded children on the
Leiter scale. *Except. Child.,* 1961, *28,* 99–102.

HUTT, M. L. *A tentative guide for the administration of the Bender Gestalt
test.* U.S. Army: Adjutant General's School, 1945.

——— and BRISKIN, G. *The clinical use of the revised Bender-Gestalt test.*
New York: Grune and Stratton, 1960.

JONES, R. W. Cross-sectional views of visual reproduction and the effects of
distraction on visual reproduction by brain-damaged retardates, familial
retardates and normal children. Unpublished doctoral dissertation, University of Miami, 1964.

——— and ALLEN, R. M. The effects of visual distraction. Paper read at
American Psychological Association, Los Angeles, 1964.

KELLER, J. E. The use of a Bender Gestalt maturation level scoring system
with mentally handicapped children. *Amer. J. Orthopsychiat.,* 1955,
25, 563–573.

KEPHART, N. C. *The brain-injured child in the classroom.* Chicago: National
Society for Crippled Children and Adults, 1963.

KIRK, S. A. Research in education. In H. A. Stevens and R. Heber (Eds.),
Mental retardation. Chicago: University of Chicago Press, 57–99.

———— and McCARTHY, J. J. The Illinois test of psycholinguistic abilities: An approach to differential diagnosis. *Amer. J. ment. Def.*, 1961, *66*, 399–412.

KITAY, J. I. The Bender-Gestalt test as a projective technique. *J. clin. Psychol.*, 1950, *6*, 170-174.

KNEHR, C. A. Progressive matrices findings with cerebral histopathology. *Percept. mot. Skills*, 1956, *6*, 249–254.

KOPPITZ, E. M. The Bender Gestalt test and learning disturbances in young children. *J. clin. Psychol.*, 1958, *14*, 292–295. (a)

————. Relationship between the Bender Gestalt test and the Wechsler intelligence scale for children. *J. clin. Psychol.*, 1958, *14*, 413–418. (b)

————. The Bender Gestalt test for children: a normative study. *J. clin. Psychol.*, 1960, *16*, 432–435.

————. Diagnosing brain damage in young children with the Bender Gestalt test. *J. consult. Psychol.*, 1962, *26*, 541–546.

LEITER, R. G. Part I of the manual for the 1948 revision of the Leiter international performance scale: Evidence of the reliability and validity of the Leiter tests. *Psychol. Service Center J.*, 1959, *11*, 1–72.

LETON, D. A. Visual-motor capacities and ocular efficiency in reading. *Percept. mot. Skills*, 1962, *15*, 407–432.

LOEFFLER, F. J. An extension and partial replication of Mayers *et al.* primary abilities at mental age six. In B. Bateman, *The Illinois test of psycholinguistic abilities in current research: Summary of studies.* Urbana: University of Illinois Press, 3–4.

LURIA, A. R. *The role of speech in the regulation of normal and abnormal behavior.* New York: Liveright, 1961.

————. *The mentally retarded child.* New York: Macmillan, 1963.

———— and YUDOVICH, R. I. *Speech and the development of mental processes in the child.* London: Stapes Press, 1959.

MAISEL, R. N., ALLEN, R. M., and TALLARICO, R. B. A comparison of the adaptive and standard administration of the Leiter international performance scale with normal children. *Cerebral Palsy Rev.*, 1962, *23* (5), 3–4, 16.

MALPASS, L. F., BROWN, R., and HOKE, D. The utility of the progressive matrices with normal and retarded children. *J. clin. Psychol.*, 1960, *16*, 350.

MASLOW, P., FROSTIG, M., LEFEVER, D. W., and WHITTLESEY, J. R. B. The Marianne Frostig developmental test of visual perception, 1963 standardization. *Percept. mot. Skills*, 1964, *19*, 463–499.

McCARTHY, D. A study of the reliability of the Goodenough drawing test of intelligence. *J. Psychol.*, 1944, *18*, 201–206.

McCARTHY, J. J. A test for the identification of defects in language usage among young cerebral palsied children. *Cerebral Palsy Rev.*, 1960, *21* (1), 4–7.

————. The importance of linguistic ability in the mentally retarded. *Ment. Retard.*, 1964, *2*, 90–96.

————. Notes on the validity of the ITPA. *Ment. Retard.*, 1965, *3* (2), 25–26.

McCARTHY, J., and KIRK, S. A. *Illinois test of psycholinguistic abilities examiner's manual.* Urbana: University of Illinois, Institute of Research for Exceptional Children, 1961.

————, ————. *The construction, standardization and statistical characteristics of the Illinois test of psycholinguistic abilities.* Urbana: University of Illinois Press, 1963.

—— and OLSON, J. L. *Validity studies on the Illinois test of psycholinguistic abilities*. Madison, Wis.: Authors, 1964.

MCCARTHY, S. A. *Children's drawings*. Baltimore: Williams and Wilkins, 1924.

MUELLER, M., and SMITH, J. O. The stability of language age modification over time. *Amer. J. ment. Def.*, 1964, *68*, 537–539.

MURPHY, M. M. A Goodenough scale of evaluation of human figure drawings of three non-psychotic groups of adults. *J. clin. Psychol.*, 1956, *12*, 397–399.

OKI, T., SAKAI, T., KIZU, M., and HAGASHI, H. A comparative study concerning the psychological traits of children with organic brain damage and subnormal oligophrenia. *Jap. J. child Psychiat.*, 1960, *1*, 126–134.

OLSON, J. L., HAHN, H. R., and HERMANN, A. L. Psycholinguistic curriculum. *Ment. Retard.*, 1965, *3* (2), 14–19.

ORME, J. E. The colored progressive matrices as a measure of intellectual subnormality. *Brit. J. med. Psychol.*, 1961, *34*, 291.

OSGOOD, C. E. Motivational dynamics of language behavior. In M. R. Jones (Ed.), *Nebraska Symposium on Motivation*, Lincoln: University of Nebraska Press, 1957, 348–424.

PASCAL, G. R., and SUTTELL, B. S. *The Bender-Gestalt test*. New York: Grune and Stratton, 1951.

PEEK, R. M., and QUAST, W. *A scoring system for the Bender-Gestalt*. Minneapolis: Authors, 1951.

PINKERTON, P., and KELLY, J. An attempted correlation between clinical and psychometric findings in senile arteriosclerotic dementia. *J. ment. Sci.*, 1952, No. 411.

RAVEN, J. C. *Guide to the standard progressive matrices*. London: Lewis, 1960.

ROHRS, F. W., and HAWORTH, M. R. The 1960 Stanford-Binet, WISC and Goodenough tests with mentally retarded children. *Amer. J. ment. Def.*, 1962, *66*, 853–859.

SCHIEFELBUSCH, R. L. A discussion of language treatment methods for mentally retarded children. *Ment. Retard.*, 1965, *3* (2), 4–7.

SCHRAMM, C. D. An evaluation of the WISC and the full-range picture vocabulary test in clinical use. *Paper* read at Kentucky Psychological Association, Lexington, 1954.

SHARP, H. C. A comparison of slow learners' scores on three individual intelligence scales. *J. clin. Psychol.*, 1957, *13*, 372.

——. A note on the reliability of the Leiter international performance scale, 1948 revision. *J. consult. Psychol.*, 1958, *22*, 320.

SIEVERS, D. J. Development and standardization of a test of psycholinguistic growth in preschool children. Unpublished doctoral dissertation, University of Illinois, 1955.

SILVERSTEIN, A. B. Psychological testing practices in state institutions for the mentally retarded. *Amer. J. ment. Def.*, 1963, *68*, 440–445.

——. Variance components in the developmental test of visual perception. *Psychol. Rep.*, in press.

—— and MOHAN, P. J. Bender-Gestalt figure rotation in the mentally retarded. *J. consult. Psychol.*, 1962, *26*, 386–388.

SKODAK, M., and SKEELS, H. M. A final follow-up study of one hundred adopted children. *J. genet. Psychol.*, 1949, *75*, 85–125.

SLOAN, W., and BENSBERG, G. J. An exploratory study of the full-range picture vocabulary test with mental defectives. *Amer. J. ment. Def.*, 1954, *58*, 481–485.

SLOSSON, R. L. *Slosson intelligence test (SIT) for children and adults.* East Aurora, N.Y.: Slosson Educational Publishers, 1963.

SMITH, B. S. The relative merits of certain verbal and non-verbal tests at the second-grade level. *J. clin. Psychol.,* 1961, *17,* 53–54.

SMITH, J. O. Group language development for educable mental retardates. *Except. Child.,* 1962, *29,* 95–101.

SMITH, L. M., and FILMORE, A. R. The Ammons FRPV test and the WISC for remedial reading cases. *J. Consult. Psychol.,* 1954, *18,* 332.

STACEY, C. L. and CARLTON, F. O. The relationship between Raven's colored progressive matrices and two tests of general intelligence. *J. clin. Psychol.,* 1955, *11,* 84–85.

——— and GILL, M. R. The relationship between Raven's colored progressive matrices and two tests of general intelligence for 172 subnormal adult subjects. *J. clin. Psychol.,* 1955, *11,* 86–87.

STARR, A. S. The Rutgers drawing test, form A. *Train. Sch. Bull.,* 1952, *49,* 45–65.

———. *The Rutgers drawing test, form B.* New Brunswick, N.J.: Author, 1961.

STEVENS, H. A. Overview. In H. A. Stevens and R. Heber (Eds.), *Mental retardation.* Chicago: University of Chicago Press, 1964, 1–15.

STIPPICH, M. The mental development of children of feebleminded mothers. *National Soc. Study Educ. Yearb.,* 1940, 337–350. Part II.

TATE, M. E. A study of the performance of selected groups of five-year-olds on the Leiter International Performance Scale. Unpublished doctoral dissertation, State University of Iowa, 1950.

———. The influence of cultural factors on the Leiter international performance scale. *J. abnorm. soc. Psychol.,* 1952, *47,* 497–501.

TEMPERO, H., and IVANOFF, J. *Effectiveness of the Peabody Picture Vocabulary Test with seventh-grade pupils.* Lincoln: University of Nebraska, Department of Educational Psychology, 1960.

THWEATT, R. C. Prediction of school learning disabilities through the use of the Bender Gestalt test: A validation study of Koppitz' scoring technique. *J. clin. Psychol.,* 1963, *19,* 216–217.

TOBIAS, J., and GORELICK, J. The utility of the Goodenough scale in the appraisal of retarded adults. *Amer. J. ment. Def.,* 1960, *65,* 64–68.

———, ———. Validity of the Peabody picture vocabulary test as a measure of intelligence of retarded adults. *Train. Sch. Bull.,* 1961, *59,* 92–98.

TOLOR, A., and SCHULBERG, H. *An evaluation of the Bender-Gestalt test.* Springfield, Ill.: Charles C Thomas, 1963.

WARREN, S. A., and COLLIER, H. L. Suitability of the Columbia mental maturity scale for mentally retarded institutionalized females. *Amer. J. ment. Def.,* 1960, *64,* 916–920.

WITSAMAN, L. R., and JONES, R. L. Reliability of the Columbia mental maturity scale with kindergarten children. *J. clin. Psychol.,* 1959, *15,* 66–68.

Personality Evaluation

RUE L. CROMWELL

4

PERSONALITY evaluations often have low initial priority in professional work with the mentally retarded. Sometimes this is justified, sometimes not. In situations where a medical judgment is needed on the possibility of an active brain lesion, the personality manifestations—whether in reaction to the lesion or otherwise—are certainly of secondary importance. In other cases, only a quick estimate of learning capacity is needed. The reasons for the reduced capacity are not considered important.

Unless there are clear signs of psychosis or other abnormal behavior, personality evaluation often has been ignored altogether. Major legal and placement decisions regarding a retarded person usually are based on which gross category the retardate fits, usually involving intelligence, social competence, and brain damage. Rarely are personality evaluations adequately used at this level of decision making.

Ignoring personality factors in the retardate is often both unfortunate and paradoxical. The retardate's personality is often the factor that brings him to the attention of legal or mental health professionals—that is, the retarded individual usually displays some behavior that arouses the concern of the family or community. In such cases, the usual approach is to examine only the intellectual level and other factors that would be a basis for placing benign controls on him. Subsequently, the possibilities of legal incompetence, commitment, guardianship, and residential treatment are considered. In this way, the understanding and treatment of his disturbing personality is relegated to secondary importance.

In other situations, the question of personality functioning is clearly the prime reason for psychological evaluation. Parents of a child may seek help in understanding why he acts the way he does and what they can do to help him behave more effectively. A teacher may need increased understanding of a child's personality to help him attain certain educational goals. A mental health professional may need a personality evaluation in order to plan psychotherapy or other means of behavior modification. A social worker or rehabilitation counselor may request a personality evaluation of a person in order to be of more assistance to him. A worker in a residential setting may wish to solve disciplinary or adjustment problems. Or, the worker may seek a basis for planning the retardate's personal, educational, and social development. In each case, meaningful decisions follow an understanding of the individual's personality.

The purpose of this chapter is to describe how personality factors are related systematically to other major concepts in mental retardation. Then, attention will be given to the way in which personality develops in mentally retarded and normal children. Finally, the process of conducting a personality evaluation and communicating its findings will be discussed.

PERSONALITY, INTELLIGENCE, AND SOCIAL COMPETENCE

The problem of defining concepts in behavioral science is uniquely difficult. For the physical scientist, the criteria of clarity, utility, and generality of definition must be met. For the behavioral scientist, there are additional demands. Man, having been concerned with his own behavior long before the age of science, has already become accustomed to ways of conceptualizing behavior. These modes are fraught with differences in usages from person to person and from time to time. Surplus and diffuse meanings go beyond the usual limits of acceptable scientific definition. Given this heritage, the behavioral scientist must deal with the subject matter of personality, intelligence, and other constructs that have been a part of the common language.

If the behavioral scientist were to use traditional terms and traditional meanings, the problem of linguistic diffusion and ambiguity would overcome him. If he were to devise different labels and different denotable meanings, the prior language learnings of his colleagues would produce the tendency either to object or to retranslate loosely the new concepts into ones to which they were originally accustomed. Moreover, the innovator would be accused of confusing a familiar issue with strange terminology. If the behavioral scientist were to choose conventional terms and to ascribe single operational meanings to them, the negative transfer from past learnings would again cause a communication problem with his colleagues. No one solution seems to be the perfect one. Nevertheless, I have chosen the latter course for this discussion, realizing that these terms probably won't have all the connotations and denotations that the reader has held for them.

Once it is agreed that conventional terms, such as personality and intelligence, will be useful with newly prescribed systematic definitions, another problem emerges—that is, intelligence and personality have usually been studied separately. Intelligence constructs typically do not have systematic relationship to personality constructs, and vice versa. Historically, two relatively compartmentalized language systems have evolved. Especially in the area of retardation, the development of an understanding of the interrelationship of these two construct systems seems important. Otherwise, personality and intellectual evaluations could be conducted and reported with the psychologist having only a limited view of how one affects the other.

With the definitions that follow, an attempt

will be made to describe some essentials of systematic interrelationship.

Personality refers to the recurring, long-term aspects of behavior that characterize individual differences among people. *Personality theories* are systems of constructs that serve to describe and predict these relatively long-term aspects of individual behavior. Depending upon what we are trying to predict, our constructs vary. Also, the events we attempt to construe vary. The notion of one "true" or "real" conception of a personality is rejected as meaningless.

Various common approaches to personality theory may be depicted by means of Figure 1.

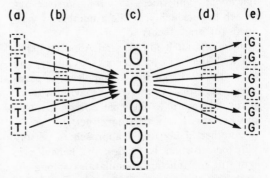

FIG. 1. Threat-avoidance and goal-approach behavior as a basis for (a) threat constructs, (b) defense mechanism constructs, (c) typology constructs, (d) trait constructs, and (e) need constructs in personality theory.

This figure illustrates the subject matter on which personality constructs are built. The *O*s represent human organisms interacting with stimulus objects in their environmental fields. The relevant stimulus objects are divided into two categories, the *G*s (goal objects) and the *T*s (threat objects). These basic constructs of goal and threat are inferred directly from the directional behavior of the individual. If a particular stimulus object or situation is observed to be one toward which behavior is directed, it may be called a goal. If it is one away from which behavior is directed, it may be called a threatening object or situation. The shafts of the arrows symbolize the kind of behaviors that are displayed, and the points of the arrows indicate the greater relative utility of referring to them as approach or avoidance behaviors respectively. The dotted lines indicate the ways in which personality theorists have abstracted constructs in order to describe and predict the individual's personality functioning.

A primitive approach to personality theory, as denoted by (c) in Figure 1, has been to classify individuals into groups. Introverts, extraverts, and ambiverts might be categorized in this way. The best known categorization of this nature is the classification of mental disorders (e.g., paranoid schizophrenia, anxiety neurosis, etc.), developed originally by Kraepelin (1913). This approach is referred to as a *type theory* of personality.

Another approach, as indicated by (d) in Figure 1, consists of classifying the approach behavior in terms of its formal aspects and functional similarities—the *trait theory* approach to personality. While a number of variations of trait theory occur, the theoretical systems of Cattell (1950) and Allport (1937) are well known as trait theories. Actually, any term, such as honesty, compulsivity, pessimism, etc., that categorizes behavior without particular regard to the goal objects involved can be viewed as a trait construct.

Another highly useful approach to personality construction is to describe behavior in terms of the functional similarities among the goals that the organism approaches—the *need theory* approach. For example, on the biological level, it can easily be observed that organisms approach food objects. Without further data on the physiological level, the functional similarity and intersubstitutability of food objects provide a sufficient basis for a behavioral construct of hunger. Once defined, it can be studied in terms of physiological, social, or other behavioral correlates. On the psychological level, goal objects may be classified in terms of types of people and social interactions a person seeks. From this data, we develop constructs of need for academic achievement, need for affiliation, need for dependence, heterosexual need, homosexual need, etc. Rotter (1954) and Murray (1938) have proposed well-known need theories of personality.

Moving to (b) in the left side of Figure 1, the avoidant behavior may be classified in terms of its functional similarities. This area of personality theory has been developed primarily in the field of psychoanalysis. The constructs are commonly referred to as *defense mechanisms*. Typical examples include pro-

jection, repression, rationalization, physical avoidance, intellectual control, etc.

Finally, in section (a) of Figure 1, the threat objects may be classified in terms of their functional similarities and intersubstitutabilities. In spite of the importance of such constructs to personality description, no one particular system of construction of threat objects and situations has attained formal usage. So, the clinician typically describes behavior in such terms as fear of female authority figures, school phobia, homosexual threat, anxiety re vocational responsibility, fear of swimming, water, etc.

Once an individual has been described in terms of these recurring interactions with his environment, one has by definition described his personality. The final step would be to look at the *personal constructs* that the individual himself uses in describing his own role in this socioenvironmental field (see Kelly, 1955).

Intelligence refers to the generalized adequacy an individual is able to maintain in achieving the goals and meeting the demands of his environment. The phrase, "generalized adequacy," refers to the level of performance the individual is able to display across different areas of ability. Performance that deviates from the person's own typical level ought to be described in terms of special abilities. The phrase, "is able to maintain," refers to the fact that the construct of intelligence is concerned with the long-term level of functioning rather than the "ups and downs" that occur as a function of hunger, distracting discomfort, sleep and drowsiness, other motivational factors, sensory deficits, temporary emotional disturbance, etc. However, to rule these factors out of the picture does not mean that intelligence is a constant. On the contrary, as will be noted in Butterfield's chapter, specific factors can be identified that will lead to increases or decreases in intelligence over time.

The phrase, "achieving the goals and meeting the demands of his environment," refers to the fact that intelligence must be defined operationally in terms of whether the individual can utilize his behavioral repertoire to obtain goals and subgoals successfully. Intelligence is sampled by especially constructed situations, that is, test items, which set up goals and subgoals. In each instance the individual must bring forth his skills to meet the demands of the situation. Intelligence is scaled in terms of how well he can do this as compared with his fellows.

This definition of intelligence rejects the distinction between cognitive process and product as a fallacious one. When cognitive process is defined operationally, it must be in terms of a sequence of observable behaviors. Each step or subgoal of the sequence may be viewed either as part of the cognitive process or as behavioral products and subproducts. These sequential steps (cognitive process, if you will) are very much in need of research as compared with other aspects of intelligence. However, they do not tell the whole story. Intelligence depends upon the ability of the individual to integrate his components of functioning in order to "deliver the goods" through holistically complete sequences of accurate goal-achieving behavior.

Social competence refers to the adequacy a person can display in meeting the demands of society, especially the demands that are made by others in his immediate environment. The subject matter used to define social competence is part of that used- to define intelligence. Thus, the two constructs are inherently correlated. Whereas the intelligence construct focuses on the areas of ability the individual displays in attaining goals, the social competence construct focuses upon the areas of demand that the social environment makes upon him. The examiner of intelligence will take a broad sample of the individual's range of skills. The examiner of social competence will sample broadly the range of social demands as they exist or are likely to exist in the living situation of the individual.

To an extent, social competence, unlike intelligence, is not focused upon generalized adequacy as much as upon specific areas where the individual falls crucially short of meeting social expectations. For example, social expectations occur regarding a person's learning to walk, learning to talk, doing passing work in school, avoiding violations of law, holding down a job, etc. If only one of these were to fall crucially short, the individual would be judged low in social competence, regardless of his standing on the others.

The effect of social change represents another distinction between intelligence and social competence. The evolution of man's intellectual functioning is not occurring as

quickly as the evolution and diversification of the demands made on man by society. Consequently, measures of intelligence usually are more similar to each other and, therefore, more intercorrelated. Measures of social competence, on the other hand, must vary with the changing demands of the culture.

Because of the focus on crucial shortcomings rather than generalized level of competence and because of the faster evolution of societal demands, the value of describing social competence in terms of a single index is limited. The major exception to this is in the pre-school years where physical development is a major and common expectation in all cultures.

How, then, does the construct of personality relate to the constructs of intelligence and social competence? As one looks at the definitions in the preceding paragraphs, certain commonalities become apparent. First of all, in accordance with scientific method, all of the constructs are defined operationally in terms of subject matter within a time-space framework. Second, all three constructs deal with a single class of events: the interaction of the individual with his environment. Third, within this interactive event, the behavior of man is assumed to be goal-directed. That is, we assume that behavior may usefully be described in terms of objects and situations the individual is approaching or avoiding. Fourth, the environment is assumed not just to be a passive source for goal-seeking but rather one that places some demands on the individual. To the extent these demands come from other people, they may be viewed as social demands. Fifth, all of the constructs abstract from relatively long segments of time in the lives of individuals. While having some modest utility in predicting the reactions of an individual in a specific time and place, they are designed primarily to predict how the individual will interact with his environment over a long period of time.

Having noted these common elements, how can the constructs of personality, intelligence, and social competence be differentiated? Indeed, one must remember that the same set of observations may have relevance for personality, intelligence, and social competence. If one is interested in the specific behaviors, goals, and threats that characterize a specific individual, the investigator would be assessing personality. If one were interested in how well the behavior achieved these goals he would be evaluating intelligence. If one were interested in whether the behavior met the society's expectations, he would be assessing social competence. To use the game of baseball as an analogy, personality refers to what techniques, strategies, and demeanor are peculiar to a given player. Intelligence refers to his batting average or his win-loss record. Social competence refers to the spectators' judgment of his performance and how well they felt he stayed within the rules.

PERSONALITY DEVELOPMENT

Having viewed personality in terms of various possible construct systems and in relation to two other constructs, let us now examine aspects of how an individual's personality develops. While Figure 1 illustrates how the individual's personality pattern may be viewed at any one time, the personality may also be described in terms of certain orderly changes in structure over the life of the developing individual. Since the retarded individual is slow in personality as well as intellectual development, evaluating his level of development in functioning is important. This approach has the clinical value of predicting where and how the retardate can be expected to change (or mature) next.

The following five arbitrary levels of personality development seem to be useful for psychoeducational purposes. They should not be viewed as discrete segments placed end to end over the developmental period of the individual. Instead, they represent overlapping and sometimes concurrent phases. They do not conform precisely to developmental construct systems that have been previously described by others. Instead, they arise from the clinical and research observations by my students and me. Research citations will occur where they are relevant to the description being presented.

The first phase of this development involves basic boundary discrimination. The second phase is that of intact hedonic functioning. The third phase is the development of a conceptual motivational system. The fourth phase concerns the development of effective interpersonal functioning. A fifth phase is the development of awareness of cultural expectations.

While these phases apply to normal children, the adequately functioning retardate would be expected to progress on each of these dimensions according to his mental age level (see Bialer, 1960).

BASIC BOUNDARY DEVELOPMENT

A primary step in the development of an infant is the differentiation of boundaries of the self, the thought processes, and the basic elements of goal and threat in the environment. Without this conception of basic boundaries, the child cannot know that he is a complete entity, that his body parts are also a part of him, that his mother and the milk bottle are not parts of him, and that his thoughts are not part of actual external events.

When the child is undeveloped or deficient in his basic boundary discriminations, concepts such as poor reality contact, deficit in object relations, and autism are often used to describe his behavior. The child will not have developed an organized response of approach or avoidance (i.e., an ability to relate) to total human beings. Instead, he may show positive or negative reactions to specific objects such as a person's hand or part of his clothing. While the mature infant will look to a person's face to interpret a slap he received on his bottom, the infant with less or retarded development likely will not associate the actions of a person with looks of approval or disapproval on his face.

Bizarre behavior and mannerisms may occur as a function of confusion between thought and external events. If the child can talk, his language may not be directed toward interpersonal conversation except when a certain relatively strong need or external demand occurs. Instead, the language may be directed toward an inner world of fantasy. Neologisms, gutteral sounds, and sentence fragments may occur as a function of vocal and other auditory self-stimulation. Especially missing from sentence structure will be the appropriate use of pronouns and prepositions that reveal adequately the relation between himself and other people and objects.

Poor body identification may be displayed in many ways. The child may stare at his hands as if they are not his. He may have an apparent disregard for parts of his body. For example, he may fail to pull his hand away from danger. He may actively injure or burn himself and then show anguish only when the pain is felt. While self-stimulation of the body would be frequent, no total body admiration or grooming would be observed. While a mirror may be used out of interest or self-entertainment, no reaction of self-consciousness, admiration, or other response to the total self can be detected. His reactions to others may appear confusing because another person's facial expressions, spoken words and overt behaviors (such as helping, giving, pinching, taking away, or pointing) may not be viewed as all originating from the same source. Nor will the child always view these responses as having relevance to himself or to other objects in the environment.

THE INTACT HEDONIST

Once the child has developed an adequate set of boundaries, he is then able to react to himself and the world in a relatively consistent hedonistic fashion. That is, his behavior becomes oriented consistently toward achieving immediate gratifications and avoiding unpleasant circumstances (see Cromwell, 1963). This will occur on a psychological as well as a biological level. Thus, positive valences are acquired for the mother, other figures, toy objects, and dominance over other children, as well as food, tactual-kinesthetic stimulation, and the other biologically based satisfactions. This appetite for primary and secondary reinforcements is one that the child has in common with lower animals, and, although language and higher-level processes are developing, most of his behavior is describable on this level.

Actions tend to be impulsive, and any attempt of the child to control his own impulses would be the result of external coercion or the threat of it. Self-restrictions in such situations as staying out of danger, obeying the rules, and declining some gratification would be done only on the basis of avoidance learning rather than from the positive satisfaction of having acted "properly."

When given high standards for performance, put under pressure, or informed of failure, the child on this level of development will tend to decrease effort or try to withdraw from the situation (Gardner, 1958; Miller, 1961). For example, the child will more readily return to a previously succeeded puzzle than a previously failed one (Bialer, 1960; Bialer and Cromwell, 1965; Spradlin, 1960). The negative hedonic aspects are more potent than the challenge to overcome the situation. Sustained effort over a period of time is rare, since gratification must be immediate. Consequently, the child may be observed to shift quickly from one activity to another in what is apparently a meaningless fashion. While a short attention span and other types of distractability may arise in other cases from brain damage (see McKinney, 1961; Schulman, Kasper, and Throne, 1965), the type described here is to be expected as an indication of the natural developmental level of the child. In the older retarded child, this behavior is often frustrating to persons who are trying to teach the child.

Since such a child does not conceptualize his performance in terms of success of final product, he may likely destroy a finished product rather than preserve or cherish it. On the other hand, he may be upset if another child destroys it.

Another characteristic of the child on this level is to see others, external forces, or unknowns as being in control of the outcome of events. Compared with the conceptually mature child, the hedonistic child will see himself less often as being in control of the outcome of various events in his living situation. This "external-locus-of-control" attitude is not to be confused with the displacement of responsibility that occurs in older blame-conscious children. The latter child has a concept of responsibility and control but is defensively avoiding personal failure. The child on the hedonistic level does not even conceive of personal responsibility and control except for limited situations or on occasions when others point this out to him.

For the retarded child or for the normal child who is retarded in personality development, the phase of intact hedonism may persist longer than in the child who is developing normally. In the older child, where this level of functioning is not expected to be predominant, some aspects of his behavior may be viewed incorrectly as hyperkinetic. This erroneous view results from the fact that the child frequently shifts behavior and "gets into everything." A child with a more advanced stage of personality development may work or play vigorously at one activity, and the observer who tends to respond to the progress and meaningfulness rather than the motor output of the activity may tend not to see it as highly active.

Should the child on the intact hedonistic level be submitted to stress or trauma, he would develop phobic reactions, generalized anxiety, tics, and other mannerisms. Should the stress be highly intense, the child may regress to a level of functioning wherein he fragments his basic boundaries. Should the child fail to experience basic need satisfaction and increasing control over his life situation, he may fixate on this level and continue to display a selfish need for immediate gratification into his teens or adulthood.

THE CONCEPTUAL MOTIVATIONAL SYSTEM

As the child is moving toward his teens, he learns that his behavior is effective in more life situations. In the early years, these would include playing with toys, buttoning his buttons, and verbalizing his wants, and in later years, mastering more complex and long-term goal-directed activity. With this favorable circumstance comes the development of a more mature level of personality functioning. The child comes more and more to respond to conceptualized goals rather than immediate gratification. This development includes what this author has referred to previously as the success-failure motivational system (Cromwell, 1963). In short, the child becomes more and more aware of the acceptability and the shortcomings of his own actions. Furthermore, he becomes motivated to approach success and avoid failure (as he conceptualizes each of these). This system gradually takes predominance over the hedonistic system. Since the success-failure motivational system is a conceptually based one, it develops in parallel with mental rather than chronological age (Bialer, 1960). Thus, retarded children are expected to be behind in this development compared with other children of the same chronological age. At any given mental age level, however, wide differences occur among all children in the development of the success-failure motivational system.

The acquisition of this conceptual motivational system can be seen in many ways. The child is more able to choose to delay gratification (Bialer, 1960). This ability to delay occurs not as a function of a "thou shalt not" reaction from avoidance learning but from a positive approach tendency toward successful and proper decisions that reap a larger reward in the future. In a problem-solving situation, the success-failure motivated child is more prone to attend to the cues relevant to the correctness of his performance than to the hedonistic aspects of verbal praise or material reward (Miller, 1961). He is much less upset when he is told he has failed or has not done well. He is less disturbed by penalties or punishments during the learning situation. Instead, he is more likely to increase effort and to modify his performance to correct the situation. Although his actual speed of learning will depend upon his intellectual level, the conceptually mature child will attempt to accomplish more in his learning activity than the less mature child (Northcutt, 1963).

Another important characteristic of the conceptually mature child is the tendency to see the outcome of events and life circumstances as being greatly determined by himself (Bialer, 1960). This attitude has been referred to as "internal locus of control (ILC)," following from various short personality scales that have been used to measure it (Bialer, 1960; James, 1957; Liverant, unpublished; Phares, 1955; Rotter, Seeman and Liverant, 1962). These scales often have been used as operational measures to gauge the effect of the S-F motivational system as an intervening variable.

Contrary to what might be expected, the child with the mature success-failure motivational system may not excel in academic achievement compared with his less mature counterpart. One reason for this is that the conceptually mature child has "a mind of own," thus pursuing types of learning that may not be a part of the teacher's expectations. On the other hand, the external locus-of-control (ELC) child in a warm, accepting climate will be more inclined to direct his efforts toward pleasing and conforming to the expectations of the teacher who is providing that climate. Consequently, the ELC children in certain situations have been found to have a higher academic achievement record than ILC children (Butterfield and Butterfield, 1961). A second explanation for the ILC child having lower academic achievement is that the child with extremely high needs for academic achievement has so much invested emotionally in his performance outcome that he cannot admit an ILC attitude in this particular situation (Chance, 1965). That is, he needs an "out," such as being able to say the examination of his performance was poor, the whims of the teacher controlled the grading, or that it all is a matter of luck when one is tested. This attitude, known as a "false external" one, can account for high achievers scoring more in the ELC direction than average achievers (Wright, 1964).

Whether either or both of these explanations are valid must depend on further investigation. Intelligence is a relevant variable in the locus of control-academic achievement relationship. Since high intelligence is significantly associated with both internal locus of control and high academic achievement, the locus of control-academic achievement relationship will vary as a function of how the intelligence variable is controlled.

Numerous kinds of personality difficulties also can emerge in a child who has developed a conceptual motivational system. These possibilities may be arbitrarily classified into four different categories. First, a number of different reactions may occur as a result of failure experience. Second, omnipotence reactions may occur. Third, depressive reactions may occur. Fourth, regression may possibly occur.

Typical examples of excessive failure are:

(1) A parent may place such high expectations on a child that he may feel his behavior is consistently inadequate.

(2) Siblings or peers, in reaction to their own problems of hostility, may torment a child until he believes he is socially unacceptable.

(3) A teacher may conclude that a child is lazy rather than retarded or disturbed; whereupon, she may hold him excessively responsible or "ride" him for every shortcoming he displays.

Each of these situations can produce a child who will quickly disclaim any responsibility or control over situations where he has performed poorly. He will feel "put upon" or pressured by others. He will whine or cry or "act like a baby." Since this behavior in children is typically viewed as unattractive, the child usually is admonished or rejected all the more. Thus, his opportunities for firm advancement in personality development must await a situation where people respond more favorably or where he has moved into a different and more favorable setting.

The most frequent reaction to prolonged situational failure is decreased effort. At first, the conceptually mature individual will increase effort. However, he can cope with and be challenged by only a certain amount of failure. After this, his behavior will start to deteriorate. After continued failure, the child begins to think the situation is outside his control. When this happens, he will start responding to this particular situation like the intact hedonistic child, decreasing effort, withdrawing from the situation or developing anxiety reactions toward it. In addition, he will display false external (and later, perhaps, genuine external) locus-of-control attitudes about the situation. These will be recognized in the language of defense mechanisms as projection in response to external stress and rationalization. Other threat-avoidance mechanisms may also occur. If compensation occurs, it would indicate a good prognosis, suggesting that a regression to the intact hedonistic stage has not occurred.

Another reaction to failure is "failure avoidance." While similar to and overlapping with the reaction already described, the failure-avoider is best characterized in opposition to the success-striver orientation. The former is primarily alert to cues in his life situation that are associated with failure and may overlook the cues that are directly relevant to success. By contrast, the success-striver may "plunge ahead" in response to cues relevant to success and be oblivious to cues that would warn of failure (Moss, 1958). While predispositions toward either of these extremes may be carried on into adulthood, the optimal behavior, realized only in a person with maximal functioning, is in accordance with the "minimax theory." The solutions of maximal gain and minimal loss are conceptualized and pursued within this framework.

Another type of reaction to failure experience is an unstable level of aspiration. The individual will set his goals so high that he is destined almost inevitably to failure. Then, he will shift to an unrealistically cautious level of behavior with low goal-setting and every effort to prevent failure. Finally, in response to this unsatisfying state of affairs, he will shift back to an unrealistically high aspiration and fail again. This pattern typically results from a prolonged amount of aperiodic failure after a child has developed success-failure awareness. Consequently, the child has a need to achieve a particular level of performance that he has desired but has not reached. The unstable pattern that emerges usually prevents the child from acquiring some of the useful skills and strategies in goal-setting. Such skills are more easily acquired by the child who has a sufficiently stable pattern to predict and accepts his own ratio of success to failure.

Perhaps the most general form of personality disturbance for a child with success-failure motivation is the "feeling of inadequacy (or inferiority)." This reaction cannot occur in an earlier phase of personality development, since the child does not conceptualize events at that time in terms of success and failure. Thus, some favorable personality development must precede the potential development of feelings of inadequacy. The individual must come to feel responsible for managing his own life situation but then, in one way or another, must feel he is not doing a good job of it. Large areas of life are emotionally blocked off by feelings of inadequacy and are viewed as not available for need satisfaction. These areas may include intellectual skill, social functioning, perception of one's own body image, etc.

Feelings of inadequacy frequently occur when a child has a sibling 18 to 30 months older and of the same sex. In this situation, the younger child can, despite much reassurance, see himself as coming up short, even in the early simple self-help skills that provide the embryonic base for ILC development. No matter how hard he tries, the older sibling is always a little better. These feelings are often resolved when the younger child finds an area of competence that is distinctly his own and does not belong to the repertoire of the older sibling. Such resolutions and compensations are often important even in determining the vocations and avocations of an individual later in life.

Not all personality disturbances on this level are related to failure. Another type of problem occurs when a child matures rapidly in success-failure motivation but does not grow concomitantly in interpersonal functioning.

Such a child may feel excessively in control of the outcome of events and consequently may display unrealistic, omnipotent reactions. As a result, he may be regarded as a "smart aleck." If so, consequent social punishment, which he would not be able to conceptualize or anticipate, may disrupt the smooth progression of his development. This situation in normal personality development is not unlike the focal situation in psychotherapy where a person has experienced a sudden feeling of growth. His omnipotent feeling may not be shared by his family and friends, and their unsympathetic reaction may tend to buffer the newfound feeling of social potency.

Another possible manifestation of the excessive ILC attitude and omnipotent feeling is the abandonment of caution. A child may become so unrealistically sure of himself that he becomes oblivious to danger. A dare will challenge him to perform a dangerous act that his more failure-avoidant peers on the same level of conceptual development would not. Clinical evidence has indicated that the excessively high ILC child, popular and well adjusted with his group, may injure or kill himself in some dangerous act such as sledding, jumping, or ice-walking.

The third kind of personality disturbance in the conceptually mature child is the child's counterpart of adult depression. In this condition, the child is excessively conscious of his own responsibility in the outcome of events. Through verbal reinforcements from parents, teachers, and others, the feelings of responsibility become developed so highly and so far beyond what a child can realistically accomplish that a condition of depression is developed. Such a child may feel his parents' quarrels or other unhappy events are his fault. He will be a worrier. He will be unable to displace blame and express hostility outwardly. He will have less spontaneity, playfulness, and narcissistic striving than other children have. He will be very conscious of the evaluational dimension of good-bad and will strive to please people with what is good. Adults will tend to view him as likable, mature, and adult-like. Yet, he will not have the happy, carefree attribute that other children his age enjoy. Opportunities to affiliate in camp or residential situations with children will often change this condition, which is usually associated with a strong identification with adult figures.

Somewhat related in psychodynamics to the depressive reaction but very different in terms of overt behavior is the hostile reaction. A child who has learned to feel reasonably in control of events but whose interpersonal experiences have led him to feel in opposition to others or blocked by others in his need satisfaction may develop reactions of hostility. Destructive reactions may result, or, if such reactions have been highly punished, latent and subtle ways of expressing hostility will be carried out unconsciously. In some cases, the inability to learn to read, enuresis, passivity, and other reactions have an underlying unconscious hostile motivation.

The fourth kind of personality disturbance in the conceptually mature child arises since the hedonic motivational system is not replaced but rather is supplanted. Thus, the possibility exists for the development of specific compulsions, specific fears, obsessions, or tics to reduce general anxiety. If the conceptually mature child is submitted to so severe a period of traumatic experience that his advanced defenses are ineffective, he may regress back through the phase of intact hedonism to one that affects his basic boundary discriminations. This possibility is not so likely if the child has acquired a stable level of conceptualized goals and a firm orientation of success-approach and failure-avoidance. Instead, the severely traumatic experience would tend to produce a severely neurotic child.

The debilitating effects of anxiety upon performance are more evident in the conceptually mature child than in the intact hedonistic child. When presented an academic chore or a test situation, the ILC child with low anxiety tends to show the greatest progress. However, the ILC child with high anxiety seems pressured and tends to make the least progress. In contrast to these two instances, the ELC child, whether with high or low anxiety, tends to have an intermediate level of performance (Brooks, 1962). Apparently, without a success-failure orientation, the ELC child neither feels pressured nor strives for productivity in this type of situation.

DEVELOPMENT OF INTERPERSONAL FUNCTIONING

Once the conceptual motivational system has developed, a part of this conceptual development becomes focused upon interpersonal functioning. While there is some evidence of interpersonal functioning during early childhood, it is limited. As defined here, interpersonal functioning refers specifically to the ability of an individual to conceptualize the feelings, attitudes, and motives of another. For example, a child may cry or be disturbed by the pain or the punishment of another child. This phase of development is to be distinguished sharply from the child's responses to another person that are oriented primarily toward his own needs, conceptual or hedonistic, and that are without regard to any conceptual picture of the other person's privately held view of the situation. It is also to be sharply distinguished from the compatible responses he makes to other people as a result of having his behavior shaped toward obtaining particular reinforcements.

The child (or adult) who has not reached the stage of interpersonal functioning may possibly be viewed as a "bull in a china shop." Such a child will be able to give at most a superficial description about what the other person's feelings are. When observed in interaction with another person, he will not show evidence of anticipating the wish or the frustration of another. In fact, he can be observed to show surprise when the other child cries or shows evidence of anger. The common result of this stage of development is sporadic fighting with other children.

Whether correct or incorrect, the child with interpersonal functioning has a conception of what the other person is thinking and feeling. He will be able to describe others in these subjective terms. He will be able to anticipate and avoid conflict with the other person. He will not be moved toward personal success or immediate gratification without being aware of the effect on the other person. In so doing, he can more often maximize his hedonistically and conceptually based satisfactions through avoiding "run-ins" with others, as well as being able to act in the interests of others. Often in institutional and isolated settings, retardates will develop deviant or idiosyncratic approaches to satisfaction. In such cases, the retardate on the advanced level of interpersonal functioning, while perhaps not modifying his behavior, will be aware of how his own behavior is viewed by another person as unacceptable and will deal with the person accordingly.

At its advanced level, the interpersonal awareness takes on motivational aspects. An individual may direct his own behavior toward achieving the best interests of others, even at some sacrifice to his own egocentric satisfaction. In addition to his own "ego defenses," he will develop "interpersonal defenses." That is, he may act in a way to protect other people from personal discomfort, threat, or humiliation.

Children with impairment in basic boundary development, hedonism, or conceptual motivation will develop interpersonal functioning in only a very limited way. However, such personality-impaired children can learn to approach others and exist amicably with them. Psychotic and other personality-impaired children may be much loved and may respond compatibly to others. They may even be treated as "pets" in their group. However, they can be viewed as having interpersonal functioning only if they can empathize and construe the feelings of others.

Initial failure or traumatic experience in interpersonal learning may lead to one of many personality impairments. Such an individual may withdraw into an isolated existence. Although becoming a "lone wolf," he would still be in contact with reality. He may develop emotional attractions and need satisfactions that are deviant from others. He may resolve his inability to construe the feelings of others by fighting his way out of situations he has failed to understand. He may orient his life toward "conning" and manipulating others. He may become an egocentric power-striver.

Having matured to the interpersonal level, however, such an individual is susceptible to other types of personality problems that would not occur on an earlier level. For example, he may use projection as a defense in a deviant or erroneous way. He may feel that other individuals regard him as inadequate or queer. Thus, the feelings of social inadequacy or deviance may arise here as well as on the basis of success-failure conceptual development. Delusions of persecutory intent by others can exist only in a person who has developed to this level.

Retardates especially would be susceptible to projective assimilation when they reach this level of functioning. That is, they would tend to assume that the feelings of others are like their own. Thus, a retardate would tend not to differentiate between his internal feelings and another person's feelings.

DEVELOPMENT OF CULTURAL FUNCTIONING

A fifth phase of personality development is cultural responsivity. In this phase, the child learns to construe a picture of what the interests and attitudes of people in general would be, even though he is not in person-to-person contact with them. Although the development of cultural functioning is usually initiated after and is continuous with the further development of interpersonal functioning, one may develop without the other. Thus, a person could be effective in a primary group but oblivious of cultural learning to the extent of being delinquent or criminal. On the other hand, he could be extremely conscious of the "rights and wrongs," the cultural taboos, etc., but be unable to get along with people around him or have an understanding of their internal frame of reference.

The development of cultural functioning may be observed when a child progresses through the following stages:

(1) He learns to discriminate between "right" and "wrong" as the people around him have taught it to him. At first, he has reference points that are immediate. That is, for example, "Mommy spanks me if it is wrong, and she is nice if it is right."

(2) Later, the moral values of "right" and "wrong" take on an absolute meaning. The child (or adult) may feel certain things are right and others wrong in the same sense that two rocks have different weight or color.

(3) Next, reasons have to be given for something to be right or wrong. Beginning with this stage, the child refrains from destroying the playroom equipment not because it is wrong per se, but because other children will want to use it. Thus, the reference point for right and wrong has shifted from specific individuals of the primary group to absolutes and finally, as in this example, to the cultural concept of "children," some of whom the child will never see or know.

(4) A further stage, seldom reached by retardates, comes with an awareness of conflicting cultural values. In this stage, the concepts of "right" and "wrong" take on relative meaning.

Defects in cultural development will be observed when a child (or adult) chronically steals, lies, disobeys rules, is destructive, has no concept of the welfare of people in general, or shows no guilt or anxiety about any violation except when threatened with personal punishment as a direct consequence. Such children also have limited time and space perspective.

Personality disturbance may result from the overdevelopment of cultural functioning. A child (or adult) may learn to be so preoccupied with "matters of conscience" that conflicts arise between these and his interpersonal, conceptual, or basic hedonistic motivations. Thus, guilt, depression, or anxiety would occur as a consequence.

Finally, the development of cultural functioning can lead to conflict between persons or groups that represent different cultural learnings. Although retardates seldom reach this level of development, individuals can learn to believe in a "cause" strongly enough to fight willingly for it. This may place them (or their group) in conflict with others who hold to different causes. Since such civilized individuals may have intact personalities, this type of conflict would more appropriately be described as cultural rather than personality related. Nevertheless, when a person enters a conflict carrying the banner of his "cause," the ramifications of it are relevant to all levels of personality functioning.

HOW TO DO A PERSONALITY EVALUATION

Understanding personality constructs and personality development is a major part of the topic of personality evaluation. Another major part is the practical understanding of how the evaluation of personality fits into the total activity of psychological evaluations. The section to follow is devoted to the practical aspects of examining personality as a part of the psychological evaluation.

RECEIVING A REFERRAL

A psychological evaluation begins with a request for help regarding the psychological understanding of an individual. Parents, school officials, physicians, social work or welfare agencies, the courts, other psychologists, and the client himself are the most frequent sources of referral.

If the exact reasons for the referral are unclear, the psychologist must ask the person making the referral to clarify the questions to be answered or the decisions to be made regarding the client. Some referral statements run the risk of getting an unsatisfactory evaluation. The referring person may ask for a "general evaluation." If so, the psychologist may focus upon aspects of the individual's functioning that are not relevant to the problems of the referring person. Or, the referring person may ask for specific tests to be given without having had training in the applicability or adequacy of these instruments. In reporting the findings, the psychologist may not focus on the test information that is relevant to the problem. Therefore, clarification should be requested. An exception to this procedure is when the referring person wants a "blind" and independent check on his own diagnostic impressions, which he is willing to make clear later.

Once the problem is clarified, the psychologist must establish whether he is adequately trained for the particular evaluation. He may wish to arrange to send all or part of the referral to another psychologist or another professional person who is better trained in a specific area.

The psychologist must receive the referral under legally and professionally acceptable procedures. Thus, the requirements of licensing, certification, or accredited agency affiliation must be considered before accepting the referral. If a student receives a referral, he may accept it only in a training facility through a supervising psychologist who is legally and professionally responsible for the case.

The psychologist must determine who is legally in custody of the client being referred. If the referring person is other than the parent or legal custodian of the child, the standard preliminary information forms (to parents, school, physician, and other relevant parties) will reveal whether the parent or legal custodian approves of the referral. If the parent or responsible person is not in approval, the referral must be declined.

The psychologist must establish to whom the report will go and to whom feedback information should be given. Whether to the parent, a teacher, the court, a psychiatrist, or another psychologist, the report should be written on a level of interpretation that will be understood by the person who will read it. If necessary, more than one version may be prepared.

If the psychological findings are to be sent to agencies and individuals other than those making the referral, a statement should be signed by the parent or legally responsible person granting permission for release of information.

The psychologist will establish whether his role involves consultation or case responsibility. In the former case, the referring person retains case responsibility. The psychologist conveys his findings to the referring person and to whomever else he might designate. In the latter case, the referring person turns over professional responsibility for the problems to the psychologist. The referring person may or may not wish further information on the case. The psychologist would communicate with the parent or responsible individual about reports, feedback communication, and appropriate treatment.

EXAMINING THE CASE FOLDER

Ordinarily, the psychologist examines the case folder materials thoroughly before seeing the client. If no case folder exists, pertinent information is obtained on report forms from the parents, teacher, physician, or other relevant parties. As a part of the clinical method, the psychologist (1) familiarizes himself with the folder material, (2) develops a set of alternative clinical hypotheses about the problems of the client, (3) decides what kinds of observations and tests are necessary to examine these clinical hypotheses, (4) examines the client, and (5) repeats the observation-hypothecation cycle.

In some situations, especially while in training, the psychologist may deliberately not look at the case materials before seeing the client. In this way he can develop independent impressions and then check them against the case folder. If so, some of the steps of the clinical method are reversed.

CONTACTING THE PATIENT

After the preliminary duties are completed and the client arrives for the appointment, the psychologist must ascertain how the client perceives the examination he is about to take.

Does he know the psychologist and his function? Does he know why he is being examined? Does he see the psychologist as a source of help (e.g., to find out why he cannot read and perhaps to teach him)? Does he see the psychologist as a threat (e.g., the person who is going to take him away from home and put him in an institution)? Has he had unpleasant experiences with professional persons in the past that will generalize to the tester and the testing situation? If the retardate can communicate, the psychologist must explain why his services have been requested. For purposes of a valid examination, this structure should be given in a positive way so that maximum performance and co-operation can be obtained. If the client is under stress, the examiner should have a clear understanding of why it exists and how it may affect the examination.

SELECTING PERSONALITY ASSESSMENT TECHNIQUES

The prime rule for selecting psychological techniques for a personality evaluation in the mentally retarded is to choose the methods that will yield the most relevant information for the problems to be solved. Since objective standardized personality tests are oriented toward predicting single criteria, they usually are inadequate for diverse and complex problems. Moreover, extremely few exist on a level appropriate for the mentally retarded. Instead, various observational situations seem to be the most valuable. Such situations allow idiographically derived clinical hypotheses to be developed. These hypotheses may then be subjected to confirmation or disconfirmation through subsequent observations in terms of specific criteria.

How does one select these observational situations? The following questions may be considered: (1) What specific referral questions are being submitted? (2) What is the evaluation of the client at first observation? (3) To what extent does the tester have to economize on time? (4) What personality theory represents the most useful attack on the problem? (5) What theory and constructs can be best translated into actions and decisions that will benefit the client? (6) Are idiographic predictions from recurrent observations or nomothetic predictions from standardized tests of prime value in this situation?

After these questions have been answered, the final question is: What stimulus and test situation will allow for the greatest range of relevant behavior and the best and most valid predictions?

METHODS OF EXAMINATION

Available methods will be described here in only a limited way. One must remember that the clinician himself is the primary tool. His understanding of clinical method and his ability to apply valid personality constructs for problem-solving are required for personality evaluation. Following from this, he will choose the methods appropriate to the situation. If a psychologist was trained to think first in terms of techniques, his range of problem-solving would be limited, and his skills would soon go out of date with the progress of research.

No attention will be given here to the evaluation of neuropathic traits or temperamental factors due to such factors as endocrine function. Although these aspects may be properly viewed as part of the study of personality, they will be discussed in other chapters.

The use of *objective behavior reports* from *different persons* is a powerful source of personality data. This method is possible in agencies and residential facilities where the child remains for an extended period of time. If the attendants, teachers, and other persons are taught how to make objective, noninferential behavior reports, then the reports at regular intervals can give recurring patterns of behavior and differential patterns of response to various individuals.

Direct observation of the client should start from the time he first appears in the waiting room and should last until he is out of sight at the end of the examination. Relevant personality data is by no means gathered only from the responses during the formal interview and testing situation. Such observations as the child's interaction with his mother or the receptionist in the waiting room, his behavior around the drinking fountain during a break, and his reaction upon greeting his mother after the testing all contribute importantly to the total evaluation.

Another important source for personality inference is the *intelligence test and other techniques* that are not intended primarily for personality data. While the routine correct answers usually do not give much of a basis for personality inference, the incorrect responses do. The psychologist should never let an incorrect response be given without recording it and asking for elaboration. One client may give wrong answers and avoid saying "I don't know." Another client may say "I don't know" even when he has a reasonably good guess. The psychologist will want to seek further evidence to confirm the extent of these different coping procedures. If the client gives any incorrect or unusual response, the psychologist should not hesitate to say, "Can you tell me more?" before continuing with the standardized testing procedure. With an incorrect picture arrangement subtest response, the psychologist should always say, "Can you tell me what is going on here?" The distortion of perception that is sometimes revealed from the story gives a valuable basis for personality inference. If the client misses easy items and gets hard ones correct, the psychologist should examine the alternative hypotheses of autistic blocking associated with basic boundary difficulty, blocking due to high situational anxiety in reaction to the test situation, ambivalent refusal to co-operate, etc.

The following are examples of atypical responses that represent leads for personality inference:

Q: Why does land in the city cost more than land in the country? *A:* Because you can't trust people in the city.

Q: What is the thing to do if someone smaller than you hits you? *A:* Hit them back.

Q: What is the thing to do if you lost one of your friend's balls? *A:* Take him to the hospital so he won't bleed to death.

Picture arrangement of man getting into a car carrying a female mannikin. *Q:* Tell me what the story is here. *A:* Well, this man and his wife are in this car fighting and finally he looks outside and sees this guy with a doll watching them.

Q: Define "fable." *A:* That's when you're nuts and they lock you up. Fableminded.

From each of these examples, what initial clinical hypothesis could be made about goal structure, threat structure, and level of personality development? Where would the examiner seek further documentation in order to determine whether a recurring response pattern is indicated?

The *behavior of the child in the testing*

room gives another source for personality inference. While the inexperienced psychologist will be devoting much of his efforts to reading the test instruction manual and administering the test adequately, the experienced clinician will be attending primarily to what the child is doing between items of the test. What does the child look at, approach, and avoid? Is he oriented more toward the examiner than the objects in the room?

Even experienced clinicians often make the mistake of failing to record observations that cannot immediately be fitted into a personality context. Observations should be recorded even if they do not seem to have any relevance at the time. Then, after playroom observations, projective techniques, and behavior reporting by others are made, the observations will often fit into a meaningful pattern and will help support or refute the clinical hypotheses that have been considered.

Of all methods for personality inference in children, the *playroom behavior* is perhaps the most fruitful and flexible. Autistic behavior associated with basic boundary development can easily be detected through idiosyncratic response to the toys, disturbances in time relationships concerning the play period, and bizarre mannerisms. Reactions to the toys may reveal phobic, aggressive, or compulsive responses in some children. To examine conceptual and interpersonal functioning, a particular child may be paired with various other children on different occasions. A conflict situation may be produced by identifying the most popular toy and having only one available for the two children. How a child resolves such conflicts with a child stronger than himself, weaker than himself, brighter than himself, and duller than himself is of particular value to observe. Children with undeveloped conceptual motivational systems, including impulse control, will be unable to delay or rationally solve the problem. They will either take the toy by force or will pout if they are not strong enough to do so. Children with more developed conceptual motivational systems will work out compromises or try to outwit the other child. Children with mature interpersonal functioning will be observed to respond in terms of the needs and rights of the other child and the psychologist.

With a one-way vision screen or auditory monitoring, a clinician can evaluate cultural development by setting up test situations to examine shared and unshared lying, stealing, or destructive behavior. Destructive-hyperkinetic behavior and destructive-hostile behavior may be differentiated. That is, immediately after some destructive act, the look of surprise or regret of the brain-damaged superactive child will be different from the defensive, rebellious, or blame-conscious look of the hostile child.

Although *projective tests* have become the hallmark of personality evaluation, they perhaps have their least value with retarded individuals. While projective tests are often used with retardates in order to see if the intelligence testing is valid, no evidence exists that projective tests will reveal any hidden intellectual potential. On the other hand, general avoidance tendencies, as revealed in projectives, the intelligence test, and the playroom may give evidence that measured intelligence and other kinds of performance are depressed by a generalized expectancy for failure.

Most projective tests, such as inkblot and picture story techniques, depend heavily upon verbal behavior. Therefore, retarded individuals with limited verbal facility give limited information with these instruments. On the other hand, the child whose lowered intelligence stems greatly from emotional disturbance may have a productive and revealing test protocol.

When projective techniques are useful, two dimensions may be conveniently assessed by thematic content. These are (1) the level of motivational development (hedonistic vs. conceptual) and (2) the tendency to view the world as rewarding vs. punishing (or, positive vs. negative). Thus, inkblot and picture story responses can be classified into hedonistic negative, hedonistic positive, conceptually developed negative, and conceptually developed positive ones.

Hedonistic negative responses would be exemplified by squashed bugs, a bear cut open, sick and diseased tissue, a child left alone, a person who got hurt, and explosions, where the subject is not identified as causing these things to happen.

Hedonistic positive responses would be exemplified in picture stories by the major figure attaining some positive outcome by chance or luck without problem solving or reasoning. Inkblot responses would include ice cream, candy, and other immediate gratification items.

Negative responses in a conceptually developed person would be exemplified by struggles without success to accomplish something (such as pleasing one's parents), feelings of inadequacy in meeting standards of self or others, guilt, escape of harm through the use of one's wits, suspicious and guarded behavior ("You have to look out for yourself in this world because no one else is going to."), and avoidance of humiliation or embarrassment.

Positive responses in the conceptually developed individual would be exemplified by use of reasoning or problem-solving in order to get a desired goal, deliberate sacrifices in order to achieve a satisfying outcome, and a positive outcome with emphasis on the obstacles that were successfully overcome. Inkblot responses could be exemplified by people dancing, people helping each other, imposed determinants that contain the positive feelings and attitudes attributed to human or human-like percepts.

Objective personality inventories are usually of little value in the personality evaluation of the mentally retarded. They have usually been standardized for predicting single-criterion dimensions; whereas, personality evaluations demand that the clinician scan data that are relevant to a large number of dimensions. Objective tests usually depend heavily upon verbal facility and are valid with retardates only when individually and orally administered. While useful in research on group differences, they generally have limited value in predicting a criterion for a single individual. However, when clinical hypotheses have been derived from other sources, an objective test may serve as a basis for getting further support or refutation.

Examples of objective tests are (1) the children's locus of control scale by Bialer and Cromwell (Bialer, 1960), (2) locus of evaluation scale by Miller (1958), (3) children's manifest anxiety scale by Castaneda, McCandless and Palermo (1956), and (4) the children's test anxiety scale by Sarason, Davidson, Lighthall, and Waite (1958). The locus of control scale has served as a basis for research in success-failure awareness (i.e., the development from the hedonistic to the conceptual motivational system). The locus of evaluation scale tells whether the child looks to others or himself to evaluate the effectiveness and acceptability of his actions. The anxiety scales give some evidence of the degree to which a child experiences the world, or test situations in the latter case, as threatening.

PREPARING THE REPORT

The psychologist assumes the responsibility for clear, effective, and immediate communication of his findings; the recipient should not have to try to interpret psychological jargon. Reports will vary greatly according to whether the recipient is a parent, teacher, social or welfare worker, pediatrician, psychoanalytically oriented psychiatrist, judge, or another psychologist. For example, a psychotherapist who is making decisions about the course of therapy would need certain findings emphasized. A school principal deciding on classroom placement or a discipline problem would find other conclusions useful.

Typically, a psychological evaluation is divided into sections on (1) basic identifying information, (2) referral information, (3) summary of findings and recommendations, and, starting on a separate page, (4) documentation of the findings and recommendations. The first three sections constitute the transmitted report; the fourth section and the protocols are kept on file. This procedure allows the psychologist and his colleagues, then or later, to see clearly what observations gave a basis for the transmitted report. The filed information will be a resource by which to answer questions that may arise later.

DOING THE FEEDBACK COMMUNICATION

A psychologist is in a position to perform his most effective service when he communicates with the referring source or when he carries out the treatment recommendations and disposition of the case. But very often in the past, he has failed. In spite of the close attention that psychologists have paid to the psychodynamics of a patient in psychotherapy, they have sometimes paid no attention to the communication dynamics involved with a parent, teacher, or physician when making a personality evaluation and giving a feedback. Often the psychologist has felt his task was accomplished when he mailed a copy of his report or gave an oral summation. Other psychologists may have taken the extra step of conveying the findings in a language that is understandable to the referring agent. Still others may have felt their duty was done when they translated their findings into the best possible treatment recommendations, taking into consideration the separate problems of the various individuals who deal with the child. While each of these considerations is important, they are not enough.

For effective clinical feedback, the psychologist, in communicating his findings to a parent, teacher, or other professional person, must view this as a clinical problem relatively separate from the evaluation of the client himself. The psychologist must assume that this person (or couple) has built up a set of needs and personal constructs about the child's behavior. There are gaps or distortions in the way they construe the child. Otherwise, they would not have sought the clinician's assistance. The problem of the clinical psychologist is to understand this construction system and set up a situation for optimal psychological change.

The validity of the psychologist's findings about the child is hardly the most relevant issue in this interaction. The findings may be adequate and the interactions not adequate, or vice versa. The relevant issue at this point is that some aspects of the psychologist's findings jibe with what the recipient already knows about the problem. Other aspects will come as welcome information that can readily be assimilated. Still other aspects will be foreign and threatening. The initial task of the psychologist is to ascertain which parts of his information will fall into these three categories. He must quickly size up the needs, threats, and personal constructs by which the individual understands the retarded child. Then, in the feedback communication process, the psychologist must unfold a sequence of communication that has the best possibility of changing attitudes and behavior in a way that would represent the best interests of the child and all concerned.

While communication dynamics is a seriously ignored area of research, clinical evidence suggests that the following sequence is useful:

(1) Begin the feedback by reviewing those aspirations and goals that the psychologist holds in common with the recipient.

(2) Continue from this common ground to the findings that the psychologist has determined to be in common with those which the recipient already holds.

(3) Move from this point to the findings that the psychologist judges will be new constructions for the recipient, alternating potentially welcome and threatening material.

(4) As negative or threatening material is introduced, the recipient frequently is asked to respond to it. This will indicate to the psychologist to what degree the individual is actually incorporating the information.

(5) To the extent he is doing so, the psychologist nondirectively allows the recipient to elaborate the information into his own construct system.

(6) If the recipient has difficulty accepting the new construction, the psychologist can discuss the new information by showing how the recipient's previous constructs can subsume and deal with it. If the recipient resists or rejects the new information, the psychologist will know that the material is too threatening for him to absorb. This cue raises a number of clinical questions and lines of action.

(7) Since the psychologist's persistence in arguing his point would merely increase the defensiveness and resistance, the psychologist must quickly move to a different level of discourse.

(8) The psychologist must ask for an elaboration of views about the child in order to get a better understanding of why the recipient rejects the information.

(9) Then he must determine if the information can be given to the recipient in a way that would not threaten his personal needs or constructs.

(10) He must determine what words or labels are potentially threatening and are susceptible to retranslation.

(11) If necessary, he must determine what observations and interactions the recipient should carry out in the days or weeks after the feedback to help him reconstrue and confirm the psychologist's findings.

(12) Finally, if, as in some cases, the recipient has a rigidly closed construct system, the psychologist should forsake his attempt to communicate the findings in full detail. Instead, he should prescribe a set of observations and investigations that would help the recipient loosen his construct system. With this, the psychologist should schedule or invite the

recipient back to discuss these experiences. In this way, the recipient is being treated as a partner in the problem-solving process and thereby the probability is increased that he will evolve a more useful construction than the one he has.

Displays of affect, such as tears or inappropriate laughter, are clinical indications that core constructs of the recipient are being influenced by the feedback information. Stony silence usually indicates an impervious construct system.

To illustrate some of the preceding points, let us review a case where a school child has been referred because he functions poorly in the classroom. The child, as it turns out, has borderline mental retardation. In addition, his personality evaluation indicates that he has had standards set so high for him that he views the classroom work as impossible. From the child's construct system, he sees no sense in attempting his work; if it is impossible, it is impossible. So, the child remains on a hedonistic avoidant level of adjustment, not concerned with success but with passive avoidance of unpleasant situations.

As the psychologist sits down for a feedback communication with the teacher, he wishes to complete his understanding of how the teacher construes the child. He begins by asking the teacher to elaborate further on the child's problems in the classroom. It soon becomes apparent that she views the child as being "lazy." To her, this construct has a number of specific connotations: (1) He will not do his work adequately. (2) He could if he would. (3) Laziness is absence of motivation. (4) This is his fault, not hers. (5) If a child is lazy, there is nothing the teacher can do about the situation.

As the psychologist listens, he gets a picture of how the teacher construes herself. She views herself as a good teacher, and this construct is important to her. As she sees it, she can teach children anything if they will only make the effort. She works hard and takes pride in the quality of her work. She feels she works harder than the other teachers and pushes the children further in achievement. She points out that her class has higher achievement scores than most of the other classes.

As the teacher reaches out for still further reasons for her adequacy, the psychologist realizes that her self-construct as a good teacher is a little shaky. Since insufficient confirmation of this comes from the principal or from other sources, she must find results of her effectiveness in the classroom. Perfectionist that she is, one child not learning as he should stands as a threat to her concept of being a good teacher. She feels anxious about this. To defend against her feeling of anxiety, she construes this child as "lazy." In this way, she is relieved of the responsibility for the child's poor learning. Although not realizing it, she looks to the psychological findings not for new ideas for handling the child. Instead, she hopes to get recognition and to confirm herself as not guilty. She retains some fear that she might be.

At this point, the psychologist's problems are to assure her that he is no threat, confirm that part of her construct system that provides a useful base of security, and then to allow her to assimilate some useful reconstructions about the child. If appropriate, while reviewing the boy's classroom shortcomings, he diverts to acknowledge the evidence that she is an effective, hard-working teacher whose children have good achievement records. With this basis of common ground, the psychologist moves on to give her some alternative constructs by which to view the child. He points out the child is more limited in ability than "the school" had originally thought. Since he was expected to perform like the average or bright normal child, he underwent a series of disappointing failures, leading him to view the classroom as a world of "impossibles." To protect himself, he withdrew from any active effort, even when he was capable. The psychologist then encourages the teacher to try for an extended period of time to lower standards and expectations so that the boy can experience repeated success for a while. Then, when he begins to respond, she can move him gradually toward performing on the level expected of a borderline mentally retarded child.

In so doing, the psychologist has attempted to create a situation where the teacher can rest on some long-term constructs. Once done, she can be led to explore and to revise constructs in areas of dealing with the child. By such a procedure, the teacher can potentially experience some reconstructions that were not even covered in the feedback session.

A FINAL PEP TALK

Among mentally retarded individuals, where by definition intellectual deficit is a central feature, the primary questions given a psychologist usually concern the nature and severity of the deficit. However, a majority of the problems of management, treatment, and life planning require an understanding of the retarded individual's personality. This presents a paradoxical situation for the psychologist who is trained to make such personality evaluations. On one hand, his answers are frequently sought. On the other hand, the body of facts, techniques, and systematic theory is limited. If he is in a clinical service position, the personality evaluations must be administered. The clinician can neither ignore the service demands nor the shortcomings of his methods.

In such a situation, the psychologist must remember his responsibility for the advancement of knowledge as well as his responsibility for service to the individual client. The advancement of knowledge is dependent upon new observations, constructs and theoretical models about personality functioning. No setting is more valuable for these developments than one where the clinician is observing and interacting with another person. Through the clinical method, new ideas can be developed; later they can be submitted to a controlled test of validity. Often the service clinician feels he has no role in the advancement of new thinking since the demands on his time do not allow him to place a major focus on the final controlled investigation of the validity of a new idea. This attitude is unfortunate. The great contribution is made by the one who develops the ideas in the first place. The service clinician should more often see this as his rightful role. If he accepts the obligation to clarify and communicate his new observations and formulations, he will be the pioneer of the richest advances of knowledge in his field.

REFERENCES

ALLPORT, G. W. *Personality; a psychological interpretation.* New York: Henry Holt, and Co., 1937.

BIALER, I. *Conceptualization of success and failure in mentally retarded and normal children.* Ann Arbor, Mich.: University Microfilms, 1960. (Also, in brief, *J. Pers.,* 1961, *29,* 303–320.)

———— and CROMWELL, R. L. Failure as motivation with mentally retarded children. *Amer. J. ment. Defic.,* 1965, *69,* 680–684.

BROOKS, S. *Effects of locus of control and anxiety on the ability of mentally retarded children to use context cues in reading.* Ann Arbor, Mich.: University Microfilms, 1962.

BUTTERFIELD, E. C., and BUTTERFIELD, GAIL B. Locus of control and academic achievement in familial retardates. Unpublished manuscript, 1961.

CASTANEDA, A., McCANDLESS, B. R., and PALERMO, D. S. The children's form of the manifest anxiety scale. *Child Developm.,* 1956, *27,* 317–326.

CATTELL, R. B. *Personality: a systematic theoretical and factual study.* New York: McGraw-Hill, 1950.

CHANCE, JUNE E. Internal control of reinforcements and school learning process. Paper presented at meetings of Society for Research in Child Development, Minneapolis, March, 1965.

CROMWELL, R. L. A social learning approach to mental retardation. In N. R. Ellis (Ed.), *Handbook of mental deficiency.* New York: McGraw-Hill, 1963. Pp. 41–91.

GARDNER, W. I. *Reactions of intellectually normal and retarded boys after experimentally induced failure: a social learning theory interpretation.* Ann Arbor, Mich.: University Microfilms, 1958.

JAMES, W. H. *Internal versus external control of reinforcement as a basic variable in learning theory.* Ann Arbor, Mich.: University Microfilms, 1957.

KELLY, G. A. *The psychology of personal constructs.* New York: W. W. Norton, 1955.

KRAEPELIN, E. *Psychiatric.* Leipzig: Barth, 1909–1913.

McKINNEY, J. P. *A multidimensional study of the behavior of severely retarded boys.* Ann Arbor, Mich.: University Microfilms, 1961.

MILLER, J. O. *Role perception and reinforcement conditions in discrimination learning among culturally deprived and non-deprived children.* Ann Arbor, Mich.: University Microfilms, 1958.

MILLER, M. B. *Locus of control, learning climate, and climate shift in serial learning with mental retardates.* Ann Arbor, Mich.: University Microfilms, 1961.

MOSS, J. W. *Failure-avoiding and success-striving behavior in mentally retarded and normal children.* Ann Arbor, Mich.: University Microfilms, 1958.

MURRAY, H. A. *Explorations in personality.* New York, London: Oxford University Press, 1938.

NORTHCUTT, MARY P. *The comparative effectiveness of classroom and programmed instruction in the teaching of decimals to fifth-grade students.* Ann Arbor, Mich.: University Microfilms, 1963.

PHARES, E. J. *Changes in expectancy in skill and chance situations.* Ann Arbor, Mich.: University Microfilms, 1955.

ROTTER, J. B. *Social learning and clinical psychology.* New York: Prentice-Hall, 1954.

————, SEEMAN, M. R., and LIVERANT, S. Internal versus external control of reinforcement; a major variable in behavior theory. In N. F. Washburne (Ed.), *Decisions, values and groups,* Vol. 2. London: Pergamon Press, 1962.

SARASON, S. B., DAVIDSON, K. S., LIGHTHALL, F., and WAITE, R. A test anxiety scale for children. *Child Developm.,* 1958, *29,* 105–113.

SCHULMAN, J. L., KASPER, J. C., and THRONE, FRANCES M. *Brain damage and behavior.* Springfield, Ill.: Charles C Thomas, 1965.

SPRADLIN, J. E. Task resumption phenomena in mentally retarded Negro children. *Abstracts of Peabody studies in mental retardation,* 1960, *1* (40).

WRIGHT, L. *The performance of overachieving males on certain measures of efficiency and divergence; a study in personality integration.* Ann Arbor, Mich.: University Microfilms, 1964.

Speech, Language, and Hearing of the Mentally Retarded

5

CLARENCE E. WEBB and STEWART KINDE

DIAGNOSIS AND MEASUREMENT

COMMUNICATION disorders constitute a major problem area for the mentally retarded. Speech, hearing, and language deficits have been identified in over 25 investigations as occurring markedly more frequently among mental retardates than among normal persons (Batza, 1956; Bradley, Evans, and Worthington, 1955; Brandfon, 1951; Carlton and Carlton, 1945a; Foale and Paterson, 1954; Goertzen, 1957; Hardy, 1948; Johnson, Copobianco, and Miller, 1960; Kennedy, 1930; Kodman, Powers, Phillip, and Weller, 1958; Lewald, 1932; Lubman, 1955; Mecham, 1955; Rigrodsky, Prunt, and Glousky, 1961; Rittmanic, 1959; Sachs, 1955; Schlanger, 1953a, 1953b, 1954; Schlanger and Gottsleben, 1956, 1957; Siegenthaler and Krzywicki, 1959; Sirkin and Lyons, 1941; Tarjan, Dingman, and Miller, 1960; Webb, Kinde, Weber, and Beedle, 1964). Despite the prevalence of these problems direct professional attention has not been broadly available.

Yet, workers in the field do not know whether the prognosis for speech, hearing, or language improvement of the mental retardate is different from that for the normal individual because:

(1) Speech, language, and/or hearing training is usually a time-consuming task. Children who are not retarded often are enrolled in such training for one, two, three, or even more years. The available evidence (Kolstoe, 1958; Lassers and Low, 1960; Rigrodsky, and Steer, 1961; Smith, 1962) does not indicate that mentally retarded individuals require more time than normal individuals to reach desirable communication goals.

(2) Speech and language development are related to mental age and IQ (Bangs, 1942; Carroll, 1964). This circumstance may create a more favorable prognosis for mentally retarded children, since optimal ages for learning good articulation, rhythm and other speech skills occur early in a child's life (Van Riper, 1963). The mental retardate may be more likely to benefit from communication training at this time since he may still be in the optimal period for learning communication skills at the time he is considered for training. Although work at younger ages may be desirable, most direct communication training is done at CA 5 and older.

(3) The relatively simple tasks necessary to bring about communication improvement appear to be within the capability of the majority of mental retardates. Good speech and language are not high-level skills. Most 6-year-olds talk acceptably well.

In view of the foregoing, the reader may wonder why more communication training has not been attempted with retardates. Personnel shortages, inadequate training, antipathy towards working with retardates, and concern for getting more cases released as "cured" appear to be the reasons why speech and hearing clinicians in the past have often excluded such cases from their work load.

Yet attention to communication improvement for the mentally retarded is greatly needed (Schiefelbusch, 1962) and well justified. The changes in a retardate's life resulting from such training are potentially as significant as the changes in the life of the individual who is not retarded.

DIFFERENTIAL DIAGNOSIS

The etiology and nature of language disorders, hearing loss, and speech problems in mentally retarded children and adults may be crucial to the education of these individuals. Just as mental retardation, communication disorders often result from brain injury, brain deficit, environmental factors, emotional problems, sensory impairment, etc. Identifying a communication problem may contribute to improved evaluation of the level of retardation and to better solutions for habilitation. For example, the child with a language deficiency caused by emotional problems is crippled in his learning capabilities not only because of the emotional problem but because of his difficulty in communicating.

CONSULTATIVE SERVICES

Direct speech, hearing, and language clinical services are often needed by the mentally retarded person. However, consultative services to all personnel involved in the training of retardates in other areas represent an even greater contribution by speech and hearing specialists. Such consultative services may include appropriate ways an attendant, parent, or teacher should respond to a pattern of stuttering in the teen-age retardate, improved ways of bringing about speech improvement in a kindergarten program for retardates, or methods of establishing communication with aphasic retardates.

Parental counseling and guidance on means of fostering speech development and the possibility of conducting a hearing conservation program for the mentally retarded also represent ways in which realistic contributions can be made.

LANGUAGE DISORDERS

CHARACTERISTICS

A number of studies have shown that the quality and quantity of language produced by the retardate are consistently inferior to that of the non-retarded.

Abstraction is less common in the language of the retarded (Badt, 1958; Bijou and Werner, 1954; Feifel and Lorge, 1950; Griffith and Spitz, 1958; Hess, Mohr, Bartelme, 1934; Mein and O'Connor, 1960; Papania, 1954). Sentences are often shorter and the syntax is usually inferior to that expected for the age of the child (Carlton and Carlton, 1945; Goda, 1957; Mein and O'Connor, 1960). Copeland (1963) reported the quantity of vocalization produced in response to delayed feedback is greater in low-ability than in high-ability retardates. Retarded children, according to Luria (1963), do not use language to effectively direct behavior, learn, or fixate the significance of experience as other children do. Jordan and deCharms (1959) found that stories given by trained retarded children were significantly longer than those given by matched retarded children who were not in special classes. Badt (1958) used the vocabulary items of the Binet scale to develop an "abstraction score," which correlated negatively and significantly with length of institutionalization. Carlton and Carlton (1945a, 1945b) found that retarded children were unable to match verbs with their subjects. Sievers and Essa (1961) evaluated language structure of 74 institutionalized children and 74 matched subjects living in the community. They found that the use of pronouns, verbs and prepositions rose with increased mental age while the proportion of nouns dropped. Similar findings in normally intelligent young children have occurred.

Mein and O'Connor (1960) analyzed the vocabularies of 80 retarded persons between CA 10 and 30. The individual vocabularies varied in size from 106 to 677 words. Mental ages for this group ranged from 3 to 7. Only 2,419 different words were produced by all of the subjects.

Schlanger (1954) found the mean sentence length of institutionalized children was significantly less than that of matched children in the community.

Wood's (1960) study indicated that while language delay was frequently found in children who were mentally retarded, only 20 per cent of her sample of 1,200 children with delayed language was found to be mentally retarded. She interpreted this to mean that a full evaluation of children with language delay was crucial to avoid potential erroneous diagnoses for mental retardation. Karlin and Strazzulla (1952) indicated that for their subjects with IQs of 15 to 20, 26 to 30, and 51 to 70 babbling occurred at 25 months, 20.4 months, and 20.8 months respectively. Word use occurred at 54.3 months, 43.2 months, and 34.5 months respectively. Sentence use began at 153 months, 93 months, and 89.4 months respectively. Blanchard (1964) indicated that subjects she observed in the institution seldom went beyond the 4th-year level in normal speech development.

In summary, language delay, shortened sentence length, syntax disproportion and restricted vocabulary size have been found to occur in the developmental pattern associated with mental retardation. The effects of institutionalization, chronological age, and mental age on these variables seems to be negatively related to negative (for institutionalization) and positive (for CA and MA) states of the retardate's well-being.

INCIDENCE

The usual procedure for determining incidence is to identify deviation from the norm and to establish a cut-off point. Subjects below the cut-off point are then described as having the disorder measured. In the retarded population, separation from the normal group on the basis of intelligence and behavior has been done before testing for speech, language, or hearing. The use of intelligence as a prior separating criteria from the normal population means that most of the subjects identified will have language delay since intelligence and behavior are often measured or observed by means of language.

For example, one of the authors (Webb, 1965) has observed an incidence of 70 per cent of language disorders in a sheltered workshop population (as defined by two or more years below MA on the Illinois Test of Psycho-Linguistic Abilities, Kirk and McCarthy, 1961). Karlin and Kennedy (1936) found 50 per cent of 32 subjects below IQ 20 were mute. Lewald (1932) gave an incidence of 57 per cent in a similar population.

In evaluating the frequency with which language disorders occur in mental retardates, one should recall that Binet and Simon (1914) defined idiocy and imbecility in terms of communication. Verbal communication difficulty characterized idiots while problems in writing characterized imbeciles.

On the basis of normal patterns of speech and language development, one might postulate a delayed continuum of language growth in the mentally retarded based on mental age. However, this does not hold—at least for institutionalized retardates. The report by Blanchard (1964) indicates retardates in institutions do not progress much beyond age 4 in speech development. However, evidence suggests that a sizable number of retardates living in the community reach language maturity (as defined on the Illinois Test of Psycho-Linguistic Abilities). For lower level retardates, particularly those in institutions, the incidence of language disorders appears to be 100 per cent.

ETIOLOGY

Etiology of language disorders in the mentally retarded population has been viewed as the result of organic deficit, developmental delay, or the effects of an inadequately stimulating or reinforcing environment.

Organic disorders and their relationship to language and mental retardation are described by Luria (1963). Beckey (1942) found delayed speech associated with gestation and pregnancy disorders. Rigrodsky and Goda (1951) found great variability in a group of brain injured children in their expressive and receptive language processes. Children who were advanced receptively were also advanced expressively.

Delayed development may be expressed as a language disorder resulting from organic or environmental factors. Schiefelbusch (1963) postulated four stages of language development: (1) sensory stimulation and smile, (2) attachment, (3) word acquisition and social exploration, and (4) language acquisition and experience. Schiefelbusch believes that developmental delay may occur in any of these stages and that critical periods for stimulation of these developmental stages exist. The developmental significance of language has also been pointed out by Luria (1963), who contended that speech involves "traces of past expression" and that generalizations in language acquisition are based on previously learned words and concepts.

Two results of favorable development training appear to be improved spontaneity and longer sentence length. Rigrodsky and Steer (1961) found that children who had received 40 daily lessons of training were more spontaneously verbal. Mecham, Courtney, and Soderberg (1955) reported mentally retarded children used longer sentences after speech therapy.

Environmental concomitants of language behavior of the mentally retarded are well illustrated by the work of Siegel (1963) and Siegel and Harkins (1963). They found that adult expectations affect and are affected by the language behavior of retarded children. The significance of stimulation from the environment is frequently viewed in the "fun, food and friendly companionship" category of Mowrer (1960). Disruption of mother-child relationships and institutional living constitutes a further detriment to the language development of retarded children (Jordan, 1963). Schlanger (1954) has demonstrated how language changes may occur as a result of institutionalization. Retardates who had an average stay in the institution of 3 years, 7 months, used shorter sentences than retardates who were in the community. Lyle (1960) has shown that institutional living for retarded children may be more significant at one stage of language development than another. Those children who had developed language prior to institutional placement adjusted better to the institution. McCarthy (1954) recommended changing the home atmosphere with psychotherapy along with language therapy in order to bring about significant language gains for children with language disorders.

Factors affecting the degree of verbal interaction of the child (or retardate) with others seem to be related to language growth, when organic factors are matched between groups. Thus, environmental deficit may contribute to the language delay of many mental retardates.

MEASUREMENT

Measurement of language in mentally retarded children and adults has been carried on in a variety of ways. Language may be evaluated on the basis of syntax (structure) or lexicon (vocabulary). Measures of syntax are typified by type-token ratios, sentence length, and the adjective-verb quotient. Studies of lexicon have involved analyses of core and fringe vocabulary, abstract/concrete analyses, synonym use, vocabulary size, and vocabulary repetitiousness.

The procedure of language sampling described by Johnson, Darley, and Spriestersbach (1963) appears to be an effective system. Small toys and picture books are used to elicit responses from the child. The examiner says to the child, "Now we are going to look at some books," and, "I want you to tell me about the pictures," etc. Usually the 50 utterances after the first ten are recorded. A tape recording of 50 language samples permits measurement of sentence length and other analyses with adequate reliability.

Analysis of language has been done frequently by the use of type-token ratios. The studies of Mein (1961), Mein and O'Connor (1960), O'Connor and Hermelin (1959), Siegel (1963), and Siegel and Harkins (1963) have evaluated language on a type-token basis. Analysis of pronouns, verbs and prepositions and their proportion to nouns was done by Sievers and Essa (1961).

Sampling of language with the Illinois Test of Psycho-Linguistic Abilities (Kirk and McCarthy, 1961) has also been of value. The structural model for the Illinois Test of Psycho-Linguistic Abilities (ITPA) assumes that there are various representational levels of language, processes of encoding and decoding, two basic modes of input (visual and auditory) and two basic modes of output (vocal and gestural). The two levels of organization are automatic-sequential and representational. The three psycho-linguistic processes are decoding, association, and encoding. The ITPA appears to provide a method of evaluating these processes somewhat independently of each other.

The Parsons Language Sample (PLS) represents another attempt to provide formal constructs for evaluating language. Based on the system provided by Skinner (1957), it has been further developed by Spradlin (1963). Two areas are evaluated: vocal and non-vocal. The vocal area consists of a TACT subtest (picture and object naming), the echoic subtest (repeating sentences and numbers), and the intraverbal subtest (response to simple questions). The non-vocal area consists of the echoic gesture subtest (imitation of motor acts), comprehension subtest (vocal and motor gestural directions to complete motor tasks) and the intraverbal gesture subtest. The PLS is based primarily on the assumption that observable language responses are sampled and evaluated in various situations. The Illinois Test of Psycho-Linguistic Abilities, on the other hand, assumes that the test items measure implicit processes within the person and that the language responses are the effect of these processes.

These two new formal tests of language may prove to be of great value in analyzing the language problems of the retarded. On a pragmatic basis, the language sampling procedures summarized by Johnson, Darley, and Spriestersbach (1963) seem to be of great value at the present time. These language sampling procedures provide for flexible syntactical and lexiconical analyses and may be adopted to a wide variety of purposes.

Another approach was developed by Mecham (1963), who used a scale for the measurement of language variables. Skills included listening and speaking skills and ranged from following simple instructions to telling simple stories. Mastery of articulation skill, recall of sequences, and use of pronouns are samples of the range of skills evaluated in the schedule. Although normative data is not available, the scale suggested by Mecham provides an over-all measure of language skill that may be useful both to non-specialists and specialists in the speech and hearing field.

The communicative evaluation chart from infancy to 5 years compiled by Anderson and Miles (1963) is an example of a similar approach. The chart covers language items from 3 months to 5 years old and is scored by estimates of "present," "not present," and "fluctuating." Intended as a screening procedure for non-professionals, the chart evaluates the child's capacity to gain and use language as a tool as well as the child's physical status, growth and development, motor coordination, and visual-motor perceptual skills. The child should score approximately at the standard for his age range to avoid referral to speech and hearing clinicians. Although most retarded children would be referred to speech and hearing clinicians after evaluation on the items proposed, the chart is useful because of the extensive diagnostic items provided.

Language can be evaluated pragmatically on a functional basis. That is, lexicon can be evaluated by careful attention to whether the subject has an appropriate number of words for his mental age and whether these reflect appropriate ratios of nouns to other parts of speech in his connected discourse. The second aspect, of listening to the syntactical structure, can be informally evaluated on the basis of presence or absence of incomplete sentences and sentences of short length as opposed to longer length. The relative repetitiousness of vocabulary is another pragmatic lexiconical means for clinical use. Although such informal analyses are no longer considered to provide meaningful research results, their clinical utility is defensible on the basis of economy of time, of their use in training, and of cases where complete analyses are impractical because of factors such as the presence of behavioral disorders.

ARTICULATION DISORDERS

CHARACTERISTICS

Tarjan *et al.* (1961) found articulation disorders characteristic of the mentally retarded in an institution. Speech problems [1] were reported 80 to 100 per cent of the time in admission cases age 4 and below regardless of the child's IQ. Residents in 80 to 100 per cent of their cases had speech problems up to age 5, regardless of IQ. For those with IQ age 20 and below of the resident population speech problems were observed in 80 to 100 per cent of the cases, through age 40.

The findings of Everhart (1953) bear out the strong relationship between articulation and IQ suggested in the findings of Tarjan *et al.* Bangs (1942), in a similar investigation, studied 53 institutionalized primary aments without deafness, paralysis or other organic problems. Cases whose retardation was due to birth injury or cases of stuttering or mute subjects were not included. His data indicated mental age was 4.9 times as significant as chronological age in its influence on articulatory proficiency. The sounds most frequently

---

1. Speech disorders and speech problems have often been surveyed in the mentally retarded population. Usually the bulk of these are impairments of articulation even though other problems (stuttering, voice) may be included.

substituted or avoided by retarded children were similar to the errors of non-retarded children except for a marked tendency toward omission of final sounds. TH, R, and S were the sounds for which other sounds were most frequently substituted.

Burt (1937), in evaluating children in atypical schools, found in the group with IQ 70 to 85 that 9 per cent of the children had mild speech defects and 5 per cent had severe speech defects. Those with IQs of 50 to 70 had 13 per cent with mild speech defects and 11 per cent with severe defects. He estimated that at least 25 per cent of retarded children in special classes in regular schools have speech defects. Matthews (1957), in summarizing literature on the incidence of speech defects in the mentally retarded, reported overall incidence figures varied from 14 to 79 per cent. He pointed out that the incidence figures differ because of varied definitions of speech defects and because of differences in the populations under study. Karlin and Strazzulla (1952) listed consonant defects in order of occurrence in a group of retardates. The most frequently occurring defective consonant was S, followed by Z, L, R, CH, J, voiced TH, SH, and voiceless TH.

Articulatory disorders represent the largest single speech disorder among mental retardates. Although language disorders exceed articulation disorders in frequency, language disorders at times may result from a severe articulation disorder that has prevented the child's obtaining reinforcement for his efforts in language. Institutional placement is strongly associated with the presence of articulation disorders in retardates. Age, both chronological and mental, is associated with improvement in the child's articulatory proficiency. Mental age, however, is more closely related to articulatory proficiency than any other single indicator.

ETIOLOGY

Evaluation of the etiology of articulation disorders in mentally retarded has not been investigated adequately. Those investigators who have mentioned etiology in this population typically have pointed to the effects of mental retardation. Interaction between the articulation disturbance and the mental retardation is likely, but the effects of motor difficulty, perceptual problems, and environment deprivation certainly should be considered as contributing factors in etiology.

Poor sensory acuity and discrimination in the auditory area are suggested by Van Riper and Irwin (1958) as significant causes of defective articulation in the general population. They note that there is equivocal evidence as to the relationship between poor auditory discrimination and articulation defects; however, for children with relatively severe articulation problems, the usual finding has been one of poor auditory discrimination. The possibility that some children with articulation defects have had a hearing loss for a period of time during their speech development also should be mentioned as a possible etiological factor.

MEASUREMENT

Articulation measurement in the mentally retarded has been carried out with a variety of stimuli and situational approaches. The procedure used by Bangs (1942) of exhibiting 65 picture cards and asking the subject to name the picture typifies one of the speech pathologist's major approaches to articulation testing. Rigrodsky and Steer (1961) used tape recordings of subject responses from the Bryngelson and Glaspey picture test cards, an auditory stimulus test in which the subject repeated four vowels and nonsense syllables combined with consonants, and spontaneous speech. The tapes were played to five trained judges to obtain pre- and post-therapy scores.

Schlanger (1953a) employed such techniques as repeated isolated sounds, repeated isolated words, Bryngelson and Glaspey picture cards, repeated phrases of sentences, and spontaneous non-emotional conversation in evaluating articulation. He elicited the non-emotional conversation by the use of pictures seen through a stereopticon, conversation adapted to happenings during a recent Christmas vacation, and the descriptions and comments of the subjects pertaining to activities connected with a doll house and the placement of furniture therein.

Although these procedures have been used with some success, one of the problems in obtaining a stable measure of articulation from any population is that of positional-inconsistency on any given sound. The child may misarticulate the S sound on "soup" but produce it correctly in the middle of the word "whistle."

Another problem in the testing of articulation is which aspect of speech performance should be sampled. Although ordinary conversation may be more closely identified with usual functioning, careful identification of defective speech sounds is exceedingly difficult from such a sample. Measures of such skill usually approximate an over-all judgment and do not delimit the specific defective sounds. An alternative might be to have a child repeat individual speech sounds. Where this is done, the measure of the child's articulation skill may be relatively unrelated to his abilities in conversation. Probably the most clinically useful approach is to ask a child to repeat single words or short phrases with the speech sounds to be tested contained within the repeated material. The approaches of Templin and Darley (picture responses) (1960) or MacDonald (repetition of sentences) (1964) provide such measures.

VOICE DISORDERS

CHARACTERISTICS

Schlanger (1953b) indicated that voice defects were observed in 61 per cent of 74 retarded children whose mean age was 12 years. Goertzen (1957) identified the vocal characteristics of the post-encephalitic child as unmodulated in pitch; harsh, nasal, or breathy in quality; and hesitant, drawling, or explosive. He believed the voice of the epileptic child was likely to be muffled and lacking in subtle variations of pitch. The voice of the mongoloid child was described as hoarse with no modulation of pitch and intensity. The cretin's voice was sometimes hoarse and froglike. The vocal problems of a child with cerebral palsy—pitch control problems, inadequate loudness variation, and quality disturbances—are well known to speech pathologists.

ETIOLOGY

West (1957) described the voice of the mongoloid child as typically husky and monotonous. He believed this occurs as the result of inadequate auditory control of vocalization.

Bender (1949) found that mongoloid children often have voices that are very deep, raucous, and low in pitch. Michel and Carney (1964) investigated pitch characteristics of eight mongoloid boys age 8½ to 10½ and found they appeared to be developing normally with respect to pitch level when compared with children of similar chronological ages but tended to be eighteen months to two years retarded in over-all physical development. In view of these data, one of the reasons for assuming that mental retardates have low-pitched voices may be the children's small physical size, causing the listener to interpret the relatively normal pitch level as inappropriate for an undersized child.

In our experience, vocal problems appear to be unusually frequent in the mentally retarded population. This might be expected on the basis of organic differences alone since these are generally more frequent among mental retardates. Frequent nasopharyngeal infections also may cause prolonged vocal differences in this group.

MEASUREMENT

Pitch is sometimes measured for therapy purposes by comparison with a pitch pipe or piano. The Purdue Direct Reading Pitch Meter (Dempsey, Draggart, Siskind, and Steer, 1950) has been utilized in research and in some clinics. Michel and Carney (1964) tape-recorded a minimum of 30 seconds of speech and transferred the tape to a disc and then to a phonellegraph, which produced a measurable visual representation of speech waves from which periodicity could be measured and converted to frequency. Intensity has often been measured through use of a sound pressure level meter such as the General Radio model #1551-B. Loudness levels have also been clinically evaluated, (i.e., whether the level seems to significantly interfere with communication as the result of being too loud, too soft, or occurring in patterned bursts).

Disorders of voice quality have been evaluated only on the basis of judgmental factors. Generally these are grouped into four categories: nasality, breathiness, hoarseness, and harshness. Nasality is usually defined as a whiney quality of voice, breathiness as air wastage, and harshness as a background rasp or gravelly sound. Hoarseness is typified by a combination of both breathiness and harshness, according to Van Riper and Irwin (1958).

Even though a defective voice may not typically be identified as a communicative disorder, the research evidence reported by Diehl and McDonald (1956) indicated that breathy and nasal voice quality significantly interfered with the information communicated.

RHYTHM DISORDERS (STUTTERING)

CHARACTERISTICS

Stuttering (formerly called stammering) is the major rhythm disorder among the mental retardates. Other rhythm disorders such as cluttering (too rapid use of words with periodic stoppage of the flow of speech), too slow a rate, too rapid a rate and inconsistent, jerky rhythm have also been observed in mentally retarded children and adults.

Stuttering is often described as primary or secondary. Primary stuttering is thought of as relatively effortless repetitions and prolongations in the continuous flow of speech. Secondary stuttering is characterized by struggling, forcing, and distraction devices used by the stutterer in an attempt to force the word out or avoid stuttering completely. Although stuttering develops on a continuum from effortless repetition to severe struggle, discussion of the problem in terms of the extremes of the range is useful. Effortless repetitions and prolongations are thought to diminish in a child's speech if no undue attention is called to them and if the child is in a relatively non-threatening, pleasant environment for the greater part of his day. Secondary stuttering, however, is thought to be self-maintaining since the stutterer's success in releasing the word reinforces the various devices he has used to force it out (Van Riper, 1963). Struggling symptoms and devices to postpone or avoid saying the words seem to be related to the degree of anxiety the stutterer has about talking in specific situations. Secondary stuttering is thought to be learned behavior resulting from the stutterer's perception of certain of his speech characteristics as undesirable. He then adopts a pattern of struggle and avoidance to eliminate what are essentially normal characteristics of speech (repetitions and prolongations).

Stuttering occurs much more frequently in the mentally retarded population than in the normal population. Schlanger (1953b) found stuttering to be present in 20 per cent of 74 institutionalized retarded children whose mean age was 12 years. Goertzen (1957) summarized the work of other authors in reporting that repetition of sounds and words and a pattern of speech closely resembling chronic stuttering is to be expected in epileptic children, particularly following an attack. He indicated choreatic speech is characterized by spasmodic uncontrolled bursts of sound. Gottsleben (1955) found a higher percentage of stuttering among mongoloids than among other categories of mental retardates. West, Ansberry, and Carr (1957) described the speech of mongoloids as resembling stuttering, and they believed the blocks and iterations in the speech of mongoloids could be called primary stuttering or cluttering.

ETIOLOGY

The etiology of stuttering may be viewed within two frames of reference: (1) the possible causes of the relatively effortless repetitions and prolongations, and (2) the development of secondary struggling, forcing, and avoiding devices.

The increased number of repetitions in a child's speech may come from various organic (endocrine, neurological) or environmental (emotional, learning) causes. The evidence for endocrine differences as etiologically significant to stuttering was presented by Hale (1951). He found a two-week administration of a 30 mg. daily dose of thiamin hydrochloride resulted in observable speech improvement in 55 per cent of young children. Possible improvement was observed in an additional 20 per cent of the 2- and 3-year-olds in the experiment, 80 per cent were observed to have improved. Only 50 per cent of the 4-year-olds were definitely improved. Doubtful results were found in children 5 and older.

Hansom (1951) used thiamin administration with adults who stuttered at the Ohio University Speech and Hearing Clinic and concluded that the thiamin made a possible contribution to speech improvement with the adults. Hill (1944), however, after surveying available research on metabolic and chemical agents that may be significant in the etiology of stuttering, concluded that "in the case of biochemical differences, no findings warrant any assumption of specific metabolic or chemical agents that are causal."

Schaubel and Street (1949) report the use of prostigmin, a reflex-inhibiting substance, with 10 stutterers. Each day 60 mgs. of prostigmin were administered to stutterers ranging in age from 14 to 40. The conclusions were based on qualitative observations during the sixteen-month treatment rather than quantitative data. Many of the stutterers reported less tension in their speech pattern. One of the problems was in maintaining the interest of the stutterer in the administration of the drug. Stutterers who improved felt they had no need for it; those who did not improve became discouraged. Schaubel and Street concluded that prostigmin as a part of general therapy with chronic stutterers may have value.

Palasek and Curtis (1960) suggest that stuttering frequency might be decreased by administration of lactose. While their results did not reach significance statistically, the number of words stuttered in successive readings was lower for the lactose condition than when calcium carbonate was administered. Both of these conditions resulted in less stuttering than the control condition in which no pills were used, indicating the effect of suggestion on frequency of stuttering.

Glasner and Rosenthal (1957), approaching the problem from an environmental point of view, found that 15.4 per cent of mothers with children entering the first grade reported their child had stuttered at some time. At the time the children entered first grade, 4.8 per cent were still diagnosed as stutterers by their mothers. Of 44 children who were still stuttering, 82 per cent of the parents had actively corrected the child's stuttering. Of 81 children who were no longer stuttering, only 59 per cent of the parents had actively corrected their speech. However, the memory of active correction on the part of the parent may diminish as the child's stuttering diminishes. Johnson (1961) presented another view. In summarizing research at the University of Iowa, he indicated that excessive concern about and attention to the child's repetitions and hesitations on the part of the parent seemed to be a major factor in whether the child continued to have difficulty.

MEASUREMENT

Davis (1939) studied repetitions in speech of 62 children ranging in age from 24 to 62 months and found repetition to be part of the speech pattern of all children. Phrase repetition was greater than either repetition of words or syllables. Word repetition was greater than syllable repetition. For girls her composite measure of syllable repetition of all types of repetition for ages in months 24–35, 36–49, and 50–60 were .348, .266, and .157 respectively. For boys the composite measure for similar age groups was .297, .239, and .219 respectively. The composite measure was composed of the instances of repeated words multiplied by the number of times each was repeated, plus the number of instances of syllable repetition, plus the number of words repeated in phrases multiplied by the number of times each was repeated, all divided by the number of words spoken. The composite measure appeared to give the best over-all index of the data Davis presented and indicated diminution of repetition with increasing age. This finding was also reported by Smith (1926), whose data indicated an average number of repetitions per word used at the age levels 2, 3, 4, and 5 for 88 children of .114, .045, .022, and .017 respectively. These figures were computed by dividing repetitions scored by the number of words used.

Sander (1963) evaluated stuttering by playing tape recordings prepared with single repetitions and double repetitions to college students. Varying ratios of number of repetitions per 100 words were used in the study. Single-unit repetitions were found to have an exponential curve between the number of persons who identified the speech as stuttering and the instances of single repetition. Speech samples containing fewer than eight repetitions of a single-unit type per 100 were not identified as stuttering by eight of ten listeners. Double-unit repetition, however, appeared to have a parabolic curve between the number of persons who identified the speech as stuttered and the instances of double-unit repetition. Ratios of one instance of double-unit syllable repetition per 100 received no stuttering judgments. With two instances of double-unit repetition per 100 words four of ten judges identified the speech as stuttered. With four instances of double-unit repetition per 100 words, seven of ten judges identified the speech as stuttered. Generally, double-unit repetitions occasioned twice as many judgments of the person being a stutterer than single-unit repetitions.

Clinically, stuttering is often evaluated in terms of the types of secondary symptoms and the extent of severity of the symptoms. Usually a descriptive analysis is presented including the sequence of the secondary symptoms and a description of each one. For example, "the subject has a tongue click, and eye blink, several side-to-side head jerks and then releases the word by a head jerk backward. Initiation of feared words is sometimes preceded by a quick inhalation with rapid exhalation through the nose prior to initiating the word attempt."

Psychological status of the patient over his anticipation of stuttering (or fear of speaking) may be evaluated by the Iowa Scale of Severity of Stuttering, or by comparison with the developmental phases of stuttering delineated by Bloodstein (1960). Phase one was typified by few if any emotional reactions to stuttering. In phase two, the child thinks of himself as a stutterer but speaks freely. In phase three, the child has a few deep feelings of embarrassment, but does not tend to avoid speaking. In phase four, vivid anticipation of stuttering and avoidance of certain speaking situations were present.

HEARING DISORDERS

CHARACTERISTICS

Over the last decade, numerous attempts have been made to assess the hearing of mental retardates, employing a variety of audiometric procedures. The problems encountered have been similar in nature to those faced in the measurement of hearing in normal children. Frisina (1963) pointed out that since most conventional audiometric procedures have been standardized on adult samples, the appropriateness of any test procedure and the need for special considerations with young subjects appear to be related to stimulus materials, response modes, instructional modes, and maturational factors. Consequently, the major approaches used with both the young and the retarded populations have involved

variations in the stimulus materials and response modes of pure tone audiometric procedures and speech reception tests. In addition, attempts toward the complete circumvention of stimulus/response problems have involved the use of objective measures such as electroencephalic audiometry, (EEG-Audio), electrodermal audiometry, (EDR-Audio), and operant audiometry (OPR-Audio). Most of the studies have been directed primarily toward the determination of absolute threshold and have had varying degrees of success. A few investigators have made attempts to classify the severity of hearing losses reported in their studies but variations in the hearing-loss criteria employed and the practice of excluding subjects on the basis of a lack of or inconsistent responses to auditory stimuli negates the possibility of generalizing from such data. Thus little quantitative information is available regarding the kinds of hearing problems characteristic of the mentally retarded.

ETIOLOGY

Since the pathology underlying mental retardation may often involve aberrations of the nervous system a high percentage of sensory-neural-type hearing problems might be hypothesized among such populations. In fact, two studies have reported comparatively large numbers of sensory-neural losses among populations of institutionalized mental retardates on the basis of divergent air and bone conduction thresholds. However, since most audiometric techniques employed for differential diagnosis require a degree of behavioral sophistication not possessed by most mental retardates little empirical evidence has been gathered to support such a supposition.

Similar problems have turned up in identifying conductive components of hearing loss among mental retardates by audiometric procedures alone. In anticipation of these difficulties, Webb, Kinde, Weber, and Beedle (1964) included otologic examinations for a selected group of institutionalized subjects who had failed auditory screening tests. Conductive problems were diagnosed for approximately 20 per cent of the patients examined with active otitis media recognized as the major factor. The authors suggest their findings may indicate a high incidence of middle ear infections in institutionalized patients, which, unless anticipated with preventative measures, may compound the problems of retardation.

The paucity of information available on the etiology of and diagnostic procedures for hearing problems of the mentally retarded points up the need for further research in this area.

INCIDENCE

Published studies have presented conflicting estimates of the incidence of hearing loss in mental retardates. Schlanger's (1961) survey of the literature showed a range of incidence from no hearing loss to over 50 per cent in the populations tested. The review by Kodman (1958) also indicated no consistent pattern in incidence of loss. In part, this inconsistency may be because of small samples tested or because of differences in subject selection, test procedures, and criteria for hearing loss. Probably the most useful data available on incidence of loss in the mentally retarded population is that derived from pure tone testing of institutionalized retardates. Over 5,000 subjects have been tested by pure tone methods in ten major investigations.

The criterion of a loss of 20 db or more for one or more frequencies for one or both ears was used in three of these surveys:

The results of a pure tone hearing testing survey at the Polk State School in Pennsylvania were reported by Birch and Matthews (1951). In their study of 247 subjects with a median IQ of 49 and a chronological age range of 10 to 19, 55.5 per cent had losses of 20 db or more at one or more of the frequencies tested (512 to 8,192 cps).

Foale and Paterson (1954) surveyed the hearing status of 100 boys aged 10–19 years with a mean IQ of 66 at the Lennox Castle Institution for Mental Defectives in Scotland. Hearing loss was identified in 33 per cent of the group tested according to the above-mentioned criterion.

Siegenthaler and Krzywicki (1959) attempted hearing testing of 396 school girls and 242 non-school women at an institution for potentially delinquent females of child-bearing age in Laurelton, Pennsylvania. The school girls had a mean chronological age of 21.7 and a mean IQ of 52.4. The non-school women had a mean chronological age of 35.0 and a

mean IQ of 51.0. Incidence figures for their groups were 17 per cent for the school girls and 32 per cent for the non-school women when tested over the 250 to 4,000 cps range.

The criterion of a loss of 20 db or more for two or more frequencies for one or both ears was used in the following four surveys:

Hearing testing of subjects in the educational department at the Fernald State School in Massachusetts was reported by Johnston and Farrell (1954). Data for the frequency range 250 to 6,000 cps were obtained on 270 children with a mean IQ of 61 who regularly attended academic classes. Hearing loss was present in 24 per cent of those tested.

At Vineland Training School, Schlanger and Gottsleben (1956) tested 498 subjects, who were divided into two age groups for analysis, those ages 5 to 20 and those over age 20. Frequencies tested were 125 to 12,000 cps. Incidence of hearing loss was 43 per cent and 71 per cent for the younger and older groups, respectively.

The incidence of hearing loss in the population at the Vineland Training School also was tested by Rigrodsky, Prunt, and Glousky (1961). Their data indicated percentages of hearing loss of 31 per cent, 20 per cent, 16 per cent, and 21 per cent for the IQ ranges 69–55, 54–40, 39–25, and 25–below, respectively. Of the 325 subjects tested, 25 per cent had impaired hearing.

Webb, Kinde, Weber, and Beedle (1964) carried out hearing testing at the Mount Pleasant State Home and Training School in Michigan. They tested 369 retardates with pure tone audiometry over the frequencies 500 to 2000 cps. The over-all incidence of hearing loss was 25 per cent.

Two studies used the loss of 30 db or more for one or more frequencies for one or both ears as a criterion on large numbers of retardates.

Schlanger and Gottsleben (1956) tested 498 subjects at the Vineland Training School on frequencies of 125 to 12,000 cps. Incidences of hearing loss were 25.7 per cent and 41.4 per cent for the younger and older groups respectively.

Hearing testing of 208 retardates was attempted by Kodman, Powers, Philip, and Weller (1958) with a younger group whose mean chronological age was 15.5 and an older group whose mean chronological age was

38.9. Frequencies tested were 250 to 8,000 cps. The younger group had an incidence of 19.04 per cent, the older group an incidence of 23.8 per cent.

Other systems for reporting of data from audiometric surveys on retardates have been used. The following two studies categorized data involving considerable numbers of subjects and, even though they have not been replicated, are reported for comparative purposes.

Rittmanic (1959) tested 1,220 patients (IQ range from 30 to 129) at the Dixon State School in Illinois. Patients were reported as pre-selected on the basis of predicted reliable response to a pure tone audiometric test. The criterion for a hearing loss was a loss of 15 db or more for two or more of the frequencies tested (250 to 8,000 cps) in one or both ears. On this basis, 40.5 per cent of the subjects had hearing losses. Of the 297 subjects tested in the 10-to-19 age range, 19.8 per cent were found to have hearing loss. The group over age 60 had an incidence of loss of 84 per cent.

Hearing testing with 199 subjects at St. Mary's Training School in West Virginia was conducted by Schlanger (1961). Those chosen were subjects who appeared capable of participating in audiometric screening. All of the subjects were from the institution except for 32 from special classes in the public schools. Frequencies tested were 500 to 4,000 cps. Criteria for hearing loss were failure to respond to two frequencies at 30 db or more in either ear, or irrelevant responses to pure tone stimuli, indicating that the subject was untestable or sufficiently inconsistent in his responses to raise a question concerning the validity of the responses. Although criteria for hearing loss included "untestable," a separate category was also established for this group. Excluding the 44 subjects who were defined as untestable (these were subsequently excluded from the hearing loss group), 42 per cent of the retardates were identified as having hearing loss.

VALIDITY OF HEARING TEST PROCEDURES ON RETARDATES

One of the problems in testing the hearing of the mentally retarded is validity. Tests of hearing used on retardates may measure, in part, retardation or one or more of the effects of retardation. Subjects who do not respond to the requirements of the test may be judged mistakenly as hard of hearing when their lack of response may actually be the result of retardation. Examiners may make judgment errors in the opposite direction as well, concluding that lack of response is the result of retardation instead of hearing loss.

The assumption that evidence of organic pathology would provide a criteria to authenticate the presumption of hearing loss based on hearing test results was investigated by Webb, Kinde, Weber, and Beedle (1964). Their study showed that organic pathology was identified by otologists in half of the retardates previously identified by audiologic testing as having hearing loss. Individual case reports of retardates identified as hard of hearing by audiometric procedures and subsequently authenticated by medical diagnosis, hearing aid fitting, or training are given by Schlanger and Gottsleben (1956), Foale and Paterson (1954) and Rittmanic (1959).

If the high incidence of hearing loss identified in the mentally retarded is a result of the influence of retardation or a factor common to both, one might expect the incidence of loss would be correlated with intelligence in this group. Siegenthaler and Krzywicki (1959) did not find the presence of hearing loss to be significantly related to IQ. When product moment and partial correlations were computed between hearing loss, IQ, and chronological age, no significant relationships were found. The restricted IQ range may explain this in part. Schlanger and Gottsleben (1956) presented data with similar implications. Their mildly retarded group was found to have an incidence of hearing loss of 31 per cent, the moderately retarded had an incidence of hearing loss of 20 per cent, the severely retarded had an incidence of hearing loss of 16 per cent, and the profoundly retarded had an incidence of hearing loss of 21 per cent.

Most studies of the hearing of retardates have pre-selected subjects to be tested. Even though more subjects might have been found to have hearing loss in the lower IQ range, only the ones less apt to exhibit hearing loss because of their behavioral responses were actually tested, thereby avoiding an apparent high incidence of loss. However, surveys have yet to show higher incidence of hearing loss among the more severely retarded individuals.

An appropriate conclusion might be that the incidence of hearing loss is high in retardates, but not because of the retardation (since hearing loss did not increase as retardation increased). Perhaps the high incidence occurs as a result of the pre-selection of patients for institutional placement (i.e., the syndrome of behavior necessary for commitment may include behavior of patients with hearing loss who may or may not have retardation to the extent other patients have whose behavior also "fits the syndrome").

A second possible explanation is that institutional placement, in itself, may result in hearing loss or in responses to sound that are indistinguishable from hearing loss. This latter possibility might occur in greater degree the longer a patient was in the institution. In an unpublished study, the authors found a correlation of .37 between per cent of chronological age spent in the institution and number of observed responses to free-field, live-voice sound for 30 retardates (chronological ages 3.4 to 15 years). This correlation, while low, was significant at the .01 level of confidence. The higher per cent of his life a patient had been in the institution the more responsive to sound he was. Their interpretation of this finding was that sound may become more unique with longer institutionalization and thereby the subject is more aware of it.

Schlanger (1961) provided further evidence for the validity of hearing test findings on retardates. He reasoned that if the high incidence of hearing loss in this group results in part from the behavioral responses associated with retardation, teaching of appropriate responses to sound might facilitate hearing testing and thereby lower the frequency with which hearing loss is identified. In his listening training program, he found that test-retest performance on hearing tests was variable, but he did not obtain a lowered incidence in the identification of hearing loss when pure tone air conduction results were considered. The percentages of loss before and after the training program (for a group previously selected as failing a criterion of hearing difficulty) were essentially similar. When the criterion for hearing loss was two frequencies missed at 20 db or more, the post-training incidence of hearing loss was 5 per cent more than the pre-training incidence.

INTERPRETING HEARING SURVEYS ON RETARDATES

These studies show that significant variables that possibly accounted for differences in hearing test survey results were chronological age, mental age and criteria for hearing loss including the frequencies, intensities, and number of failures to respond. Other variables that were not controlled were the number of patients excluded from testing (few studies reported this), and the procedure for determining which patients would be considered testable subjects.

Workers should report the criteria by which patients were considered testable in order that data may be compared. Subsequent studies would also be improved if data were reported by the two or three most frequently used criteria for hearing loss.

Based on these studies, the best estimates of the over-all incidence of hearing loss among retardates in institutions seemed to vary according to the criteria of loss employed. If a 15-db screening level was used and two or more frequencies failed before hearing loss was identified, the incidence was 40.5 per cent. When the criterion was a 20 db or more loss for one frequency, the incidence was 32 per cent, and when a two frequency loss was required, the incidence was 24 per cent. The free-field, live-voice testing carried out by Webb, Kinde, Weber, and Beedle (1964) on 1,093 retardates resulted in an incidence of hearing loss of 24 per cent when criteria for loss were failure to give two observable responses to 20 db live voice sounds. Incidence of hearing loss diminished to 21 per cent when the criterion was a 30 db loss at one frequency. These percentages were based, in large part, on the total group of retardates. Older age groups had higher incidences of hearing loss; some groups of higher level retardates and some younger age groups were lower. By way of comparison, hearing testing of public school children of normal intelligence usually results in hearing loss incidence figures of 4 to 5 per cent (Newby, 1964).

MEASUREMENT

Many hearing test procedures have been employed in attempts to assess the hearing of the mentally retarded. As previously pointed out these have primarily involved adaptations of standardized pure tone and speech reception. Most of these changes have utilized stimulus materials and response modes thought to be more interesting or motivational and requiring a less sophisticated response. In addition, several objective techniques have been used in the hope of precluding all such stimulus and response problems.

Among the variations in stimulus materials is the "peep show" originally suggested by Dix and Hallpike (1947). This procedure employs pictures presented in a darkened box and illuminated only when the subject responds to the auditory test tone by pushing a button. Webb, Kinde, Weber, and Beedle (1964) employed a device that displayed candies behind a locked, transparent door and dispensed pieces whenever the subject responded to a test tone. Several studies have employed modifications of a speech reception test designed for children and developed by Siegenthaler, Pearson and Lezak (1954). Groups of pictures, selected on the basis of their familiarity to the subject, are presented to the testee and followed by a stimulus word that is best represented by one of the pictures and that the subject is expected to point out. Many other stimulus modifications, including animated toys and other entertaining devices, have been used successfully with normal children and may have application with retarded populations.

A number of adaptations in response modes have been classified under the term "play audiometry." Most of these involve a kind of behavioral conditioning in which the subject stacks rings on a dowel, places blocks in a container, moves a toy, answers a telephone or engages in some similar kind of play activity in response to an auditory signal. Although there are indications in the literature (Webb, Kinde, Weber, and Beedle 1964) that these techniques are not effective with profoundly retarded children and those with extreme behavioral problems, these procedures may have widespread application with subjects functioning at less retarded levels. A modification of standard pure tone test response procedures, called the "ear choice" technique, was first suggested by Curry and Kurtzrock (1951) and is unique in that it contains a validity check of the responses elicited. During this procedure, the test tones are presented alternately to the subject's ears and he is asked to identify the location throughout randomized alternations. This technique was compared with standard response procedures for administration time in a study reported by Bradley, Evans, and Worthington, (1955). Their findings indicated that standard procedures took less time to administer but a higher incidence of loss was reported through the use of ear choice technique employing the same hearing-loss criterion for both tests.

Sound field localization techniques have been extensively employed with neonates and infants utilizing a variety of auditory stimuli. Studies such as those reported by Gesell and Armatruda (1948) and Chun, Pawsat, and Forster (1960) indicate that normal infants can localize sound in space as early as 26 weeks old. The extension of this approach to the auditory screening of institutionalized mentally retarded patients was reported by Webb, Kinde, Weber, and Beedle (1964). Taped voice materials and "attractive noises" were employed as stimuli and were randomly presented with a five-second interval between presentations. Judgments of response were made on the basis of characteristic behavioral reactions and alterations or interruptions of ongoing behavior. The results of this study indicated such procedures might make it possible to differentiate between mentally retarded subjects with hearing loss and those with normal hearing, regardless of behavioral problems that might negate the use of conventional tests.

Objective tests to evaluate hearing through means other than voluntary responses have yet to prove satisfactory when administered to young children or mental retardates. Electrodermal audiometry, which measures conditioned changes in the resistance of the skin in response to auditory stimulation paired with a mild electric shock, has been attempted by a number of investigators. Davis and Silverman (1960) said that children who are the most difficult to test with conventional procedures are also the most difficult to test with EDR-Audio. O'Neill, Oyer and Hillis (1961) reported similar results after using a battery of tests with children who showed indications of mental retardation and emotional disturbances. In no case was EDR-Audio successful when play audiometry was unsuccessful. Webb, Kinde, Weber, and Beedle (1964) found the shock to be so emotionally disturbing to young institutionalized retardates that it was impossible to identify a response to auditory stimulation because of the concomitant high level of background noise. A few reports of the successful use of EDR-Audio are to be noted in the literature (Barr, 1955; Kodman, Fein and Mixson, 1959; Sortini, 1959), but for the most part the consensus seems to be that it is no more effective than standard techniques.

Only recently has electroencephalic audiometry proven to be of limited utility. Subjective methods of scoring responses have not facilitated acute threshold measurements (Webb, Kinde, Weber, and Beedle, 1964). However, in the last few years extensive interest has been displayed in the use of computer techniques for the detection of EER-Audio responses. The first reported use of such a system to evaluate hearing was made by Lowell, Troffer, Warburton, and Rushford (1960) and Lowell, Williams, Ballinger and Alvig (1961). Using a specially constructed analog computer to "average out" responses to electronically produced clicks, they compared the summed potentials to threshold measurements taken with standard procedures and reported sufficient agreement to show promise of clinical application. Williams and Graham (1963), using both manual measurement and computer analysis to detect cortical changes in children in the waking state, found such changes were identifiable by both types of measurement. However, a trained EEG technician was employed to make the manual measurements. Derbyshire and McCandless (1964) employed summing computers and digital converters to arrive at a general description of the evoked electroencephalic response to auditory stimulation. Recently, the existence and detectability of such evoked responses in infants as young as 4 weeks old was demonstrated by McCandless and Best (1964). Continued research in this area may produce an effective and truly objective method of auditory testing that will facilitate the early identification of hearing problems in children.

An audiometric procedure employing operant conditioning recently was reported by Spradlin and Lloyd (1965). With candy as a reinforcement, their subjects were taught to push a key in response to a tone presented through a speaker. Initially the tone was paired with a light that faded out as soon as the response was established. A relatively short period of time was required to condition a child to respond to a tone presented in a sound field. By placing earphones on the child's forehead and gradually moving them down to his ears, Spradlin and Lloyd were able to obtain responses with phones and identify previously undetected hearing losses in several profoundly retarded children.

SYNDROMES ASSOCIATED WITH SPEECH LANGUAGE OR HEARING PROBLEMS

SJOGREN-LARSON SYNDROME

As described by Wittcop and Henry (1963), this disorder is characterized by speech defects ranging from dysarthric speech, use of monosyllables, inability to speak, hesitancy, stuttering, misarticulations, monotonous speech, substitution of single words for whole sentences, mispronunciation of vowels and inability to put words into sentences. Other investigators have noted that many patients keep their mouths open and have excessive drooling.

The Sjogren-Larson Syndrome appears to be inherited. The first symptoms noted are roughened skin and spacticity, and at a later date, retardation and retinal changes. Spastic convulsions are often reported at 48 months old. Swallowing is usually accompanied by a sucking motion. Frequent bouts of bruxism (gnashing of teeth) are seen for periods of up to one hour. Tactile and proprioceptive defects in the interior oral cavity and tongue are present.

HISTIDINEMIA

Wittcop and Henry (1963) also detail histidinemia speech disorders in articulation and language. The articulatory difficulty resulted from inability to move the tongue independently of the mandible, particularly during mandibular descent. For example, "la la" became "ja ja." Consonants requiring tongue-mandibular independence, especially T, D, N, and L were poorly articulated. Vowel distortion was present at times, depending on the ad·acent consonant. Articulatory mispronunciations were further accentuated by sideward movements of the mandible during elevation or descent. Among the problems of language organization were diffculties in both syntax and noun usage. Although normal peripheral hearing was observed, problems in sequential speech recall suggested central nervous system difficulty. Responses (by gesture to gesture) indicated normal visual-cortical tracking. Inability to repeat two phrase sentences even after four trials reinforced the conclusion of auditory reticulo-temporal deficit and possibly of cortical involvement. All two-phrase sentences were confused both syntactically and nominally.

Case loads of speech pathologists may include an occasional child with problems similar to this but without mental retardation. Histidinemia gives a positive PKU test result but is usually not associated with mental retardation.

POST-ENCEPHALITIC CONDITIONS

Goertzen (1957) indicated that the probable speech difficulties of the post-encephalitic child will be those generally associated with motor deficiency (i.e., unmodulated pitch, harsh nasal or breathy quality and hesitant, drawling or explosive utterance).

Kastein (1952) made a detailed evaluation of a post-encephalitic 5-year-old child. Kastein noted an awkward gait and otherwise poor co-ordination, including the tongue being curled when protruded, tongue elevation not possible, and articulation defective to the extent that the few of the child's words could be understood by the parents. Visual and auditory perception were also defective. The child could not recognize or match pictures and had a short attention span. Generally, the child had the symptoms of an aphasic brain injured child. Therapy included training in symbols, attention span, visual motor co-ordination, articulation muscle functions, the establishment of laterality, and parental guidance. She noted the child gained 11 points in IQ over a sixteen-month period. At the age of 8 years, 10 months, the child could use language well and could also make all the speech sounds. After therapy the child was able to go to a special school.

AUTISM

Scanlan, Leberfeld, and Freibrun (1963) detail the results of a language training program for eight autistic, retarded, non-verbal children CA 5 years, 2 months to 9 years, 6 months. The children were living at home and had an average of 47 sessions with a speech therapist. Therapy was oriented to training the child to respond to auditory and visual stimuli in the environment, to increase attention span, to decrease distractabiilty, to stimulate verbal comprehension and expression, to develop visual motor functions, and to develop bodily image. Qualitative findings suggested that a lack of development of receptive and expressive functions might be an important feature of at least some autistic cases. The authors stressed that adequate identification of perceptual language and speech deficits in autistic children was essential. They believed that the more therapy, the greater the extent of progress. The age at which the child began therapy did not seem crucial, although the authors felt older children might have progressed more rapidly had they begun treatment earlier.

The possibility of considering speech therapy for autistic children was suggested by a study of 63 autistic children (Eisenberg and Kanner, 1956). These children were re-evaluated at a mean CA of 15 years (they had been seen initially as pre-school children). Half of those who possessed meaningful language at the age of 5 improved. Only one of 31 children without ability to communicate at age 5 had improved significantly. Eisenberg and Kanner (1956) concluded that the failure to develop speech should be thought of as a measure of the extent of the autism.

PHENYLKETONURIA

Phenylketonuria (PKU) occurs approximately once in every 25,000 births and is transmitted as a simple Mendelian recessive trait. The disease usually results in severe mental retardation; however, according to Diedrich and Poser (1960), speech disorders (particularly language delay) may exist without severe retardation. Treatment of two sibling cases where a special diet was started at ages 3 and 4 resulted in marked improvement in language as well as in functional mentation. Speech pathologists should be certain that language-delayed children have been screened for PKU disorders.

FAMILIAL DYSAUTONOMIE

De Hirsch and Jansky (1956) detailed the speech, hearing, and language difficulties of twelve children in this category. The syndrome was characterized by vegetative dysfunctions, excessive perspiration, drooling, erythematous blotching of the skin, intermittent hypertension, diminished reflexes, and emotional instability. The most striking feature was the failure of the patient to produce normal quantities of tears when crying (defective lacrimation).

The twelve patients studied were CA 3 years, 6 months to 12 years, 10 months when first seen and were observed up to 21 months. Seven of them were slow in using words and eight were slow in using phrases. Swallowing, chewing, sucking, and breathing were frequently disordered. All of the children had difficulty in lip movement, eight had difficulty in tongue movement, eleven drooled, ten had voice quality and pitch differences. None of the children were found to have difficulty in hearing speech, but two had difficulty in understanding speech and seven had difficulty in auditory memory span. Six had difficulty in articulation, ten had difficulty in rate control, and five had difficulty in rhythm. Voice quality was often deviate.

CENTRAL NERVOUS SYSTEM DISORDERS

Worster-Drought (1953) reported speech difficulties in cases of congenital supra-bulbar agenesis. They noted weakness and spasticity of the lips, tongue, soft palate, and pharyngeal and laryngeal muscles, either separately or combined. Speech at times was extremely dysarthric with severe cases having immobile lips, tongue, and soft palate. Some children under study were able to protrude their tongue but were unable to curl it upwards, and lateral movement was impossible.

Peacher (1950) noted dysarthria and difficulty in swallowing in bilateral pyramidal lesions resulting from pseudo-bulbar palsy. Respiration and rhythm were involved if the pontine pathway was damaged. Bilabial and lingua-dental consonants and lingua-rugal sounds were most often distorted. Bulbar speech was usually described as flaccid. Rhythm difficulties were particularly frequent in cerebellar involvement. Defective articula-tion was most strongly related to pyramidal involvement and respiration and phonation disturbances were the result of basal ganglia difficulty.

Rutherford (1944) found that children with extra-pyramidal lesions had loud, low-pitched, irregular, monotonous, and aspirate speech. This problem was interpreted as due to respiratory difficulties. Zentay (1937) de-scribed corticostriopallidorubrobulbar track lesions affecting respiration, pitch, and rate of speech. At times this resulted in hyperkinesis of the vocal folds, involuntary movement of the diaphragm, and poor co-ordination, usually leading to a weak voice with variable pitch. In Robbins' (1940) discussion of patients with bulbar speech, he noted that they omitted syllables and had high-pitched, hoarse, monotonous, and nasal voices.

Characteristic motor difficulties in speech may be observed in specific central nervous system disorders, affecting any part of the speech mechanism depending on the site of neural damage.

MONGOLISM

Goertzen (1957) characterized language growth in the mongoloid child as limited and slow to develop. Articulation was often clumsy and difficult to understand; voice quality was hoarse with little pitch modulation. West, Ansberry, and Carr (1957) pointed out the structural anomalies of the lips, mouth, palate, teeth, external hair, tympanum, and eighth nerve in mongoloid children. The mongoloid child's voice was characterized as husky and monotonous, his auditory imagery as deficient and aphasia-like, and his rate as impeded by blocks and iterations. The authors did not believe this behavior should be called stutter-ing, since the mongoloid child was not embar-rassed by it and remissions were not seen in response to changes in social pressure.

MANAGEMENT AND THERAPY

NEED, PURPOSE, AND GOALS FOR THERAPY

Bibey (1951) observed mentally retarded children compensating for speech disorders by withdrawing, talking only in response to direct questions, avoiding direct speech, laughing inappropriately, and using stereotyped responses.

The need for speech improvement of the mentally retarded as identified by Bibey has not been met. One of the obstacles has been the identification of training goals for retardates. Strazzulla and Karlin (1952) indicated the aim is not necessarily to perfect speech but rather to develop useable language to the maximum of the child's ability. The term "realistic goals" of speech therapy for mentally retarded children is mentioned frequently in the literature. Often this means setting goals in regard to the child's history, intelligence level, motivation, co-ordination, environment, and organic structure for speech. Certainly many mentally retarded children have as good prognoses as individuals who are not retarded but who have poor structure, poor motivation, and poor environment. Assuming that all retarded children are poor therapy risks is not only unfair but is also illogical. For example, some poorly motivated but normally intelligent adult stutterers have poorer prognoses for better communication than a well-motivated, delayed-language, mentally retarded child. The criteria of motivation, organic structure, history, co-ordination, environment, and mental age can be used to decide whether to undertake therapy with individuals who are mentally retarded.

Several therapy approaches have been used with the mental retardate, including (1) formal skill training, involving drill, practice, and specific skills teaching, such as ear training in specific acoustic aspects of a desired sound or speech sound production; (2) communication-centered approaches, involving the use of speech related to objects, events, or activities the child may want to communicate about for speech practice; (3) unit teaching, where a given unit such as discussion of airplanes is used as a vehicle for teaching speech sounds; (4) environmental approaches, where the persons in the child's environment do not reward or reinforce defective speech when the child can produce an improved pattern of speech; and (5) speech improvement, involving formal training in a group setting on speech sound discrimination, speech sound production, and other skills related to good speech development.

Lassers and Low (1960) carried out communication-centered speech therapy with mentally retarded children whose IQs ranged from 40 to 79 and whose CAs ranged 7 to 15. Reproducing real life experiences, Lassers and Low attempted to meet the needs of the group by stimulating verbal and non-verbal activities and unifying the group. The therapists attempted to arrange conditions so that acceptable behavior would occur and then encouraged the child once it had occurred. Behavior that was unacceptable was not punished. The communicative therapy group showed significant improvement in articulation over the traditional therapy group and the control group.

Lubman (1955) carried out conventional individual therapy with 75 children once each week. Although the results were evaluated only qualitatively, the findings were that 62 of the children had improved under the program and that mongoloid children showed more rapid and permanent improvement than brain-injured children. Lubman's findings contrast sharply with the statement of West, Ansberry, and Carr (1957) regarding the futility of speech therapy with mongoloid children.

CASE LOAD, RECORD-KEEPING, ROLE WITH CO-WORKERS

The speech and hearing clinician's case load of children depends on many factors—the severity of the cases, the frequency of sessions and their length, the number of children seen each hour, the necessity to carry out other activities such as parent counseling, diagnosis of incoming cases, preparation of materials, and transportation to a number of settings, if required. Approximately five hours of case contact each day, including parent conferences and contact with other professionals, represents a maximum period, if time for preparation and record-keeping is to be allowed in the schedule. Assuming one day a week for program organization, special conferences, additional meetings with other professionals, and cases not regularly scheduled, a full-time speech and hearing clinician has a maximum number of 20 hours a week available for case contact. Obviously only seven children can be seen for three 60-minute periods a week on an individual basis with this amount of time available. Some children may require such a program of therapy that five 60-minute periods a week may be necessary. For most cases, however, a more usual practice is to schedule cases with similar problems into groups ranging in size from two to four for two 30-minute periods a week. Although scheduling should be flexible enough to meet the needs of atypical cases, a case load ranging from 30 to 50 children is not unreasonable. However, most speech and hearing clinicians who carry 50 cases a week have too little time for parental consultation. Diagnosis in regular schools is ordinarily carried out in September before scheduling therapy sessions. In institutions or special schools for the retarded, a similar practice seems appropriate with an occasional one-week break for new case scheduling. Allowing time for the clinician to participate in an out-patient diagnostic clinic is also a wise plan.

Record-keeping by the clinician ordinarily involves maintaining a 9″ x 12″ manila file folder for each case, with notes on each session regarding the child's speech, unusual problems involved (particularly adjustment), and progress reports. A case record form as suggested in Appendix A should also be kept in the file folder so that the child's problems in speech, language, and hearing status may be dealt with adequately.

The role of the speech and hearing clinician in working with other professionals such as classroom teachers, physicians, physiotherapists, attendants, and nurses needs to be well defined. Speech and hearing clinicians are fully trained professionals capable of carrying out their function without supervision of their work (although they may accept administrative supervision) by professionals in other fields. Although speech and hearing clinicians need medical evaluation on their cases before initiating therapy, their work is not medical in nature. Training a child to articulate correctly the S sound involves special teaching skills. Although many classroom teachers have done excellent and effective work in improving the speech of children, they have not been able to spend enough time with some other children to bring about success. However, classroom teachers are often very helpful in assisting speech and hearing clinicians in carrying over the child's new speech skills to his classroom speech behavior. The clinician can suggest to the teacher a system of reminder devices (such as waiting to respond to a child's speech attempts that are below his capabilities) when the child gets to the point where he can successfully maintain a newly learned sound in the classroom.

LANGUAGE, MANAGEMENT, AND THERAPY

The goals of speech therapy for mentally retarded children have been enumerated by Schneider and Vallon (1954). Typical goals should be: (1) to improve the appropriateness of the child's language; (2) to increase sentence length: (3) to build vocabulary; (4) to improve the syntax of the child's language; (5) to increase verbal output; and (6) to improve the child's receptive skills for comprehending language. Specific goals should be set for each retardate based on the level of language adequacy at the time. For example, expanding vocabulary for a child who has several hundred words but very poor syntax does not appear to be desirable. Likewise, the child who has no language ordinarily might have as his first goal the acquisition of a ten-word vocabulary (verbal mediation development as described by Carroll, 1964).

AUTISM APPROACHES

Mowrer (1960) has pointed out similarities in the language learning process for both birds and children. He believes that birds and children learn to talk as a result of association of pleasant feelings with language. They initiate speech to recall the pleasantness of having a reinforcing (talking) person about them. This line of thought has come to be known as the Autism Theory.

Rigrodsky and Steer (1961) evaluated the autism approach in improving articulation on the voiceless *th* and *v*. Although significant differences were not noted between this procedure and conventional procedures, their impression was that children in the experimental group became more spontaneously verbal and were more favorably inclined to the therapy sessions.

A major purpose of the autism approach is that of attaching pleasant associations to the sounds and words of language in the hope that the child will carry out his own practice as he attempts to duplicate and recall the pleasantness associated with speech by earlier experience.

OPERANT ANALYSES OF LANGUAGE

Skinner (1957) has pointed out how language is "shaped" on the basis of instating echoic behavior, "manding" reinforcements of chance de*mand*s and "tacting" (reinforcement of verbal demands to bring desired objects into con*tact*.) Skinner noted the withdrawal of aversive stimuli operates similarly to approval in language development. One of the present authors (CW) has observed that for children who are not on a schedule of reinforcement (severely and profoundly retarded and autistic), the first step should be to shape motor behavior, then to associate speech with it.

In view of the research reported by Schiefelbusch *et al.* (1963), it is easy to understand how language growth in mentally retarded children would be delayed in addition to or coincidentally with their retardation. The authors' findings indicated that the effect of the verbal level of the child on the listener, the type of situation in which the two are placed and the pre-instructions given to the listener have an effect on the language used to the child. Where such language stimulation is denied, initial echoic attempts (and later "manding" and "tacting") would appear to be inevitably held back. The poor performance of the retardate in language may thus be explained by the inadequate language stimulation he receives. Language stimulation should be planned to be slightly above the child's present level of language performance. Selective reinforcement should be used when the child makes appropriate responses.

Settings in which language stimulation can be useful are many. Such settings should involve language that is meaningful and useful to the child and represent a planned effort to build a specific vocabulary for him. He can talk quite well with 500 words, provided they are the right 500! Poor selection means that the words taught will not be reinforced frequently. Criteria for word selection should be the frequency with which the child will need the word and the possibility of his obtaining reinforcement for its use. The functional core vocabulary suggested by Borreca, Burger, Goldstein, and Sinches (1953) represents a good attempt at identifying a group of words that is appropriate for children with minimal language.

FACTORS INFLUENCING LANGUAGE DEVELOPMENT

Story reading, increased mothering, socio-economic level, health, and institutionalization have been shown to influence language development significantly in both retarded and normal children. These factors may be manipulated for therapeutic purposes; clues for ways of stimulating language growth may be inferred from factors that hold back growth. For example, Irwin (1960) found that reading stories to young children ages 13 to 30 months brought about significant increases in phoneme frequency over children who did not have stories read to them. Similarly, Irwin (1952) observed significantly higher phoneme frequencies among children of high socio-economic parents (professional-business-clerical workers) than among children of low socio-economic parents (laborers). Irwin (1952) also found that infants living in their own homes were more advanced on these variables than infants living in orphanages.

Schlanger (1954) found language output of institutionalized children was significantly low compared with matched peers. Apparently the institutional environment, separation from the parents, or some other factor has a significant effect on lowering language output of institutionalized children. Increased mothering of institutionalized children has been shown to have a significantly beneficial effect by McKinney and Kelly (1963). Forty-eight severely retarded boys (CA 8 to 18 years) with social quotients of 5 to 55 (and with the majority an IQ of 30 and below) were given twelve "mothers," who were selected from 20 mildly retarded residents of the institution. The "mothers," whose IQs ranged from 42 to 80 and CAs from 17 to 75, each chose two adopted boys and spent at least four hours a day five days a week for four weeks with them. Significant improvements in "blabbering" and meaningful use of words was found among the children at the .01 level of confidence.

The significance of good health in language development was noted by Meader (1940). He concluded that good health, nutrition, and adequate experience are crucial in the development of infant early childhood language and speech skills.

PARENTAL ASSISTANCE

Strazzulla (1954) and Molloy (1961) present useful approaches to language teaching for parents working with their children. Webb and Holland (1963) also present helpful information as well as specific teaching suggestions for the parents. Among the suggestions are: (1) to continue reinforcement of words until they are well established; (2) to reinforce the child's best response irrespective of the adequacy of articulation; (3) to provide continued opportunity for the child to use the new word in a meaningful context; (4) to plan the language teaching approach on the basis of the child's mental age rather than his size or chronological age; (5) to avoid demanding language of the child, continuing instead to stimulate him with the same word over and over in a pleasant way until he begins to use the word on his own; and (6) to use meaningful reinforcements appropriate to the child such as smiling, attentive listening, cogent verbal responses, and verbal approval.

ARTICULATION MANAGEMENT

The developmental nature of articulation complicates the problem of clearly identifying the speech sound goals for a given child. Speech sound development follows mental age until by the age of 8 most children have succeeded in achieving articulation without consistent errors (Van Riper, 1963). Motor and perceptual difficulties can delay development. The child with cerebral palsy, hearing loss, or dysarthria is often significantly below this age expectation.

Gross to Fine Articulation Training. In shaping behavior of organisms, as Skinner has pointed out (1957), one must begin with opposites that the organism can clearly differentiate. For example, in teaching auditory differentiation the difference between a drum and a whistle represents a fairly easy (gross) discrimination. Although this discrimination is of little value in differentiating a lateral S from an acoustically adequate S for speech purposes, it represents a beginning in the development of auditory discrimination sufficient to make such a differentiation. Steps should be planned on the basis of the gross to fine concept in

auditory skills, speech sound articulation, and other aspects of teaching improved speech. A sequence intended to culminate in discrimination of good S sounds might approximate this:

1. The difference between presence and absence of S.
2. The difference between S and R.
3. The difference between S and SH.
4. The difference between a loud S and a quiet S.
5. The difference between a lateral S and a frontal (lingual) S.
6. The difference between a good S and a lateral S.

Differentiation usually can be taught more rapidly against a background of noise or light with the noise or light being associated initially with the defective sound. Once discriminative hearing has occurred gradual fading of the noise or light leaves the desired discrimination intact.

Specific Articulation Improvement Techniques. Many techniques are available to aid speech sound training. The following ones appear to be especially useful with retarded children and adults. The work of Holland and Matthews (1963) illustrates the utility of programming auditory discrimination of S for children without mental retardation. Auditory discrimination of S was learned faster by machine programming than by teaching from a speech clinician. The indications are that speech sounds, combinations of speech sounds, and discrimination of sounds could be taught well with programmed learning. Recorded exercises requiring verbal responses of the child might significantly improve the efficiency and effectiveness of our training. These might involve the use of stories such as those prepared by Nemoy and Davis (1954) and the use of unusual or unique stimuli to attract attention to the tape with short presentations of the speech sounds to be learned presented on tape at intermittent intervals and at varying loudness levels.

Unit teaching offers another planned approach to articulation improvement. Webb and Parnell (1960) have suggested this approach for use with non-retarded children. Kinde (1962) has developed a "dairy farm" unit for this purpose that can be adapted easily for retarded children. One of its advantages is that the child may be able to build a number of new words and modify old words around a given central topic, which serves as a discriminated stimulus to the child signalling him to modify his articulation when he encounters something related to the given topic. Once the child achieves articulation adequacy in talking about a single topic, carry over to additional topics takes place more readily.

Motokinesthetic approaches may also be useful in bringing about articulation improvement. The use of manipulation of the articulatory organs or interference with old motor sequences with tongue depressors, toothpicks, zonds (wire frameworks to guide the tongue in producing a given sound as described by Clark (1961)), straws, gum, and caramels, all have the common function of modifying the child's articulatory pattern so that he can then attempt a new way of producing the sound. These procedures are most useful in cases where the old motor pattern is so strongly fixated the child does not modify it even though he recognizes it as incorrect.

Ear training, that is, the training of the child in clearly identifying the acoustic characteristics of the correct sound, identifying the differences between the incorrect and correct sound, and stimulating the child with the new desired sound, is perhaps the most universally used approach in articulation improvement. Its efficacy can be improved by the suggestions given by Van Riper (1963). Essentially these involve increasing the vividness, uniqueness, and contrast of the acoustic characteristics of the "old" and the "new" sound.

Need for Prevention and Organized Therapy. Even with children who are not retarded, articulation therapy often extends over a period of years rather than months. Prevention is thought to be much more effective than therapy. Certainly in cases when early consultation can be attained regarding the child's development of articulation patterns this is true. Such prevention consultation may involve recommendations on the child's feeding, the way the parents stimulate his speech development, and the way his speech attempts are reinforced. Suggestions for developing the child's developing perceptual and motor skills by games such as Van Riper (1952) recommended may be unusually useful in prevention of articulatory disorders in retarded children.

Therapy should help build the child's feelings of security so that he will speak freely in a dyad setting and in a group. Planning should include teaching of desirable reinforcements for good speech efforts, sequential planning for training (from speech sounds to words to sentences to connected conversation), relating good speech attempts to communication efforts rather than "for show," and participation of others in the child's environment to provide an enjoyable speech environment for the child.

VOICE MANAGEMENT

Very little voice training has been attempted with the mentally retarded. For that matter, formal evaluation of voice therapy is rare in the professional literature whether it deals with retarded or normal children. Certainly the frequent laryngeal infections, the high rate of organic differences found in some sub-groups of the mentally retarded, and vocal strain and abuse of laryngeal areas provide adequate explanations for the high rate of vocal anomalies found by Schlanger (1953b).

Peacher (1947) detailed the results of vocal re-education on patients with contact ulcer of the larynx. She found four of six patients returned to normal with cessation of all symptoms after vocal re-education. Significant improvement was shown in the other two cases as a result of vocal re-education. Patients in the control group who did not receive therapy continued to have difficulty.

The management of voice cases should include checking of pitch range to determine whether the optimal pitch is being used, observation of possible excess tension in the throat muscles, and an analysis of whether the muscles usually used for swallowing are being used during phonation. Some individuals have been observed elevating the larynx as if they were swallowing when they attempted to produce vocal sounds. Ability to discriminate the specific problem both by auditory and kinesthetic means, ability to change the voice in the direction of improvement, and the effect of special influences (such as distraction, pitch change, noise, and emotion) should be determined. The effect of relaxation by means of whispering, yawning, lying down, sighing, or wakening also is frequently valuable in planning a training program.

Hoarseness was the first symptom of laryngeal cancer in 93 per cent of 144 cases observed by Zinn (1945). Yet hoarseness is not necessarily a sign of cancer. Williamson (1946) observed and carried out voice training with 72 cases of hoarse voice, none of which had a pathological origin.

General goals for therapy should include teaching the individual to be aware of the error and the need to change, training him to discriminate the difference by auditory means, and teaching him to produce the new voice easily.

HEARING MANAGEMENT

Although few retarded children likely receive routine hearing screening on an annual basis, the reported incidence of hearing loss in this population makes it appear warranted. If such children were identified early in life, medical, surgical, and educational treatments probably could be provided and many hearing losses avoided. Language learning, educational progress, psychological adjustment, vocational training, and social adjustment would be much improved for such children.

Many retardates can be adequately tested with pure tone audiometric procedures. A screening program could be operated similar to the regular public school hearing screening programs already in operation in most states.

Assuming that a hearing conservation program identifies retarded children with auditory problems, appropriate training can be expected to be difficult with this group, since the major avenue of learning—hearing—is impaired in a group whose skill in learning is also impaired. The probabiliy of their being able to compensate for their hearing defect by other modalities is much less than with other children. The major recommended procedures for hearing habilitation include hearing aids, auditory training, lip reading, and psychological approaches.

Hearing Aids. Hearing aids have been shown to work much more successfully with younger children than with older children. Sortini (1959) found that there was a marked difference in success in getting children below age 3 to wear hearing aids compared with those fitted at a later age. His impression was that

language development, behavior, and personality benefit significantly from early hearing aids and their application in training. Rushford and Lowell (1960) found that early fitting of the hearing aid (in their survey of 1,515 families with young deaf children) resulted in more usage of the hearing aid if the aid was purchased when the child was under 2½. Of the children surveyed, 68 per cent wore a hearing aid all day if it was fitted under age 2½. Only 19 per cent wore the aid all day if it was purchased between 8.5 to 9.4 years. Hearing aid usage with mentally retarded (Hartmann, 1958) resulted in upward habilitation of six mentally retarded patients (CA 16 to 27). Subsequent improvement in ability to communicate was observed.

As hearing testing procedures are used more widely with the retarded, earlier identification of cases with hearing deficit will be possible. Resolution of the problems of obtaining and fitting hearing aids and subsequently assisting the child to wear the aid throughout the day will be needed. However, these problems have often been encountered with children not identified as mentally retarded and have been resolved at early ages.

The ideal time for hearing aid fitting and selection should be under age 3. At that time the child will adapt to the hearing aid provided the aid is introduced with favorable activities for short periods of time. When the child realizes he can use the information delivered via the hearing aid for things meaningful to him, problems of wearing the aid usually are resolved.

More serious problems arise with cases who have already developed behavioral problems and are beyond a reinforcement schedule for purposes of training. These cases may require positioning the teacher in a sound isolated booth and using free-field amplification to the child (Nichols, 1963). This should only be done at times favorable to the child with appropriate reinforcement of use of the sound on his part. One way to accomplish this is through the use of recorded music over a public address system, with the teacher and perhaps other children responding by gestures, walking, marching, or clapping in time to the music. The child who responds appropriately to the music is rewarded by smiles and attention. The basic principle underlying such training is the association of pleasurable events with the significance of sound. The child who learns to want to hear has little difficulty employing a hearing aid.

Auditory Training. Part of successful hearing habilitation is to train the child in interpreting sound. Of course, this is a learned skill that some children with normal hearing do not fully utilize. A continuum of growth of auditory discrimination exists.

Auditory discrimination is sometimes taught with young hard-of-hearing (and deaf) children by means of gross noise makers such as a drum. The child may march when the drum is beating and stop when it stops. After he has learned to discriminate the presence of sound from its absence, he then may be taught to discriminate between two or more noise makers. Ultimately discrimination of speech (which is viewed as fine discrimination) is taught. Such discrimination of speech may involve contrasting quite different sounds or words initially. For example, the words "food" and "banana" have relatively great acoustic differences whereas "nose" and "toes" sound alike. Preferential seating so the child is nearer to the speaker is ordinarily helpful as well.

Lip Reading. Lip reading is thought to be an invaluable adjunct to hearing, enabling a child or an adult to compensate for his acoustic impairment through another channel of sensory communication, vision. A clinician can teach it to non-language children by calling attention to his mouth for phrases that are readily interpretable by the children. For example, at the end of a session, the phrase "it is time to go now" spoken repeatedly over a period of several meetings can be recognized by young children as distinct from other phrases used during the hour. With older children, the use of contrasting phrases and questions in context facilitates early skill in the recognition of what is said. Words such as "luck" and "lug" are difficult to tell apart, whereas "where" and "now" are easier to learn. Teachers of lip reading incorporate the use of contextual clues with meaningful words and phrases and a consistent approach to the introduction of speech sounds. In this way the child learns to recognize all speech sounds and has special attention on each of them.

Psychological Approaches. The psychological effects of deafness or hearing loss should not be overlooked. A child may isolate himself completely unless attempts are made to include him in group activities. Insecurity regarding what other people are talking about and excess strain and tension because of the necessity to concentrate continually in order to communicate often contribute to psychological problems. Once the problem is identified, compensatory efforts on the part of persons in the child's environment should be made. Making certain the child understands, controlling adults' emotional reactions when he does not hear something, and including the child in groups are important aspects of psychological management of such children.

APPENDIX A

Speech, Hearing, and Language Record

IDENTIFYING DATA

Name   Age   Birthdate   Sex
Date first seen   Date of subsequent entries (Use another color pencil to
indicate date and for other entries)

Address   Parent or guardian   Phone
Examiner   School
Teacher (Date entries)
Grade (Date entries)
Major speech problem   Secondary speech problem, if any
Other problems

SPEECH, LANGUAGE, AND HEARING FACTORS (Complete only where applicable)

ARTICULATION (Circle defective sound, when corrected mark sound X and date)
Templin words

*su*n	*k*ite	*cl*ock	brea*the*
*sp*oon	*g*oat	sol*d*ier	ca*r*
*z*ipper	*f*ork	ma*tch*es	*cr*eam
*th*umb	va*c*uum	fla*sh*light	ba*ll*
*th*ere	bi*c*ycle	chi*ck*en	*gl*asses
re*c*ord	*st*ar	ti*g*er	ora*ng*e
*tr*ee	*sc*i*ss*ors	ele*ph*ant	wa*tch*
*l*amb	*t*oo*th*bru*sh*	en*v*elope	fi*sh*
air*pl*ane	fea*th*er	bu*s*	*sn*ake
*j*acks	*c*a*rr*ot	*squ*irrel	*p*i*g*
*ch*air	*dr*um	ho*se*	kni*fe*
*sh*oe	ba*ll*oon	tee*th*	*st*ove

Total Sounds Defective

Blends (list)   Vowels (list)

Estimated % of consistency of errors

Templin score   Normal cut-off for age level on Templin

Estimated intelligibility % understood

STUTTERING   (check)

Repetitions   Prolongations   Hesitations   Speech Muscles Tension

Phase 1   Phase 2   Phase 3

Episodic   Chronic   Some sits. more diff.

Initial word/sentence   Esp. on fast   Word subs., sound difficult

Small words   Major words   anticipates

Chara. symptom repetition   Reacts as a   Little fear-embarrass

Pressure increases   stutterer but

Speaks freely   speaks freely

Phase 4

Vivid anticipation of stutt.   1—Normally Frequent

Special diff. in response to various   2—Possible Problem
  sounds, words, sit., listeners   3—Definite Problem

Frequent word substitutions   Partword repetitions   1 2 3

Avoids speech   Word repetitions   1 2 3

Fear and embarrassment   Phrase repetitions   1 2 3

                                 Prolonged sounds   1 2 3

                                 Unvocalized intervals   1 2 3

List secondary characteristics below

Attitude toward stuttering (good)   1 2 3 4 5   (poor)

VOICE (Use read passage if possible)

1—Acceptable   2—Possible Problem   3—Definite Problem

Loudness	1	2	3
Pitch	1	2	3
Nasality	1	2	3
Breathy	1	2	3
Harsh	1	2	3
Hoarse	1	2	3
Glottal attack	1	2	3

1—Improvement   2—Possible Improvement   3—No Improvement

Result of pitch change   1 2 3

Result of loudness change   1 2 3

Check: Hard attack   Infrequent pitch breaks   Frequent pitch breaks   Whispering
   interspersed   Tremulous   Can sing up and down scale   Can imitate
   inflectional patterns   Number of tones in total pitch range   Number of tones
   habitual pitch level above lowest tone   Number of tones discrepancy between habitual
   and optimal pitch   Quality changed under: Sustained vowels   oral reading

Recognition of voice difference and motivation for improvement

(good)   1 2 3 4 5   (poor)

over-all severity of voice problem

(normal)   1 2 3 4 5   (extremely severe)

LANGUAGE

Vocabulary score on IQ test: Score   Test

Scores on PPVT   Scores on Mecham test

Estimate of language adequacy by teacher-percentile rank (100—best)

No response	1 2 3	Lack of spontaneity in verbalization	1 2 3
Brief responses	1 2 3	Excessive verbal output	1 2 3
Responses slow	1 2 3	Glib use of platitudes and cliches	1 2 3
Responses irrelevant	1 2 3	Limited vocabulary	1 2 3

50 utterance mean length

HEARING

BEA   REA   LEA   Discrimination   SRT

Whisper test   Tuning forks

Bone conduction test

Auditory memory span   1 2 3

Able to discriminate auditory aspects of the problem   1 2 3

250   500   1000   4000   8000
10
20
30
40
50
60
70
80
90
100

PHYSICAL FACTORS

List diseases and dates

PKU test result
Allergies
Anemia
Glandular problem
Chronic colds
Ear disease
Chronic laryngitis

Respiratory: Breath supply		Teeth
Muscular tensions		Lips
Larynx:		Tongue
History of growths		Hard palate
Inflammations		Soft palate
Pain		Gag reflex
Resonators:		Uvula
Palatal closure	1 2 3	Walk straight line
Size of velopharyngeal space	1 2 3	Swallowing
		Blowing balloon

Presence of reverse swallowing and/or tongue thrust (describe)

Presence of nasal emission (Describe)

Diadochokinetic rate pata   /5 sec. pataka   /5 sec.

Comments from physician

ENVIRONMENTAL FACTORS   (Circle: 1—Best,   5—Poorest)

Socio-economic status in community   1 2 3 4 5

Educational status in the school   1 2 3 4 5

Age began babbling   Amount   First word

2-word combinations   Early speech stimulation (describe)

Need as a child for speech	1 2 3	Estimate of parent-child relationship	1 2 3
Adequacy of speech models	1 2 3	Estimate of sibling-child relationship	1 2 3

Reward for speech	1 2 3	Speech ability of family	1 2 3
Prenatal		Grades failed	
Birth		Marks received	
Feeding		Problem areas	
Sitting		Social acceptance	
Walking		Father's occupation	
Handedness			

PSYCHOLOGICAL FACTORS   (Circle: 1—Best,   5—Poorest)

Estimated personal/social adjustment from Johnson/Darley, Spriestersbach (p. 147) questionnaire   1 2 3 4 5

Goodenough IQ   PPVT IQ   WISC IQ

Vineland IQ   C.A.T. results

Parental attitude to school   1 2 3 4 5 to speech   1 2 3 4 5

Child's attitude to school   1 2 3 4 5 to speech   1 2 3 4 5

Presence of suspected problem areas (Describe)

OVER-ALL PROGNOSIS AND SEVERITY   (Circle: 1—Good,   5—Poor)

Rating of prognosis for good speech   1 2 3 4 5

Rating of severity of speech/hearing/language problem   1 2 3 4 5

PROGRESS IN THERAPY

Entries   Progress notes

Date

Release date

Recommend rechecks on

(Rate each recheck: 1—completely OK,   5—definitely not OK)

First recheck   1 2 3 4 5

Second recheck   1 2 3 4 5

Third recheck   1 2 3 4 5

Final recheck date   1 2 3 4 5

REFERENCES

ANDERSON, R. M., and MILES, M. Childrens Hospital, Denver, 1963. Unpublished paper.

BADT, M. I. Levels of abstraction in vocabulary definitions of mentally retarded school children. *Amer. J. ment. Defic.*, 1958, *63*, 241–246.

BANGS, J. L. A clinical analysis of the articulatory defects of the feebleminded. *J. sp. Dis.*, 1942, *7*, 343–356.

BARR, B. Pure tone audiometry for pre-school children. *Acta Otolaryng.*, Supplement, 1955, *121*, 5–82.

BATZA, E. M. Investigation of speech and oral language behavior of educable mentally retarded children. Unpublished dissertation, Northwestern University, 1956.

BECKEY, R. E. A study of certain factors related to retardation of speech. *J. sp. Dis.*, 1942, *7*, 223–249.

BENDER, C. E. *Mongolism and cretinism.* New York: Grune and Stratton, 1949.

BIBEY, L. A. A rationale of speech therapy for mentally deficient children. *Train. Schl. Bull.*, 1951, 236–239.

BIJOU, S. W., and WERNER, H. Language analyses in brain-injured and non-brain injured mentally deficient children. *J. genet. Psychol.*, 1954, *66*, 239–254.

BINET, A., and SIMON, TH. *Mentally defective children.* Boston: Longmans, Green, 1914.

BIRCH, J. W., and MATTHEWS, H. The hearing of mental defectives: Its measurement and characteristics. *Amer. J. ment. Defic.*, 1951, *55*, 348–393.

BLANCHARD, I. Speech patterns and etiology in mental retardation. *Amer. J. ment. Defic.*, 1964, *68*, 612–617.

BLOODSTEIN, O. The development of stuttering: II. Developmental phases. *J. sp. hear. Dis.*, 1960, *25*, 366–376.

BORRECA, F., BURGER, R., GOLDSTEIN, I., and SINCHES, R. A. Functional core vocabulary for slow learners. *Amer. J. ment. Defic.*, 1953, *58*, 273–300.

BRADLEY, E., EVANS, W. E., and WORTHINGTON, A. M. An investigation of hearing loss in mentally retarded children and adults. *Amer. J. ment. Defic.*, 1955, *60*, 346–352.

BRANDFON, W. Speech problems of the mentally retarded child: A study based on case histories. Unpublished masters thesis, Louisiana State University, 1951.

BURT, C. *The backward child.* Appleton-Century, 1937.

CARLTON, T., and CARLTON, L. E. Oral English errors of normal children and of mental defectives. *Elem. Schl. J.*, 1945, *45*, 340–348. (a)

———, ———. Errors in the oral language of mentally defective adolescents and normal elementary children. *J. genet. Psychol.*, 1945, *56*, 183–220. (b)

CARROLL, J. B. *Language and thought.* New York: Prentice-Hall, 1964.

CHUN, R., PAWSAT, R., and FORSTER, F. Sound localization of infants. *J. nerv. ment. Dis.*, 1960, *130*, 472.

CLARK, R. Speech pathology (LogoPedics) in the USSR. *ASHA*, 1961, *3*, 43–45.

COPELAND, R. The effects of feedback modification on verbal behavior. In R. L. Schiefelbusch (Ed.), *Language studies of mentally retarded children. J. sp. hear. Dis. mon. Suppl.*, No. 10, 1963.

CURRY, E. T., and KURTZROCK, G. H. A preliminary investigation of the ear-choice technique in threshold audiometry. *J. sp. hear. Dis.*, 1951, *16*, 340–345.

DAVIS, D. M. The relation of repetitions in the speech of young children to certain measures of language maturity and situational factors: Part I. *J. sp. Dis.*, 1939, *4*, 308–318.

DAVIS, H., and SILVERMAN, S. *Hearing and deafness.* New York: Holt, Rinehart and Winston, 1960.

DeHIRSCH, K., and JANSKY, J. Language investigation of children suffering from familial dysautonomie. *J. sp. hear. Dis.*, 1956, *21*, 450–460.

DEMPSEY, M., DRAGGART, G., SISKIND, R., and STEER, M. The Purdue pitch meter—A direct-reading fundamental frequency analyzer. *J. sp. hear Dis.*, 1950, *15*, 135–141.

DERBYSHIRE, A., and McCANDLESS, G. Template for EEG response to sound. *J. sp. hear. Res.*, 1964, *7*, 96–98.

DIEDRICH, W. M., and POSER, C. M. Language and mentation of two phenyl-ketonuric children. *J. sp. hear. Dis.*, 1960, *25*, 124–234.

DIEHL, C., and McDONALD, E. Effect of voice quality on communication. *J. sp. hear. Dis.*, 1956, *21*, 233–237.

DIX, M., and HALLPIKE, C. The peep show: A new technique for pure tone audiometry in young children. *Brit. med. J.*, 1947, *2*, 719–723.

EISENBERG, L. The autistic child in adolescence. *Amer. J. Psychiat.*, 1956, *112*, 607–612.

———— and KANNER, L. Early infantile autism, 1943–1955. *Amer. J. Ortho-psychiat.*, 1956, *26*, 556–566.

EVERHART, R. W. The relationship between articulation and other develop-mental factors in children. *J. sp. hear. Dis.*, 1953, *18*, 332–338.

FEIFEL, H., and LORGE, I. Qualitative differences in the vocabulary responses of children. *J. educ. Psychol.*, 1950, *41*, 1–18.

FOALE, M., and PATERSON, J. W. The hearing of mental defectives. *Amer. J. ment. Defic.*, 1954, *59*, 254–258.

FRISINA, R. D. Measurement of hearing in children. In Jerber, J. (Ed.), *Modern developments in audiology.* New York: Academic Press, 1963.

GESELL, A., and ARMATRUDA, C. *Developmental diagnosis.* New York: Har-per (Hoeber), 1948.

GLASNER, P., and ROSENTHAL, D. Parental diagnosis of stuttering in young children. *J. sp. hear. Dis.*, 1957, *22*, 288–295.

GODA, S. Vocal utterances of young moderately and severely retarded non-speaking children. *Amer. J. ment. Defic.*, 1957, *62*, 244–253.

GOERTZEN, S. M. Speech and the mentally retarded child. *Amer. J. ment. Defic.*, 1957, *62*, 244–253.

GOTTSLEBEN, R. H. The incidence of stuttering in a group of mongoloids. *Train. Schl. Bull.*, 1955, *51*, 208–218.

GRIFFITH, B. C., and SPITZ, H. Some relationships between abstraction and word meaning in retarded adolescents. *Amer. J. ment. Defic.*, 1958, *63*, 247–251.

HALE, L. A consideration of thiamin supplement in prevention of stuttering in pre-school children. *J. sp. hear. Dis.*, 1951, *16*, 327–333.

HANSOM, E. M. An exploratory study of the effect of thiamin hydrochloride on adults who stutter. Unpublished masters thesis, Ohio State University, 1951.

HARDY, W. G. The relation between impaired hearing and feeblemindedness. *The nerv. Child.*, October 1948, *7*, 432–445.

HARTMAN, B. T. A study of therapeutic and functional values of hearing aids for the mentally handicapped. *Amer. J. ment. Defic.*, 1958, *62*, 803–809.

HESS, J., MOHR, G., and BARTELME, P. *The physical and mental growth of prematurely born children.* University of Chicago Press, 1934.

HILL, H. Stuttering: I. Critical review and evaluation of biochemical investi-gations. *J. sp. hear. Dis.*, 1944, *9*, 245–261.

HOLLAND, A., and MATTHEWS, J. Application of teaching machine concepts to speech pathology and audiology. *ASHA*, 1963, *5*, 474–482.

IRWIN, O. E. Speech development in the young child: 2. Some factors related to speech development in the infant and young child. *J. sp. hear. Dis.*, 1952, *17*, 269–279.

————. Infant speech: Effect of systematic reading of stories. *J. sp. hear. Res.*, 1960, *3*, 187–190.

JOHNSON, G. O., CAPOBIANCO, R., and MILLER, D. Speech and language de-velopment and mentally deficient children enrolled in training programs. *Excep. Child.*, 1960, *27*, 72–77.

JOHNSON, W. *Stuttering and what you can do about it.* University of Minne-sota, 1961.

————, DARLEY, F., and SPRIESTERSBACH, D. C. *Diagnostic methods in speech pathology.* New York: Harper, 1963.

JOHNSTON, P., and FARRELL, M. An experiment in improving medical and educational services for hard of hearing children at the Walter E. Fernald State School. *Amer. J. ment. Defic.*, 1957, *62*, 230–237.

Jordan, T. E. Language and mental retardation: Empirical and conceptual considerations. In Schiefelbusch, R., and Smith, J. (Eds.), *Research in speech and hearing for mentally retarded children*. U.S. Office of Education #FO10, 1963.

———— and deCharms, R. The achievement motive in nomal and retarded children. *Amer. J. ment. Defic.*, 1959, *64*, 457–466.

Karlin, I. W., and Kennedy, L. Delay in the development of speech. *Amer. J. Dis. Child.*, 1936, *51*, 1138–1149.

———— and Strazzulla, M. Speech and language problems of mentally deficient children. *J. sp. hear. Dis.*, 1952, *17*, 286–294.

Kastein, S. Speech and language habilitation in a post-encephalitic child. *Amer. J. ment. Defic.*, 1952, *56*, 570–577.

Kennedy, L. Studies in the speech of the feebleminded. Unpublished doctoral dissertation, University of Wisconsin, 1930.

Kinde, S. A unit approach to speech therapy. Unpublished masters thesis, Central Michigan University, 1962.

Kirk, S. A., and McCarthy, J. J. The Illinois test of psycholinguistic abilities —An approach to differential diagnosis. *Amer. J. ment. Defic.*, 1961, *66*, 399–412.

Kodman, F. The incidence of hearing loss in mentally retarded children. *Amer. J. ment. Defic.*, 1958, *62*, 675–678.

————, Fein, A., and Mixson, A. Psychogalvanic skin response audiometry with severely retarded children. *Amer. J. ment. Defic.*, 1959, *64*, 131–136.

Kodman, F., Jr., Powers, T., Phillip, P., and Weller, G. M. An investigation of hearing loss in mentally retarded children and adults. *Amer. J. ment. Defic.*, 1958, *63*, 460–463.

Kolstoe, O. P. Language training of low-grade mongoloid children. *Amer. J. ment. Defic.*, 1958, *63*, 17–30.

Lassers, L., and Low, G. *A study of the relative effectiveness of different approaches of speech therapy and mentally retarded children; final report.* U.S. Office of Education, Cooperative Research Program #6904, 1960.

Lewald, J. Speech defects as found in a group of five hundred mental defectives. *Proc. Amer. Assoc. Study Feebleminded*, 1932, *56*, 291–301.

Lowell, E. L., Troffer, C. I., Warburton, E. A., and Rushford, G. M. Temporal evannation: A new approach in diagnostic audiometry. *J. sp. hear., Dis.*, 1960, *25*, 340–345.

————, Williams, C. T., Ballinger, R. M., and Alvig, D. P. Measurement of auditory thresholds with special purpose analog computer. *J. sp. hear. Res.*, 1961, *4*, 105–112.

Lubman, Charlotte. Speech program for severely retarded children. *Amer. J. ment. Defic.*, 1955, *60*, 297–300.

Luria, A. R. *The mentally retarded child*. New York: Pergamon Press, 1963.

Lyle, J. G. Some factors affecting the speech development of imbecile children in an institution. *J. Child psychol. Psychiat.*, 1960, *2*, 121–129.

McCandless, G. A., and Best, L. Evoked responses to auditory stimuli in man using a summing computer. *J. sp. hear. Res.*, 1964, *7*, 193–201.

McCarthy, D. Language development in children. In Carmichael, L., (Ed.), *Manual of child psychology*. New York: John Wiley and Sons, 1954.

MacDonald, E. T. *Articulation testing and treatment: A sensory-motor approach*. Pittsburgh: Stanwix House, 1964.

McKinney, J., and Kelly, T. The effects of increased mothering on the behavior of severely retarded boys. *Amer. J. Ment. Defic.*, 1963, *67*, 556–562.

MATTHEWS, J. Speech problems of the mentally retarded. In Travis, R. (Ed.), *Handbook of speech pathology*. New York: Appleton-Century-Crofts, 1957.

MEADER, M. H. The effect of disturbances in the developmental processes upon emergent specificity or function. *J. sp. Dis.*, 1940, *5*, 211–220.

MECHAM, M. J. The development and application of procedures for measuring speech improvement in mentally defective children. *Amer. J. ment. Defic.*, 1955, *60*, 301–306.

————. Developmental schedules of oral-aural language as an aid to the teacher of the mentally retarded. *Mental Retardation*, 1963, 359–369.

————, COURTNEY, S., and SODERBERG, G. Effects of tolserol on the speech errors of mentally defective children. *Amer. J. psychol. Med.*, 1955, *34*, 535–536.

MEIN, R. A study of the oral vocabularies of several subnormal patients: II. Grammatical analysis of speech samples. *J. ment. Defic. Res.*, 1961, *5*, 52–62.

———— and O'CONNOR, N. A Study of the oral vocabularies of severely subnormal patients. *J. ment. Defic. Res.*, 1960, *4*, 130–143.

MICHEL, J., and CARNEY, R. Pitch characteristics of mongoloid boys. *J. sp. hear. Dis.*, 1964, *29*, 121–125.

MOLLOY, J. *Teaching the retarded child to talk.* New York: John Day, 1961.

MOSS, J., MOSS, M., and TIZARD, J. Electrodermal response audiometry with mentally defective children. *J. sp. hear. Res.*, 1961, *4*, 41–47.

MOWRER, O. *Learning theory and the symbolic process.* New York: John Wiley and Sons, 1960.

NEMOY, E., and DAVIS, S. *The correction of defective consonant sounds.* Magnolia, Mass.: Expression Co., 1954.

NEWBY, H. *Audiology,* New York: Appleton-Century-Crofts, 1964.

NICHOLS, W. Personal communication, 1963.

O'CONNOR, N., and HERMELIN, B. Some effects of word learning in imbeciles. *Lang-Speech.* 1959, *2*, 63–71.

O'NEILL, J., OYER, H., and HILLIS, J. Audiometric procedures used with children. *J. sp. hear. Dis.*, 1961, *26*, 61–66.

PALASEK, J., and CURTIS, W. Sugar placebos and stuttering. *J. sp. hear. Res.*, 1960, *3*, 223–226.

PAPANIA, N. A. Qualitative analysis of vocabulary responses of institutionalized mentally retarded children. *J. clin. Psychol.*, 1954, *10*, 361–365.

PEACHER, G. Contact ulcer of the larynx. Part 4: A clinical study of vocal reeducation. *J. sp. Dis.*, 1947, *12*, 179–190.

PEACHER, W. The etiology and differential diagnosis of dysarthria. *J. sp. hear. Dis.*, 1950, *15*, 252–265.

RIGRODSKY, S., and GODA, S. Language behavior of a group of non-speaking brain-damaged mentally retarded children. *Train. Schl. Bull.*, 1951, *58*, 52–60.

————, PRUNT, F., and GLOUSKY, L. A study of the incidence, types and associated etiologies of hearing loss in an institutionalized mentally retarded population. *Train. Schl. Bull.*, 1961, *58*, 30–34.

———— and STEER, M. D. Mowrer's theory applied to speech habilitation of the mentally retarded. *J. sp. Dis.*, 1961, *26*, 237–243.

RITTMANIC, P. A. Hearing rehabilitation for the institutionalized mentally retarded. *Amer. J. ment. Defic.*, 1959, *63*, 778–783.

ROBBINS, S. Dysarthria and its treatment. *J. sp. Dis.*, 1940, *5*, 113–120.

RUSHFORD, J., and LOWELL, E. Use of hearing aids by young children. *J. sp. hear. Res.*, 1960, *3*, 354–560.

Rutherford, B. A comparative study of loudness, pitch, rate, rhythm and avality of speech of children handicapped by cerebral palsy. *J. sp. Dis.*, 1944, *9*, 263–271.

Sachs, M. H. A survey and evaluation of the existing interrelationships between speech and mental deficiencies. Masters thesis, University of Virginia. Reported by Eisenson, J., The nature of defective speech, in *Psychology of exceptional children and youth*. New York: Prentice-Hall, 1955.

Sander, E. Frequency of syllable repetition and "stutterer" judgments. *J. sp. hear. Dis.*, 1963, *28*, 19–30.

Scanlan, J. B., Leberfeld, D. T., and Freibrun, R. Language training in the treatment of the autistic child functioning on a retarded level. *Mental Retardation*, 1963, *1*, 305–310.

Schaubel, H., and Street, R. Prostigmin and the chronic stutterer. *J. sp. hear. Dis.*, 1949, *14*, 143–146.

Schiefelbusch, R. L. Language studies of mentally retarded children. *J. sp. hear. Dis. mon. Suppl.* No. 10, 1963. (a)

————. The development of communication skills. In Schiefelbusch, R. and Smith, J. (Eds.), *Research in speech and hearing for mentally retarded children*. Conference report. U.S. Office of Education, #FO10, 1963. (b)

————. (Chairman), *et al*. Report to the President's Panel on Mental Retardation: Speech pathology and audiology needs. *ASHA*, 1962, *4*, 453–456.

Schlanger, B. B. Speech examination of a group of institutionalized mentally handicapped children. *J. sp. hear. Dis.*, 1953, *18*, 339–349. (a)

————. Speech measurements of institutionalized mentally handicapped children. *Amer. J. ment. Defic.*, 1953, *58*, 114–122. (b)

————. Environmental influences on the verbal output of mentally retarded children. *J. sp. hear. Dis.*, 1954, *19*, 339–343.

————. The effects of listening training on the auditory thresholds of mentally retarded children. U.S. Office of Education, #8936, 1961.

———— and Gottsleben, R. H. Testing the hearing of the mentally retarded. *J. sp. hear. Dis.*, 1956, *21*, 487–492.

———— and ————. Analysis of speech defects among the institutionalized mentally retarded. *J. sp. hear. Dis.*, 1957, *54*, 5–8.

Schneider, B., and Vallon, J. A speech therapy program for mentally retarded children. *Amer. J. ment. Defic.*, 1954, *58*, 633–639.

Sheridan, M. D. High tone deafness in school children simulating mental defect. *Brit. Med. J.*, 1944, *2*, 272–274.

Siegel, G. M. Verbal behavior of retarded children assembled with pre-instituted adults. In Schiefelbusch, R. (Ed.), *Language studies of mentally retarded children*. *J. sp. hear. mon. Suppl.*, 1963, No. 10.

———— and Harkins, J. P. Verbal behavior of adults in two conditions with institutionalized retarded children. In Schiefelbusch, R. (Ed.), *Language studies of mentally retarded children*. *J. sp. hear. Dis. mon. Suppl.*, 1963, No. 10.

Siegenthaler, B., and Krzywicki, D. Incidence and patterns of hearing loss among an adult mentally retarded population. *Amer. J. ment. Defic.*, 1959, *64*, 444–459.

————, Pearson, J., and Lezak, R. A speech reception test for children. *J. sp. hear. Dis.*, 1954, *19*, 360–366.

Sievers, D., and Essa, S. H. Language development in institutionalized and community mentally retarded children. *Amer. J. ment. Defic.*, 1961, *66*, 413–420.

SIRKIN, J., and LYONS, W. F. A study of speech defects in mental deficiency. *Amer. J. ment. Defic.* 1941, *46,* 74–80.

SKINNER, B. F. *Verbal behavior.* New York: Appleton-Century-Crofts, 1957.

SMITH, J. Group language development for educable mental retardates. *Except. Child.,* 1962, 95–101.

SMITH, M. E. Investigation of the development of the sentence and the extent of vocabulary in young children. University of Iowa studies in child welfare, 1926, *5,* 1–92.

SORTINI, A. Importance of individual hearing aids, and early therapy for preschool children. *J. sp. hear. Dis.,* 1959, *24,* 346–353.

SPRADLIN, J. Assessment of speech and language of retarded children: The Parsons language sample. *J. sp. hear. Dis. mon. Suppl.,* 1963, No. 10, 8–31. (a)

————. Language and communication of mental defectives. In Ellis, N. (Ed.), *Handbook of mental deficiency.* New York: McGraw-Hill, 1963. (b)

———— and LLOYD, L. Operant audiometry with profoundly retarded. AAMD convention paper, Miami, 1965.

STRAZZULLA, M. Speech problems of the mongoloid child. *Pediat.,* 1953, *8,* 268–273.

————. A language guide for the parent of retarded children. *Amer. J. ment. Defic.,* 1954, *59,* 48–58.

———— and KARLIN, I. Speech and language problems of mentally deficient children. *J. sp. hear. Dis.,* 1952, *17,* 286–294.

TARJAN, G., DINGMAN, H., and MILLER, C. Statistical expectations of selected handicaps in the mentally retarded. *Amer. J. ment. Defic.,* 1960, *65,* 335–341.

———— et al. Natural history of mental deficiency in a state hospital: III. Selected characteristics of first admissions and their environments. *Amer. J. Dis. Child.,* 1961, *101,* 195–205.

TEMPLIN, M., and DARLEY, F. The Templin-Darley test of articulation. Iowa City: University of Iowa Bureau of Education Research and Service, 1960.

VAN RIPER, C. *Helping children talk better.* Chicago: Science Research Associates, 1952.

————. *Speech correction: Principles and methods.* (4th ed.) Englewood Cliffs, N.J.: Prentice-Hall, 1963.

———— and IRWIN, J. Voice and articulation. New York: Prentice-Hall, 1958.

WEBB, C. Language disorders in a workshop for retarded. Unpublished study, 1965.

———— and HOLLAND, H. Parents as speech teachers, *SPAN,* 1963, *6,* 13–15.

————, KINDE, S., WEBER, B., and BEEDLE, R. *Procedures for evaluating the hearing of the mentally retarded.* U.S. Office of Education, CRP #1731, 1964.

————, ————, and ————. Incidence of hearing loss in institutionalized mental retardates. *Amer. J. ment. Defic.,* 1966, *70,* 563–568.

———— and PARNELL, J. Unit teaching in speech and hearing at the elementary school level. *J. sp. hear. Dis.,* 1960, *25,* 302–303.

WEISS, D. Speech in retarded children. *Nerv. Child.,* 1950, *9,* 21–30.

WEISS, D. A. Organic lesions leading to speech disorders. *Nerv. Child.,* 1948, *7,* 29–37.

WEST, R., ANSBERRY, M., and CARR, A. *The rehabilitation of speech.* (3rd ed.) New York: Harper, 1957.

WILLIAMS, G., and GRAHAM, J. EEG responses to auditory stimuli in waking children. *J. sp. hear. Res.,* 1963, *6,* 57–63.

WILLIAMSON, A. Diagnosis and treatment of seventy-two cases of hoarse voice. *Quart. J. sp.,* 1946, *31,* 189–202.

WINITZ, H. Research on intelligence and articulation. *Child Develpm.,* 1964, *35,* 287–297.

———— and BELLEROSE, B. Effects of pretraining on sound discrimination learning. *J. sp. hear. Res.,* 1963, *6,* 171–180.

WITTCOP, C. J., and HENRY, F. V. Sjögren-Larsson syndrome and histidinemia: Hereditary biochemical diseases with defects of speech and oral functions. *J. sp. hear. Dis.,* 1963, *28,* 109–122.

WOOD, N. E. *Communication problems and their effect on the learning potential of the mentally retarded child.* U.S. Office of Education, CRP #184, 1960.

WORSTER-DROUGHT, C. Dysarthria. *Speech,* 1953, *17,* 48–57.

ZENTAY, A. Motor disorders of the central nervous system and their significance for speech. Part I: Cerebral and cerebellar dysarthrias. *J. sp. Dis.,* 1937, *2,* 131–138.

ZINN, W. The significance of hoarseness. *Transactions of the Laryngological, Rhinological and Otological Society,* 1945, 133–134.

The Role of Environmental Factors in the Treatment of Institutionalized Mental Retardates[1]

EARL C. BUTTERFIELD

6

MOST workers in the field used to believe that little could be done to cure or ameliorate mental retardation. Some authors even included the notion of incurability in their definition of mental retardation (e.g., Doll, 1941). Recently, more and more authors have expressed the view that retardation is sometimes remediable through educational, psychological, and medical treatment (e.g., Kirk, 1958; Sarason and Gladwin, 1958). Whether this current optimism is factually based or not, the belief that retardation may be curable does raise interesting questions about the contributions of environmental conditions to retarded persons' development.

The rendering of many services to retarded people assumes that certain environmental modifications can favorably affect their development. Many workers have believed that environmental conditions can contribute to or cause mental retardation (Heber, 1959; Sarason and Gladwin, 1958). Still, little specific attention has been given to the possibility that general environmental conditions might contribute positively to the development of retardates. Manipulating the general environment in which a retarded person lives has seldom been explicitly regarded as an important part of his treatment regimen.

One's conclusions about the effects of various environmental conditions upon the retarded and one's response to these depend largely upon his evaluation and interpretation of the available evidence. While some research bears upon the question, none of it is conclusive. Furthermore, the complexities of the problem suggest that definitive research may not be done for some time. Some would argue this means the only appropriate course of action is to defer judgment and collect more and sounder data. It is true that more and better data are needed, but until one appreciates the shortcomings of existing evidence, he is quite unlikely to gather better evidence.

The purpose of this chapter is to consider evidence that bears upon the utility of regarding general environmental conditions as important in the treatment of retarded children. For both practical and technical reasons, this chapter is concerned only with the effects of environmental conditions upon retardates in institutional settings.[2] The practical reasons are: (1) this class of retardate is easily defined, (2) institutionalized retardates present the most serious adjustment problems, and (3) the institutionalized retardate has been studied much more than the noninstitutionalized retardate. The technical reason is that institutionalized and noninstitutionalized retardates differ in several important ways (e.g., the institutionalized retardate has a lower IQ, comes more often from broken and otherwise disturbed families, and has had the unique experiences associated with institutionalization [Bienenstok and Coxe, 1956; Goffman, 1957; Nye, 1958; Saenger, 1957; Sommer, 1959; Windle, 1962].)[3]

1. This chapter was prepared while the author was supported by United States Public Health Service Grant MH-0809. Dr. Herschel Berkowitz provided invaluable critical comments throughout the preparation of this paper.

2. For reviews of evidence concerning the effects of institutionalization upon non-retarded children, the reader should see Butterfield (1963), Casler (1961), and/or Yarrow (1961).

3. See Sarason and Gladwin (1958, p. 1282) for a presentation of the view that institutionalized and noninstitutionalized retardates are not substantially different from one another.

THE EFFECTS OF DIFFERENT ENVIRONMENTS UPON INTELLECTUAL FUNCTIONING

One could conclude from common-sense or casual observation alone that markedly different environments differentially affect retarded persons' intelligence. Thus, upon becoming acquainted with institutions for the retarded, many observers have concluded that institutions cause a decrease in intelligence, although some institutional personnel are convinced that institutionalization leads to an increase in the intelligence of some retardates. Such casual conclusions should be questioned, if for no other reason than that until recently the persons who had had most intimate contact with retardates (i.e., institution personnel and parents) acted as if they believed that little could be done to change retardate intelligence either for better or worse.

COMPARISONS OF INSTITUTIONALIZED AND NONINSTITUTIONALIZED RETARDATES

One of the more common empirical methods of studying the effects of environmental conditions upon the retarded has been to compare the intellectual performance of groups of retardates residing in markedly different settings. Almost invariably investigators have compared institutionalized retardates with those living at home or in foster homes. This is the grossest and least useful way to study environmental effects upon intelligence. Establishing that institutionalized retardates are less intelligent does not justify the conclusion that the institutional environment caused the lesser intelligence. Retardates may be institutionalized precisely because they are less intelligent. Furthermore, merely reporting that an institution lowers intelligence while a home does not is of little value to those who wish to change institutions for the better. They must know which of the many differences between institutions and homes is causing the lowered intelligence. Nevertheless, institutions and homes are probably as different as are any two existing environments in which retardates are found. Therefore, comparing retardates in them has seemed a natural first step in determining whether environmental variations do affect retardate intelligence.

Four investigations have shown that institutionalized retardates were less intelligent or less well developed than supposedly comparable groups of noninstitutionalized retardates (Centerwall and Centerwall, 1960; Lyle, 1959, 1960a, 1960b; Stedman, Eichorn, Griffin, and Gooch, 1962). The importance of these studies depends largely upon whether the institutionalized and noninstitutionalized groups would have differed if the retardates who were institutionalized had remained in their own homes. The two studies conducted by Lyle (1959, 1960a) reported neither the circumstances that led to the institutionalization of his groups nor the age at which their institutionalization occurred. Nevertheless, his findings are of interest because they indicate that institutionalized retardates are inferior to noninstitutionalized retardates only in verbal measures of intelligence. He found no differences between institutionalized and noninstitutionalized retardates in performance measures of intelligence. This discrepancy between findings with verbal and performance measures is what one might expect if institutionalization causes a lowering of retardate intelligence. Familiarity with the general lack of verbal stimulation in institutional settings suggests that if institutions do have adverse effects, they should be more marked in verbal than in performance areas of ability. Regardless of whether one attributes Lyle's findings to the effects of institutionalization, the results do suggest that institution personnel should give particular attention to stimulating retardates' verbal performance.

Particular attention probably should be given to the verbal stimulating of mongoloid retardates, since Lyle's findings indicate that mongoloids have a relatively greater verbal deficit than other kinds of retardates. Centerwall and Centerwall and Stedman, Eichorn, Griffin, and Gooch reported that all of their subjects were mongoloids and that all of those who were institutionalized were admitted during the neonatal period on the recommendation of the attending obstetrician. In the study of Centerwall and Centerwall, no differences were observed between the institutionalized and noninstitutionalized mongoloids on such factors as birth weight, age at which the diagnosis of mongolism was made, the presence of congenital defects, and various family characteristics. The primary reason for institutionalization seems to

have been the personal belief of the delivering obstetrician that it was inadvisable to keep
a mongoloid child at home. Since this belief
seems unlikely to have been related to the subsequent intelligence and development of the
child, the findings of Centerwall and Centerwall and Stedman, Eichorn, Griffin, and
Gooch that institutionalized mongoloids developed less quickly and were less intelligent
than those raised at home may reasonably be
attributed to the effects of institutionalization.
However, some qualifying considerations arise.
Both groups of authors used infant intelligence
scales. Since infant intelligence scales predict
later intelligence very inaccurately (Pinneau,
1961), there is no assurance that the difference
in IQ between groups reflects the effects of
institutionalization or that the difference would
exist when the children were older. All of the
subjects in both of these studies were mongoloids and all were institutionalized at a very
early age. It is impossible to tell from these
studies whether other kinds of retardates and
retardates who were admitted to an institution
at a later age would also show intellectual impairment that appeared to be a result of
institutionalization.

CROSS-SECTIONAL STUDIES OF LENGTH OF INSTITUTIONALIZATION

Another approach to the study of institutional environments upon the retarded has
been to compare the IQs of retardates who
have been institutionalized a short time with
the IQs of those who have been institutionalized a long time. The rationale for this cross-
sectional approach is that if institutions depress
intelligence, then long-term patients should
have lower IQs than short-term patients. A
major difficulty with this approach is that it
provides no way of knowing whether the long-
term patients have changed in intelligence since
their admission. Numerous reasons can be
given for long-term patients being less intelligent than short-term patients, even though the
long-term patients have not decreased in intelligence. For example, more intelligent patients would not stay in an institution as long
as less intelligent patients. Another possibility
is that all retarded people become less intelligent as they grow older.

To avoid the shortcomings of the cross-
sectional approach in the study of length of

institutionalization, Cutts and Lane (1947)
selected short- and long-term patients who had
the same chronological age and full-scale IQ.
Comparing the verbal and performance IQs of
their groups, Cutts and Lane found that the
short-term patients were more capable verbally than the long-term patients, but that the
two groups were the same in performance IQ.
This study is consistent with those of Lyle
(1959, 1960a) in suggesting that institutions
may be more detrimental to verbal than to
performance abilities. Cross-sectional studies
by Iscoe and McCann (1965) and Badt
(1958) suggest that abstract ability may also
be impaired by increasing length of
institutionalization.

LONGITUDINAL STUDIES OF THE EFFECTS OF INSTITUTIONALIZATION

A logical refinement of the matching procedure used by Cutts and Lane is testing the
same patients after different amounts of institutional experience. In using this longitudinal
approach, one must provide some means of
determining that any observed changes are
influenced by the environment rather than
some other factor associated with increasing
age. The best way to do this is to examine
two groups over time: an experimental group
that is experiencing the particular environment
under study and a control group that is not.
Provided that the experimental and control
groups are comparable on such factors as age,
family background, etc., differences between
them in changes over time may be attributed
to the effects of their different environments.

Some longitudinal studies of IQ changes in
institutionalized retardates did not employ a
control group of any kind (Alper and Horne,
1959; Chipman, 1929; Hoakley, 1932; Minoque, 1926; Prouty, 1930). These studies tell
us very little about the effects of institutional
residence upon retarded persons. Nevertheless,
they are interesting because a misinterpretation
of their findings (described by Windle, 1962)
has led to a host of longitudinal studies in
which institutionalized retarded persons have
been grouped according to either age, sex,
diagnosis, or preinstitutional experiences.[4] In

4. It would probably be more accurate to
say that the misinterpretation of these studies
preceded rather than led to more sophisticated
studies. However, assuming a more causal association facilitates the present exposition.

the following paragraphs, these investigations will be viewed as if they were studies of the effects of environmental conditions.[5] The rationale for considering them this way is that differential changes in intelligence between various subgroups may reflect different effects that institutions have on different kinds of retardates. Strictly speaking, this rationale is incorrect. One would have to have a matched noninstitutional control group for each of the institutionalized subgroups in order to reach any conclusive decision about the effects of institutions upon different kinds of retardates. Unfortunately, very few studies employ noninstitutional control groups of this kind. Consequently, in using studies that compare intellectual change among subgroups of the institutionalized retarded population for the purpose of understanding the effect of the institutional environments, I am relying upon findings that are not very suitable for my purpose. The reader should understand that considerable judgment and risk of incorrect conclusions are involved in this practice.

Longitudinal studies by Crissey (1937) and Kephart and Strauss (1940) suggest that retardates who are institutionalized at an early age (CA less than 12 years) lose more IQ points with increasing length of institutionalization than do retardates who are older (CA 12 to 20 years) when they are institutionalized. Several studies (Clarke and Clarke, 1953, 1954; Clarke, Clarke, and Reiman, 1958; Collman and Newlyn, 1958; Fisher, 1962a, 1962b; Fisher, Kilman, and Shotwell, 1961; Mundy, 1957) show that increasing length of institutionalization is unrelated to IQ change in adult and young adult retardates. A practically conservative interpretation of these findings would be that institution personnel should take particular care in the education and stimulation of younger retardates since they may be more adversely affected by institutionalization than are older patients.

Several studies of male and female retardates residing in institutions (Camp and Waite, 1932; Chipman, 1929; Kaplan, 1943; Minoque, 1926; Sloan and Harman, 1947) show no consistent differences between the sexes in IQ change.

Some studies suggest that retardates with different diagnoses show differential IQ changes.

5. The authors of these studies frequently did not consider them to be that.

Strauss and Kephart (1939) employed four general diagnostic categories: (1) exogenous—evidence of physical damage to the central nervous system and no family history of retardation; (2) endogenous—no evidence of physical damage to the central nervous system, but a family history of retardation; (3) mixed—evidence of both brain damage and retardation in the family; and (4) psychopath—no evidence of brain damage, but evidence of psychopathic personality traits. They found that the endogenous and psychopathic groups showed more IQ gains, the exogenous showed more IQ losses, and the mixed group fell between the others in IQ change. Studies by Kephart and Strauss (1940), Kirk (1958), and Mitchell (1955) confirm these findings with endogenous and exogenous groupings. Findings by Minoque (1926), Skeels and Dye (1939), and Chambers and Zabarenko (1956) failed to support Strauss and Kephart's findings. However, the diagnostic classifications of these non-supportive studies were somewhat different from those of Strauss and Kephart (1939). It seems fair to suggest that different diagnostic groups of retardates probably show different intellectual changes over the course of institutionalization. While these studies don't show clearly that differential changes depend in any crucial way upon the retardates' being in an institution, they do suggest that different institutional conditions might be desirable for retardates of different diagnostic categories.

Retardates from different preinstitutional backgrounds seem to show differential intellectual change. Clarke and Clarke (1953, 1954) gave intelligence tests to 59 mentally retarded persons when they were institutionalized and then retested them two years later. Without knowledge of the results of the intelligence tests, they rated the social histories of their retarded subjects for the presence or absence of adverse family backgrounds (e.g., having been taken from their parents because of neglect). They found that the IQs of persons from more adverse family backgrounds increased substantially more than did those of persons from less adverse backgrounds. Clarke and Clarke's subjects were retested again after six years of institutionalization by Clarke, Clarke, and Reiman (1958). The nine patients from more adverse backgrounds, who were still in the institution, again showed significantly greater increments in IQ from the time of institutionalization. Clarke, Clarke, and Reiman also administered intelligence tests to 32 other retardates who had been tested upon admission to and had remained in an institution for five years. Again, those from more deprived backgrounds showed significantly greater IQ gains. Cross-sectional findings by Jones and Carr-Saunders (1927) and Mitchell (1955) lend support to these findings. Longitudinal results by Collman and Newlyn (1958) and Zigler and Williams (1963) failed to support the Clarkes' findings, but this could have resulted from too short an interval between examinations (Collman and Newlyn, 1958), the use of different ratings of preinstitutional experiences (Zigler and Williams, 1963), or the fact that these authors were studying different institutions. All things considered, retardates from more adverse backgrounds seem to respond more favorably to an institutional environment. This could be due to the removal of the child from the poor home environment rather than to any positive feature of institutions.

We have now considered longitudinal studies that grouped retardates in four ways: according to age, sex, diagnosis, or preinstitutional background. These are not completely separate or independent kinds of groupings. Diagnostic categories depended in part upon background factors (Butterfield and Zigler, 1965; Dingman and Miller, 1959; Heber, 1959; Tarjan, Wright, Dingman, and Eyman, 1961; Windle, 1962; Zigler, 1963; etc.). In almost none of the studies that used one of these factors as a basis for grouping were the other possible grouping factors controlled. This may account for some of the inconsistency in the literature and perhaps justifies the rather liberal interpretations made at some points above. At any rate, studies that simultaneously investigate each of these factors are clearly necessary. In the meantime, institutional personnel should consider providing different kinds of programs for patients of different diagnoses and different preinstitutional backgrounds, and they might re-evaluate the programs that exist for patients of different ages.

A final class of longitudinal study relevant to the question of environmental influences upon the intelligence of institutionalized retardates compares intelligence test change for retardates who leave an institution with that of retardates who remain. The rationale for this kind of comparison is that if released patients show intellectual changes that retained patients do not, then the change must be a result of the difference between the environments of retained and released patients. This rationale is correct only if the released and retained patients are comparable at the time of release. This condition has probably never been met. For example, Mundy (1957) reported that a group of retarded girls who were released from an institution in order to assume rehabilitative jobs increased significantly more in IQ than did a group that remained. The girls who were released were highly motivated to improve their status, while those who remained were not. Consequently, the differential IQ change that Mundy observed may have been due to motivational factors rather than, or in addition to, environmental factors. Bodman (1950) and Dingman and Miller (1959) have shown that released and non-released retardates also differ in nonmotivational ways: released patients less frequently have criminal records and are more intelligent. For reasons of this kind, the other longitudinal study of released and non-released retardates (McKay, 1942) is also inconclusive.

MANIPULATIONS OF ENVIRONMENTAL CONDITIONS

None of the studies considered so far indicated the kinds of environmental modifications that would best suit the needs of different patients. What needs to be done is to compare groups of retardates who experience environments that are different in known ways. The surest way to know how two environments differ is to construct them to be different. Studies that use this manipulative approach should be given particular attention because they reveal which factors cause any observed differences and provide the best basis for practical action. A less satisfactory approach is to select existing environments that seem to differ in only a few ways. The problem with this approach is that assessing environments is an extremely complex and subjective task; one can never be certain that he knows exactly how two naturally occurring environments differ.

Lyle (1960b) has reported an investigation that combined the approach of creating an environment and using an existing one. He selected sixteen pairs of retarded children from an existing institution, choosing them on the basis of comparability in age, etiology, non-verbal intelligence, and verbal intelligence in cases where children could speak. One child from each pair was left in the institution, and the other was transferred to an experimental institution. Lyle described the institution from which children were selected as follows:

There were formal programs and organized activities, often, it seemed to the writer, of doubtful educational value. For the juniors, the fitting together of jigsaw puzzles; and for the seniors, simple kinds of handwork were much in evidence. Activities requiring speech did not figure very much in the programme at all. The children sat at desks or tables for most of the school day, and the main endeavor of the teacher was necessarily to control the children. . . . The wards contained some 50 children, and here again the routine was necessarily rigid and controlling, with too few ward staff to manage too many children. Generally, throughout the institution, verbal communication between children, or between children and staff, seemed not to be a very frequent occurrence.

Lyle described the experimental institution as follows:

The children were divided into two families of eight, each with two house mothers concerned primarily with the same group of children. In this way intimate relations between individual children and particular adults were fostered . . . there was no *formal* instruction. Instead, interest was the main motivating force, and much of the day was spent by the children in play, a supply of suitable equipment being gradually accumulated. This meant that for example no direct instruction was given in speech and language; but the children had many opportunities to talk to the staff and to other children and were encouraged to do so. The educational programme was based largely upon nursery school principles, instruction taking place informally, and in the context of real life situations rather than in formal lessons.

Lyle found the experimental group had gained appreciably more in verbal skills after twelve months than had the group that remained in the older institution—a gain that was even greater after eighteen months. The experimental group gained six months more in verbal mental age over the course of eighteen months than did the other group, but the groups did not differ in performance ability gain. However, considering that the mean non-verbal IQ of the two groups was only 39 at the beginning of the study, a differential gain of this magnitude is quite substantial. Moreover, the gain was obtained without the use of highly trained personnel or formal instruction. Skeels and Dye (1939) performed a quite similar experiment using very young children and also found that increased contact with adults and nursery school instruction increased the IQs of institutional children.

Two investigators (Gallagher, 1960, 1962; Kirk, 1958) have studied the effects of adding special educational techniques to typical institution programs. Kirk employed a preschool type of program and found after one year that it had increased social maturity as well as IQ. These increases seemed to persist for a year after the nursery school experience was terminated. Using very specialized educational procedures for only a brief part of each day with brain-injured retardates, Gallagher found increases in both verbal and performance abilities. However, the verbal ability increases were not maintained after the special tutoring was stopped.

SUMMATION

The limitations of empirical evidence concerning the effects of environmental variation upon institutionalized retardate intelligence have been made clear. Still, several findings have appeared consistently enough to deserve reiteration. Institutions probably have most detrimental effects upon verbal and abstract abilities. These effects are probably more marked for younger retardates and for retardates from more favorable home environments. Retardates from very adverse backgrounds may benefit from an institutional environment.

All of this suggests that one of the most beneficial things an institution could do for its retarded residents would be to increase opportunities for verbal expression. Highly trained personnel probably are not needed for this; simply providing a greater number of child care workers who talk directly and frequently to their charges would probably help a great deal.

One of the justifications for a cottage rather than a dormitory system of residential organization in an institution is that it allows closer contact between caretakers and patients. The desirability of this closer contact has not often been made clear. The research reviewed above suggests that one desirable feature of closer contact would be greater intellectual growth.

THE EFFECTS OF ENVIRONMENTAL DIFFERENCES UPON RETARDATE PERSONALITY

A surprisingly small number of investigations have dealt with the effects of environmental variation upon retardate personality. Retardate personality has been regarded as an important determinant of prognosis (cf. Windle, 1962), yet apparently it has not often been regarded as something that might be changed by environmental factors. Rather, the changing of personality seems to have been regarded as something that can be accomplished only by means of very specialized therapeutic procedures and drugs.

Why haven't more studies been conducted of the effects of such factors as institutional environment upon retardate personality? For some time now, psychiatrists and psychologists have believed the unfortunate fictions that retardates were less variable than intellectually normal persons in personality, that they possessed largely uninteresting personality characteristics, and, at any rate, that little could be done to change retardate personality. Professional persons who are competent in personality research have not often been employed by institutions for the retarded because many institutions have seen no value in research of any kind and because capable research people often regard institutions as undesirable places to work. The measurement of personality characteristics is more an art than a science so that the use of personality dimensions in research is often regarded as too unscientific to be worthwhile. Psychologists and psychiatrists have alternately perpetuated and bickered about the belief that only they could ethically treat personality characteristics. Finally, personality has not been conceived broadly enough. There is more to personality than those extreme disturbances we call mental illness.

The few studies of the effects of environmental factors upon retardate personality have been carried out by researchers who subscribed to a broad view of personality. Typical psy-chiatric descriptions of personality do not appear in a consideration of their findings. Consequently, the following discussion is unhampered by the difficulty of communicating subtle psychiatric distinctions. Nevertheless, understanding the practical significance of research into retardate personality is difficult. All these studies have grown out of particular theoretical views about the nature of personality development. They were designed to test these views and their authors have been relatively unconcerned with determining the practical significance of the personality measures they employed. In drawing practical conclusions from these studies, one must rely upon judgment and educated guesses.

The limitations and rationale of the different types of studies were described during the consideration of the effects of environmental variation upon intelligence. These same limitations and rationale apply to many of the evaluations of the following studies of retardate personality.

COMPARISONS OF RETARDATES IN DIFFERENT ENVIRONMENTS

Green and Zigler (1962) compared institutionalized retarded children with noninstitutionalized retarded and noninstitutionalized normal children, all matched on mental age. They found that the institutionalized retarded children persisted longer in a monotonous task for which they were given either praise or attention than did either of the noninstitutionalized groups. Green and Zigler interpreted this to mean that institutionalization leads to a heightened need for social reinforcement. These findings may be a result of some characteristic of retardates that leads to institutionalization rather than some characteristic which results from institutionalization.

Zigler (1963) compared four groups of children who were matched on mental age. Two of the groups were normal and two were retarded. One retarded and one normal group were institutionalized and one retarded and one normal group were not institutionalized. Zigler found that the two institutionalized groups persisted longer at a monotonous task than did the two noninstitutionalized groups both under conditions of attention and verbal reinforcement and under conditions of attention alone. These results are cosistent with those of Green and Zigler (1962) but could also be due to some selective factor leading to institutionalization.

LONGITUDINAL STUDIES OF THE EFFECTS OF INSTITUTIONS UPON PERSONALITY

Butterfield and Zigler (1965) introduced a novel notion into research on the effects of institutionalization. They started from a simple idea that researchers have somehow overlooked —that institutions are quite different from one another. On the basis of this premise, they suggested that different institutions probably have different effects upon the personality or motivation of their retarded residents. Accordingly, they decided to compare residents in two institutions that seemed quite different. A definite strength of this strategy is that there are probably fewer differences beween retardates admitted to different institutions than there are between institutionalized and noninstitutionalized retardates. Therefore, differences between retardates in different institutions are likely a result of the environmental differences between the institutions. The disadvantage of this approach lies in the difficulty involved in specifying just how two institutions differ.

Butterfield and Zigler studied two institutions in the same state that had identical admission policies. They relied upon intensive personal experience in describing how the institutions differed. Their descriptions of the two institutions are given below because the reader will appreciate more fully what the term institutionalization refers to and because their descriptions of institutions and those of Lyle reported above are among the very few in the literature.

In institution A, all except the most severely retarded children are regarded by the staff as being potentially capable of returning to the community. Every effort is made to provide a noninstitutional (i.e., homelike) environment. School classes, residential units at the younger age levels, movies, and social events, which are quite frequent, are coeducational. Meals are prepared in the living units where the children eat in small groups. Emphasis is placed upon individual responsibility rather than upon external control by the staff. No buildings are locked and all children who are ambulatory move freely about the grounds to school, work, and recreational activities. Isolation is rarely used as a punishment. Essentially no security force is employed. There are a large number of small residential units and a number of

factors are considered before assigning a child to a unit (e.g., age, sex, intellectual level, the child's attitude toward the caretakers and other children residing in the unit, and their attitude toward him).

In institution B, most patients are regarded as incapable of returning to the community. Little effort is made to provide a homelike environment for them. School classes, all residential units, movies, and most social events are segregated by sex. Meals are prepared and children eat in a large central dining room with virtually no individual supervision. Emphasis is upon external control of the children by the staff rather than upon inculcating individual responsibility. All buildings are locked and no child moves about the grounds unattended by an employe. Isolation is frequently used as a punishment. A large staff of security officers patrol the grounds regularly. Residential units are all of the large, dormitory type and no effort is made to group children except by gross sex, age, and intellectual criteria. The climate at institution A strikes one as being much more conducive to constructive, supportive interactions between the children and their adult caretakers than the climate at institution B. In the light of earlier work concerning the effects of social deprivation on children's desire for social reinforcement, one would hypothesize that children in institution B would be more motivated to receive social reinforcement than the children in institution A.

In two separate investigations, Butterfield and Zigler found evidence that retardates in institution B had a greater need for social reinforcement. This seems to be strong evidence that different institutions have different effects upon retarded children.

Stevenson and Knights (1962) made repeated examinations of retarded children after they had returned to an institution for the retarded from summer vacations at home. One group (A) was examined one, twelve, and thirty weeks after returning to the institution. Another group (B) was examined twelve and thirty weeks after returning. Some children were examined under conditions of verbal reinforcement, while other children were given no verbal reinforcement. Male retardates in neither group (A nor B) showed neither time of examination nor type of reinforcement effects. Stevenson and Knights interpreted this lack of differences to mean that male reinforcers (the experimenters were males) were not effective social reinforcers for male children. The female retardates in group A had a greater rate of response on a monotonous task under conditions of verbal reinforcement than under conditions of attention only. This difference was found in all three examinations.

The female children in group B showed no differences between the two conditions of reinforcement. Females from both groups A and B showed no differences over time. On the basis of the differences between the females from groups A and B, Stevenson and Knights suggested that "separation from home and family results in more intense feelings of deprivation and isolation than occur after the child has readjusted to the institutional setting." This conclusion seems logically unsound. If there was a period of heightened social motivation immediately following return to an institution from home and this motivation was reduced following a readjustment to the institution, then there should be differences between the group A children's performance immediately after return from home and, later, after there has been time for readjustment to the institution. Stevenson and Knights found no such difference. Rather, their results indicated that the group A girls were different from the group B girls. Why these two groups of girls should have differed is not clear, but a readjustment process could not account for their having differed.

Stevenson and Knights employed a rate of response measure. However, Zigler (1963) and Green and Zigler (1962) have found that rate measures are not correlated with persistence measures in institutionalized retardates. Furthermore, the findings of the latter two authors suggest that rate measures are not as sensitive to the effects of institutionalization as are persistence measures. The study of changes in motivation after returning to an institution might be more enlightening if a persistence measure were used.

Zigler (1961) found greater persistence in a socially reinforcing task among institutionalized retarded subjects who had come from less socially deprived backgrounds. By itself, this study does not tell anything about the effects of institutionalization. However, most of the same subjects who were examined by Zigler were re-examined two years later by Zigler and Williams (1963). They found that all subjects persisted longer at the time of re-examination than they had initially. Furthermore, the increase in persistence was much more marked for those children who had come from non-deprived preinstitutional environments than it was for children from deprived preinstitutional environments. The

conclusion drawn by Zigler and Williams was that institutional residence is more socially depriving for subjects from deprived backgrounds. This interpretation would be stronger if the same experimenter had conducted both examinations and if noninstitutional deprived and non-deprived control groups were employed.

INTERPRETATIONS

All of the studies on retardate personality arose from the conviction that frequent, warm interactions between adults and children are necessary for normal personality development. The view of personality development that these studies support is that if children experience sufficient positive interaction with adults, they gradually become more oriented toward achieving independence and less needful of frequent, indiscriminate support from adults and peers. A corollary of this view is that if children, whether retarded or normal, do not receive sufficient positive adult contact (as they probably do not in institutions), they will remain more immaturely oriented toward receiving attention from adults. They will not become sufficiently motivated toward achieving independence to make a satisfactory adjustment as an adult. Furthermore, this view suggests that retardates are even more susceptible to the detrimental effects of insufficient or inadequate adult support than are normal children. The reason for this is that retardates, because of their lesser intelligence, are more frequently incapable of meeting conventional standards of achievement and are more likely to learn that they cannot rely upon themselves.

The studies of environmental influence upon retardate personality suggest that one of the hallmarks of a desirable institutional environment is the provision of intimate positive contact between adult caretakers and residents. This suggestion is strikingly similar to those derived from studies of environmental influences upon retardate intelligence. Zigler (1963) has suggested that one of the reasons institutions seem to depress intellectual functioning may be that institutions foster an immature orientation toward other persons to the detriment of such things as intellectual pursuits. Be that as it may, empirical evidence seems to justify a strong plea for increasing the number of attendants per patient in institutions for the retarded. A more favorable attendant-patient ratio could make institutions more therapeutic places to send retardates. I am not urging more attendants be hired in order to reduce the work load of those already working in institutions; what I emphasize is that the prime consideration is the treatment benefits for the retardate.

Merely having more attendants would do little good if they were not interacting appropriately with the residents. Just what is the proper way is hard to say on the basis of the studies reported above. Intuitively, however, if attendants tried, within the very realistic limitations of their jobs, to interact frequently, realistically, and warmly with their patients, they probably would be close to the ideal. This statement has considerable implication for attendant selection and training (see Chapter 12).

Other suggestions arise from the studies reviewed in this section. Adequate personality development likely would be helped by employing both male and female attendants for patients of both sexes. Since institutions seem to differ, one source of stimulation for and knowledge of improving them would be for their personnel to visit other institutions. In this regard, let me point out that institutions are probably not just good or bad relative to one another. Rather, institutions have different strengths and weaknesses. Probably no institution exists that could not improve itself by careful consideration of its and others' policies.

THE EFFECTS OF DIFFERENT ENVIRONMENTS UPON VOCATIONAL ADJUSTMENT, PLACEMENT, SUCCESS, ETC.

Increasing intelligence and fostering positive personality development are surely worthy goals of a treatment program for the mentally retarded. For many institutions and for many retarded persons, these are tremendously ambitious goals in and of themselves. For other institutions and other retardates, increased intelligence and better personal adjustment are simply means to the goals of being placed outside of the institution, securing and keeping gainful employment, establishing satisfying social relations in the community, etc. When an institution holds these latter goals for some or all of its retardates, it must recognize that the relationship is far from clear between increased retardate intelligence and personal adjustment on one hand and community placement and success on the other. (Windle, 1962). Accordingly, such institutions would seem well-advised in planning their treatment environment to attend more closely to studies of the relationship between environmental conditions and placement success than to studies of relationships between environmental conditions and intelligence or personality.[6]

Studies of the determinants of placement success (hereafter referred to as outcome studies) suffer from the same limitations as studies of the determinants of increased intelligence and positive personality development. In addition, they have other shortcomings that make them difficult to interpret. Defining community adjustment is extremely difficult, and few agree about what constitutes a successful placement outcome (Humphreys, 1937). Accordingly, there have been great differences between studies in criteria used to define successful community placement. These different criteria are probably not very highly related to one another (Scott, 1958). Consequently, comparing different studies of community placement is often fruitless.

Several complications arise in the interpretation of outcome studies because institutions are hesitant to experiment with their placement procedures. Understandably enough, institutions that have active placement programs exercise great care in the selection of placement candidates. Quite probably, different institutions use different selection criteria, although this is uncertain because almost all institutions' criteria are relatively subjective and inexplicit. Differences between the results of studies may well be due to differences in the kinds of retardates whom different institutions return to the community. This may be true even when institutions have quite similar treatment environments. This problem is no less serious in institutions that do not have active placement programs. In these institutions, the characteristics of retardates placed in the community vary with the nature of the agent (i.e., family,

6. There are, of course, many determinants of placement success besides environmental background. The reader is referred to Windle (1962) for a review of studies of those determinants.

employer, etc.) initiating return to the community. Another problem is that when only certain kinds of patients are returned to the community one never knows whether other kinds of patients, given the proper institutional and release environments, might be successfully placed outside of the institution. Furthermore, the kinds of patients who are most often returned to the community may be those who would succeed or fail regardless of the character of the institution from which they came. If this were the case, then the goal of understanding institutional effects would have been defeated before it began.

Administrative conventions about returning retardates to the institution once they have been placed in the community also make outcome studies difficult to evaluate. Generally speaking, institutions are probably rather conservative in their judgment about whether a retardate should be left in the community once he has been placed. For the presumed "good" of the retardate, the community, and the public view of the institution, it is often deemed necessary to return a retardate to the institution before he makes a conspicuous failure of his placement. Consequently, some retardates who would have been successful are probably not given sufficient time to demonstrate that fact. Accordingly, the desirable effects of an institution's environment upon some retardates may be masked by lack of sufficient opportunity for the retardate to demonstrate those effects. On the other hand, some institutions probably do not maintain enough contact with their released patients to determine whether they have been successful. Consequently, retardates from those institutions may not be returned from the community until their failure becomes extremely conspicuous. For reasons such as these, length of placement is probably not a very trustworthy criterion of the effects of an institutional program. The use of other criteria is also highly complicated by such factors as these.

This consideration of some of the problems in interpreting outcome studies raises a very thorny question about doing research in an institutional setting. The needs of program administrators often seem to conflict with the needs of those who would use research procedures to evaluate existing programs or to develop new programs. The question that both the administrator and the researcher in an institution must consider in order to resolve this conflict is "Upon what basis will decisions be made when administrative and research needs conflict?" The failure to provide a satisfactory answer to this question has been partially to blame for the fact that few institutions for the retarded have research programs. The answer that must be given to this question if research is to flourish is that administrative and research conflicts will be resolved by a mutual determination of how important the researcher's efforts and answers will be. The more critical the administrator's need, the more important the knowledge sought by the researcher must be in order that the administrator alter his usual practices to suit the researcher's needs. On the other hand, any administrative practice may be altered if the probable gain in knowledge seems great enough.

All too frequently some other answer is given to the question of how to resolve administrative and research conflicts. One answer is that no administrative need is so small that it can give way to any research need. The implication of this answer is that administrative leaders of institutions know all they need to know to run a satisfactory institution. That is patently false and means no research is done. The patient ultimately suffers from this state of affairs. Another answer is that no research will be undertaken if it interferes with major institutional programs such as schooling and extra-institutional placement to more than a minor degree. The result of this answer is that few questions of any major importance to administrative practices will be answered with research techniques, although large-scale investigations of basic scientific issues may be pursued vigorously. Another conceivable answer is that research needs always take precedence over administrative needs. This approach could lead to a failure to apply the knowledge that we already possess to the treatment of retarded people.

In summary, questions of both practical and theoretical significance can be answered by research in an institutional setting. By focusing upon the importance of the answers to those questions and exercising a modicum of good will, administrators and researchers can find mutually satisfactory ways to answer those questions.

PREINSTITUTIONAL ENVIRONMENT AND LIKELIHOOD OF RELEASE FROM AN INSTITUTION

Clarke, Clarke, and Reiman (1958) found a greater discharge and placement rate among institutionalized patients who came from very low socioeconomic, rejecting, and broken homes than among those who came from more typical homes. Dingman (1959) found that patients whose preinstitutional guardians held semiskilled or lower-status jobs were more often released than were patients whose guardians came from higher-status occupations. Urban-rural preadmission residence has been found to be unrelated to likelihood of release (Krishef, Reynolds, and Stunkard, 1959; Reynolds and MacEachern, 1956).

The relationship between kind of preinstitutional residence (Clarke, Clarke, and Reiman, 1958; Dingman, 1959) and release probably reflects the fact that retardates from poor homes are quite different from those from better homes. Some evidence suggests that retardates from poorer homes are less retarded and have less serious emotional problems (Dingman, 1959; Greene, 1945). Accordingly, many doubt whether the above studies show that preinstitutional environment *per se* affects likelihood of release from an institution.

PREINSTITUTIONAL ENVIRONMENT AND RELEASE OUTCOME

Several studies have investigated the effects of number of foster home and orphanage placements prior to residence in an institution for the retarded upon vocational placement, family care placement, or planned discharge from the institution. Cohen (1947), Krishef (1957), and Shafter (1957) found no relationship between preinstitutional residence and postinstitutional success. Wolfson (1956) and Shafter (1957) found no relationship between the degree of intactness of the preinstitutional home and success upon discharge and parole respectively. Socioeconomic status of preinstitutional home has been found to be unrelated to adjustment upon release (Krishef, 1957; Popenoe, 1927; Potter and McCollister, 1926; Shafter, 1957; Wolfson, 1956). Whether the patient came to the institution from a rural or urban home seems to have no bearing upon his success in placement after institutionaliza-

tion (Krishef, 1957; Krishef, Reynolds, and Stunkard, 1959; Shafter, 1957).

INSTITUTIONAL EXPERIENCES AND RELEASE OUTCOME

Many investigators have studied the relationship between length of institutionalization and release outcome. A majority of these investigations have found either no relationship between the two factors (Craib and Woodward, 1958; Krishef, 1957; Krishef, Reynolds, and Stunkard, 1959; Town, 1931; Wallace, 1918; Windle, 1959, 1962; Wolfson, 1956) or have attributed the relationship found to administrative practices in the institution rather than to the environmental effects of the institution (Pense, 1943; Potter and McCollister, 1926).

One of the considerations in evaluating all studies of release outcome is the kind of setting into which patients are released. No such distinctions were made in the studies that showed no relationship between length of institutionalization and release outcome. Hiatt (1951) and Brown, Windle, and Stewart (1959) found that older patients who were placed in family-care settings were more likely to succeed the longer they had been institutionalized. These findings are probably a result of the similarity of institutional and family care settings. The longer patients had to become adjusted to one institutional way of life, the more likely they were to adjust to another similar way of life. This rationale cannot account for the findings of Hartzler (1953), Grant (1956), and Tong and McKay (1959) that patients who had been institutionalized longer prior to relatively independent vocational placements were less likely to have to be reinstitutionalized. The retardate's age at time of release quite possibly may account for these latter findings. The patients who had been institutionalized longer were older and possibly, therefore, more stable (Windle, 1962).

These findings clearly do not support the conclusion of some authors (e.g., Sarason and Gladwin, 1958), that long institutionalization is detrimental to later social adjustment. Whether more well-executed studies would support this contention is hard to tell. Clearly, more investigations are needed.

A few studies have tried to analyze institutional experiences more finely than those that observed the effects of length of institutionalization. They have examined the effects of psychotherapy (Astrachan, 1955; Tarjan and Benson, 1953) and work experiences (Megaw and Sullivan, 1945; O'Brien, 1952; Shafter, 1957; Thomas, 1943) during institutionalization. While the authors frequently felt that therapy and work experience did contribute to release adjustment, none of them presented evidence that supported this conviction.

None of these studies seem to have come to grips with the difficult problem of specifying and assessing the character of a retardate's institutional experience. Until this is done, outcome studies are unlikely to clarify our understanding of the effects of institutionalization.

POST-INSTITUTIONAL ENVIRONMENT AND OUTCOME

Several studies indicate that when retardates are released to homes in which the adults are relatively more sympathetic and child-oriented, they are more likely to remain on placement (Abel, 1940; Camp and Waite, 1932; Harold, 1955; Hartzler, 1953; Schroeder and Bartelme, 1928). Similarly, placements to rural settings usually last longer than placement to urban settings (Krishef, 1957; Kuenzel, 1939; Stebbins, 1931), although Shafter (1957) found no differences between urban and rural settings. All of these significant findings probably indicate that some settings tolerate retardates better than others. Whether these settings also have more beneficial effects upon retardates is problematic.

CONCLUSIONS

I suggested earlier that release outcome studies might provide a better basis for some aspects of institutional program planning than studies of environmental effects upon intelligence or personality. Rationally, that is still correct despite the fact the results of outcome studies are of little help. Indeed, no clear conclusions about institutional programming follow from them—a disappointing and ironic situation. The irony stems from the fact that institution administrators have considerable control over the factors that make outcome studies difficult to execute. Furthermore, these are the studies that should be of most help to them in planning their programs. Possibly the outcome studies are less clear-cut because

outcome is not influenced by environmental factors. However, better outcome research will have to be done before that conclusion can be made confidently.

The premise on which this chapter was based is that empirical, research-derived knowledge provides the firmest possible foundation for the selection of a treatment environment for the retarded. By implication, commonsense, experientially based knowledge provides a less adequate foundation. The reader should ask himself, now that he is acquainted with a considerable amount of empirical evidence, whether research has provided him with a better foundation on which to build a treatment environment than his common sense alone had given him. Different readers will undoubtedly answer this question differently. Some, at least, will decide that the research studies reviewed here have not told them anything they hadn't figured out from their personal experiences. What, then, may one say to these readers about the utility of research, about the validity of the premise upon which this chapter is based?

The failure of research studies to contribute more to knowledge of treating retardation may be ascribed to two things. On a practical level, relatively little research has been done on the treatment of retarded. Furthermore, many limitations prevail in much of the empirical work that has been done. While it may be avoiding the issue of the utility of research to say that more and better studies are needed, nevertheless, more and better studies are needed. On a more abstract level, the potential contribution of research studies should be made clear. Most research does not result in sweepingly new and startling ideas. This is particularly true of research into problems that require social action for their solution. People, not experiments, create new ideas, and people base their ideas on many things besides research. The most typical contribution of an experiment is to confirm existing ideas and perhaps, but just perhaps, to provide evidence upon which new ideas can be built. By confirming existing ideas, research can provide a basis upon which confident action may be taken. Accordingly, the importance of research to the person who would take action, in this case to treat the retarded, is determined directly by his confidence in the outcomes of the actions he takes. If he wants to be certain that his actions will do some good or will not do any harm, then he will probably want empirical evidence to supplement his best judgment. On the other hand, if he does not feel a need to be certain about the outcomes of his actions, then he may well wish to rely upon his own best judgment, unaided by research findings.

Let us now return to a consideration of why existing outcome studies have not provided a more substantial basis for planning a treatment environment for the retarded. At least part of the reason is that persons with administrative responsibility for placement have either felt no need for adequate outcome studies, or have been unable, through lack of knowledge or resources, to see that they were done. It is difficult to conceive of any effort at providing a better treatment environment that would do any harm. Whether it would do any good is more difficult to tell, but most of the things that one would think of doing to improve an environment are, by nature, things which at least appear to be beneficial. For example, few would quarrel about efforts to improve the living conditions of the retarded. On humane grounds alone, it is a reasonable thing to do. Accordingly, research into its efficacy has probably seemed relatively superfluous. One can also understand why persons who are responsible for administering treatment programs may not know how, or have the resources, to execute outcome studies.

Perhaps the most basic reason that more research, including outcome studies, has not been done in institutional settings is that research is a time-consuming and demanding endeavor and requires a very special kind of environment. If a person must spend much of his time involved in other activities, he will get little research done. Unfortunately, institutions seldom have been financially able to hire highly trained persons without requiring that they spend most, if not all, of their time in treating the retarded. Moreover, one person is seldom enough to conceive sound research designs. Research is much more likely to occur and to be of a high quality when a number of persons within an institution are able to consult with each other about their research problems. The lack of competent research people within institutions is probably not due entirely to the lack of funds to hire them. On the contrary, those few institutions that do have funds for research personnel find them hard to attract. Researchers' reluctance to work for institutions probably stems from their convictions that institution administrators are not sympathetic to their needs, that they will find few research-oriented colleagues in institutions, and that they would prefer to do more basic and less practical research. Finally, the execution of any investigation as involved as the release outcome study requires the time and co-operation of many people, both within and outside of the institution.

None of the reasons cited for the relative lack of research in institutional settings is insurmountable. It is hoped that more people will try to surmount them in the future than have in the past.

REFERENCES

ABEL, T. M. A study of a group of subnormal girls successfully adjusted in industry and the community. *Amer. J. ment. Defic.,* 1940, *45,* 66–72.

ALPER, A. E., and HORNE, B. M. Changes in IQ of a group of institutionalized mental defectives over a period of two decades. *Amer. J. ment. Defic.,* 1959, *64,* 472–475.

ASTRACHAN, MYRTLE. Group psychotherapy with mentally retarded female adolescents and adults. *Amer. J. ment. Defic.,* 1955, *60,* 152–156.

BADT, M. I. Levels of abstraction in vocabulary definitions of mentally retarded school children. *Amer. J. ment. Defic.,* 1958, *63,* 241–247.

BIENENSTOK, T., and COXE, W. W. *Census of severely retarded children in New York State.* Albany: State of New York, 1956.

BODMAN, F. The social adaptation of institution children. *Ment. Hlth. London,* 1950, *9,* 68–69.

BROWN, S. J., WINDLE, C., and STEWART, E. Statistics on a family care program. *Amer. J. ment. Defic.,* 1959, *64,* 535–542.

BUTTERFIELD, E. C. The effects of institutionalization: methodological and hypothetical issues. Yale University: Unpublished manuscript, 1963.

—— and ZIGLER, E. The influence of differing institutional social climates on the effectiveness of social reinforcement in the mentally retarded. *Amer. J. ment. Defic.*, 1965, *70*, 48–56.

CAMP, B. M., and WAITE, T. E. Report on four cases of mental deficiency on parole. *Amer. Assn. Study Feebleminded*, 1932, *37*, 381–394.

CASLER, L. Maternal deprivation: A critical review of the literature. *Monogr. Soc. Res. Child Develpm.*, Ser. No. 80, 1961, *26*, 2.

CENTERWALL, S. A., and CENTERWALL, W. R. A study of children with mongolism reared in the home compared to those reared away from home. *Pediatrics*, 1960, *25*, 678–685.

CHAMBERS, G. S., and ZABARENKO, R. N. Effects of glutamic acid and social stimulation in mental deficiency. *J. abnorm. soc. Psychol.*, 1956, *53*, 315–320.

CHIPMAN, CATHERINE E. The constancy of the intelligence quotient of mental defectives. *Psychol. Clinic*, 1929, *18*, 103–111.

CLARKE, A. D. B., and CLARKE, A. M. How constant is the IQ? *Lancet*, 1953, *2*, 877–880.

—— and ——. Cognitive changes in the feebleminded. *Brit. J. Psychol.*, 1954, *45*, 173–179.

——, ——, and REIMAN, S. Cognitive and social changes in the feebleminded—three further studies. *Brit. J. Psychol.*, 1958, *49*, 144–157.

COHEN, J. Survey of a school program for family care of school age children. *Amer. J. ment. Defic.*, 1947, *51*, 502–509.

COLLMAN, R. D., and NEWLYN, D. Changes in Terman-Merrill IQs of mentally retarded children. *Amer. J. ment. Defic.*, 1958, *63*, 307–311.

CRAIB, M. F., and WOODWARD, M. A survey of 44 children admitted to the Fountain Group Hospital under the Mental Deficiency Act and subsequently accepted as educable. *J. ment. Sci.*, 1958, *104*, 115–122.

CRISSEY, O. L. The mental development of children of the same IQ in differing institutional environments. *Child Develpm.*, 1937, *8*, 217–220.

CUTTS, R. A., and LANE, MARGERY. The effect of hospitalization on Wechsler-Bellevue subtest scores by mental defectives. *Amer. J. ment. Defic.*, 1947, *51*, 391–393.

DINGMAN, H. F. Some uses of descriptive statistics in population analysis. *Amer. J. ment. Defic.*, 1959, *64*, 291–295.

—— and MILLER, C. R. Note on use of correlation statistics and population analysis. *Amer. J. ment. Defic.*, 1959, *64*, 636–637.

DOLL, E. A. The essentials of an inclusive concept of mental deficiency. *Amer. J. ment. Defic.*, 1941, *46*, 214–219.

FISCHER, G. M. Further evidence of the invalidity of the Wechsler Adult Intelligence Scale for the assessment of intelligence of mental retardates. *J. ment. defic. Research*, 1962, 6, 41–43. (a)

——. A note on the validity of the Wechsler Adult Intelligence Scale for mental retardates. *J. consult. Psychol.*, 1962, *26*. (b)

——, KILMAN, BEVERLY, and SHOTWELL, ANNA. Comparability of intelligence quotients of mental defectives of the Wechsler adult intelligence scale and the 1960 revision of the Stanford-Binet. *J. consult, Psychol.*, 1961, *25*, 192–195.

GALLAGHER, J. J. *The tutoring of brain-injured mentally retarded children: an experimental study.* Springfield, Ill.: Charles C Thomas, 1960.

——. Changes in verbal and non-verbal ability of brain-injured mentally retarded children following removal of special stimulation. *Amer. J. ment. Defic.*, 1962, *66*, 774–781.

GOFFMAN, E. Characteristics of total institutions. In *Symposium on preventive and social psychiatry*. Washington, D. C.: Walter Reed Army Institute of Research, 1957, 43–84.

GRANT, J. R. Results of institutional treatment of juvenile mental defectives over a 30-year period. *Canad. Med. Assn. J.*, 1956, *75*, 918–921.

GREEN, C., and ZIGLER, E. Social deprivation and the performance of retarded and normal children on a satiation type task. *Child Develpm.*, 1962, *33*, 499–508.

GREENE, CHARLOTTE L. A study of personal adjustment in mentally retarded girls. *Amer. J. ment. Defic.*, 1945, *49*, 472–476.

HAROLD, E. C. Employment of patients discharged from the St. Louis State Training School. *Amer. J. ment. Defic.*, 1955, *60*, 397–402.

HARTZLER, ETHEL. A ten-year survey of girls discharged from the Laurelton State Village. *Amer. J. ment. Defic.*, 1953, *57*, 512–517.

HEBER, R. A manual on terminology and classification in mental retardation. *Monogr. Supp. Amer. J. ment. Defic.*, 1959, *64*, No. 2.

HIATT, M. S. Casework services in community placement of defectives. *Amer. J. ment. Defic.*, 1951, *56*, 204–211.

HOAKLEY, Z. PAULINE. The variability of intelligence quotients. *Amer. Assn. Study Feebleminded*, 1932, *37*, 119–148.

HUMPHREYS, E. J. Questionnaires of the 1936–1937 Committee on Research of the American Association on Mental Deficiency. *Proc. Amer. Assn. ment. Defic.*, 1937, *42*, 188–222.

ISCOE, I., and McCANN, J. The perception of an emotional continuum by older and younger mental retardates. *J. abnorm. soc. Psychol.*, 1965, *1*, 383–385.

JONES, D., and CARR-SAUNDERS, A. The relation between intelligence and social status among orphan children. *Brit. J. Psychol.*, 1927, *17*, 343–364.

KAPLAN, O. Mental decline in older morons. *Amer. J. ment. Defic.*, 1943, *47*, 277–285.

KEPHART, N. C., and STRAUSS, A. A. A clinical factor influencing variations in IQ. *Amer. J. Orthopsychiat.*, 1940, *10*, 343–350.

KIRK, S. A. *Early education of the mentally retarded*. Urbana: University of Illinois Press, 1958.

KRISHEF, C. H. An analysis of some factors in the institutional experience of mentally retarded discharges from the Owatonna State School that influence their successful or unsuccessful community adjustment. Unpublished manuscript, School of Social Work, University of Minnesota, 1957.

————, REYNOLDS, M. C., and STUNKARD, C. L. A study of factors related to rating post-institutional adjustment. *Minn. Welfare*, 1959, *11*, 5–15.

KUENZEL, MYRA W. Social status of foster families engaged in community care and training of mentally deficient children. *Amer. Assn. ment. Defic.*, 1939, *44*, 244–253.

LYLE, J. G. The effect of an institution environment upon the verbal development of imbecile children: I. Verbal intelligence. *J. ment. defic. Res.*, 1959, *3*, 122–128.

————. The effect of an institution environment upon the verbal development of imbecile children: II. Speech and Language. *J. ment. defic. Res.*, 1960, *4*, 1–13. (a)

————. The effect of an institution environment upon the verbal development of imbecile children: III. The Brooklands residential family unit. *J. ment. defic. Res.*, 1960, *4*, 14–23. (b)

McKay, B. E. A study of IQ changes in a group of girls paroled from a state school for mental defectives. *Amer. J. ment. Defic.*, 1942, *46*, 296–500.

Megaw, D. C., and Sullivan, L. C. Relationship of specialized vocational training and community adjustment in higher grade mentally defective boys. *Amer. J. ment. Defic.*, 1945, *49*, 383–387.

Minoque, Blanche M. The constancy of the IQ of mental defectives. *Ment. Hyg.*, 1926, *10*, 751–758.

Mitchell, Anna. A study of the social competence of a group of institution-alized retarded children. *Amer. J. ment. Defic.*, 1955, *60*, 354.

Mundy, Lydia. Environmental influence on intellectual function as measured by intelligence tests. *Brit. J. med. Psychol.*, 1957, *30*, 194–201.

Nye, F. I. *Family relationships and delinquent behavior.* New York: John Wiley and Sons, 1958.

O'Brien, M. W. A vocational study of a group of institutionalized persons. *Amer. J. ment. Defic.*, 1952, *57*, 56–62.

Pense, A. W. The problem of the male defective delinquent in the state school. *Amer. J. ment. Defic.*, 1943, *47*, 467–472.

Pinneau, S. R. *Changes in intelligence quotient.* Boston: Houghton-Mifflin, 1961.

Popenoe, P. Success on parole after sterilization. *Proc. Amer. Assn. Study Feebleminded*, 1927, *32*, 86–103.

Potter, H. W., and McCollister, Crystal. A resumé of parole work at Letchworth Village. *Proc. Amer. Assn. Study Feebleminded*, 1926, *31*, 165–188.

Prouty, Ruth A. Psychological classification versus clinical diagnosis. *Psychol. Clinic.* 1930, *18*, 213–220.

Reynolds, M. C., and MacEachern, D. G. The prediction of the adult status of high grade mental defectives. In M. E. Wright and H. T. Croley (Eds.), *Research in the management of the mentally retarded child.* Winfield, Kan.: Winfield State Training School, 1956, 175–193.

Saenger, G. *The adjustment of severely retarded adults in the community.* Albany: New York State Interdepartmental Health Resources Board, 1957.

Sarason, S. B., and Gladwin, T. Psychological and cultural problems in mental subnormality: A review of research. *Amer. J. ment. Defic.*, 1958, *62*, 1115–1307.

Schroeder, P. L., and Bartelme, P. A mental health program as a juvenile court method of supervising the feebleminded. *Amer. Assn. Study Feeble-minded*, 1928, *33*, 37–58.

Scott, W. A. Research definitions of mental health and mental illness. *Psychol. Bull.*, 1958, *55*, 29–45.

Shafter, A. J. Criteria for selecting institutionalized mental defectives for vocational placement. *Amer. J. ment. Defic.*, 1957, *61*, 599–616.

Skeels, H. M., and Dye, H. A study of the effects of differential stimulation on mentally retarded children. *Proc. Amer. Assn. ment. Defic.*, 1939, *44*, 114–136.

Sloan, W., and Harman, H. H. Constancy of IQ in mental defectives. *J. genet. Psychol.*, 1947, *71*, 177–185.

Sommer, R. On writing "little papers." *Amer. Psychologist*, 1959, *14*, 235–237.

Stebbins, I. F. An evaluation of homes for parole placement of mental defec-tives. *Amer. Assn. Study Feebleminded*, 1931, *36*, 50–69.

Stedman, D. J., Eichorn, D. H., Griffin, J., and Gooch, B. A comparative study of growth and developmental trends of institutionalized and noninstitutionalized retarded children: A summary report. Paper read at AAMD national convention, New York, 1962.

STEVENSON, H. W., and KNIGHTS, R. M. The effectiveness of social reinforcement after brief and extended institutionalization. *Amer. J. ment. Defic.*, 1962, *66*, 589–594.

STRAUSS, A. A., and KEPHART, N. C. Role of mental growth in a constant environment among higher grade moron and borderline children. *Amer. Assn. ment. Defic.*, 1939, *44*, 137–142.

TARJAN, G., and BENSON, F. Report on the pilot study at Pacific Colony. *Amer. J. ment. Defic.*, 1953, *57*, 453–462.

———, WRIGHT, S. W., DINGMAN, H. G., and EYMAN, R. K. Natural history of mental deficiency in a state hospital. *Amer. J. Diseases Children*, 1961, *101*, 195–205.

THOMAS, B. E. A study of the factors used to make a prognosis of social adjustment. *Amer. J. ment. Defic.*, 1943, *47*, 334–336.

TONG, J. E., and MACKAY, G. W. A statistical follow-up of mental defectives of dangerous or violent propensities. *Brit. J. Del.*, 1959, *9*, 276–284.

TOWN, CLARA H. An investigation of the adjustment of the feebleminded in the community. *Psychol. clinic*, 1931, *20*, 42–54.

WALLACE, G. L. Parole of the feeble-minded. *Proc. Amer. Assn. Study Feeble-minded*, 1918–9, *23*, 60–81.

WINDLE, C. An exploratory study of unauthorized absences from Pacific State Hospital. *Trng. Sch. Bull.*, 1959, *55*, 73–75.

———. Prognosis of mental subnormals. *Monogr. Supp. Amer. J. ment. Defic.*, 1962, *66*, No. 5.

WOLFSON, I. N. Follow-up studies of 92 male and 131 female patients who were discharged from the Newark State School in 1946. *Amer. J. ment. Defic.*, 1956, *61*, 224–238.

YARROW, L. J. Maternal deprivation: Toward an empirical and conceptual reevaluation. *Psychol. Bull.*, 1961, *58*, 459–490.

ZIGLER, E. Social deprivation and rigidity in the performance of feebleminded children. *J. abnorm. soc. Psychol.*, 1961, *62*, 413–421.

———. Social reinforcement, environment, and the child. *Amer. J. Orthopsychiat.*, 1963, *33*, 614–623.

——— and WILLIAMS, J. Institutionalization and the effectiveness of social reinforcement: A three-year follow-up study. *J. abnorm. soc. Psychol.*, 1963, *66*, 197–205.

Psychotherapy and Other Adjustment Techniques with the Mentally Retarded[1]

IRV BIALER

CUSTOMARILY, one begins a discussion of psychotherapy by proposing a definition. However, in synthesizing the views of experts toward that end, one sees readily that a simple definition of "psychotherapy"—or even a complex one that will meet everyone's criteria—is well nigh impossible. Nevertheless, psychiatrists and clinical psychologists, while disagreeing among and between themselves as to just what psychotherapy is, generally agree that it refers broadly to effecting behavioral or personality changes in the direction of more effective adjustment through planned psychological, as opposed to medical, means. At the same time, because the emphasis is on *psychological procedures,* the opinion is commonly held, even among many professionals, that the term may only be applied legitimately to therapeutic procedures employed by psychiatrists and psychologists. One of the purposes of this chapter is to examine the construct's general relevance to procedures used by a variety of professional disciplines.

In rendering services to the mentally retarded—particularly in an institutional setting—a number of other disciplines are engaged in efforts to effect positive behavioral change or social and emotional adjustment—efforts that seem to fit under the general rubric of "adjustment techniques," but are not commonly given the appellation "psychotherapy." These disciplines include social service, chaplaincy, adjunctive therapies, and nursing service.

In concluding an excellent chapter on psy-

1. Preparation of this chapter was aided in part by the support of the Joseph P. Kennedy, Jr., Foundation.

chotherapy with the exceptional child, Cowen and Trippe (1963) state:

Fundamentally, . . . , it would be a mistake to view psychotherapy as the only weapon in the mental health armamentarium. It is not! . . .

Psychotherapy should not be oversold, nor should it be sold down the river. There is . . . , an important place for it in a balanced . . . overall approach to the mental health problems of the disabled. But progress in this area will be accelerated only if we do not constrict ourselves by thinking of psychotherapy first and grafting other approaches on to that corpus. . . . Indeed it may be more useful in future compendia to replace a chapter on psychotherapy . . . with a somewhat broader one on mental health approaches with the disabled. . . . (pp. 582-583)

While retaining the major emphasis on those procedures commonly labeled "psychotherapeutic," I have attempted to replace a chapter on psychotherapy with a somewhat broader one. More specifically, I also have attempted to examine the treatment roles of such "helping techniques" as casework and social group work (social service), pastoral counseling (chaplaincy), art, music, occupational and recreational therapies (adjunctive therapies), and remotivation (nursing service).

Throughout, I have made a deliberate effort to avoid couching the discussion in the form of an extensive, comprehensive review of the literature on psychotherapy with the mentally retarded. The interested reader is referred to representative summaries of research in Cowen and Trippe (1963), Gunzburg (1958), and Sternlicht (1965) and to an as-yet-unexcelled collection of reprinted studies in Stacey and DeMartino (1957). Further, Sternlicht (in press) presents the most comprehensively documented review of work in this area.

DEFINITIONS AND THERAPEUTIC ROLES

PSYCHOTHERAPY

To provide a clear and coherent frame of reference for our discussion, I propose a "best fit" definition, which has been culled from a survey of representative viewpoints of what constitutes the essential elements of the construct (Coleman, 1949; Gunzburg, 1958; Hadley, 1958; Kaplan, 1963; Leland and Smith, 1962; Robinson and Robinson, 1965; Rotter, 1964; Snyder, 1947; Wolberg, 1954).

Psychotherapy may be defined as *the systematic utilization of psychological techniques, chief of which is a close interpersonal relationship, by a professionally trained therapist in order to help individuals who need or seek his assistance in the amelioration of their emotional or behavioral problems. The procedures involved may include nonverbal as well as verbal techniques, and the subjects may or may not be aware of the dynamics of the therapeutic process.*

The elements of this definition cover what most authorities, regardless of theoretical bent, seem to agree psychotherapy is. At the same time, some of these elements indicate what most people would consider it is not. Let us analyze the definition along these lines.

What Psychotherapy Is: 1. It is primarily (and this is probably its most distinguishing characteristic) psychological treatment applied with a certain amount of regularity and consistency. The chief medium through which the psychological treatment is effected is a close and oftentimes emotional relationship between the subject (primarily referred to as either "patient" or "client") and the therapist. However, in some cases, as with the schizophrenic child who cannot tolerate close interpersonal contact, the technique may require the deliberate maintenance of a relationship that is more "distant."

2. It requires an adequate level of preparation and training on the part of the therapist that provides him with the tools—theoretical background and practical experience—with

which to treat emotional or behavioral problems.

3. Psychotherapy may be effected in either an individual or group setting.

4. Individuals in need of psychotherapy often seek this assistance; however, other individuals who need therapy but do not seek it (for example, young children and many mentally retarded individuals) must be referred in one way or another.

5. The amelioration of problems requiring psychotherapy may be carried out through verbal or nonverbal procedures (for example, play and activity media).

6. Since children may very often be unaware that they are undergoing a personality reorganization and since, indeed, such reorganization need not necessarily be the goal of all psychotherapeutic relationships, awareness on the part of the subject is not seen as necessary to the present definition.

What Psychotherapy Is Not: 1. It is not medical treatment in the sense of utilizing drugs and other medication. Thus its practice is not necessarily limited to any given profession. While psychotherapy is generally accepted as part of the repertoire of the psychiatrist, psychoanalyst, and clinical psychologist, Grinker, MacGregor, Selan, Klein, and Kohrman (1961) point out: "Psychological intervention is a form of drugless therapy and not subject to restrictions of licensure. . . . Who does psychotherapy depends only on the individual's qualifications" (p. 115). The licensure Grinker refers to is that which limits medical practice. Of course, some sort of regulatory or supervisory procedure is necessary to ensure that only those individuals who are properly qualified through training and experience are permitted to function as psychotherapists.

2. Psychotherapy does not include any type of physical treatment—including speech therapy, although the latter may be used in conjunction with psychotherapy in those cases where the speech disorder reflects emotional problems.

3. Teaching procedures and guidance activities that are primarily oriented toward information dissemination and advice-giving are not considered psychotherapeutic.

4. There is some general disagreement over whether procedures involving environmental modification and subsumed under such labels

as "milieu therapy" or "environmental therapy" may legitimately be designated as *psycho*therapy.

Considerations of the various viewpoints indicate that environmental treatment may be viewed as having two (not necessarily mutually exclusive) aspects. One of these involves its utilization as an integral part of the psychotherapeutic process and is exemplified by the treatment of parents along with their children. In this aspect, a change in behavior and attitude on the part of parents is seen as an improvement in the child's social environment, with consequent facilitation of the child's own therapy. The other aspect centers around fostering alterations in the child's surroundings for purposes of effecting behavioral modification without necessarily directly involving the child in a psychotherapeutic relationship. This is exemplified, in the community, by removing the child from his own inadequate home and placing him in a foster home or by "marked changes in the behavior of a delinquent or obstructive school child when the school sees fit to recognize some talent or to give the child a position of importance in the classroom" (Rotter, 1964, p. 87), and, in an institutional setting, by altering the resident's cottage or ward placement or his work supervisor. In the first sense, environmental manipulation may be considered an indispensable adjunct to psychotherapy with the child; in the second sense, it could probably more meaningfully be construed as an independent "helping" technique.

SOCIAL CASEWORK AND GROUP WORK

Psychiatric social workers, while designating their treatment approaches "casework" or "social group work," seem to feel that often the members of their profession must differentiate between or point out the similarities of what they do and what may be defined as psychotherapy. Hadley's definition is representative: "Psychiatric social work is one of many social work fields. It is distinguished . . . by the fact that the psychiatric social worker has had . . . courses and field experience with psychiatric orientation, and works . . . in a psychiatric setting" (1958, p. 618). Since the question of whether casework and social group work can or should be designated as psychotherapy seems to preoccupy not only

social workers (e.g., Garrett, 1949; Hollis, 1964; Konopka, 1963) but psychiatrists (e.g., Allen, 1963; Coleman, 1949; Kaplan, 1963) definitional and conceptual problems have been rampant.

Social Casework. Mary Richmond (1922), whose efforts served to systemize social work as a professional discipline, provided an early conceptual framework for the role of the social caseworker. Richmond conceived the special field of casework as "the development of personality through the conscious and comprehensive adjustment of social relationships, and within that field the worker is no more occupied with abnormalities in the individual than in the environment, is no more able to neglect the one than the other. The distinctive approach of the case worker, in fact, is back to the individual by way of his social environment" (1922, p. 98).

More recently, Hollis (1964) described casework as a form of psychological therapy which "has its own identity, its own philosophy and its own methodolgy, related to but not identical with those of any other 'healing professions' [i.e., psychiatry, psychoanalysis, psychology]" (p. 266).

Consideration of the preceding definitional statements makes it readily apparent that casework treatment is covered by our "best fit" definition of psychotherapy. Nevertheless, I must agree with the stand taken by Coleman (1949), whose position, while it was stated many years ago, still is strongly congruent with that of the more recent psychiatric and social work sources cited above.

Coleman said, "The practice of the qualified caseworker may be considered a form of psychotherapy . . . , since it is a procedure directed toward the alleviation of emotional distress through the use of psychological means, based upon an adequate educational foundation . . . , however, I see no value in calling casework anything but casework, even though it is a genuine psychotherapeutic endeavor" (p. 245).

Social Group Work. Richmond (1922) conceived of group work as an extension of casework in that the former "includes a wide variety of activities . . . in which the individual, though still met face to face, becomes one of a number" (p. 223). Konopka (1963) retained these essential ingredients in her more comprehensive (albeit general) definition:

"Social group work is a method of social work that helps individuals to enhance their social functioning through purposeful group experiences and to cope more effectively with their personal, group, or community problems" (p. 20).

As with casework, the practice of social group work is very much akin to the practice of group psychotherapy, using our definition of the latter. However, again, as with casework, there seems to be little to gain from calling social group work by any other name. On the contrary, labeling as "psychotherapists" psychiatric social workers who are providing therapeutic services would have the effect of losing for them both part of their professional identity and the value of differentiating their contribution to the joint effort of a number of disciplines.

By and large, psychiatric social workers do not appear to seek the label, "psychotherapist." They are rather concerned with having it understood by the professions with which they work most closely (i.e., psychiatrists and psychologists) that they are providing a distinct therapeutic service by techniques which have much in common with those of the other professions.

PASTORAL COUNSELING

Pastoral counseling may be defined as: "A verbal interchange between an individual with theological as well as psychological training (i.e., a specially trained minister or pastor) and a member of his congregation for purposes of solving the member's personal or religious problems."

As an adjustment technique, pastoral counseling seeks ultimately to help the individual "so that he can live as socially useful, emotionally mature, and personally satisfying a life as he is able to in [his] environment" (Golden, 1962, p. 33). The procedures involved may sometimes be very similar to those therapeutic approaches utilized by psychologists, psychiatrists, and psychiatric social workers.

What, then, distinguishes pastoral counseling from the other "helping professions"? Two distinctive dimensions come to mind: The first revolves around the symbol of the minister as a representative of God and the church. The second involves the durable or continuing relationship that the individual has with his pastor.

Both the symbolic representation of the minister and the nuances of his extra-counseling relationships with the parishioner distinguish the pastoral counselor very sharply from the psychologist, the psychiatrist, and the social worker.

The religious dimension of the minister's role imbues it with awe and respect, and the counselee tends to identify the pastor's values with love and "correct" behavior. In direct contradistinction to the other professions, pastoral counseling often apparently involves consideration of moral issues insofar as the behavior of the individual is concerned. Nevertheless, both Golden (1962) and Stubblefield (1965, chapter 7) emphasize that the religious symbolism attached to the clergyman's role and the perception of his values by the troubled person may have positive therapeutic value.

In his durable relationship, the minister is often involved in every phase of his church members' lives. He often plays a significant role for the individual before any trouble develops, and he will continue to have a relationship after the problem is solved. Because of this continuing involvement, the pastoral counselor is perceived in a somewhat different light than is the psychologist or social worker, with whom a given client maintains a very specific, temporally limited interaction.

The combination of role representation and continuous interaction probably predisposes the church member to bring to the clergyman many different kinds of problems, so that the pastor is often faced with the necessity of deciding which problems he can handle and which ones he should refer elsewhere. As Sivley (1963) puts it: "When an individual brings his spiritual problems to the pastor, he often brings his psychological problems, too. When does one stop and the other start? When should a pastor refer his parishioner for other professional help?" (p. 33). Stubblefield (1965, chapter 6), while discussing this problem from the viewpoint of pastoral care to the mentally retarded, seems to sum up a viewpoint that is relevant to other groups as well. Stubblefield points out that the minister must work within the larger context of other relationships that impinge upon the individual and that the pastoral counselor, when faced with emotional or adjustment problems that appear to be outside his own realm of competence, should correlate his work with other professional and community resources, including physicians, psychologists, and psychiatric social workers.

ADJUNCTIVE THERAPIES

The term "adjunctive," when applied to therapeutic procedures, may be construed as having two meanings that are pertinent to the present topic. On one hand, it may refer to media that are used as auxiliaries or aids to other treatment or counseling activities. Thus, artistic activities such as drawing or finger painting may be utilized as nonverbal psychotherapeutic techniques. Art provides a medium through which an individual of limited expressive ability may give vent to feelings and ideas without having to put them into words. Robinson and Robinson (1965) indicate that: "A number of workers have utilized artistic media as adjuncts to psychotherapy with both retarded adults and retarded children" (p. 490). By the same token, Hadley (1958) in describing music as an adjunctive medium, reports that "music often provides an opening wedge to help the counselor . . . gain rapport with the client" (p. 206). Further, the use of recreational activities in a psychotherapeutic relationship may play a role in facilitating the therapist-client interaction. DeMartino (1957) characterizes recreational therapy as a psychotherapeutic approach through which the therapist has an additional opportunity to impart "basic need gratification," which DeMartino suggests is one of the chief avenues through which therapy occurs—particularly among institutionalized retardates.

Under the second meaning of the term, adjunctive therapies are adjustment techniques that, as part of an over-all institutional program, are designed to effect positive behavioral change and effectiveness among the residents; yet these techniques do not always fit under the aegis of such recognized "therapeutic" departments as medicine (including psychiatry), psychology, and social service. A department of adjunctive therapies may include subsections on recreation, occupational therapy, music therapy, and art therapy. Ideally, each of these sections—which may function as autonomous "departments" in some settings—is under the direction of an individual with specialized training in his respective field. The point to be noted is that psychological training is not a prerequisite to filling these positions or conducting these programs. The important variable is a level of technical skill on the part of the staff member in his own area of specialization and the ability to provide the resident with the means through which his sense of well-being, his behavioral effectiveness, and his social relationships may be enhanced without psychotherapeutic intervention.

Another important difference between adjunctive therapies and psychological therapies is that, whereas the latter are extended only to those who are diagnosed as needing them, the former may in many instances be extended to all residents. This is particularly true of recreational activities and, to lesser degrees, of art, music, and occupational activities. The point here is that the resident does not necessarily have to manifest "maladjusted" behavior before he is included in these "therapeutic" programs.

While psychological training on the part of therapist and maladjustment on the part of the resident are not necessarily requisite to conducting an adjunctive therapies program, I contend that the various activities contribute to positive behavioral change or social and emotional adjustment. Toward that end, the following definitions are advanced.

Art Activities. When the artistic media are employed as nonverbal psychotherapeutic techniques (e.g., Freeman, 1936, 1957; Kadis, 1957; King, 1954) the label "art therapy" might be appropriate. However, the term "art activities program" seems more meaningful and less equivocal when such media as drawing, painting, or finger painting are employed as part of a large-scale recreational program under the supervision of a (nonpsychologically) trained person (e.g., Schlotter and Svendsen, 1959; Southern Regional Education Board, 1964). The goal here is to improve an individual's adjustment by giving him interesting and creative tasks through which he might be able to (1) express himself, (2) gain a feeling of accomplishment, (3) develop his talent, or (4) enhance his general feeling of well-being.

Music Activities. Procedures involving musical instruments, songs, rhythm, and musical games may also be subsumed under two categories. They may be recreational (i.e., used for fun, relaxation, profitable use of leisure time, or entertainment) or they may be therapeutic (i.e., designed to treat pathological behavior that may or may not be amenable to other forms of therapy). Activities falling under both of these categories may be within the purview of an adjunctive therapies department; and both are very often administered or supervised by a qualified staff member who is identified as a music therapist (i.e., "a person engaged in the application of music as a rehabilitation or treatment method" [Shatin, Longmore, and Kotter, 1963, p. 18]). Recreational programs for the mentally retarded typically include musical activities (e.g., Schlotter and Svendsen, 1959; Southern Regional Education Board, 1964) that are designed to effect positive behavioral changes along the same lines as those propounded above for an art activities program. However, music therapy involves a planned approach by a trained person directed toward one or more other individuals with a view toward modifying specific maladaptive or pathological behavior through the use of musical techniques and media (e.g., Heimlich, 1960; Joseph and Heimlich, 1959; Nordoff and Robbins, 1965; Weigl, 1959).

Occupational Therapy. The American Association on Mental Deficiency manual on standards for state institutions (AAMD, 1964) defines occupational therapy (OT) as "medically prescribed and professionally guided physical or mental activity devised to treat specific disorders or disabilities" (p. 82). This broad statement, which could very easily be applied to a number of other therapeutic procedures is then further qualified: "In mental retardation occupational therapy may be especially valuable in the treatment of residents manifesting physical disabilities, emotional disturbances and [a] wide variety of perceptual handicaps" (p. 82).

While the AAMD manual suggests that OT be considered a program of therapies, the definition and its accompanying statements are too general and do not in any way indicate how OT differs from other treatment techniques. However, a number of authors have attempted to delineate the exact nature of this method of treatment with various degrees of precision.

For example, Flaherty (1956) provides a concise definitional statement that distinguishes the technique from others: "In any field of service, occupational therapy is treatment by means of participation in occupations or activities devised for a specific problem" (p. 758).

Hutt and Gibby (1958), in describing OT as a therapeutic approach with the retarded child, indicate that: "This approach involves creative activity on the part of the retarded child (such as simple woodworking, clay modeling, weaving, and the like). Occupational therapy enables the child to develop his interests and aptitudes, and provides a means through which specific disabilities of the child may be corrected" (p. 298).

There appears to be some concern, some disagreement, and perhaps some preoccupation with the question of whether occupational therapy is an educational or a medical function.

Soper (1946, 1957) holds at one point that for the institutionalized mentally retarded, occupational therapy is essentially "teaching behavior" (i.e., designed to instill patterns of acceptable behavior into such residents by utilizing such media as arts and crafts, music, games, and recreation activities). However, Soper further notes that occupational therapy must be prescribed by a staff physician before a resident is enrolled in such a program.

Menzel (1952, 1957) considers occupational therapy as warranting inclusion under the rubric "psychotherapeutic techniques." She uses the term "psychiatric occupational therapy," and makes it very clear that the therapist is following through on the referring psychiatrist's prescription—with never an intimation that an educational process is in any way involved.

In striking contrast to Menzel's approach, Dewing (1952, 1957) conceptualizes an OT program (in this case specifically with severely retarded children) as one of educational and constructive activities aimed at modifying behavior—with no mention of medical prescription or supervision.

The dual conceptualization of the function and place of OT in an institutional program at present is illustrated in the AAMD manual on institution standards (AAMD, 1964). As previously noted, the manual defines OT as a "medically prescribed" activity. It then goes on to recommend that the occupational therapist be a graduate of a program accredited by the Council on Medical Education and Hospitals of the American Medical Association (p. 83). Nevertheless, in previously describing the functions of a department of education and training, the same manual notes: "In some institutions . . . there will be other functions assigned to this department such as occupational therapy" (p. 79).

Having raised the question of a function that is assigned to the education department yet which is medically prescribed and apparently medically oriented, the manual makes a recommendation that may serve to solve at least that segment of the "education vs. medical function" controversy. It suggests "that occupational therapy should be established as a separate and independent discipline" (p. 83), under a director or supervisor of occupational therapy.

Recreational Services. Under the previous section on music activities, I indicated that the term "recreational" connotes those activities that are "used for fun, relaxation, profitable use of leisure time, or entertainment." Other, more authoritative authors have included these elements in their more formal definitions. Lawler (1964) in presenting a rationale for recreational services to institutionalized retardates, states, for example: "the following definition, simple as it is, [is] most appropriate: 'If it's fun, it's recreation!' Another definition of recreation might be: 'Any form of leisure time experience or activity in which an individual engages because of the enjoyment and satisfaction it brings to him'" (p. 2).

The term "recreational therapy" is often loosely applied to such services that are rendered to the mentally retarded in the institution or the community. The AAMD manual on institutional standards (AAMD, 1964) seems to give the term formal recognition and status by listing "recreational therapy" under the heading "Therapies and Activities" (p. 39) along with "occupational therapy," "physical therapy," and several others. The manual does not define the therapeutic role of recreation, but the point is stressed that "recreation programming should provide each resident with enjoyable leisure-time activities and promote mental and physical health through interesting and worthwhile recreational pursuits" (p. 49).

Remotivation. Remotivation is a therapeutic technique that was originally developed for use by the psychiatric aide or ward attendant in the mental hospital (APA/SKF, 1964; Long, 1962; Robinson, 1964), and that has subsequently been adapted and modified for use with the institutionalized mentally retarded (APA/SKF, 1962; Wright, Erb, and Lawrence, 1961). The technique, which is primarily a nursing service function (i.e., supervised by professional nurses) was specifically designed to provide ward personnel with a means of re-establishing the severely disturbed patient's contact with and appreciation of reality through the use of a structured yet flexible group relationship. At the same time, the remotivation technique provides an additional dimension by which the attendant becomes an active and recognized member of the total therapeutic effort. Thus, it has reportedly resulted in changing the behavior and attitudes not only of the mental patient, but those of the ward attendant as well (Long, 1961, 1962; Long and Ferrel, 1962).

Accordingly, remotivation has been defined as "a technique of simple group interaction which can be used by the psychiatric aide with his own patients. It is a structured activity which enables him to reach his patients in a meaningful and constructive way, over and above the daily custodial care which has previously constituted the somewhat limited role of the psychiatric aide" (Robinson, 1964, Introduction).

Robinson emphasizes further that "remotivation is not psychotherapy in the strict sense of the word. It is, instead a method of aide-patient interaction which increases and strengthens the contact between the aide and his own patients" (1964, p. 2).

The technique follows a structured procedure consisting of five carefully organized "steps," the ultimate aim of which is to "re-awaken interest in the environment and re-establish the basic techniques of social adjustment" (Long, 1961, p. 8). The procedure is seen as accomplishing the aim through: (1) stimulating the patient—providing him with something new and different to think about; (2) interesting him in the objective world—thereby reducing autistic behavior; and (3) providing him with group interaction (APA/SKF, 1964; Long, 1962).

Although the remotivation technique was originally developed for use in mental hospitals, its potential applicability to residents of institutions for the mentally retarded was quickly recognized and implemented with some modification (Wright, Erb, and Lawrence, 1961). However, it has been suggested that the term "motivation" be applied to the adaptation of the remotivation technique to schools and hospitals for the mentally retarded (APA/SKF, 1962). At present, this suggestion (although it may have some merit) does not seem to have met with wide acceptance among proponents of the technique with retarded residents.

OBJECTIVES AND AIMS

Traditionally, all the therapeutic and adjustment techniques that were discussed in the previous section have been applied primarily in institutional settings; and probably with very few exceptions, (e.g., some art and music activities and other recreational services including what has been alluded to as "therapeutic recreation") the various services will continue to be extended and applied primarily to institutionalized retardates. This supposition is based on several reasons:

1. As community training programs for both educable and trainable retardates increase in number and in scope, and as vocational training and rehabilitation efforts in the community increase in effectiveness, the characteristics of the institutional residents are undergoing a subtle but steady and apparently inexorable change. The institutionalized population is becoming younger or more severely retarded (Scheerenberger, 1965); and when an older, higher level retardate is institutionalized, it is usually after he has manifested behavior that has brought him to the attention of the authorities or that has made him a family or community problem. As Beier (1964) points out, the presence of a behavioral disorder is among the primary causes of institutionalization of the mildly or borderline mentally retarded.

2. In some of the latter cases, institutionalization may be the only resort because of lack of community facilities or interested professional personnel for treating behavior disorders and emotional problems among retardates. For example, Robinson and Robinson (1965) note that largely because of negative attitudes prevalent among mental health professionals who are not primarily affiliated with facilities for the retarded, "in many community clinics, children tend to be turned away simply because they are retarded . . .

without regard for their needs or amenability to treatment" (p. 480). The gloomy picture is accentuated when one considers that with some notable exceptions (e.g., Chess, 1962), even in clinics that have been specifically established to provide services to the mentally retarded and their families, professional workers for a number of reasons as pointed out by Wolfensberger (1965), may be emphasizing diagnosis and "shying away from other services"—including psychotherapy and counseling.

3. Long-time institutionalized individuals who are amenable to habilitative programs and discharge eventually find their way back to the community. However, a number of high-level retardates of both sexes who might otherwise be eligible for habilitative or rehabilitative services from the institution may manifest behavioral pathology that is incompatible with community placement—thus requiring therapeutic services within the institution.

4. As Leland and Smith (1962) indicate, the fact of institutionalization itself may create a need for extending adjustment procedures to given children. This appears to be particularly true of those children who construe institutionalization as verification of their fears of rejection by their family and who consequently cannot respond well to the hospital or school.

5. Organized, purposeful effort to extend wide-scale psychological, psychiatric and social service therapies to retardates has been and still is prevalent with few exceptions only in an institutional setting. The same may be said of pastoral counseling, since it is only in the institution that the pastor or chaplain is available to the retardate on a convenient and continuing basis. On the other hand, occupational therapy has been developed and is conducted primarily within a hospital or institutional milieu; and remotivation has been, by definition, similarly circumscribed in its application since its inception.

Probably only in the area of those services subsumed under the rubric "recreational activities"—including "therapeutic recreation"—has a definite trend developed toward extending pertinent programs and services to the retardate in the community in a purposeful, organized, large-scale manner.

Consequently, while community programs may be mentioned where appropriate, the discussion that follows will emphasize services extended to the retardate in the residential facility. Needless to say, while objectives and aims may be somewhat different, most of the various techniques may be applied with little or no modification to community programs for the retarded.

PSYCHOTHERAPY

The major goals of workers who direct psychotherapeutic efforts toward the mentally retarded fall into three principal categories: IQ change, emotional or behavioral adjustment, and milieu or (environmental) modification.

Historically, the psychotherapeutic objective of changes in the IQ referred to attempts at reversing, attenuating, or "curing" the condition by raising the level of measured intelligence significantly—thus removing the "fundamental cause" of the retardation. Under this objective, effectiveness of treatment was gauged by the extent to which test scores rose from pre- to post-treatment. The earliest studies apparently were directed primarily toward "curing" the condition rather than toward the alleviation of emotional or behavioral distress. Findings under this general approach were contradictory and confusing. For example, while Chidester and Menninger (1936) reported a marked increase in IQ score (from 62 to 90) along with "near-normal functioning" in the single case history that constitutes their report, Clark (1933) came away with the conclusion that: "psychoanalysis as a therapy would not claim to remove the fundamental causes of amentia . . . the innate defect is not curable" (quoted by Beier, 1964, p. 474).

Later research which utilized the criterion of IQ change or which cited this as a significant aspect of therapeutic effectiveness was more directly aimed at modifying emotional problems. Cowen and Trippe (1963) and Gunzburg (1958) have presented reviews and critiques of such research. While many of these studies report positive changes in measured intelligence following psychotherapy, it would probably still be wise to heed Beier's injunction that "increases in intellectual measures through psychotherapy are still generally suspect" (1964, p. 480).

With all, I am in essential agreement with the categorical statement of Cowen and Trippe that "there are some children, competently diagnosed as defective . . . , who are capable of making significant . . . intellectual improvements following a psychotherapeutic . . . experience" (1963, p. 554).

The second objective, emotional or behavioral adjustment, is concerned with the treatment of the relevant pathology in an individual who is mentally retarded with a view toward enhancing social relationships and general behavioral effectiveness. Here, the primary emphasis is on treating the personality problem, and increases in IQ ratings when they occur, may be considered incidental to the alleviation of emotional and behavioral distress. For example, Axline's report (1949, 1957) deals with children who were referred for nondirective play therapy on the basis of emotional disturbance or behavior problems. As a result of the therapy experiences, about one-third of the children, in addition to showing improvement in the presenting problem, showed striking gains in measured intelligence. However, Axline specifically disclaims the notion that the given treatment raised the IQ, insisting rather that "the explanation that seems apropos is that the child was freed from emotional constraint and could thus express his capacities more adequately" (1957, p. 220). Chess (1962), reporting on an experimental psychiatric program in a community mental retardation clinic, notes that of nineteen children in the program (all of whom responded to therapy with varying degrees of success in terms of emotional or behavioral improvement), two children made such significant gains, both behaviorally and in measured intelligence during the course of psychotherapy, that they could no longer be considered retarded.

In contrast to such studies as those of Axline and Chess, the trend at present seems to be toward emphasizing improvement in behavior and emotional adjustment and of applying pertinent (albeit not always sensitive) criteria to the exclusion of IQ change. Thus, Subotnick and Callahan (1959), using short-term play therapy on retardates with "emotional difficulties," measured effectiveness with projective tests and behavior ratings; Snyder and Sechrest (1959), in a study on directive group therapy with delinquent retardates, used the criterion of institutional adjustment as measured by housing reports; and Albini and Dinitz (1965) utilizing a combination of group play and individual interview therapy with disturbed retardates, employed a combination of measures including teacher ratings of behavior and attitudes, grades, attitude toward parent, and parental attitude toward and interest in the child.

Intellectual behavior may be adversely affected by the individual's emotional state, and, consequently, improved emotional stability may be reflected by a significant gain in measured intelligence on the part of the retardate. However, as Leland put it recently, this is "the cherry on the sundae, the ice cream and syrup being the actual improvement . . . in the areas of adaptive behavior and institutional or community living. The curable or reversible aspects [of psychotherapy] thus relate to changes in adaptive behavior rather than measured intelligence" (personal communication, 1964). This is a stand with which I heartily concur.

The concept of environmental modification is broadly equivalent to what Cowen and Trippe (1963) refer to as "the improvement of sociopsychological factors through more wholesome environments" (p. 560). At the institutional level, this may involve the interweaving of therapeutic activities into the overall program design. For example, in the study by Maisner (1950), play-therapy experiences were one aspect of a "special personality reeducation program"—which in turn was part of an over-all rehabilitative design, and Thorne (1948) describes a modification in an institutional program whereby counseling or psychotherapy — rather than punishment — were used to handle serious breaches of discipline.

For the retarded child in the community, milieu modification may involve treatment of parents along with children in order to facilitate the child's own therapy; or it may take the form of some of the modifications in home surroundings along the lines of those suggested by Wiest (1955) for strengthening the child's conception of himself as an individual (e.g., the strategic placement of mirrors to help the child see himself as a whole individual and as distinct from his surroundings).

SOCIAL CASEWORK AND SOCIAL GROUP WORK

With the exception of the sometimes overstressed aim of achieving significant positive changes in measured intelligence, the general categories of objectives for social work therapy are remarkably similar to those discussed in the previous section, namely: the enhancement of emotional adjustment and behavioral effectiveness, and adapting or "tailoring" the environment. However, an important difference between the therapeutic approaches of the disciplines involved is that the social worker puts much greater emphasis on the second objective as a means of achieving the first.

Specific goals of social work therapy with institutionalized retardates seem to be related to a number of very important factors:

1. The retarded individual is often completely unprepared for separation from his family and community. Thus, the transition from the family to the institution may often prove extremely traumatic.

2. The social worker, by virtue of the fact that he is intimately concerned with the intake process, is often viewed by the retardate as a sympathetic link between the institution and the family, In addition, the retardate may often seek out "his" social worker for contacts should later problems arise (Stewart, 1960).

3. Many of their problems "derive from unhealthy parent-child relationships, or uncompromising and hostile community attitudes" (Begab, 1963, p. 70). In addition, "some of these retarded individuals have come to regard all persons in authority as a source of punishment and persecution" (Begab, 1963, p. 71).

4. Nevertheless, where possible, the ultimate aim is to return the individual to his home, to his community, and to eventual social and vocational independence.

With these factors as a background, let us very briefly present some of the specific aims or goals of social work therapy with the institutionalized retardate.

Howell (1957) considers the aims of casework under six general headings:

(1) To assist the child in making a satisfactory adjustment to the life and routine of the training school; (2) To assist the child in handling emotional problems so that he will be able to profit from the various aspects of his training; (3) Preplacement planning with the child as he begins to reach the end of his training program; (4) To assist with the inevitable feelings that arise just prior to and immediately after leaving the training school; (5) To assist the parents with their feelings about original placement and the child's

possible return to his own home or to a more advised setting; (6) Simple interpretation to the community (p. 592).

The emphasis on follow-up treatment and community relations is what probably most strongly differentiates social work treatment from that of psychology and psychiatry.

Social work treatment is based on a supportive relationship between the worker and his clients and may include any or a combination of the following techniques (Begab, 1963; Community Service Society of New York, 1958; Stewart, 1960):

REASSURANCE. Here the emphasis is on recognition and approval of the client's abilities, capabilities, and strengths.

DISCUSSION. In this approach, which is ideally followed with motivated clients who can verbalize meaningfully, the primary effort may be a conscious focus on problem-solving. This technique employs the client's reasoning ability, helps him to interpret reality, to appreciate alternative courses of action, and to foresee possible consequences of specific behaviors on his part. Thus, this is probably most appropriate with older, higher level retardates.

ADVICE AND GUIDANCE. This technique is deemed appropriate "when the client is unable to find his own solution and when his need and motivation enable him to use direction or permission as a means toward achieving a socially acceptable goal" (Community Service Society of New York, 1958, p. 17). Begab (1963) sees this technique as being most appropriate with lower level retardates.

VENTILATION. This allows the individual to express his feelings regarding his experiences and to release pent-up emotion in a safe, permissive situation.

DIRECT INTERVENTION. This technique is readily recognized as being closely related to the general objective of environmental modification. As Stewart (1960) put it: "If there is any aspect of the retardate's social milieu that tends to be maladaptive, the worker can recommend changes in reality situations such as vocational, ward, or recreational placement" (p. 36). This is in line with the aim toward adapting the institutional environment in order to relieve undue emotional stress and to provide opportunities for learning and promoting new social skills. Other forms of en-

vironmental manipulation which involve direct intervention (although they are not usually thus labeled) are: effecting foster home placement that will suit the retardate's needs better than are those of the institution or his own family, and bringing about changes in the attitudes toward and expectations of the resident on the part of his family and community in order to foster more effective behavior both while the retardate is institutionalized and upon his release.

PASTORAL COUNSELING

More and more, clergymen are realizing that mentally retarded individuals are entitled to and can profit from a pastoral ministry— including help with personal, as well as religious problems through a counseling relationship (e.g., Agee, 1962; Golden, 1962; Stubblefield, 1965). However, the extent to which such services are being provided in most communities is questionable.

In a survey of 220 clergymen of various Christian denominations in a large southern city, Stubblefield (1964) found that 90 per cent or more of the ministers felt the church was responsible for the religious care of the retarded and that a pastoral ministry to the retarded was possible. Nevertheless, only a relative minority indicated that they had ever entered into a counseling situation with a retarded person or his family; and those who had done so tended to characterize their work as "pastoral care" (i.e., short-term, unstructured relationships, rather than long-term, structured counseling). If the sample surveyed in this study is representative of most U.S. communities, it is likely, as Stubblefield (1965) suggests, that clergymen in general have some trepidation about making themselves available to retarded members of their congregation on two accounts: (1) the general belief that pastoral ministry to the retarded is limited by the fact that these individuals always remain children, with the interests and needs of children; and (2) the assumption that retardates are so different from other members of the congregation that special training in the area of mental health is necessary before a helping relationship can be established.

In striking contrast to the relative inaccessibility of the clergyman in the community, the institutional chaplain not only offers his services freely, but is often sought out by the resident as a staff member who has something special to offer (i.e., spiritual help in coping with problems).

The prime objective for the institutionalized retardate is similar to that of other "helping" professions, with the added dimension of providing or shoring up spiritual resources when this is feasible.

Following the basic philosophy that the retarded individual is more like the average person than he is different, insofar as the problems that bring him to the counselor are concerned, some writers (e.g., Golden, 1962; Stubblefield, 1965) hold that no different or new concepts or principles of counseling are required, but that techniques, methods, or procedures may require modification from client to client—or perhaps even for a given client—depending on special problems, particular needs, and individual abilities.

ADJUNCTIVE THERAPIES

In discussing the objectives and aims of those adjustment procedures that employ artistic and musical media, we will adhere to the distinction previously made between art therapy and an art activities program and between music therapy and a musical activities program.

Art Therapy. It has been previously suggested that the label "art therapy" might be most appropriate when artistic media are employed to help the retarded individual of limited expressive ability communicate ideas and feelings without having to verbalize them. When employed in this sense the term seems to have the connotation: "the use of art in therapy."

Thus, the major objective of art in therapy is to facilitate a psychotherapeutic relationship by providing a channel of communication between the subject and the therapist. Nor is this channel a one-way avenue. Kadis (1957) points out that activities such as painting and drawing allow the child to express his feelings about his world and himself in his own set of symbols at a level appropriate to his conceptual ability. Kadis then goes on to emphasize that while these symbols become the child's means of approaching the therapist and of giving him necessary clues, the therapist on

his part must respond actively to these "messages" in order that the child may experience himself as understood, and that therapy may proceed.

Gondor and Levbarg (1958), in describing the value of artistic productions (including drawings and paper cutouts) for giving the play therapist information regarding the child's feelings about himself, his social relationships and family, his fears, and the nature of his defenses, make the point: "The therapist's skill, understanding of personality-dynamics and use of the verbal and non-verbal communication of the child, combined with warm empathy, remain the decisive agents in helping the patient" (p. 61).

In summary, the major aim, when art is used in therapy, is to establish lines of reciprocal communication and thus to facilitate the therapeutic relationship. However, while creative production is not the immediate goal of art therapy, the creation of a tangible product may have therapeutic side effects.

As Robinson and Robinson (1965) point out, "for an artistically talented individual, his art may win him deserved recognition, which in itself may be extremely therapeutic" (p. 490). This point is amply demonstrated in the case of Selma (Schaefer-Simmern, 1948), an institutionalized adult retardate, whose artistic and behavioral growth occurred while she was serving as a subject in a study designed to "observe the nature and development of the artistic form in the efforts of defective individuals" (Sarason, 1959, p. 316).

Kadis (1957) indicates that artistic production (in finger painting at least) also may have a kind of cathartic effect that is therapeutic "through the direct tactual contact and the impact of color, fantasy life and personal associations seem to be strongly provoked and elicited. Thus, as the child feels increasingly able to express, to sense, and to explore his world . . . through his own symbolic language, he will feel a greater degree of mastery over himself and his world. . . . As he is able to produce his images and master them, he also tends to be better able to verbalize" (p. 256).

If the artistic endeavor and its tangible product lead to therapeutic outcomes, then we may conceptualize the term "art therapy" as also carrying the meaning "art as therapy."

Music Therapy. The construct "music therapy" may also be conceptualized as consisting of two components: music in therapy, and music as therapy.

The primary objective of music in therapy is to establish contact and facilitate rapport with the subject. As Weigl notes, "children who have been in constant motion may at least temporarily quiet down and listen" (1959, p. 672). In this sense, the aesthetic and rhythmic qualities of music may provide the previously mentioned "opening wedge" between the therapist and client.

However, in considering the dimension "music as therapy," we are not concerned with the aesthetic and "mood" producing qualities of a musical composition, but rather with "functional music" (i.e., the isolation and use of such basic musical elements as rhythm, harmony, melody [Knight, Ludwig, Strazzulla, and Pope, 1957] for "reaching practical therapeutic goals outside of music itself" [Weigl, 1959, p. 673]).

In describing her use of "functional music" (which she equates conceptually to "music therapy"), Weigl indicates that the goals of this approach vary with the needs of the retarded child, with the major emphasis on social adaptation.

Knight, Ludwig, Strazzulla, and Pope (1957) describe the use of functional music as part of the remedial program of a hyperactive retarded boy in both individual and group settings "to strengthen voluntary inhibition of motor acts, and to offer the child a series of successful experiences" (p. 510).

Joseph and Heimlich (1959) consider music therapy as a specific psychotherapeutic discipline that has particular utility where other, more traditional psychotherapeutic efforts may be ineffective. In the program described by the authors, children are selected for music therapy on the basis of a number of specific maladaptive or pathological criteria; and in addition those chosen all show the inability to relate satisfactorily to adults or peers.

In further delineating the various aspects of music as a therapeutic tool, Joseph and Heimlich make the following points:

1. Music provides an opportunity for immediate satisfaction by allowing the direct, safe, and constructive discharge of emotion through sound.

2. Songs may serve as media of communication, providing opportunities for individual as well as group expression and allowing for expression of feelings, wishes, and activities that the child often finds difficult to talk about directly.

3. Percussion instruments are useful with all children; however they are of particular value with timid, withdrawn children. "With a percussion instrument to speak for them they are on safe ground. The instrument talks, not they" (1959, p. 45).

4. Encouraging the child to paint or use chalk to music gives him an opportunity to express his feelings through another medium, with music providing the springboard for design, color, and movement on paper. Some children derive sensuous pleasure from the combination of color and music. Others derive feelings of self-worth through production of something of value. For all, the fact that there is no "correct" response in this situation fosters free expression and active fantasy.

In describing techniques for the use of percussion instruments, Joseph and Heimlich (1959) note that one way to draw a child into responsive activity is for the therapist to listen carefully to a child's random drum-beating, to catch a pattern in the random beats, and to pick up and carry out this pattern on the piano "in a series of dynamic improvisations" (p. 44).

While the improvisation technique is almost incidental in the program described above, Nordoff and Robbins (1965) depend almost entirely on musical improvisation in their work with individual children. The particular approach of these workers is based upon the rationale that the manner in which the child responds to improvisation yields a "musical self-portrait," that there is a detectable connection between the child's pathology or personality and this self-portrait, and that the therapist can effectively utilize that relationship to give direction to his own efforts.

Occupational Therapy. Occupational therapy has been earlier defined as "treatment by means of participation in occupations or activities devised for a specific problem." If we examine the objectives and aims of OT from the standpoint of this general definition, we must agree with Kille (1956) that: "the effort in the field of retardation . . . becomes one of applying occupational therapy principles and methods specifically to those individuals regardless of age, who have one or more disabilities or special problems in addition to mental retardation" (p. 769).

In discussing the following objectives and their implementation in a total program for the institutionalized mentally retarded, Kille also indicates the adjunctive nature of occupational therapy as a discipline:

1. Assignment of a newly admitted individual to a well-designed OT program allows for early assessment of his general physical ability, as well as of his personality, abilities, and interests—thus providing diagnostic material for "members of the medical, psychological, and educational team."

2. For young children with physically handicapping skeletal deformities, a program employing OT methods can aid in the general improvement of muscle tone and can often help achieve improved general development. However, the value of such a program would be greatly enhanced if the activities were linked to a physical therapy regimen.

3. For those retarded residents who are emotionally disturbed and present difficult management problems, OT can do much to help these people live more comfortably with themselves as well as with others. In the case of such residents, the occupational therapy program should be closely associated with a program of psychological therapy.

4. Occupational therapy may allow for prevocational exploration by exposing the individual to various job situations. When the need for occupational treatment-training has abated, the therapist may offer valuable guides to the work-placement supervisor for finding a suitable work-training situation for the individual.

Dewing (1952, 1957) delineates the aims and objectives of an OT program with a group of retardates who are severely retarded—thus needing prolonged institutional care—and with whom the main objective is to foster adjustment to institutional life. Specific objectives for which Dewing outlines appropriate activities include development of : (1) co-operation and group relationships; (2) constructive techniques and creative expression; (3) mental processes such as "thinking, perception, discernment, and imagination, on a very fundamental level"; (4) attention-span and concentration; and (5) better physical co-ordination.

These aims are purportedly achieved through activities which include: block building, picture coloring, paper cutting, stringing beads, working with peg-boards, assembling educational puzzles, completing sewing cards, weaving paper mats, and various forms of group play.

The implementation of an occupational therapy program and the attainment of its varied objectives in specific cases begins with what Kille (1956) calls "activity analysis." In activity analysis, the therapist considers the mental and physical processes involved in carrying out a given activity along with a consideration of the practicability of that activity. Also evaluated as part of the detailed study are the psychological effect on the patient, the adaptability and variability of the activity, and the contraindications for its use as a medium in the treatment of the specific problem.

Recreational Services. The AAMD manual on institutional standards (AAMD, 1964) lists the purposes of recreational services in residential facilities for the mentally retarded with the admonition that recreation programming should be designed to "promote mental and physical health through interesting and worthwhile recreational pursuits" (p. 49). This admonition suggests that the aim of such services transcends the philosophy of providing "fun, relaxation, and entertainment" and more closely approximates the enhancement of a sense of well-being, behavioral effectiveness and social relationships. In short, a long-term goal is more effective adaptive behavior.

Upon careful consideration, the purposes listed in the manual are apparently congruent with the principles of therapeutic recreation in an institutional setting (Hillman, 1965); and at the same time, they are relevant to the concept of "socio-recreative programming" (Avedon and Arje, 1964) as applied to retardates in the community. The manual emphasizes that it is the responsibility of institutional recreational services to provide:

1. Planned recreational activities that will ensure participation by all residents according to their interests and abilities. Thus, it is construed that such activities may be made available to individuals at all levels of retardation—including the profoundly retarded (see Hillman, 1965).

2. Planned coeducational activities that will foster healthy heterosexual relationships and generally acceptable social behavior. These activities may include dances, entertainment activities (e.g., movies and concerts), field

trips (e.g., shopping, museums, industrial plants), and coed sports (e.g., boy teams vs. girl teams).

3. The enhancement of healthy social relationships by providing an opportunity for social interchange in varied environmental settings—including those away from the institution. For example, residents may use bowling alleys in the community; they may attend state fairs and baseball games in nearby towns; they may be taken off grounds for concerts and art exhibits.

4. Intra- and extra-mural sports activities with others of comparable ability in order to encourage competition and instill principles of sportsmanship and fair play. For example, baseball "leagues" may be formed whereby cottage plays cottage and institution is pitted against institution.

5. Instruction in various hobbies and games. A most informative manual published by the Southern Regional Education Board (SREB, 1964) provides detailed rationales and descriptions for activities subdivided according to the following categories: (a) active games (e.g., hop scotch, follow-the-leader); (b) music and rhythms (e.g., singing, marching, percussion activities); (c) quiet and table games (e.g., dolls, card games); (d) arts and crafts (e.g., pasting, cutting, painting, making puppets); and (e) homemade games and equipment (e.g., shuffleboard).

6. Instruction in the safe use of recreational equipment and supplies. This may serve to enhance the effective use of these materials and to develop a sense of pride and ownership.

Remotivation. As originally devised, the remotivation technique follows five carefully organized "steps" designed to involve the resident in a stimulating group interaction in which he is encouraged to attend to the objective world with an aim toward reawakening his interest in his surroundings and of re-establishing the basic techniques of social adjustment.

The technique of remotivation consists of a series of regular (usually weekly) meetings held under the leadership of a psychiatric aide or attendant. The usual series consists of twelve sessions, with each meeting lasting from 30 minutes to an hour; and the participants are encouraged, but not required, to attend.

In each of the meetings, the leader guides the group interaction through specific steps:

1. First he creates a *climate of acceptance.*

The leader moves around the circle of members, greeting each by name, expressing appreciation to each for attending, making personal contact and including each member in the discussion, even though no visible response may be elicited.

2. The leader creates a *bridge to reality* by the reading of objective poetry. This rather odd approach, which was originally developed for use with psychiatric patients, seems to have special merit for use with retarded residents. The poetry selected is simple, rhythmic, and pertinent to the topic selected for that particular remotivation session. Pictures and other visual aids relevant to the topic of the poem are often utilized; and as the leader reads, he circles within the group, encouraging members to read passages or to discuss the ideas expressed in the poem.

3. In this step, the resident learns to *share the world we live in.* The purpose here is the development of the topic to be covered in that session. Objective questions, carefully planned in advance by the leader, serve to stimulate group discussion and to keep it focused on the topic. Various "props," such as pictures, pamphlets, maps, samples of cloth, etc., foster interest and discussion regarding the realities of the world.

4. In the fourth step, the resident is helped to develop an *appreciation of the work of the world.* Here the attendant-leader attempts to help the resident think and talk about work in relation to himself, to tell how a particular job is done, to talk about the kind of work he likes, and to discuss jobs related to the subject.

5. In the last step, the attendant creates a *climate of appreciation.* The leader expresses his pleasure at meeting with the group. He thanks each member for joining the group and lets each know that he is respected for whatever he has contributed to the session. The leader finds out from the members what they would like to discuss at their next meeting or indicates his plans for the next session.

Wright, Erb, and Lawrence (1961) sum up the value of the five-step method in concluding a discussion of the last step:

This step is basically a continuation of the first step which sets the climate carried out throughout the group session. . . . The method, as exemplified particularly in the first and fifth steps, the introductions and good-byes, facilitates the exchange of consideration and respect which are so often felt, but frequently difficult to express. It is perhaps this basic ingredient that has brought about some of the responses from the mentally retarded which had not been thought possible (p. 9).

PROCESS AND OUTCOME

A comprehensive discussion of the various psychotherapeutic techniques requires attention to: (1) the need for theory-based procedures, (2) factors common among the various approaches to psychotherapy, (3) the controversies surrounding the questions of feasibility and effectiveness of psychotherapy with the mentally retarded—along with the attendant question as to which theoretical and methodological approaches may be more effective, (4) the issues involved in measuring effectiveness, and (5) a discussion of individual and group methods as applied in various situations by the various disciplines.

However, we are confronted with space limitations and with the fact that a number of other sources have discussed all of these issues at great length in their comprehensive reviews and compendia (e.g., Cowen and Trippe, 1963; Gunzburg, 1958; Robinson and Robinson, 1965; Sarason, 1959; Stacey and DeMartino, 1957; Sternlicht, 1965; Sternlicht, in press). Consequently, I will touch on topics (1), (2), (3), and (4) briefly in order to devote the major portion of this section to topic (5)—with some modification from the usual review-of-the-literature approach.

NEED FOR THEORY

Most authorities agree that psychotherapy and others of the adjustment media discussed above should involve the systematic employment of a group of techniques by a therapist, counselor, or leader. Theory-based procedures facilitate adherence in treatment to a system of concepts which the therapist has mastered. Such procedures give structure and direction to the process and provide a framework for the prediction and evaluation of outcome in research.

Theory-based approaches to psychotherapy with the mentally retarded have characteristically been associated with a particular personality theory (e.g., psychoanalytic or client-centered). However, the potential value of theory for giving structure and direction to process and for enhancing prediction and evaluation of outcome is also demonstrated by some newer theoretical models that have evolved independently of a given theorist's formal conception of the nature of personality (Haywood, 1964; Leland and Smith, 1962, 1965; Sternlicht, 1964a).

Haywood's proposed approach to fostering mental health in the retarded is through the principles of the "motivator-hygiene" concept (i.e., "motivator therapy"); and the theoretical approach of Leland and Smith holds essentially that the manipulation of structure (in both play materials and therapist's role) will lead to differential therapeutic outcomes. Both of these fit under the rubric of "novel psychotherapeutic strategies" and will be further elaborated upon in the subsequent discussion of methodological approaches.

Sternlicht's (1964a) prognostic-etiological model for the psychological treatment of mental retardation is an attempt to relate psychotherapeutic outcome with predetermined goals. It is based on the philosophy that the questions of feasibility and effectiveness are prognostic ones that must take into account the etiology of the mental retardation and the goals of the therapy. Thus, the model is said to enable one to predict for which goals and under which circumstances psychotherapy is or is not indicated. Conversely, it also indicates what a feasible goal might be for certain etiological groups. Sternlicht's theoretical position might be summarized as follows:

1. If the goal of psychotherapy is to raise the IQ, thus "curing" the condition, then: (a) it is not indicated in the case of mental retardation due either to neurological deficit (which is primarily a medical problem, and which cannot be reversed or improved by psychological means) or to severe cultural deprivation (which is more responsive to special educational methods); however (b) it *is* indicated where the cause has been established as "primary emotional maladjustment," with the expectation that the intellectual deficit can be attenuated in proportion to the extent of the restoration of the individual's emotional stability.

2. If the goal is personality adjustment and improved adaptive behavior, then: (a) psychotherapy is indicated, again, where the established primary cause is emotional disturb-

ance; and (b) where maladjustment is the result of an emotional reaction to or resulting from the existing intellectual deficit—whatever the etiology of that deficit.

If the primary problem is neurological defect or cultural deficiency (i.e., if under this model no "cure" of the intellectual deficiency through psychotherapy is thought possible), Sternlicht's model does not define the child out of therapy as some authors have contended (e.g., Leland and Smith, 1965 [2]). The model only says that in these cases, psychotherapy should not be employed with the goal of raising the IQ, but that it is nevertheless to be employed to relieve the distress of: "the patient who feels his intellectual handicap, and all of the unique concomitants which this handicap embraces, such as social and familial rejection, . . . *the impulsive disinhibition resulting from cortical inefficiency,* . . . *the social-psychological influence of a subnormal culture,* and so on . . . *without necessarily raising the IQ*" (pp. 621-622; italics added).

COMMON FACTORS IN DIVERSE APPROACHES

As Cowen and Trippe (1963) point out, the frequent observation that each of the various schools of psychotherapy (in spite of widely diverging techniques) succeeds in helping some people, suggests that a common core of factors exists in all forms of successful psychotherapy. The authors include the following among their "common denominators in the process of psychotherapy" (pp. 529-531):

1. An individual seeking help—whether or not he is directly responsible for the action and regardless of his motivation for treatment.

2. A client-therapist relationship and interaction—which Cowen and Trippe hold to be the most important single common denominator to all approaches. "The essence of therapy is not the response of the client to therapeutic techniques . . . it is his response to another person" (p. 529).

3. The impact of the therapist's personality

2. For an interesting and illuminating discussion of the whole question of intelligence as it relates to psychotherapy with the mentally retarded child, the reader is urged to see the section on "Intelligence and the Use of Play Therapy" in Leland and Smith (1965).

in the relationship—facilitating client movement through "warmth, sensitivity, understanding, spontaneity, and empathy" (p. 529).

4. A "safe" opportunity for expression of feeling and release of emotional tension (catharsis).

5. The systematic employment of a set of operating techniques by the therapist.

6. Initiation of positive behavior changes in real life situations.

Gunzburg (1958) evaluates the different psychotherapeutic approaches employed with institutionalized retardates—including those in individual and group interview, play, and activity settings, and employing psychoanalytic, nondirective, directive (non-analytic), and eclectic procedures—and he comes away with the conclusion that: "in the last analysis, the common factor among the various methods appears to be that individualized attention, reassurance, and acceptance by the therapist have in themselves a soothing effect on the patient and make him accessible to help and guidance" (p. 392).

FEASIBILITY AND EFFECTIVENESS

The reviews and compendia alluded to earlier make it abundantly clear that the early pessimism regarding the question of whether retardates can engage in and profit from a psychotherapeutic regimen is no longer justified. Despite serious shortcomings in reported literature, there is now abundant evidence, drawn from reports of programs and investigations conducted in various settings and under radically different theoretical orientations, to support the conclusion that various types of therapeutic practices have been "shown to be successful with some children, under some conditions, and with some therapists" (Robinson and Robinson, 1965, p. 500). The various reviewers are also in substantial agreement that the few comparative studies of therapy with the disturbed retardate and the maladjusted child of average intelligence do not support the belief that the therapeutic prognosis is automatically poorer for the retarded individual.

Granting the validity of the observation that psychotherapy has been "shown to be successful with some children, under some conditions, and with some therapists," the following questions present themselves: (a) are feasibility and effectiveness related to etiology and level of retardation? and (b) are any specific methodological approaches more effective with specific kinds of individuals? For example, what are the relative merits of structured vs. unstructured, directive vs. nondirective, and verbal vs. nonverbal procedures? Among those who have addressed themselves to these issues are Chess (1962), DeMartino (1957), Leland and Smith (1962, 1965), Snyder and Sechrest (1959), Sternlicht (1963, 1964a, 1965, 1966, in press), and Wanderer and Sternlicht (1964).

In a study that may be conceptualized as attacking both of the above questions simultaneously, Chess (1962) reports an experimental program in group psychotherapy at a community mental retardation clinic—involving young children (CA 4 to 16) of various IQ levels (from less than 30 to 72), and varying diagnostic categories—in which, following detailed observation of the child's behavior under varying circumstances, a plan was made for an individualized psychotherapeutic approach. The individual plan took into account the child's diagnosis, mental age, concentration ability, and interests. Intellectual level was a factor in deciding whether to approach the child on a conceptual level, via relationship therapy, or through "conditioning techniques." Chess concludes that the best results were obtained in the diagnostic group "mental retardation with secondary [neurotic] behavior disorder." For children with "behavior symptoms due to brain damage," results were reportedly encouraging within the limited goals set; and with the "mentally retarded schizophrenics," treatment results were generally poor.

Leland and Smith (1962) argue that for the emotionally disturbed, brain-injured, mentally retarded child, the form of play therapy that utilizes unstructured play materials together with an unstructured approach on the part of the therapist (the "U-U pattern") shows the most promise of achieving the therapeutic goals set for such children. These goals include: recognition of self, understanding that impulses can be controlled, and learning to live within social boundaries.

With regard to the directive-nondirective and verbal-nonverbal dichotomies, the aforementioned reviews and reports indicate that, under certain conditions and with certain individuals, various combinations of these elements may be efficacious in producing positive behavioral change. For example, Snyder and Sechrest (1959), working with male delinquent retardates, report a favorable outcome with a directive, structured, verbal (didactic) approach; while Sternlicht (1966) indicates that with female delinquent retardates, a directive approach incorporating nonverbal activity and communication should be the treatment of choice.

The consensus seems to be that a directive approach is generally more effective, and that verbal methods, when employed, are most feasible with older, higher level retardates. Nevertheless, some authors (e.g., DeMartino, 1957; Sternlicht, 1963) conclude that an eclectic approach (i.e., utilizing a combination of directive and client-centered elements) may be necessary with some retarded individuals; and Robinson and Robinson (1965) note that "difficulty in formulating and understanding ideas through words requires psychotherapy with many retarded persons to include a very large nonverbal component" (p. 484). Of course, the use of various expressive media and play techniques have been directed to that end.

MEASURING EFFECTIVENESS

If we come away from the literature with the increasing conviction that psychotherapy with the mentally retarded is a feasible and often successful form of treatment, we are nevertheless faced with the serious question of adequately delineating the criteria to be used for determining therapeutic success or effectiveness.

The question of criteria is intimately related to preset goals since we may judge a procedure as effective if it has enabled us to reach a predetermined therapeutic goal. However, again, goal-setting must be contingent on the nature of the individual's behavioral or emotional problem and on the extent to which his unique characteristics render him capable of responding to given treatment procedures. Therefore, perhaps the questions: "Is psychotherapy effective?" or "Does psychotherapy work with retardates?" serve to raise pseudo issues and should not be asked. With respect to these issues, Ford and Urban (1965), in introducing a method for comparing systems of psychotherapy, indicate that emphasis on specific behavior changes may be a more fruitful point of departure in establishing criteria.

If therapeutic effectiveness is to be determined by the extent to which given procedures produce specific behavioral changes in given individuals, the measurement of such effectiveness immediately presents a two-fold problem: (1) How does one decide which changes are necessary (i.e., which aspects of the client's behavior are to be altered by therapy)? and (2) Which instruments are available or can be devised to objectively measure whether and to what extent the desired behavioral change has occurred? When these questions are answered, we then are faced with the issue of establishing that a relationship exists between the modifications in the client's behavior or symptomatology and the given treatment procedure. The latter issue involves not only the validation of a given treatment approach or philosophy but the utilization of proper controls to ensure that the changes noted are reasonably due to the therapeutic regimen and not to any number of other factors in the client's life space.

The available literature indicates that these are momentous issues for research and practice in psychotherapy with retarded (as well as nonretarded) subjects. Specifically in the case of retardates, failure (either through neglect or inability) to take the first two considerations into account seems to have resulted in negative findings in some instances. For example, the reports of controlled studies by Albini and Dinitz (1965) and by Subotnick and Callahan (1959) both indicate that their respective failures to produce measurable improvement in retardates with emotional problems may have stemmed from difficulties such as those involved in: (1) identifying the subjects who needed treatment as well as which specific aspects of behavior required modification, and (2) the utilization of sufficiently sensitive instruments for detecting and measuring change. On the other hand, Snyder and Sechrest (1959), while using a fairly loose criterion of change ("institutional adjustment" as indicated by positive comments on routine housing reports), chose subjects who answered the behavioral description of "defective delinquent" and assigned their subjects to directive-treatment, nondirective-treat-

ment ("placebo"), and no-treatment groups, with the apparent validation of their hypothesis that a directive procedure was more effective with that population.

METHODOLOGICAL APPROACHES

The following discussion of procedures that I consider to be novel, interesting, unusual, or especially fruitful will be organized according to the specialty involved.

Psychotherapy. In this section, we will briefly outline newly developed or perhaps somewhat unusual approaches which seem to show promise of enhancing process and outcome in psychotherapy with retardates.

"Shadow therapy," a novel technique conceived and developed by Robertson (1964, 1965) for facilitating therapeutic communication and for fostering the integration of the severely disturbed child's fantasy life with reality, is based on the following concepts: (1) Night time is the most traumatic period of the 24-hour, day-night, cycle. During this period, the subject is alone with his anxieties in the darkness and among its component shadows. (2) Disturbed children often find it difficult to distinguish between reality and unreality. By the same token, shadows are perceived as images that exist yet which have an unreal quality. (3) Re-creating the physical aspects of night time by the use of a dark room may provide a means whereby, in the security of the therapeutic situation, the subject can focus on anxieties that he could probably control in the daytime, but that he found overwhelming at night. Robertson conjectures that by manipulating or responding to shadows under such conditions, the child can safely reveal and cope with his conflicts, thus accelerating the therapeutic process.

The shadow therapy environment consists of three types of shadows, produced by the illumination from a flashlight or projector, and including: "free shadows" (those cast by the subject as he moves about the room); "controlled shadows" (cast by silhouettes that are controlled by the therapist or subject— and that consist of various shapes including birds, human beings, and geometric designs); and "static shadows" (random environmental shadows).

In concluding her discussion of the use of this method with twelve retarded children who had manifested marked emotional problems, Robertson (1964) observes that the technique "appears to be [especially] effective with disturbed children who have become completely indifferent to their environment" (p. 222). Advantages of the process apparently lie in the fact that the subject is allowed to control his own reality and unreality levels. Thus, "he can be in his fantasy world or . . . in the real world, or . . . partially in both worlds . . . until [he] can handle the sources of [his] disturbance more adequately" (pp. 222–223).

On another front, proceeding from the poetic hypothesis that "to see ourselves as others see us would from many a blunder free us," and from the more scientific assumption that social skills and employability among adult retardates may be facilitated by confronting such individuals with an objective, realistic, vivid, and concrete message about their own behavior in social situations, the research group at MacDonald Training Center in Tampa, Florida, has been conducting an excellently designed project on the use of audio-visual feedback in group counseling with noninstitutionalized retarded adults of both sexes (Ricker and Pinkard, 1964; Ricker, 1965).

This project, now in its fourth and final replication, compares three ways of conducting counseling sessions with matched groups of five to seven subjects. Group A (the experimental group) sees previously taken sound motion pictures of their own behavior during social and work situations as part of group counseling sessions, which are generally oriented toward improving social and emotional maturity. Group B (the first control group) is shown a series of films of retarded individuals (other than themselves) in similar social situations during group counseling experiences with the same general orientation. The second control group, Group C, receives group counseling with this orientation, but does not view any films. Statistical and procedural methods of partialling out group leader effects are utilized to control that important variable. An independent research team views all the film and rates each subject's behavior toward measurement of his progress in social development; and a variety of criterion measures are used at the beginning and end of each four-month counseling period to evaluate changes in personal and social maturity.

While the study is not yet completed, preliminary inspection and analysis of the raw data seem to suggest the validity of the prediction that Group A would show more effective development of personal and social skills than would the clients in the other two matched groups.

Another imaginative (if sometimes controversial) approach is represented in the work of Sternlicht. Proceeding from the premise that the first few sessions are crucial for establishing group-therapist relationships in working with institutionalized retarded male adolescents who are exhibiting serious destructive, aggressive, uninhibited, or impulsive behavior, Sternlicht (1964b) employed an Indian hand-wrestling technique to demonstrate his physical superiority over the "strongest" member of the group. While rapport-establishment had previously been impossible with similar groups, the "awe and admiration" of group members following the novel procedure reportedly made for the rapid development of a working therapeutic interaction with beneficial results.

Following from his viewpoint that the emphasis in the group treatment of female delinquent retardates should be upon nonverbal activity and communication, Sternlicht (1966) employed several unorthodox nonverbal techniques—in addition to the more traditional ones of play therapy, finger painting, and psychodrama in pantomime.[3] The novel methods included a "silence-insult" technique and the use of mirrors and balloons. In the "silence-insult" technique, the therapist maintains silence until all loud, raucous group behavior subsides, following which the group is informed that the silence is the therapist's way of insulting the members for their boisterousness, of which he highly disapproves. Used in the first session, this approach, too, reportedly produces rapid, therapeutic movement.

---

3. Apropos of psychodrama and of rapport-establishing techniques, Arnholter (1955) suggests an interesting variation which is obviously simple and reportedly effective for helping retarded adolescents enter into socio-drama. The "paper bag technique" utilizes faces drawn on bags and mounted on sticks—which apparently provides the subject with a tangible symbol of his role and consequently allows for less self-consciousness and freer projection.

Mirrors are used to illustrate how the individual's actions and interactions appear to others and to demonstrate suggested behavioral modifications. Balloons are employed diagnostically and therapeutically, since the manner in which group members blow up and break balloons gives the therapist some indication of such variables as subject's degree of aggressiveness and need for structure, while providing the individual with a safe outlet for hostility. Rubbing the balloon against the cheek is also reportedly relaxing and tension-reducing.

In a study using the "progressive anaesthesia" technique for inducing hypnosis in retardates ranging in age from 7 to 15 years and in IQ from 37 to 68, Sternlicht and Wanderer (1963) conclude that their findings (twelve of the twenty subjects were hypnotizable) rule out the position that relatively unintelligent people are not susceptible to hypnosis. However, those authors regard their results as only provocative and call for more research in this area.

Finally, the "alternative guidance" approach (Wanderer and Sternlicht, 1964) is presented as a means by which the negative aspects of directive counseling (e.g., fostering dependency and possible weakening of the retardate's self-image) can be eliminated while still taking into account the retarded subject's difficulty in perceiving alternatives to unacceptable behavior. This is reportedly accomplished by having the therapist serve as a "source of data, a library of alternatives" from which the client chooses one tentative approach, which—while it may not be the best one—is his own choice. Alternative guidance is seen as "a synthesis, retaining the best elements of the [directive] therapy relationship while filling an objective need for the patient" (p. 15). The similarity is fairly obvious between this approach and what Golden (1962), on the one hand, advocates in "advisory counseling" in pastoral counseling situations, and, what Yepsen (1952, 1957), on the other hand, dubs "sound advisory technique." However, the larger context within which the "alternative guidance" concept is promulgated distinguishes it somewhat from the others.

An area of increasing interest and concern to psychologists is the application of behavior-shaping strategies and techniques (i.e., classical and operant conditioning principles) to

psychotherapeutic goals. In the general literature, the issues involved in such an approach are discussed under various headings, such as "behavior therapy" (Kalish, 1965), or "operant techniques" (Sidman, 1962); or under the general rubric, "conditioning therapies" (Wolpe, Salter, and Reyna, 1964)—the latter being a compendium of assorted approaches (including those subsumed under the other two headings) that are designed to develop a more effective behavioral repertoire in the client through varying and manipulating what Sidman calls "the concurrent controlling environment," through applying learning principles.

None of the sources cited make any reference to studies or programs describing the application of behavior-shaping strategies to psychotherapeutic goals (which would be my broad definition of "behavior therapy") with the mentally retarded—although some early exploratory studies involving operant conditioning of retardates in learning situations are given brief mention. Nevertheless, there have been some interesting recent developments which, if they are not or cannot be called "behavior therapy" in a formal sense, certainly are designed to reshape maladaptive behavior by the manipulation of selected variables.

An important case in point is the work of Leland and Smith (1962, 1965), which seeks to adapt the techniques of an accepted therapeutic model (play therapy) to conditions prescribed by the individual characteristics of the retarded subjects involved and by the specific therapeutic goals (i.e., prescribed response changes for given individuals); and which in so doing uses a combination of learning theory and behavior principles to establish the conditions and procedures for different play therapy "patterns."

Leland and Smith base their approach on the following two major premises, which respectively reflect their general theoretical orientation and the rationale of their specific therapeutic "patterns":

1. "The combination of the functions of conditioning and the functions of cognition . . . [are] the two major instruments in a successful play therapy procedure [with the retarded child]" (1965, p. 55). Thus, the authors conceptualize the whole therapy process as taking the form of "forcing the child

to think" through "selective reinforcement" (i.e., rewarding behavior that is congruent with the therapeutic goals, and withholding reward [or punishing] if a given behavior is antithetical to those goals).

2. In applying procedures for behavioral modification, "the atmosphere of the therapeutic setting and the attitudes of the therapist become extremely important in terms of the conditioning processes that are to be established . . . this general idea [is] best represented by the concept of structure" (1965, p. 66). From this follows the principle that the manipulation of structure in both the play materials (therapeutic "form") and in the therapist's role (therapeutic "order") will lead to differential treatment outcome in keeping with the specific needs of given individuals.

An elaboration of the first premise is best accomplished by the authors' own words. In concluding and summarizing the discussion of their generalized theory of behavior in play therapy, Leland and Smith state:

It [the theory] is based on the premise that all behavior is lawful, that behavior tends to be tension-relieving, and that aberrations of behavior tend to be self-reinforcing; that the way to deal with these aberrations is through a process of building and/or unblocking cognitive functions, that this may be done through a reward and punishment situation where reward becomes the permission to carry out behavior of the patient's choice, and punishment becomes intrusion in this sphere (1965, p. 38).

The second premise stems from the philosophy that in general, the behavioral changes we wish to achieve most with the child who is "functionally retarded" relate to making the child aware of the social forces that surround him and to modifying his responses appropriately. Since the concepts of social acceptability and personal reward (as well as the extent to which awareness of social forces and consequent response modification can be accomplished) vary with different children because of varying personality, environmental, developmental, and symptomatological considerations, the setting and procedures under which the conditioning processes are established must be tailored to the individual differences of the children involved. Toward that end, Leland and Smith (1965) have developed and described four different types of (individual and group) play therapy patterns, each of which differentially stresses structure (or the lack of it) in play materials and in therapeutic approach and each of which is seen as accomplishing differential goals. These patterns are:

1. Unstructured materials with an unstructured therapeutic approach (U-U). This is seen as best serving the needs of "the emotionally disturbed, brain damaged, mentally retarded child" (Leland and Smith, 1962), who is severely retarded intellectually, or whose adaptive behavior is extremely low. The therapeutic goals for such children are described as recognition of self, understanding that impulses can be controlled, and learning to live within prescribed environmental boundaries. As noted previously the processes employed for accomplishing these aims (and those of the "patterns" which follow) are essentially those of conditioning both functional and verbal behaviors by the therapist's selectively rewarding responses leading toward the goals, and punishing behavior that is detrimental to goal-attainment. In addition, the therapist's role includes "cognitive stimulation," whereby he serves as a model for appropriate goal-oriented behavior on the part of the child.

2. Unstructured materials with a structured therapeutic approach (U-S). This is considered to be most typical of that found in occupational, recreational, music, and other ancillary therapies. The child suitable for the U-S form has already developed more complex cognitions regarding self, impulse control, and social limits. He has awareness of responsibility for his behavior but is not sufficiently aware of the manifestations or implications of such responsibility. This method is seen as being most valuable with those children who are emotionally disturbed through CNS pathology rather than through psychogenic cause —the same CNS damage having produced retarded intellectual functioning. The aims here are improvement in self-concept, impulse control, and social interaction through "the development of fantasy, imagination, and social reality. . . ."

3. Structured materials with an unstructured therapeutic approach (S-U). This arrangement is viewed as being typical of traditional psychotherapeutic play procedures. This method is indicated for the child who, while his self-concept and impulse control are rela-

tively adequate, is unable to relate properly to people and things—with consequent feelings of aggression, hostility and general uneasiness in his environment. The S-U method is intended to build relationships with things and people; help in dealing with social and cultural realities; and help in establishing and developing realistic personal goals for the child.

4. Structured materials in a structured therapeutic approach (S-S). This pattern is reportedly most descriptive of that used in special educational or other modified classroom situations. Individuals most suited for this method are children who are functioning at the levels indicated by the goals prescribed for the S-U or U-S forms of treatment (whether through exposure to these approaches or not), and who, while still showing specific areas of difficulty manifest "high training potential." The approach is designed to deal with specific symptoms by way of "a finishing procedure" and is aimed at: improvement of social maturity through improved cognition; developing the child's understanding regarding his place in the world and his self-worth; and building realistic levels of aspiration.

While the foregoing approach is only more-or-less tangentially related to the formal and rather highly structured behavior-shaping procedures involved in what has been defined as behavior therapy, there is a striking similarity in elements (i.e., looking to learning theory and behavior principles for establishing the conditions of therapy, and letting the therapeutic conditions depend upon the nature of the response to be changed). Nevertheless, Leland and Smith show no disposition to include their approach under the "Behavior Therapy" rubric; and I have no intention of doing so for them. By the same token (to my knowledge), the preceding discussion outlines the only fully developed ongoing program of psychotherapy with retardates in which learning principles have been consciously employed toward a therapeutic goal.

Nevertheless, other investigators are concerning themselves with behavior-shaping strategies that eventually may have direct or indirect implications for treatment of the retarded child with emotional or behavior problems.

Reference has already been made to Haywood's proposed application of the "motivation-hygiene" concept—originally developed by Herzberg and Hamlin (1961, 1963)—to psychotherapy with retarded individuals under the appellation "motivator therapy" (Haywood, 1964).

Central to the motivator-hygiene concept is the construct that individuals in general may be characterized as being primarily oriented either toward "self-actualization" or "task" (motivator) variables or toward "environmental" (hygiene) variables. As Haywood (1964) expounds it, the motivator person is seen as one who "seeks his personal satisfactions through those factors inherent in the task itself; that is, achievement, increasing responsibility, meaningfulness of the work, recognition, and advancement" (p. 4). On the other hand, "the hygiene individual . . . seeks his personal satisfactions in the comforts and reassurances of the environment, being motivated to seek such things as personal comfort, low-effort tasks, and high material reward" (p. 4).

Further, some think it possible to measure the extent of motivation vs. hygiene orientation in given individuals by means of a simple instrument—the "choice-motivator scale" (Hamlin and Nemo, 1962). The findings of research by the latter investigators, employing that scale on a population including schizophrenic adults and "normal" college students, reportedly seem to support the original assumption of Herzberg and Hamlin that the motivator orientation is associated with "mental health," while the hygiene orientation is more characteristic of "mental illness."

After the contention of Herzberg and Hamlin (1961) that adjustment to the environment is primarily an avoidance adjustment, Haywood and Dobbs (1964) found that high school boys who show high hygiene orientation (on the choice-motivator scale) tend to avoid tension inducing situations; while those who score high in motivator orientation tend to seek out such situations. This finding then led the latter authors to formulate the tentative hypothesis that a primary environmenal orientation—as opposed to concern with motivator variables—develops as a consequence of *conditioned avoidance behavior;* and they further suggested that if the hygiene orientation is a reflection of learned behavior, it can be unlearned by the substitution of incompatible approach behaviors in therapeutic social situations such as psychotherapy groups.

In applying all the foregoing concepts to personality dynamics in retardates, Haywood (1964) suggests that since successful accomplishment of interesting tasks is relatively unlikely among the retarded, "such a . . . person may easily learn to . . . avoid engaging in tasks in which he is likely to fail" (pp. 6-7), with the consequent "establishment of conditioned avoidance behaviors resulting in a primary hygiene orientation" (p. 7)

In outlining his rationale for the extension of motivator-hygiene principles to treatment of retardates, Haywood (1964) asserts:

Programs of personality change based on its principles lend themselves readily to group manipulations, and do not require the richness of verbal interchange that characterizes current psychotherapies. In fact *the activity therapy paradigm seems to be most readily adaptable to the motivator hygiene concepts.* By arranging an appropriate series of rewards in the form of opportunities to participate in a series of tasks of increasing complexity and intrinsic interest, one should theoretically be able to foster a motivator orientation, thus to establish attitudes more consistent with mental health, even in completely non-verbal persons (pp. 8-9; italics added).

After preliminary efforts at assessing the feasibility of measuring motivator vs. hygiene orientation in retardates, Haywood has tentatively noted that "adolescent patients with IQs as low as 40 can give quite scorable responses to the choice-motivator scale" (1964, p. 9).

Another and more direct application of behavior-shaping techniques that seems to provide fringe benefits with therapeutic implications, but may turn out to be a therapeutic approach in its own right, is described by Blau (1965) in a preliminary report on the results of the employment of automated learning procedures (i.e., programmed instruction) with retarded children who have not been in school because of various physical difficulties.

Blau reports that not only has the procedure been effective in producing academic achievement, but that parents have been reporting other interesting behavioral changes in the children. The reported changes include: cessation of bed wetting, decrease in aggressiveness, increase in ability to relate to other children, more amenability to parental scheduling, and increased creative exploration of their surroundings.

The possibility of therapeutic benefits from programmed instruction approaches is also supported by the findings of Blackman and Capobianco (1965), who report that although no academic superiority was evidenced by their teaching machine groups (of retarded adolescents), greater improvement in deportment was shown by the latter groups as compared with the no-teaching machine groups studied. The latter investigators offer as a rationale for the significant improvement in the deportment of the experimental groups the possibility that "the teaching machine and its accompanying program . . . , may have operated to improve the classroom behaviors of the (subjects) . . . by reducing frustration and maximizing attention" (pp. 268-269).

Some investigators, both in and out of the area of mental retardation, are employing more formal conditioning procedures in programs whose techniques may eventually be employed profitably in behavior therapy with the retarded individual. Thus, Ellis (1963), suggesting that psychologists working with retardates should be "behavior engineers," presents an S-R reinforcement model for toilet-training severely retarded persons. Bricker, in papers dealing respectively with differential diagnosis (1965a) and speech training (1965b) in populations including mentally retarded children, outlines an approach that he describes as being firmly rooted in Skinnerian principles of behavior. Birnbrauer (1963) summarizes laboratory studies over a wide range of subject characteristics and clinical problems which "have shown that deviant behavior in humans . . . can be eliminated and replaced by socially desirable behavior using reinforcement principles" (p. 9). In the same paper, Birnbrauer briefly outlines a new approach employed at the University of Washington, where reinforcement procedures have been incorporated into outpatient therapy with children by teaching parents effective operant techniques that can be applied in a therapeutic regimen at home. The study by Wolf, Risley, and Mees (1964), an exciting example of the modification of behavior in an institutionalized autistic child through the combination of positive reinforcement, extinction, and negative reinforcement (punishment), also indicates the possibilities of utilizing parents to carry on the therapeutic reinforcement-extinction procedures when the child has improved enough to go home. Also, in a paper that is broadly representative of work with autistic children and that seems to have important ramifications for application to the retarded, Ferster and DeMyer (1962) describe a procedure by which the behavior of severely autistic children was brought under the control of an artificial environment by techniques of operant reinforcement. The techniques in the controlled setting made it possible to sustain and widen the repertoire of the previously inaccessible children.

Before leaving the discussion of behavior-shaping techniques, brief mention must be made of an approach that utilizes the methods of free-operant conditioning for the combined purposes of automatic direct measurement of behavior deficits in retarded children and of designing corrective (prosthetic) environments for maximizing the over-all behavioral efficiency of such children (Barrett and Lindsley, 1962; Lindsley, 1964; NARC, 1964). A more complete description of this methodology is provided in Chapter 8.

Those investigators, theorists, and clinicians who insist that a major therapeutic element in psychotherapy is the establishment of a "close" client-therapist "relationship" may object that behavior therapy is not "really" psychotherapy since the major source of reinforcement therein may not necessarily be the therapist. For an interesting discussion of this point, I recommend Kalish (1965, pp. 1249-1250). However, the reader will recall that from my point of view, the most distinguishing characteristic of psychotherapy is considered to be the fact that it is psychological treatment applied with regularity and consistency, toward the amelioration of emotional or behavioral distress. There is little doubt that behavior therapy is such treatment applied toward such goals. By the same token, successful applications of the principles of behavior therapy may well require modifications in those definitions that specify the inevitable requirement of a close interpersonal relationship for therapeutic effectiveness (e.g., Leland and Smith, 1965) and in lists of "common denominators" that delineate the relationship as "a basic common aspect of diverse approaches" (e.g., Cowen and Trippe, 1963).

Social Work Therapy. I have been unable to find detailed descriptions of individual casework with retardates wherein specific cases are cited for purposes of delineating novel, unusual, or especially fruitful techniques. On the other hand, novel and interesting experimental or clinical approaches to social group work with the mentally retarded, while by no means abundant, have appeared in recent published and unpublished reports; and this section will sample these briefly. Nevertheless, lest the reader be misled regarding the availability of general material on casework with retardates, he is referred to the excellent and extensive monograph by Begab (1963) as a source and resource for background, philosophy, objectives, and general approaches to both casework and group work with institutionalized retardates. Those unique client problems that must be handled by the caseworker in the institution (e.g., reaction to the intake process, separation from family, etc.) are also discussed in such sources as the aforementioned reports by Howell (1957) and Stewart (1960). Regarding the sampling of papers on group work approaches, those that I found especially enlightening and apparently promising were descriptions of institutional programs by Scheer and Sharpe (1963, undated, 1965) and Smith and Hartford (1959) as well as reports of an ongoing demonstration program in a community mental retardation clinic (Goodman, 1966; Goodman and Budner, 1964; Goodman and Giannini, 1965).

Scheer and Sharpe (1963) describe an unique approach to social group work with institutionalized delinquent retardates—"day camping"—which is seen as deriving its essential value by being an intensive group experience that is physically removed from the institutional setting. Not only does such a program apparently put the group in comparative isolation from institutional pressures and influences, but it also reportedly fosters independence (e.g., campers must pitch their own tents, build their own fires, cook their own meals) and co-operation with the staff and peers. Indeed, reported (Scheer and Sharpe, undated) immediate results of the camping experience include: (1) development of meaningful peer and staff relationships, (2) an increased willingness of residents to work co-operatively with staff, (3) noticeable improvement in campers' "self-reliance, independence, and initiative," (4) the enrichment of "social competence skills," and (5) reduction in delinquent behavior. However, there seems to have been little transfer back to cottage living since "many residents rapidly slipped back into their old familiar social patterns once they concluded their camp experience" (1963, p. 147). Consequently the program administrators decided to follow up the camp experience with more effective utilization of a cottage environment for providing opportunities for social and emotional growth. Scheer and Sharpe describe such a program utilizing a special cottage with a fraternity-house atmosphere as a "reward" cottage. "Both the staff and residents saw placement at Centerville [the name given the cottage] as being the result of staying out of trouble and conforming to institutional routines" (undated, p. 84). Utilization of this setting by the group work staff to develop a "therapeutic community" reportedly led to more permanent behavioral changes among treated residents.

In a paper which attempts to examine what the institution in general and the group worker in particular can do to promote and develop "social-adaptive skills" in the retardate with social-emotional problems, Scheer and Sharpe (1965) delineate the differential needs, therapeutic goals, and treatment approaches that the social group worker should consider for residents who fit into the following categories: (1) a product of a deprived environmental background, (2) a product of an overprotected home environment, (3) openly defiant adolescents (called "delinquent defectives"), or (4) individuals whose "primary" problems lie in other than social or psychological realms (i.e., "the brain-damaged, the aphasiac, the epileptic, or the physically handicapped"). Noting that "because of the complexity of the needs of residents, as well as differences in age, functioning level, or social maturity coupled with the ever-present problem of staff shortages, many group work services have not been fully developed" (p. 24), the paper describes how many of the objectives of group work within the institution are met through existing programs that are divided into "play groups," "teen-age groups," and "young adult groups."

Smith and Hartford (1959) describe a "dynamic group approach" to the problems of the delinquent male adolescent retardate in a state school in the form of a structured social club, called "The Kings." In the course of group meetings with the worker, there reportedly emerged among "The Kings" a strong sense of belonging to the group ("we feeling"), a constructive need to function as a unit, positive attitudes of individual responsibility not only to the group but to society, and new attitudes toward authority.

With regard to the community project, in 1963, the social work staff of the Mental Retardation Clinic of Flower–Fifth Avenue Hospital in New York City, began a "demonstration-evaluation project" of the effectiveness of modified group counseling with mildly retarded female adolescents and their parents (Goodman, 1966; Goodman and Budner, 1964; Goodman and Giannini, 1965). While the primary aims of the project are to demonstrate and evaluate the effectiveness of therapeutic group work "adapted to the needs, limitations and capacity of mildly retarded adolescent girls," parallel groups for mothers and involvement of fathers were from the beginning viewed as "primary requisites for the therapeutic success of the adolescent groups." This project has the unique feature of being a controlled and apparently well-designed research study in the field of social group work (as opposed to the more prevalent program description), and it is therefore worthy of some extended discussion.

During the first year of the project, the following was accomplished: (1) Four groups, each consisting of eight retarded adolescent girls (IQ 55 to 75), were established—along with four parallel groups of the mothers of these girls; (2) A control group of sixteen retardates was designated; (3) A special activity group for girls who did not meet the criteria for this project was set up as a "satellite" service; and (4) Individual meetings with the fathers of the experimental Ss were initiated.

From the beginning, three of the four experimental groups were composed of predominantly white subjects from "middle class" families. However, in order to include a better representation of the retarded population and of the clinic caseload, the fourth group was made up of Puerto Rican adolescents (with corresponding treatment of their parents); and meetings with these latter subjects were conducted in Puerto Rican Spanish. In addition, during the second year of the project, a fifth therapy group was added, comprised predominantly of girls from low-income Negro families—but including some Puerto Rican and other socially deprived girls—along with the corresponding parents.

The girls in all experimental groups were selected for group work treatment on the basis of the psychiatric diagnosis proposed and described by Chess (1962), after a screening process involving social service, psychological, psychiatric, and pediatric examinations.

A major approach with the parent groups is to help the mother examine her role and her feelings in relation to the child and the way in which her own behavior affects that of the child, positively or negatively. With the adolescent groups, role playing has been found to be an extremely useful technique. However, in spite of the limited verbal facility of many subjects, it is reported that the quality of participation in planned discussion in all groups "is more focused, pertinent, and better related to reality problems than most previous reports on therapeutic approaches with the retarded would indicate."

A very interesting phase of the project, initiated during the second year with the cooperation of the Hospital Volunteer Department, was the establishment of a six-week summer prevocational training program for 14 girls in the two "middle class" groups. The girls were exposed to a variety of jobs within the hospital setting; but all activity was related back to group membership. Aside from the training implications, the prime rationale for this program was to give the girls opportunities that would directly foster concepts of themselves as able to function apart from their mothers. After the six-week period, it was judged that the results were extremely positive in many dimensions—from a vocational as well as a social-emotional standpoint; and in the third year, the procedure was successfully repeated with the members of the two Puerto Rican and Negro (i.e., "socially handicapped") groups.

Published reports of social work programs with retardates are characteristically devoid of mention regarding instruments for measuring change in clients' behavior following treatment. Therefore, permit me to note that a number of instruments are being utilized for gathering data to be used in evaluating the effectiveness of the above-described project. Instrumentation includes: (1) a 75-item "social work

[parent] interview" questionnaire—including questions regarding child-rearing practices and attitudes, child behavior, discipline, and parental expectations; (2) an "attitude and opinion scale" (regarding mental retardation and retarded children in general)—administered to parents; (3) a series of "initial screening" materials, including data on family structure and socio-economic situation, observation of child, parent's report of child's behavior, and intellectual and emotional evaluation of the mother; (4) psychiatric and psychological evaluations; and (5) a teacher rating form regarding the child's classroom behavior. All of these are supplemented by a "running log" of services supplied to the adolescent and her family.

The above project is now (1966) in its final year; and although a good deal of data has been secured, it has not yet been analyzed formally. However, tentative findings and impressions include the following:

1. The members of the two older middle-class groups have made a good deal of progress—reflecting marked improvement in social functioning and often "significant improvement in intellectual functioning." Improvement in family interrelationships is indicated by a "significant change in attitude, handling, and quality of acceptance on the part of their mothers. The girls are functioning much more independently."

2. The younger middle-class group has as a whole been least successful, although some marked individual gain has been noted. Perhaps these girls were too young for the treatment program employed, and a structural social activity group would have been more suitable.

3. The Puerto Rican group shows strong group cohesion, but is most dependent on planned activities (i.e., dances, music sessions, role playing). They act out feelings more readily, but are more resistant to discussing problem areas. In the summer work program, they showed greater maturity than had the "middle class" girls the previous summer.

4. Puerto Rican mothers have shown movement toward a greater awareness of their child, increased tolerance of the girls, and greater encouragement of independence among their children.

5. In the predominantly Negro group, co-

hesiveness among the girls has formed slowly. They are beginning to show progress in establishing communication with each other and in relating to the group worker. Specific individual gains among the latter group include improvement in school performance and in peer relations outside of school. The mother's group here has not shown as much promise as have the mothers of the girls in the other groups. The final report is expected to offer clues to effective methods of reaching and working with deprived adolescents and their families, and also to offer guidelines to help other communities establish programs similar to those used for the project as a whole.

As previously noted, the literature indicates a dearth of measuring instruments designed to be used by social workers to chart changes in their clients. The only such instrument that has come to my attention is that of Hunt and Kogan (1952). This device, a manual for judging client movement in social casework, apparently is designed to facilitate the measurement of "movement" *per se,* without differentiating that part resulting from the casework treatment. In addition, it requires extensive and intensive record keeping. Conceivably, some imaginative application could render the instrument more sensitive and less unwieldy, as well as extending its applicability to social group work.

Pastoral Counseling. Few references can be found in the available literature to illustrate the dynamics of the pastoral counseling situation with the mentally retarded—with the notable exception of the book by Stubblefield (1965).

As noted earlier, pastoral counseling seems to be characterized by two distinct dimensions: (1) It revolves around the symbol of the minister as a representative of God and the church; and (2) It involves (and may stem from) the durable or continuing relationship that the individual has with his pastor. For the institutionalized retardate, these dimensions apply to the role of the chaplain. Stubblefield (1965) provides case histories to demonstrate how both religious symbolism attached to the chaplain's role and the day-to-day contact as the chaplain moves among the residents may be used for establishing and maintaining a therapeutic relationship. As Stubblefield points out, in an institution where several disciplines

work therapeutically with the residents, counseling assignments or "case loads" are made on the basis of the presenting problem of the resident and the ability of a particular counselor to work with the person and his problem. The cases for which the chaplain assumes responsibility are generally those in which the unique dimensions of his role are considered to be important assets. The following case outlines, summarized from histories in Chapters 4 and 7 of Stubblefield's presentation, are illustrative.

An 18-year-old girl (IQ 53), whose institutionalization had been deemed necessary because of "anti-social behavior," originally was referred for casework treatment in the institution. In the course of such treatment, she expressed many religious concerns such as "becoming a Christian again" and "living for God"; therefore she was referred to the chaplain for pastoral counseling. In subsequent sessions, the counselor found that before coming to the institution, the resident had been baptized, had become a member of her church, and had accepted her pastor's invitation to be "saved." However, shortly thereafter, she had begun to associate with "the wrong crowd," to take "God's name in vain," and to do "things she shouldn't." Consequently, she began to feel she was no longer a Christian. Her religious experiences were marked by intense conflict among ideas derived from early religious training (in which the concept of a "punishing God" was stressed), a positive desire to be a Christian, and guilt over her social misdeeds. In several counseling sessions with the chaplain, the girl was encouraged and enabled to express her deeper feelings freely and "was helped to understand the nature of God's forgiveness when we sin." After some months, she was able to accept membership in a community church near the institution.

The counseling relationship with "James," a 28-year-old resident (IQ 52) who presented frequent behavior problems, was initiated by the chaplain, who in the course of his ward rounds, indicated to James that he was concerned about the continual trouble in which the resident was involved and that he would like to talk to him about the situation. Because James was a behavior problem and, in addition, had only limited use of his right hand, he had not been included in the institution's educational and vocational training programs. Nevertheless, the vocational training officer thought that James could be productive in a carefully supervised situation. Indeed, the first counseling interview indicated that part of the resident's behavior problems could be attributed to boredom and lack of purpose. James expressed a strong desire for inclusion in the work program of the institution. In addition, early interviews established that James was immature, impulsive, and manipulative, and also that his misbehavior was often a reaction to his family's neglect in writing or visiting him. Nevertheless, the chaplain decided that an important goal of the counseling relationship would be to prepare James for a job in the institution. Interviews were conducted twice a week for 45 minutes each, and James expressed himself freely and with some apparent understanding of what was motivating his behavior. The chaplain "was reflective, seeking to help James to be honest about his feelings, but at the same time representing reality to him." Religion *per se* was seldom mentioned, but the identity of the chaplain as a minister was clearly maintained by the client. "On several occasions, James commented that a preacher wanted people to be good and live right." Over a three-month period, James showed greatly improved behavior, and he was referred for job assignment with careful instructions that continued placement depended upon his behavior. James worked on the farm for two months—presenting no serious problems—until he became "upset" and had to be removed from the job. Nevertheless, he had apparently demonstrated his ability to modify his behavior with proper motivation and support.

Adjunctive Therapies. ART. With the exception of those programs already delineated, I am not aware of any interesting new contributions toward the use of art *as* therapy. However, two approaches to the use of art *in* therapy seem to deserve notice. The first of these, painting or chalking to music (Heimlich, 1960; Joseph and Heimlich, 1959), has already been mentioned briefly, but the exact technique will bear more elaboration. The second involves the use of finger painting as an adjunct to therapeutic recreation with the mentally retarded (Davis, 1965).

MUSIC. The work of Nordoff and Robbins (1965), to which brief reference has already

been made, represents an outstanding contribution to the use of music as therapy with "handicapped" children—including the mentally retarded. What follows is a brief overview of the elements of their methodology.

In the individual working situation, a child entering the music room for the first time finds a drum beside the piano at which the therapist is seated. The child is encouraged to "make music" with the therapist by beating the drum. "The initial aims of the therapist will be to discover to what extent the child can 'make music,' what music-making means to the child, and how he makes music. The therapist will discover all this through the use of improvised music" (p. 51). In the course of the session, the therapist, working with the child's unique musical and personal responses to his "exploratory improvisations," seeks to "build a channel of communication." The process reportedly involves trial and error over many sessions since each child's responses are unique and idiosyncratic. Each session is recorded on high-quality tape; and consequent detailed study of the recording allows for clearer definition and more precise description of the child's responses.

Based on observations of work done with 145 children over a considerable period of time, Nordoff and Robbins have been able to delineate 13 "categories of response," which describe both the "hindrances and malformations" manifested by the children (Categories 2 to 10) and the "therapeutic avenues of approach that the children extend toward the therapist" (Categories 11 to 13). The unelaborated list is: (1) complete rhythmic freedom, (2) unstable rhythmic freedom (including psychological and neurological components), (3) limited rhythmic freedom, (4) compulsive beating, (5) disordered beating, (6) evasive beating, (7) emotional-force beating, (8) chaotic creative beating, (9) piano playing, (10) responses by singing, (11) responses to singing, (12) responses to specific musical idioms, and (13) responses to mood or changes of mood through music.

In working with the responses, the musical experience for the child is effected by the developing and modelling of a particular quality in the therapist's improvisation:

This [quality] may fall into any of the well-defined categories of music, or it may be a musical expression that is completely new and belongs only to the particular needs of a child. The experience so mediated may be predominantly rhythmic, melodic, harmonic, or structural (p. 61).

A very interesting point made by these authors is that "dynamic, dissonant music does not necessarily excite or disturb psychotic children" (p. 34). Indeed, "this appeared to be a more significant experience for the children than quiet, soothing music, which might be considered more suitable" (p. 34).

A number of case histories are set forth to demonstrate "that the use of improvised music with [disturbed] children has diagnostic and therapeutic significance" (p. 94). Apparently, the technique as employed by Nordoff and Robbins can be extremely helpful in attaining important therapeutic objectives with retardates both on an individual basis and through group musical activities.

OCCUPATIONAL THERAPY. Previous references to programs of occupational therapy (OT) with the mentally retarded—covering definitions, objectives, and aims—indicate the awakening of a strong feeling of responsibility on the part of members of this profession for the enhancement of the retardate's adaptive behavior along a number of dimensions. However, while most residential institutions and a number of community clinics seem to have departments of occupational therapy, and while the AAMD manual on standards (AAMD, 1964) recognizes this discipline as an important cog in the "interdisciplinary" machine, reports of current OT programs with retardates are sparse and widely scattered. Indeed, it was only with considerable difficulty that I was able to locate relatively recent material in this area.[4]

First, let us consider the few sources that deal with modification of adaptive behavior in retardates with emotional or behavioral problems. Gottwald (1964) describes the organization, functions, and philosophy of the Spe-

cial Treatment Center (a "therapeutically oriented living situation") established at the Wayne County (Michigan) Training School for disturbed male retardates who "do not respond to the regular institutional program." The special program involves all departments of the institution, and occupational therapy was included in order to provide a nonacademic program in which the child was free to express himself through activities that included ceramics, woodworking, leathercraft, painting, weaving, and other minor crafts. Dawson and Reger (1961) and Reger and Dawson (1962) describe in considerably more detail the role of an occupational therapy program in treating, respectively, the hyperactive and the emotionally disturbed retardate in the Special Treatment Center at Wayne County Training School. They discuss a method of behavioral control and modification with these populations that involves a "consistent, rigorous schedule of stimulus-response programming" —somewhat reminiscent of the approach described by Leland and Smith (1965), but much less formalized.

Much closer to the philosophy advocated by Leland and Smith is the approach described by Fairman (1965) in delineating the occupational therapy philosophy, approach, and objectives at Parsons (Kansas) State Hospital and Training Center. Fairman advocates a detailed initial behavioral analysis for establishing a baseline against which to determine the value of the occupational therapy process and to help classify the individual into one of the five levels of adaptive behavior described by Leland (1964). In discussing the responsibility of OT for achieving the differential behavioral objectives for individuals at various functional levels, Fairman states: "In our setting we have found new information, technique, and some success by turning to learning theory as the basis for an approach to the mentally retarded" (p. 274). He then suggests the feasibility of utilizing "operant therapy" in occupational therapy for "the development of prosthetic environments that will enable the individual to achieve a higher level of independent functioning" (p. 275).

The remaining papers run a gamut in application of occupational therapy approaches to various needs of and goals with the retarded. Erhardt (1965) describes a pilot study concerning the role of OT in the admission eval-

---

4. I am indebted to the following for their gracious aid in locating and providing much of the cited material: June Mazer, Director of the Psychiatric Field Services Project, American Occupational Therapy Association; Caroline Aggarwald, chief occupational therapist, Bird S. Coler Memorial Hospital; and Alice Trei, senior occupational therapist, New York State Psychiatric Institute—all of New York City.

uation procedures at the Orient (Ohio) State Institute. Among the reported aims of the OT evaluation on admission is the pointing up of such specific needs of retardates as are "easily overlooked or discounted by routine, standardized procedures" (i.e., perceptual problems, emotional disturbance, and minor speech and hearing defects). Izutsu (1965) provides a brief description of the manner in which OT fits into the general institutional program for low-level retardates in Hawaii. Kramer (1965) and Patrick (1960) describe the role of OT in what appear to be essentially vocational rehabilitation programs for retardates in community facilities (i.e., respectively, the Fort Worth [Texas] Society for Crippled Children and Adults, and the Hartford [Connecticut] Rehabilitation Center).

Insofar as formal evaluation of the effectiveness of occupational therapy with retardates is concerned, only one available source (Fairman, 1965) touches upon the problem. However, while Fairman analyzes the concept of "evaluation"—emphasizing that it is observable behavior that must be measured and recorded—with the initial behavioral analysis serving as a baseline for noting change, he presents no formal instrument for measuring changes in adaptive behavior as a function of an OT regimen.

Nevertheless, fruitful efforts toward objective measurement of the effectiveness of particular OT programs seem to have been made among children with severe physical impairment (Herring, 1965; Tyler, 1965). Herring describes a series of peg-board tests that have been devised to measure small degrees of improvement in prehension and eye-hand coordination in "severely handicapped patients;" and Tyler outlines the development and use of the "children's hand skills survey" for measuring the ability of preschool cerebral palsied children to use their upper extremities.

RECREATIONAL SERVICES. An important contribution to the field of therapeutic recreation has been made by Avedon and Arje (1964) through their introduction of the concept of "socio-recreative programing" for the retardate in the community. Another major contribution—in this case concerning the institutionalized profoundly retarded child—seems to be developing at the Woodbine (New Jersey) State Colony, where a tailor-made program of therapeutic recreation for

such residents (Hillman, 1965) appears to be "demonstrating the feasibility of changing the behavior of the profoundly retarded . . . [through] recreation activities." [5]

Socio-recreative planning is aimed at minimizing the effects of social isolation and at promoting the socialization process among retardates. Avedon and Arje (1964) emphasize that "socio-recreative programing has an educational focus" with the objective of teaching the retardate, his family, and his community how recreation may be used as a means of promoting physical and mental health, enhancing mental and social development, and developing realistic and appropriate prevocational skills in the retarded person. The phases of such programming involve the introduction of appropriate activities at appropriate stages of development ranging from infancy, through preschool, school-age, teen-age, and adult periods. At each of the various phases, preventive, supportive, or remedial services are emphasized, depending on the extent to which the person's needs have been met previously and the extent to which he has achieved socially independent functioning. For those groups who may wish to sponsor specific programs in their communities, Avedon and Arje offer as guidelines: (1) a model comprehensive program; (2) an outline for a suggested demonstration project in the form of a remedial program for teen-agers and young adults —including a procedure for determining the effectiveness of the program; (3) a model instructional program for a local school system; and (4) examples of programs currently in operation in the United States.

One of the more significant aspects of the socio-recreative approach is the element of recreation counseling. As Avedon and Arje (1964) describe it:

The objective of recreation counseling for the retarded person and his family is to enable them to make independent use of a variety of recreative resources . . . To do this, the recreation specialist adapts standard counseling techniques . . . i.e., gives information about available resources . . . in the community, arranges opportunities for learning and practicing recreative skills in various community settings, gives advice about how to behave . . . in various social . . . situations with the nonretarded (p. 5).

5. W. A. Hillman, Jr., personal communication, July 1965.

Interestingly enough, in light of our present context, Arje (1960) describes a recreational counseling service (for mental patients) in which individual counseling is conducted by a psychologist who reportedly employs techniques similar to those used in vocational counseling, but with the apparent goal of social satisfaction rather than job satisfaction.

Hillman (1965) reports that, under the auspices of a hospital improvement project grant sponsored by the National Institute of Mental Health, an activity program has been developed for the profoundly retarded resident based on some of the principles of therapeutic recreation and has been in progress at Woodbine State Colony since September, 1964.

The three cottage groups involved in the project include approximately 300 male residents with a median MA of 1 year, 3 months, and a median IQ of 12. However, the three groups vary in chronological and mental age, mobility, self-help skills, and interests over a wide range of individual differences. Thus, the recreational approach varies according to cottage and grouping within each cottage; and all activities are scheduled with concern for individual abilities. A recreation therapist and a recreation aide work in pairs in each cottage; and the program consists of small-group activities (involving from four to ten residents) in an area of the cottage isolated from the community living sections. Activities that have been developed include:

1. Free play and social integration. During periods of free play and instruction in use of toys, social interaction among residents is encouraged and rewarded.

2. Co-operative play. Progress from free play into co-operative play activities involves music, tumbling, croquet, physical training, and other play activities for the development of large muscles, co-ordination, and locomotion.

3. Self-help activities. Activities such as dressing and brushing teeth are adapted into games, according to the resident's capabilities and needs.

Progress in the therapeutic recreation program is charted on a quarterly evaluation form, which covers the areas of co-ordination and locomotion, manipulation, and social needs. While the project is still in progress, early data indicate that: "continued experience and exposure to toys, games, social stimuli, and play

in general has generated significant movement toward increased sociability, improvement in manipulation . . . and small changes in physical co-ordination" (Hillman, 1965, p. 5).

The need for determining effectiveness of therapeutic and general recreation services has been recognized in various sources. As has already been noted, Avedon and Arje (1964) outline procedures for evaluating the effectiveness of their suggested pilot demonstration of a remedial recreational program for retarded teen-agers and young adults, and the Woodbine therapeutic recreation program provides for a quarterly evaluation form on which to chart residents' progress. Such a chart could be utilized for the dual purpose of measuring both change in the subject and efficacy of the program. In other sources that do not deal directly with retarded populations, the problem of the evaluation of recreational services is also given earnest consideration. For example, Haun (1965) sets forth eight indices by which such services to patients can be measured "purely in terms of effectiveness as recreation" (i.e., the extent to which patients are "having fun"), along with "A Suggested Check List for Evaluating Hospital Recreation Services" (pp. 70-74).

Remotivation. The fifth edition of the Remotivation Directory (APA/SKF, 1965) lists 29 state schools for the retarded (among a total of 237 institutions) "with some sort of remotivation program" as of December 31, 1964. In spite of the strong probability that a substantial proportion of the 29 programs are viable, they have yielded only two published reports to date in which procedures and results are delineated (APA/SKF, 1962; Wright, Erb, and Lawrence, 1961). In line with a previous description in this chapter of the procedures and objectives of the remotivation technique with retardates, the Woodbine (New Jersey) State Colony has recently established a recreational motivation training program (Resnick and Hillman, 1965), whereby attendants are trained as recreation aides for the purpose of applying the basic concepts of the traditional remotivation technique in a recreation setting in cottages for the severely and profoundly retarded.

"Motivation for the Mentally Retarded" (APA/SKF, 1962) is a report of the adaptation of the remotivation technique to male residents in two wards at Fairview State Hospital, Costa Mesa, California. Enthusiastic optimism is evident in the following excerpt:

In March, 1962, the first motivation sessions were held on Wards 81 and 83. In one, a maximum security ward, a heterogeneous group of eight boys was selected including psychotic mentally retarded, severely retarded, moderately and mildly retarded children. These patients were abusive both to themselves and others, and their antisocial behavior did not permit them to be cared for on other wards. Some had been diagnosed as functioning . . . with IQs of 12 to 20. They did not speak and they were not considered educable. Yet only three months after their first motivation session, these patients were accepting instruction (p. 3).

The paper by Wright, Erb, and Lawrence (1961) is a brief report of the experiences in carrying out a program of remotivation by nursing personnel in two state schools for the retarded in Pennsylvania (i.e., Pennhurst State School and Selinsgrove State School) during the period 1959 to 1961. Under this program, standard remotivation procedures were applied (with positive results) to selected residents of the two institutions in order to determine whether a technique originally developed for working with psychiatric patients could have application for nursing care programs with the mentally retarded. After successful adaptation of remotivation principles to the two relatively high-level retarded populations, the staff at Selinsgrove carried the efforts a step further. In June, 1961, "motivation" sessions for "dependent" mentally retarded children were begun. The program was based along the same lines as the remotivation sessions already established in the school. Particularly emphasized was basic habit training—including such activities as brushing teeth, washing face, using handkerchief, tying shoes, and developing table manners. Each session, which lasted from 30 to 45 minutes, was started with a five-minute review of the previous sessions. This was usually followed by singing songs or playing a game which was always related to the subject to be discussed subsequently. Wright, Erb, and Lawrence concluded that, "among the twelve patients participating in the program, it is felt that two did not benefit. The other ten showed great improvement in their own personal care as well as assisting with small routine ward duties. There is a marked increase in meaningful conversation among these patients with the nurses and aides" (p. 18).

The recreational motivation technique is an adaptation of the basic remotivation technique hereinbefore described—together with a combination of various recreation theories, practices, and new techniques originated by the therapeutic recreation staff at Woodbine State Colony. A recreational motivation training manual (Resnick and Hillman, 1965) has been developed as a guide to be used in the training of attendants for working as recreation aides directly with this technique in their cottages. The procedure calls for the aide to meet each of the severely or profoundly retarded residents (in groups of five or ten) at least once a week for between 30 minutes and an hour, depending on the group and activity. During these meetings, the leader follows the five structured steps previously described—but with some modifications that take into account the particular environment and the functional characteristics and needs of the participants. The five steps in recreational motivation are:

1. *Climate of Acceptance:* Greeting and welcoming residents.

2. *Bridge to the Real World:* Introduction of the activity for that session (e.g., dressing, free play, tying shoes).

3. *The World of the Cottage:* An attempt to develop the resident's awareness and understanding of his environment by carrying out the prescribed activity.

4. *The Simple Tasks of the Cottage:* An attempt to teach the resident simple cottage tasks or self-help tasks by which he may have an opportunity to develop a sense of self-worth and successful accomplishment.

5. *The Climate of Appreciation:* Constant praise for each resident for every accomplishment, and praise for the group as a whole at the end of the session.

In a very real sense, recreational motivation at Woodbine is an integral part of the over-all therapeutic recreation program at that facility.

RESEARCH CONSIDERATIONS

Research endeavors and suggestions have already been indicated in preceding sections for the professions involved. At this point, we will briefly highlight some of the problems, needs, and directions that seem to deserve re-search attention among the various disciplines.

PSYCHOTHERAPY

Research efforts in psychotherapy, as in the other techniques, may be grouped under the general headings of "process studies" and "outcome studies." Of these, the bulk of pub-lished material in the field of mental retarda-tion has apparently been on outcome, with the major question being: "Is psychotherapy ef-fective with retardates?" As already noted, the question of effectiveness is no longer pertinent —since numerous investigations have indicated that benefits have accrued to some individuals under some procedures and with some thera-pists. Allusion has already been made to studies addressed to the more relevant ques-tion (which combines considerations of both process and outcome): "What works best for whom under what conditions?" However, a good deal of work is still obviously called for in that direction. Toward that end, Cowen and Trippe (1963) delineate important meth-odological considerations regarding outcome research in psychotherapy with exceptional children. Among the methodological problems that must be dealt with in outcome research, Cowen and Trippe discuss sampling, design, control, and criteria. For example, they note that: (1) Sampling should be done through "controlled observations"—a condition not ful-filled by case-study data; (2) The design of a study must include provision for follow-up. Since changes resulting from therapy should persist, therapy cannot always be evaluated accurately at its conclusion; (3) Proper con-trols should make it possible for the investi-gator to attribute changes in personality and behavioral measures to the specific therapeutic intervention—thus minimizing the probability that change results from the intervention of other program resources; and (4) The prob-lem of what constitutes successful therapy must be given much consideration. On this last point, extended discussion has been presented in this chapter. Nevertheless, I must emphasize that criteria should stress changes in reliably reported observable behavior (i.e., behavioral criteria) rather than in protocols on such in-struments as projective techniques and other devices for probing depth dynamics.

Process research (i.e., investigation of the active elements in treatment) bears on the question of feasibility, and again the question is not "Is psychotherapy feasible with re-tardates?" but rather: "What methods and procedures work best with which populations; and what is the nature of the therapeutic ex-perience under these approaches?"

Psychotherapy research with the retarded must turn toward investigation of the nature of the therapeutic process. Strupp (1962), within the context of extremely pertinent re-marks on research in psychotherapy, notes that "there has been since 1950, a steady increase, both in quantity and quality, of objective in-vestigations of the therapeutic process" (p. 579). Obviously this increase has not reflected work within the field of mental retardation. However, most of the work outlined in the preceding section on methodological ap-proaches may serve as examples of potentially fruitful lines of investigation. In addition, one other study (Butler, 1964) identifies itself as being specifically concerned with critical vari-ables in the counseling process; and a research approach that would probably offer the most exciting promise for the enhancement of proc-ess would be the effective application of be-havior-shaping strategies to psychotherapeutic goals with the mentally retarded.

In conducting process research, we should also seek to understand the nature of the therapeutic experience for the client under var-ious procedures (e.g., how does the child per-ceive the dynamics of the process?). Here the literature with children in general and with re-tarded individuals in particular seems to be so scarce as to be almost nonexistent. I know of only two sources wherein the meaning of the therapeutic experience to child participants has been considered; and neither deals with re-tardates. Axline (1950) considers nondirective play therapy experiences as viewed by children who participated; and Littner (1962), exam-ines some of the meanings of the analytic re-lationship to the child. Here then is another potentially exciting avenue of investigation in psychotherapy with the retarded.

SOCIAL WORK THERAPY

Almost everything that can be said of re-search in psychotherapy may be applied to re-search in social work therapy with retardates —with the additional comment that published reports of formal research in the latter area are seemingly extremely scarce. Indeed, the one project that came to my attention as worthy of the designation "research study" is not yet published. I refer to the ongoing "demonstration-evaluation" project conducted by Goodman and his staff at the Mental Retardation Clinic, Flower–Fifth Avenue Hospital, New York City. Thus, the most immediate need in this professional area is more formal research of all kinds. In that connection, the research aspirant in the field of social work will find useful general guidelines in the paper by Wolins (1963), which suggests approaches and procedures to possible research problems and issues arising out of the programs in community clinics for the retarded.

Two specific contributions that investigators in social work could seek to provide are: (1) novel, fruitful approaches in individual casework; and (2) the development of instruments for measuring process and outcome in casework and social group work.

PASTORAL COUNSELING

As previously indicated, published material relative to process dynamics in the pastoral counseling of the mentally retarded is almost nonexistent. Formal studies aimed in that direction could contribute materially to both theory and practice in this discipline. Investigations covering process research in pastoral counseling are suggested by previously discussed material and might include: (1) analysis of the extent to which retardates at various functional levels conceptualize the chaplain as symbolic of God and Church; (2) the extent to which the individual perceives his everyday relationship with the chaplain as "durable" or "continuing"; (3) the relationship between early religious training (including such elements as specific religious background of the client and the "religiosity" of his family) and the need to seek pastoral counseling; (4) the client's perception of the counseling relationship, and (5) the development of appropriate instruments for recording and measuring process and outcome in this "helping" technique.

ADJUNCTIVE THERAPIES

In therapeutic endeavors involving art and music, further exploration seems warranted regarding the combination of painting or chalking to music.

Insofar as music therapy *per se,* is concerned, it should prove of great interest to explore further the therapeutic effect of dissonance, which is suggested by Nordoff and Robbins (1965).

In occupational therapy, controlled formal research on the suggested utilization of learning principles for behavioral control and modification in an OT setting, should certainly prove a significant adjunct to research on behavior therapy conducted by other disciplines —as well as adding an important dimension to the contribution of the occupational therapist. Here, too, appropriate instruments should be devised for the objective and controlled measurement of process and outcome of OT programs with retardates.

Research in recreational services should investigate further the concepts of therapeutic recreation with the profoundly retarded; and a large-scale, cross-sectional and longitudinal study to investigate the preventive, supportive, and remedial aspects of "socio-recreative programing" seems to be called forth by the developmental aspects of the program as delineated by its proponents.

REMOTIVATION

Apparently the only formal research that has been reported on the remotivation technique has been the earlier described work done in a mental hospital setting by Long and his associates. Those investigations (which might serve as excellent paradigms for similar studies in facilities for the retarded) led to the conclusions that: (1) The remotivation technique can be instrumental in modifying the behavior of disturbed patients—making them more communicative and increasing their participation in other activities; and (2) The custodial attitude so often prevalent among attendants in mental hospitals can be modified considerably through the involvement of ward personnel in a technique that presumably allows them to be identified as members of the treatment team.

Wright, Erb, and Lawrence (1961) suggest that research in remotivation with retardates should follow similar lines as those just mentioned; and they go on to outline additional questions for investigation: (1) What techniques from fields such as special education and psychology might be useful to the psychiatric aide or attendant in using this technique with retardates? (2) What elements in the technique have made this an apparently satisfying experience to ward personnel? and (3) How has involvement in remotivation changed the attendants' concepts of themselves?

I feel that the technique offers considerable benefit for severely and profoundly retarded individuals—for whom involvement in most other therapeutic programs may be very difficult. A series of formal, controlled studies to determine the feasibility and effectiveness of this approach with such subjects would make an interesting and significant contribution. Hillman's work seems heuristic.

SUMMARY

The term "psychotherapy" refers broadly to effecting positive behavioral or personality changes through planned psychological procedures. The term is traditionally applied to therapeutic techniques employed by psychiatrists and psychologists. However, other disciplines in rendering services to retardates, particularly in an institutional setting, employ planned approaches that are designed to effect behavioral change or emotional adjustment among the individuals receiving service. These approaches, which may be designated as "adjustment techniques" and are designed to raise the retardate's level of adaptive behavior, are not commonly included under "psychotherapy."

While retaining the major emphasis on those procedures commonly labeled "psychothera-peutic," this chapter has also attempted to examine the treatment roles and helping techniques of such adjustment media as casework and social group work; pastoral counseling; art, music, occupational, and recreational therapies; and remotivation.

Throughout, an effort has been made to communicate practical information, while giving due consideration to findings of both theoretical and empirical research. Toward that end, the material has been discussed under four main headings: (1) definitions and therapeutic roles of the several media—including a "best fit" definition of psychotherapy; (2) treatment objectives and aims and the techniques for their implementation by the various professions —with emphasis on service to the retardate in the residential facility; (3) process and outcome, including discussions of: the need for theory-based procedures; common factors in various approaches to psychotherapy; controversies regarding the feasibility and effectiveness of adjustment procedures (particularly psychotherapy) with the retarded; and an extended discussion of novel, interesting, and fruitful methodological approaches employed by the various specialties; and (4) research considerations—highlighting some of the problems, needs, and directions for research by the disciplines covered.

In conclusion, if this chapter serves in any way to facilitate understanding, communication, and cooperation among the many disciplines who are engaged in serving the mentally retarded in our institutions and communities, it will have accomplished the author's major intent in grouping together all the "helping techniques" and discussing them as related units.

REFERENCES

AAMD. Standards for state residential institutions for the mentally retarded. *Monogr. Suppl., Amer. J. ment. Defic.*, 1964, *68* (4).

AGEE, J. W. The minister looks at mental retardation. *Pastoral Psychol.*, 1962, *13,* 12–22.

ALBINI, J. L., and DINITZ, S. Psychotherapy with disturbed and defective children: An evaluation of changes in behavior and attitude. *Amer. J. ment. Defic.*, 1965, *69,* 560–567.

ALLEN, H. *Positive aspects of child psychiatry.* New York: W. W. Norton, 1963.

APA/SKF. *Motivation for the mentally retarded: A report from Fairview*

State Hospital, Costa Mesa, California. Philadelphia: APA/Smith Kline and French Laboratories, Remotivation Project, 1962.

————. *Remotivation: Basic facts about a useful mental hospital program.* (Rev. ed.) Philadelphia: APA/Smith Kline and French Laboratories, Remotivation Project, 1964.

————. *Remotivation directory.* (5th ed.) Philadelphia: APA/Smith Kline and French Remotivation Project, 1965.

ARJE, FRANCES B. Recreation counseling. *Hosp. Management,* 1960, *89* (4) (Reprint).

ARNHOLTER, ETHELWYNE. Social drama for retarded adolescents. *Except. Child.,* 1955, *21,* 132–134.

AVEDON, E. M., and ARJE, FRANCES B. *Socio-recreative programing for the retarded: A handbook for sponsoring groups.* New York: Bureau of Publications, Teachers College, Columbia University, 1964.

AXLINE, VIRGINIA M. Mental deficiency—symptom or disease? *J. consult. Psychol.,* 1949, *13,* 313–327. (Also reprinted in Stacey and DeMartino, 1957, 219–240).

————. Play therapy experiences as described by child participants. *J. consult. Psychol.,* 1950, *14,* 53–63.

BARRETT, BEATRICE H., and LINDSLEY, O. R. Deficits in acquisition of operant discrimination and differentiation shown by institutionalized retarded children. *Amer. J. ment. Defic.,* 1962, *67,* 424–436.

BEGAB, M. J. *The mentally retarded child: A guide to services of social agencies.* Washington, D.C.: Dept. of Health, Education, and Welfare, Children's Bureau, 1963. (Publication No. 404.)

BEIER, D. C. Behavioral disturbances in the mentally retarded. In H. A. Stevens and R. Heber (Eds.), *Mental retardation: A review of research.* Chicago: University of Chicago Press, 1964, 453–487.

BIRNBRAUER, J. S. Applications of reinforcement theory to clinical problems. Paper read at American Association on Mental Deficiency, Portland, Oregon, 1963.

BLACKMAN, L. S., and CAPOBIANCO, R. J. An evaluation of programmed instruction with the mentally retarded utilizing teaching machines. *Amer. J. ment. Defic.,* 1965, *70,* 262–269.

BLAU, THEODORE H. Psychotherapy through educational success. Paper read at American Association on Mental Deficiency, Miami Beach, 1965.

BRICKER, W. A. Learning approach to differential diagnosis among mentally retarded children. Paper read at S.E. Region, American Association on Mental Deficiency, Nashville, 1965. (a)

————. Speech training with autistic and mentally retarded children. Paper read at Society for Research in Child Development, Minneapolis, 1965. (b)

BUTLER, A. J. Client-counselor communication and interaction in counseling with the mentally retarded. Grant application to U.S. Department of Health, Education, and Welfare, Vocational Rehabilitation Administration. Madison: University of Wisconsin, 1964.

CHESS, STELLA. Psychiatric treatment of the mentally retarded child with behavior problems. *Amer. J. Orthopsychiat.,* 1962, *32,* 863–869.

CHIDESTER, LEONORA, and MENNINGER, K. A. The application of psychoanalytic methods to the study of mental retardation. *Amer. J. Orthopsychiat.,* 1936, *6,* 616–625. (Also reprinted in Stacey and DeMartino, 1957, 156–166).

CLARK, L. P. *The nature and treatment of amentia.* Baltimore: Williams and Wilkins, 1933.

COLEMAN, J. V. Distinguishing between psychotherapy and casework. *J. soc. Casework*, 1949, *30*, 244–251.

Community Service Society of New York. *Method and process in social casework*. New York: Family Service Association of America, 1958.

COWEN, E. L., and TRIPPE, M. J. Psychotherapy and play techniques with the exceptional child and youth. In W. M. Cruickshank (Ed.), *Psychology of exceptional children and youth*. (2d ed.) Englewood Cliffs, N.J.: Prentice-Hall, 1963, 526–591.

DAVIS, MARGARET. Implications of finger painting for the child with retarded mental development. *Recreation for the ill and handicapped*, 1965, *9*, 5–6.

DAWSON, ANTOINETTE, and REGER, R. Occupational therapy program for emotionally disturbed mentally retarded children. In *Conference proceedings*. New York: American Occupational Therapy Association, 1961, 67–69.

DEMARTINO, M. F. Some observations concerning psychotherapeutic techniques with the mentally retarded. In C. L. Stacey and M. F. DeMartino (Eds.), *Counseling and psychotherapy with the mentally retarded*. Glencoe, Ill.: Free Press, 1957, 461–472.

DEWING, DOROTHY. Use of occupational therapy in the socialization of severely retarded children. *Amer. J. ment. Defic.*, 1952, *57*, 43–49. (Also reprinted in Stacey and DeMartino, 1957, 366–372).

ELLIS, N. R. Toilet training the severely defective patient: An S-R reinforcement analysis. *Amer. J. ment. Defic.*, 1963, *68*, 98–103.

ERHARDT, RUTH C. Occupational therapy admission evaluation in a residential facility for mental retardates. Paper read at American Occupational Therapy Association, Miami Beach, 1965. (Abstracted in R. K. Bing [Ed.], *Abstracts and summaries, forty-fifth annual conference*. New York: AOTA, 1965, #26).

FAIRMAN, C. W. Evaluation of the institutionalized retardate. In Wilma L. West (Ed.), *Occupational therapy for the multiply handicapped child*. Chicago: University of Illinois, College of Medicine, 1965, 263–277.

FERSTER, C. B., and DEMYER, MARIAN K. A method for the experimental analysis of the behavior of autistic children. *Amer. J. Orthopsychiat.*, 1962, *32*, 89–98.

FLAHERTY, VERA. History and development of occupational therapy. *Amer. J. ment. Defic.*, 1956, *60*, 755–759.

FORD, D. H., and URBAN H. B. *Systems of psychotherapy: A comparative study*. New York: John Wiley and Sons, 1965.

FREEMAN, MABEL. Drawing as a psychotherapeutic intermedium. *Amer. J. ment. Defic.*, 1936, *41*, 182–187. (Also reprinted in Stacey and DeMartino, 1957, 258–262).

GARRETT, ANNETTE. Historical survey of the evolution of casework. *J. soc. Casework*, 1949, *30*, 219–229.

GOLDEN, E. S. Pastoral counseling and guidance with the mental retardate. *Pastoral Psychol.*, 1962, *13*, 31–36.

GONDER, E. I., and LEVBARG, M. Techniques and expressive therapy integrated into the treatment of mentally retarded children. *Amer. J. ment. Defic.*, 1958, *63*, 60–63.

GOODMAN, L. A demonstration project evaluating the effectiveness of group therapy with retarded adolescent girls. A progress report to the U.S. Children's Bureau. New York: Flower–Fifth Ave. Hospital, M.R. Clinic, 1966.

———— and BUDNER, S. A demonstration program evaluating the effectiveness and methodology of group therapy for retarded adolescents (mildly retarded girls): A progress report to the U.S. Children's Bureau. New York: Flower–Fifth Ave. Hospital, M.R. Clinic, 1964.

———— and GIANNINI, MARGARET, J. A demonstration project evaluating the effectiveness of group therapy with retarded adolescent girls. A progress report to the U.S. Children's Bureau. New York: Flower–Fifth Ave. Hospital, M.R. Clinic, 1965.

GOTTWALD, H. L. A special program for educable-emotionally disturbed retarded. *Ment. Retard.,* 1964, *2,* 353–359.

GRINKER, R. R., MacGREGOR, HELEN, SELAN, KATE, KLEIN, ANNETTE, and KOHRMAN, JANET. *Psychiatric social work: A transactional case book.* New York: Basic Books, 1961.

GUNZBURG, H. C. Psychotherapy with the feeble-minded. In Ann M. Clarke and A. D. B. Clarke (Eds.), *Mental deficiency: The changing outlook.* Glencoe, Ill.: The Free Press, 1958, 365–392.

HADLEY, J. M. *Clinical and counseling psychology.* New York: Alfred A. Knopf, 1958.

HAMLIN, R. M., and NEMO, R. S. Self-actualization in choice scores of improved schizophrenics. *J. clin. Psychol.,* 1962, *18,* 51–54.

HAUN, P. *Recreation: A medical viewpoint.* New York: Bureau of Publications, Teachers College, Columbia University, 1965.

HAYWOOD, H. C. A psychodynamic model with relevance to mental retardation. Paper read at American Association on Mental Deficiency, Kansas City, Mo., 1964.

———— and DOBBS, VIRGINIA. Motivation and anxiety in high school boys. *J. Pers.,* 1964, *32,* 371–379.

HEIMLICH, EVELYN P. Music as therapy with emotionally disturbed children. *Child Welf.,* 1960, *39,* 3–7.

HERRING, MARJORIE B. Creation of an object-related test system. Paper read at American Occupational Therapy Association, Miami Beach, 1965. (Abstracted in R. K. Bing [Ed.], *Abstracts and summaries, forty-fifth annual conference.* New York: AOTA, 1965, 2).

HERZBERG, F., and HAMLIN, R. M. A motivation-hygiene concept of mental health. *Ment. Hyg., N.Y.,* 1961, *45,* 394–401.

———— and ————. The motivation-hygiene concept and psychotherapy. *Ment. Hyg., N. Y.,* 1963, *47,* 384–397.

HILLMAN, W. A., JR. Therapeutic recreation with the profoundly retarded. Paper read at American Association on Mental Deficiency, Miami Beach, 1965.

HOLLIS, FLORENCE. *Casework: A psychosocial therapy.* New York: Random House, 1964.

HOWELL, J. E. Casework with retarded children in an institutional setting. *Amer. J. ment. Defic.,* 1957, *61,* 592–594.

HUNT, J. McV., and KOGAN, L. S. *Measuring results in social casework: A manual for judging movement.* (Rev. ed.) New York: Family Service Association of America, 1952.

HUTT, M. L., and GIBBY, R. G. *The mentally retarded child: Development, education, and guidance.* Boston: Allyn and Bacon, 1958.

IZUTSU, S. A motivation and training program for the very severely and profoundly mentally retarded. In Wilma L. West (Ed.), *Occupational therapy for the multiply handicapped child.* Chicago: University of Illinois, College of Medicine, 1965, 278–321.

JOSEPH, H., and HEIMLICH, EVELYN P. The therapeutic use of music with "treatment resistant" children. *Amer. J. ment. Defic.,* 1959, *64,* 41–49.

KADIS, A. L. The use of fingerpainting in psychotherapy with mentally retarded children. In C. L. Stacey and M. F. DeMartino (Eds.), *Counseling and psychotherapy with the mentally retarded*. Glencoe, Ill.: Free Press. 1957, 255–258.

KALISH, H. I. Behavior therapy. In B. B. Wolman (Ed.), *Handbook of clinical psychology*. New York: McGraw-Hill, 1965, 1230–1253.

KAPLAN, A. H. Social work therapy and psychiatric psychotherapy: An attempt at differentiation. *Arch. gen. Psychiat.*, 1963, *9*, 497–509.

KILLE, ELEANOR C. Clarifying the role of occupational therapy in a program for the mentally retarded. *Amer. J. ment. Defic.*, 1956, *60*, 765–771.

KING, F. W. The use of drawings of the human figure as an adjunct in psychotherapy. *J. clin. Psychol.*, 1954, *10*, 65–69.

KNIGHT, D., LUDWIG, A. J., STRAZZULLA, M., and POPE L. The role of varied therapies in the rehabilitation of the retarded child. *Amer. J. ment. Defic.*, 1957, *61*, 508–515.

KONOPKA, GISELA. *Social group work: A helping process*. Englewood Cliffs, N.J.: Prentice-Hall, 1963.

KRAMER, J. Work adjustment, training, and evaluation for teenage retardates. In Wilma L. West (Ed.), *Occupational therapy for the multiply handicapped child*. Chicago: University of Illinois, College of Medicine, 1965, 241–262.

LAWLER, W. Why recreation? In SREB Recreation Committee, *Recreation for the mentally retarded: A handbook for ward personnel*. Atlanta: Southern Regional Education Board, 1964, 1–10.

LELAND, H. Some thoughts on the current status of adaptive behavior. *Ment. Retard.*, 1964, *2*, 171–176.

———— and SMITH, D. Unstructured material in play therapy for emotionally disturbed, brain damaged, mentally retarded children. *Amer. J. ment. Defic.*, 1962, *66*, 621–628.

———— and ————. *Play therapy with mentally subnormal children*. New York: Grune and Stratton, 1965.

LINDSLEY, O. R. Direct measurement and prosthesis of retarded behavior. *J. Educ.*. 1964, *147*, 62–81.

LITTNER, N. Self-awareness by the analyst as one source of information concerning the child's conflicts and conflictual experiences. Paper read at Chicago Psychoanalytic Society, 1962.

LONG, R. S., JR. Changing attitudes about mental illness through remotivation. Paper read at American Psychological Association, New York, 1961.

————. Remotivation: Fact or artifact. *Ment. Hosp. Serv. Suppl.*, 1962 (June), No. 151.

———— and FERREL, ELIZABETH T. Behavioral changes observed during remotivation sessions. Paper read at Midwest Psychological Association, Chicago, 1962.

MAISNER, EDNA A. Contributions of play therapy techniques to total rehabilitative design in an institution for high-grade mentally deficient and borderline children. *Amer. J. ment. Defic.*, 1950, *55*, 235–250. (Also reprinted in Stacey and DeMartino, 1957, 241–255).

MENZEL, MARIELLA Z. Psychotherapeutic techniques among the mentally deficient: Occupational therapy. *Amer. J. ment. Defic.*, 1952, *56*, 796–802. (Also reprinted in Stacey and DeMartino, 1957, 359–365.)

NATIONAL ASSOCIATION FOR RETARDED CHILDREN. Behavior patterns reveal many cues. *Children Limited*, 1964, *13* (3), 7.

NORDOFF, P., and ROBBINS, C. *Music therapy for handicapped children: Investigations and experiences*. Blauvelt, N.Y.: Rudolph Steiner Publications, 1965.

PATRICK, DONNA. Retardates in a work adjustment program. *Amer. J. Occup. Ther.*, 1960, *14*, 297–300.

REGER, R., and DAWSON, ANTOINETTE. The hyperactive educable mentally retarded child: Occupational therapy program. *Amer. J. Occup. Ther.*, 1962, *16*, 182–184.

RESNICK, M. I., and HILLMAN, W. A., JR. *Recreational motivation handbook.* Woodbine, N.J.: State Colony, 1965.

RICHMOND, MARY E. *What is social case work?* New York: Russell Sage Foundation, 1922.

RICKER, L. H. Research use of audiovisual feedback in improving social skills of mentally retarded young adults. Panel presentation at American Association on Mental Deficiency, Miami Beach, 1965.

———— and PINKARD, C. M., JR. Three approaches to group counseling involving motion pictures with mentally retarded adults. *Proceedings of the international Copenhagen congress on the scientific study of mental retardation*, 1964, *2*, 714–717.

ROBERTSON, MARY F. Shadow therapy. *Ment. Retard.*, 1964, *2*, 218–223.

————. Shadow image perception: A communicative device in therapy. Paper read at Southeast Region, American Association on Mental Deficiency, Nashville, Tenn., 1965.

ROBINSON, ALICE M. *Remotivation technique.* (Rev. ed.) Philadelphia: APA/ Smith Kline and French Laboratories, Remotivation Project, 1964.

ROBINSON, H. B., and ROBINSON, NANCY M. *The mentally retarded child: A psychological approach.* New York: McGraw-Hill, 1965.

ROTTER, J. B. *Clinical psychology.* Englewood Cliffs, N.J.: Prentice-Hall, 1964.

SARASON, S. B. *Psychological problems in mental deficiency.* (3d ed.) New York: Harper, 1959.

SCHAEFER-SIMMERN, H. *The unfolding of artistic activity.* Berkeley, Calif.: University of California Press, 1948.

SCHEER, R. M., and SHARPE, W. M. Social group work in day camping with institutionalized delinquent retardates. *Train. Sch. Bull.*, 1963, *60*, 138–147.

———— and ————. Group work as a treatment. *Ment. Retard.*, 1965, *3*, 23–25.

———— and ————. Centerville—social mobilization within a cottage for the institutionalized retarded. In R. M. Scheer, W. M. Sharpe, and Ann Webster (Eds.), *Social group work with the institutionalized retardate.* Fort Wayne (Indiana) State School, undated.

SCHEERENBERGER, R. C. A census of public and private residential facilities for the mentally retarded in the United States and Canada. In *Directory of residential facilities for the mentally retarded.* Willimantic, Conn.: American Association on Mental Deficiency, 1965, iv–viii.

SCHLOTTER, BERTHA E., and SVENDSEN, MARGARET. *An experiment in recreation with the mentally retarded.* Springfield, Ill.: Dept. of Public Welfare, 1959.

SHATIN, L., DOUGLAS-LONGMORE, GLADYS, and KOTTER, W. L. A quantified criterion for evaluating the music therapist. *J. Rehab.*, 1963, *29*, 18–19.

SIDMAN, M. Operant techniques. In A. J. Bachrach (Ed.), *Experimental foundations of clinical psychology.* New York: Basic Books, 1962, 170–210.

SIVLEY, R. B. The church as a mental health resource. *Mind over matter*, 1963, *8*, 30–36.

SMITH, ROMAINE V., and HARTFORD, R. J. A social group work program in an institution for the mentally retarded. *Amer. J. ment. Defic.*, 1959, *63*, 897–902.

SNYDER, R., and SECHREST, L. An experimental study of directive group therapy with defective delinquents. *Amer. J. ment. Defic.*, 1959, *64*, 117–123.

SNYDER, W. U. The present status of psychotherapeutic counseling. *Psychol. Bull.*, 1947, *44*, 297–386. (As quoted in Cowen and Trippe, 1963, 527).

SOPER, R. L. Occupational therapy, its contribution to the training of mentally deficient patients at the Newark State School. *Amer. J. ment. Defic.*, 1946, *51*, 296–300. (Also reprinted in Stacey and DeMartino, 1957, 353–359).

SREB RECREATION COMMITTEE. *Recreation for the mentally retarded: A handbook for ward personnel.* Atlanta: Southern Regional Education Board, 1964.

STACEY, C. L., and DeMARTINO, M. F. (Eds.) *Counseling and psychotherapy with the mentally retarded.* Glencoe, Ill.: The Free Press, 1957.

STERNLICHT, M. The inapplicability for mental defectives of the client-centered approach. *J. client-centered Counsel.*, 1963, *1*, 11–12.

———. A theoretical model for the psychological treatment of mental retardation. *Amer. J. ment. Defic.*, 1964, *68*, 618–622. (a)

———. Establishing an initial relationship in group therapy with delinquent retarded male adolescents. *Amer. J. ment. Defic.*, 1964, *69*, 39–41. (b)

———. Psychotherapeutic techniques useful with the mentally retarded: A review and critique. *Psychiat. Quart.*, 1965, *39*, 84–90.

———. Treatment approaches to delinquent retardates. *Int. J. group Psychother.*, 1966, *16*, 91–93.

———. Psychotherapeutic procedures with the retarded. In N. R. Ellis (Ed.), *International review of research in mental retardation*, Vol. 2, New York: Academic Press, in press.

——— and WANDERER, Z. W. Hypnotic susceptibility and mental deficiency. *Int. J. clin. exp. Hypn.*, 1963, *11*, 104–111.

STEWART, C. A. The role of the psychiatric social worker as a participant in the interdisciplinary team in a residential facility for the mentally retarded. Unpublished MSSW thesis, University of Tennessee, School of Social Work, Nashville, 1960.

STRUPP, H. H. Patient-doctor relationships: Psychotherapist in the therapeutic process. In A. J. Bachrach (Ed.), *Experimental foundations of clinical psychology.* New York: Basic Books, 1962, 576–615.

STUBBLEFIELD, H. W. The ministry and mental retardation. *J. Relig. Hlth.*, 1964, *3*, 136–147.

———. *The church's ministry in mental retardation.* Nashville: Broadman Press, 1965.

SUBOTNICK, L., and CALLAHAN, R. J. A pilot study in short-term play therapy with institutionalized educable mentally retarded boys. *Amer. J. ment. Defic.*, 1959, *63*, 730–735.

THORNE, F. C. Counseling and psychotherapy with mental defectives. *Amer. J. ment. Defic.*, 1948, *52*, 263–271. (Also reprinted in Stacey and DeMartino, 1957, 75–85).

TYLER, NANCY B. Measuring the effectiveness of occupational therapy for the cerebral palsied child. Paper read at American Occupational Therapy Association, Miami Beach, 1965. (Abstracted in R. K. Bing [Ed.], *Abstracts and summaries, forty-fifth annual conference.* New York: AOTA, 1965, #3.)

WANDERER, Z. W., and STERNLICHT, M. Alternative guidance: A psycho-therapeutic approach to mental deficiency. *Int. ment. Hlth. Res. Newsltr.*, 1964, *7*, 13–15.

WEIGL, VALLY. Functional music, a therapeutic tool in working with the mentally retarded. *Amer. J. ment. Defic.*, 1959, *63*, 672–678.

WIEST, G. Psychotherapy with the mentally retarded. *Amer. J. ment. Defic.*, 1955, *59*, 640–644.

WOLBERG, L. R. *The technique of psychotherapy.* New York: Grune and Stratton, 1954.

WOLF, M. M., RISLEY, T. R., and MEES, H. L. Application of operant con-ditioning procedures to the behaviour problems of an autistic child. *Behav. Res. Ther.*, 1964, *1*, 305–312.

WOLFENSBERGER, W. Embarrassments in the diagnostic process. *Ment. Retard.*, 1965, *3*, 29–31.

WOLINS, M. Social work research in mental retardation clinics: Possibilities and prospects. In *Child health projects for mentally retarded children: The role of the social worker.* Washington, D.C.: Dept. of Health, Edu-cation, and Welfare, Children's Bureau, 1963.

WOLPE, J., SALTER, A., and REYNA, L. J. (Eds.). *The conditioning therapies: The challenge in psychotherapy.* New York: Holt, Rinehart, and Winston, 1964.

WRIGHT, MARGARET M., ERB, ALMA, and LAWRENCE, PEARL. *Remotivation technique in the nursing care of the mentally retarded.* Philadelphia: APA/Smith Kline and French Laboratories, Remotivation Project, 1961.

YEPSEN, L. N. Counseling the mentally retarded. *Amer. J. ment. Defic.*, 1952, *57*, 205–213. (Also reprinted in Stacey and DeMartino, 1957, 65–75).

Learning Abilities of the Mentally Retarded

ALFRED A. BAUMEISTER

8

THE last decade has witnessed an increased scientific interest in the learning, or more properly, the learning deficiencies of mental retardates. McPherson in 1948 was able to list only a dozen studies devoted to a consideration of learning in mentally defective individuals. Since then a steady stream of research has been making its way into the literature. Almost every area and aspect of learning has been touched. Furthermore, attempts have been made to develop theories applicable to the learning deficits characteristic of defective individuals (e.g., Ellis, 1963; Zeaman and House, 1963).

The purpose of this chapter is to discuss, describe, and extrapolate the results of research as they suggest techniques for changing and controlling the behavior of retarded individuals. Considerable attention will be devoted to consideration of applications of operant techniques. In addition, some of the suggestions that grow out of certain recent and relevant theories will be interpreted in light of their applications in practical situations.

The suggestions and interpretations that follow can only be viewed as tentative. One of the reasons for this is that the manipulations that produce certain changes in behavior under controlled laboratory conditions may interact with uncontrolled variations in a more "natural" setting. For example, the motivation of the subject is likely to differ from laboratory to school room. The results of such confounding may be to produce an effect other than the expected one. Many of the principles that have been observed in the laboratory have yet to be put to the test in a practical learning situation. A considerable amount of intermediate research remains to be conducted. Another related precaution concerns the types of subjects investigated. Frequently these have been unrepresentative of the general population of retardates. What may be successful with one subgroup may not with another.

What the experimenter defines as learning may be very different from what the teacher views as learning. The experimenter, in attempting to control as much of the behavioral variation as possible, often deliberately attempts to use a task that is divorced from the subject's experience. The teacher, on the other hand, usually proceeds from the opposite point of view. The fact that correlations among the various laboratory learning measures are far short of perfect should be ample indication of the need for caution in generalization. Furthermore, in the laboratory we treat most individual differences as "error." Of course, the only error is the investigator's inability to account for these differences. The teacher cannot afford to ignore them for he is less interested in mean performance of the group than in the individual performances of each individual.

Finally, before any principle can be accepted, it should be subjected to cross-validation. Only in a relatively few instances have replication experiments been conducted, which is to be expected in any new field of scientific inquiry. Time and more research will remedy this situation.

RELATIVE ABILITIES OF NORMAL AND RETARDED CHILDREN

Retardates are frequently assumed to be inferior learners. A not uncommon attitude concerning the abilities and skills of retarded individuals is that they inevitably learn more slowly and retain less than normal children. Accordingly, educational programs for these children have been formulated on the assumption that the learning deficit experienced by the intellectually retarded is general and unitary, i.e., he lacks "intelligence." The retardate is usually assumed to be inferior in all aspects of the learning process, including acquisition and retention. Moreover, implicit in this notion is the further assumption that whatever is causing the difficulty in one area is responsible for maladaptive behaviors in other areas. As a consequence, the "special" in special education has meant giving the retarded individual essentially the same materials in the same manner as is given to the normal individual, but in lesser amounts and at a slower rate.

However, the research that is available on the abilities of retardates suggests something different: that the learning deficiency of mildly and moderately retarded persons is task-specific or related to only certain aspects of the learning situation. Some evidence even suggests that under certain conditions the learning and retention of retardates are quite adequate—comparable, in fact to the normal.

This, of course, complicates matters; for now we are obliged to specify the ways in which retarded individuals are retarded and the circumstances under which this retardation is manifested. For instance, does distractibility or poor retention represent a significant source of inferiority? Or does the problem lie in inferior verbal mediation, or is a perceptual difficulty the important factor, or is poor discrimination? But, by the same token, a more optimistic light is cast on the problem. Knowledge of the circumstances in which the retarded child performs better may lead to more effective means of educating and training him. If we know the specific deficits in a particular case, we may be able either to eliminate the deficit or to create a prosthetic environment to mitigate the defect.

This is not to say that we should expect to see a set of behavioral laws that apply to retardates and not to normals and vice versa. In writing a formula for behavioral output, one might expect to see essentially the same set of terms for both populations but with the values of certain constants differing. Ellis, Pryer, and Barnett (1960b), for example, have shown

that the learning curves of normal and retarded subjects can be described mathematically by essentially the same equations. A universality to certain principles seems to exist that exceeds even phylogenetic boundaries. Thus men and rats learn better when they receive rewards for doing so. Both organisms learn better when the reward closely follows the response. Both learn faster when the associations to be formed are between familiar events, and so on. Hence, we can expect retardates and normals to respond in qualitatively and even quantitatively the same manner to many variations in their environments. In fact, lacking specific knowledge about what to predict of the retardate's behavior, the best prediction is that it would closely resemble behavior of the normal individual in the same situation.

Several studies suggest that the abilities of retardates and normals are, in some respects, qualitatively different, although intelligence test performance is made equal in terms of an MA match. Thus, for example, Girardeau (1959) has reported that mongoloid retardates are significantly inferior in their abilities to form learning sets. Baumeister, Beedle, and Hawkins (1964) and many others have found retardates to be relatively disadvantaged in learning a response when discrimination is difficult. On the other hand, Sanders, Ross, and Heal (1965), in reporting that retardates are *superior* to their MA-matched normals in making nonreversal discrimination learning shifts, have also suggested differences in the learning processes of mentally retarded and normal individuals. As one possible explanation of these data, Girardeau suggests that the structures of abilities for the two groups are made of different factors. Other learning studies and investigations of test performance seem to bear out these observations.

Studies of intelligence test performances are relevant here, first because they add further evidence of qualitative behavioral differences between normals and retardates and, secondly, because intelligence test scores correlate well with some measures of learning, particularly those that involve the use of language. It is not too surprising that verbal intelligence test scores are better predictors of learning by retardates than are performance intelligence measures (Brengelmann and Hillman, 1965). Comparing the Stanford-Binet performance of normal and deficient subjects of equal MAs, two studies (Thompson and Magaret, 1947; Magaret and Thompson, 1950) showed that items requiring rote memorization were more difficult for the retardates. Also, retarded youngsters did poorer on items requiring verbal response or verbal presentation. This seems to agree with the finding that retardates are generally more retarded in verbal than in performance abilities (Baumeister, 1964). The findings of Thompson and Magaret suggest that, contrary to much professional and lay opinion, rote memory does not constitute a special ability of the retarded. They observe that, ". . . dull (subjects) differ from brighter ones not only in being less bright but in showing other characteristics to a greater degree" (p. 165).

Other studies (Baumeister and Bartlett, 1962; Baumeister, Bartlett, and Hawkins, (1963) using factor analytic techniques have shown that the structure of abilities tapped by the Wechsler Intelligence Scale for Children may be different for normals and retardates. Both groups were characterized by verbal and performance abilities as well as by a "general" ability. However, in the case of the retardates, a fourth factor emerged, which the authors have tentatively called "concentration" or "stimulus trace." This suggests that a portion of the variability in the scores of the retarded subjects must be explained by reference to another variable. Thus, for example, certain items such as digit span require the subject to remember over a short period of time certain stimulus events. The retardate may be less able to do this than the normal. Virtually the same results have been reported with the WAIS (Sprague and Quay, 1965). In another factor analytic study of the WISC, Tillman (1965) has identified three factors unique to normal children and one, which he has called "freedom from distractibility," unique to retarded children. Other similar studies (e.g., Gallagher and Lucito, 1961) indicate the retardate to be relatively weak in tests of attention, comprehension, and concept formation. As a result of his studies with English children, Burt (1958) found the retarded to be particularly defective in tests of reasoning, memory, and attention.

In reviewing studies of learning abilities in relation to intelligence, Johnson (1955) concluded that there is little evidence that a general learning factor is related to general intelligence. Learning tasks that require verbalization abstraction, and conceptualization correlate higher with tests of intelligence than do other tasks. Intelligence test scores also are generally unrelated to recall, a finding that will be considered in more detail later.

VERBAL LEARNING

Possibly the most extensively researched area of learning in relation to mental retardation involves the use of language. This is not unexpected. For one thing, the use of language is obviously the main function we are measuring with most intelligence tests. Hence, one might expect intelligence test performance to correlate well with verbal learning ability. Another reason for the interest in verbal learning tasks is that the bulk of classroom learning is essentially verbal in nature.

The term "verbal learning" is quite loose and applies to a wide variety of procedures that share in common the use of some form of language as an integral process in the performance of the task. Among the more commonly employed procedures are those of paired-associates and serial learning, although these do not necessarily require verbal learning.

PAIRED-ASSOCIATES LEARNING

The paired-associates problem involves the successive presentation of a list of pairs of items. On each presentation, the order of the list is changed to prevent serial learning. These items can be words, pictures, symbols, and even sounds. The members of each pair are not required to be in the same category of stimuli or even in the same modality. The subject's task is to associate the members of each pair so that when presented with only one, he can indicate its associate. Of course, many variations of this basic theme have been devised.

Several experimenters have compared the paired-associates learning of normals and mental retardates matched on MA (Cantor and Ryan, 1962; Girardeau and Ellis, 1964; Iscoe and Semler, 1964; Johnson and Blake, 1960; O'Conner and Hermelin, 1963; Ring and Palermo, 1961). The results of these investiga-

tions are equivocal, some suggesting that retardates learn the paired-associates as well as
normal individuals of the same MA, but two
indicating a retardate inferiority. Surprisingly,
when the intelligence groups are matched on
CA, the retardate does fairly well (Akutagawa
and Benoit, 1959; Eisman, 1958; Ford, 1962;
Vergason, 1964). Some exceptions are Baumeister (1963), Blue (1963), Jensen (1965),
and Madsen (1963).

SERIAL LEARNING

The serial learning procedure involves successive presentation of a number of stimuli
with the requirement that the subject be able
to anticipate the stimulus following the one
that he is shown. Thus, each item is both
stimulus and response.

As opposed to the near comparable performance of normals and retardates that characterized the paired-associates learning situation, serial learning deficits appear to be quite
marked in the retardates when they are
matched on CA with normals (e.g., Barnett,
Ellis, and Pryer, 1960; Ellis, Pryer, Distefano,
and Pryer, 1960; Pryer, 1960). High IQ seems
to be more necessary for adequate serial learning than for paired-associates learning.

In general, the serial learning studies have
tended to employ less meaningful materials
than those concerned with paired-associates
learning. The nonsense syllable has been used
almost exclusively. Moreover, the subjects
tested in the serial learning studies generally
were considerably less intelligent than those
employed in the other studies. Possibly the
serial learning task renders the application of
verbal mediators more difficult. If, as several
studies indicate, retardates do not make effective use of verbal mediators, they may suffer
relatively more than normals in serial learning.
A study by Jensen and Rohwer (1963a) has
cast some light on this problem. They found
that instructions to their retarded subjects to
use verbal mediators greatly facilitated paired-
associates learning but had no effect at all
upon serial learning. One tentative implication
to be drawn from these results is that the
paired-associates methodology should be utilized with retardates whenever the teacher
has a choice of procedures.

Investigations comparing brain-damaged and
non-brain-damaged retardates have pointed to
a marked inferiority on the part of the or-
ganics in serial learning (Barnett, Ellis, and
Pryer, 1960; Mitchell, 1952), but not in
paired-associates learning (Dent and Johnson,
1964).

VERBAL MEDIATION

A close examination of the paired-associates studies reveals that all those that report
comparable performance for normal and retarded groups have employed meaningful and
easily mediated materials. That is, the subjects would have had little difficulty in assigning labels to the items represented in the task.
On the other hand, the studies that have reported an inferiority on the part of the
tardate have tended to use either more abstract materials (nonsense syllables and forms)
or conceptually confusing materials. Wallis
(1962) has demonstrated that while both normal and retarded subjects learn semi-concrete
faster than abstract material, the tendency is
more marked in the latter group.

Quite probably, much of the learning inferiority of retardates, where such inferiority
is found to exist, can be linked to the lack of
spontaneous mediation among these individuals. Thus, the retardate's learning is apparently affected by the meaningfulness of the
material to be learned or, more properly, by
the extent to which he is able to apply distinctive verbal mediators to the cues. Increasing abstraction produces differences in favor
of the normals. In a somewhat related vein,
Iscoe and Semler (1964) have shown a difference between rate of paired-associates
learning depending upon the similarity of the
stimuli to be associated.

Some evidence indicates that when retardates are taught first to mediate cues with
distinctive labels, their discriminative and associative learning performance improves (Barnett, Ellis, and Pryer, 1959; Cantor and
Hottel, 1957; Smith and Means, 1961). A
study by Dickerson, Girardeau, and Spradlin
(1964), however, demonstrated that under
some conditions the effect may not be particularly pronounced. Rieber (1964) has found
that although retardates utilize pretraining experiences in a mediational fashion, they do not
thereby benefit as much as normal children.

In general, mediation seems to be dependent upon the meaningfulness of the stimuli that are to serve as the mediators and upon the conflicting associations that they may produce.

According to Wallace and Underwood (1964), implicit associative responses (IARs) normally accompanying the act of perceiving a stimulus word. For example, the IAR to the word "apple" may be "orange" or "red" or "fruit." Such responses could hinder or facilitate learning depending upon the nature of the materials and the type of task. In a free learning task, for instance, where the subject is asked to recall a list of items in any order, high conceptual similarity of the material should facilitate learning. On the other hand, in paired-associates learning, the reverse should be true. Wallace and Underwood have shown this to be the case for normal children. However, retarded children fail to demonstrate such an effect, suggesting that retardates do not spontaneously produce mediating responses. Nevertheless, retarded children may, under some conditions, make IARs yet fail to use them. O'Connor and Hermelin (1963) have demonstrated that the stimulus situation can be arranged to promote and encourage the use of such responses by these children.

In a series of studies designed to explore, in some detail, the effects of verbal mediation on the paired-associates learning of retardates, Jensen and Rohwer (Jensen, 1963, 1965; Jensen and Rohwer, 1963a, 1963b) have shown quite conclusively the significant benefits that accrue from verbal coding of the stimulus materials. Moreover, they have found that if the associates are first presented together in a meaningful context (e.g., in the form of a sentence as opposed to mere labelling), performance is even further enhanced. Absolute retention over a long period does not appear to be affected so beneficially, suggesting that the technique of using the specific mediators may be forgotten by the subject. Nevertheless, the associations acquired through the use of verbal mediators are retained just as well as associations that were initially formed over a great deal of practice without benefit of verbal mediation.

All these studies imply that meaningful materials should be used whenever possible and that when new material is to be presented, the retardate should be given opportunity to apply mediators to the material. The normal individual undoubtedly has a much larger reserve of labels to attach to the stimulus events that he encounters. Furthermore, when confronted with a new stimulus event, he probably will attempt to give meaning to it, having found it adaptive to do so in the past. On the other hand, the retardate has fewer mediators and, probably of greater importance, less experience in using them. The teacher must make a more direct attempt to supply these labels and to bring about a more effective use of them. For instance, learning has been shown to be facilitated if the subject is required to name the stimulus before responding (Weir and Stevenson, 1959). This procedure probably serves to increase the use of implicit associative responses as mediators. However, the mediational response, in order to be effective, need not be necessarily verbal. That is, any implicit response that adds distinctiveness to the relevant cues, could be considered a mediator. A subject may code stimuli with a variety of motor responses. House (1964b) has suggested that retardates with very low IQ scores can be taught to use gross motor acts as non-verbal, cue-producing responses to increase discrimination of external stimuli. Language may not be a necessary precondition for the effective use of mediators.

The research on verbal learning suggests, in short, that when the material to be learned is familiar and concrete the retardate does as well as the normal. As more abstract concepts are used, his performance falls off.

The way in which the to-be-learned materials are programmed appears to affect the rate of verbal paired-associates learning in mentally retarded children. Madsen (1963) has found that distributed practice is of considerably greater benefit to retarded children than to bright or average youngsters. Madsen reasons that consolidation time (i.e., time required for a transient memory trace to result in a relatively permanent structural change) is slow in mental retardates. Consequently, distributed practice is particularly beneficial to these subjects since it allows a longer interval for the trace to consolidate. Dent and Johnson (1964) have also concluded that subnormal children benefit greatly from conditions of distributed practice. Finally, Baumeister, Hawkins, and Davis (1966) have reported that increased exposure duration, within limits, benefits retardates more so than normals.

MEMORY IN VERBAL LEARNING

Learning and memory are inseparable. The only possible way to demonstrate what an individual has learned is to measure his retention of that material. Studies that are intended to investigate acquisition are actually dealing with memory, albeit on a rather short-term basis. Aside from this consideration, memory is important to our discussion from a practical point of view. That is, what is the good of having learned something if no relatively durable residual of that effort remains?

The question to be posed here is whether retarded individuals, after achieving some criterion of learning, can retain and draw upon this material after a lapse of time. Very few studies have been concerned with the durability of learning in the defective. The few that are available (e.g., Baumeister, 1963a, 1963b; Eisman, 1958; Hetherington and Banta, 1962; Johnson and Blake, 1960) suggest that verbal associations once acquired by the retardate are remembered by him almost as well as by the normal individual. Vergason (1964) has found that retention of paired-associates is as good with retardates, up to periods of one month, as with normals of like chronological age. Other paired-associates studies in which intelligence groups were matched on mental age (Cantor and Ryan, 1962; O'Connor and Hermelin, 1963) have reported similar results. In addition, Hawker, Geertz, and Shrago (1964) have found the long-term retention of verbal materials by severely retarded children to be rather remarkable. At least one worker, however, has found poorer retention of paired-associates material by retardates (Madsen, 1963).

Again, the meaningfulness of the material is suggested as a relevant factor. Baumeister (1963), employing nonsense syllables, found little retention by retardates after one month as opposed to the substantial savings of normal subjects. However, in this case, acquisition rate also differed and the retention scores therefore might be confounded with differences in original learning.

Over-learning of the material apparently benefits the retention of retardates more so than that of normals. Vergason (1964), in particular, has demonstrated the role of over-learning in acquisition upon retention. The effects of additional practice, however, seem to diminish as the retention interval increases. Frequency of presentation is probably not as crucial in this regard as is degree of initial learning. Obviously, some relationship exists between these two factors.

In a study designed to produce forgetting, Ford (1962) apparently has found that proactive inhibition effects on relearning of verbal materials are greater in retardates than in normals. In his control condition, where no interfering material was introduced, Ford found the retention of the defectives to be as good as that of the normals. In other studies designed to study the effects of proactive inhibition, House, Smith, and Zeaman (1964) and Scheerenberger (1964) also indicated that this is an important factor related to forgetfulness in retardates. The greater the number of learning tasks encountered by these subjects, apparently the greater the amount of forgetting on subsequent tasks.

Retroactive inhibition effects are also apparent in retention of verbal materials by retardates (Pryer, 1960), although, in this particular study, the retardates were not found to be any more handicapped by the interpolated material than the normal individuals. This is consistent with the results of a similar study by Cassel (1957). On the other hand, using a considerably different procedure, Hawkins and Baumeister (1965) found that when highly similar material is interpolated between repetitions of a digit series, retardates are much more disadvantaged than normal individuals. Johnson and Blake (1960) have reported that intellectually normal children are affected, in a digit substitution task, by retroactive inhibition while retarded subjects are not. However, since the normal and retarded groups did not reach the same degree of initial learning (the retardates were superior), a direct comparison is not possible. Such differences in retroactive inhibition as exist between the intelligence groups may be a result of acquisition differences rather than of differential inhibition effects. Certainly, well-learned materials do not seem as likely to be affected by retroactive inhibition. Studies have shown that as the original materials are more differentiated, the interference decreases. In any case, some evidence suggests that the interference effect resulting from interpolation of new materials is of short duration. Pro-active inhibition is probably the most serious of the two effects.

From a practical point of view, one might tentatively propose that lessons for retarded children be planned to minimize proactive and retroactive inhibition effects. Such inter-ference effects could be attenuated by some attention to the types of materials that are to be learned, the ways in which the materials are presented, and the order in which they are taken up. For example, each lesson should contain material highly dissimilar to that which precedes or follows. A substantial rest period should be introduced between lessons. The most important material could be pre-sented first (to avoid proactive effects) or last (to avoid retroactive effects). The mate-rial should be overlearned when strong inter-ference effects are likely. Such considerations do not appear to be as crucial for normals.

Apparently, if the material is meaningful, and if learning is reinforced by additional practice, if the materials are programmed ap-propriately, and if the learner is not pro-foundly retarded, he will remember as well as the normal individual over fairly long inter-vals. The process involved in acquisition seems to represent the greater impairment for the retardate. Associations, once formed, are fairly durable.

DISCRIMINATION LEARNING

Of all the sub-areas of learning that have been studied in relation to mental retarda-tion, none has been so thoroughly investigated as discrimination learning. Among the several reasons for this development, the ability to discriminate and to selectively respond on the basis of this discrimination is obviously an ele-mental aspect of higher forms of learning. Secondly, discrimination learning tasks can be made relatively easy and do not necessarily involve language, as evidenced by the exten-sive use of these procedures with animals. Discrimination learning tasks are particularly well suited for comparative studies. Finally, they readily lend themselves to experimental manipulations. Adding impetus to research in this area is the extension of discrimination learning theory proposed by Zeaman and House (1963).

Some recent reviews of studies have dealt with the discrimination learning of mental re-tardates (Stevenson, 1963; Denny, 1964). Zeaman and House (1963; House and Zea-man, 1963) have described their intensive ex-perimental and theoretical analyses of the discrimination learning abilities of mental de-fectives. Because of the coverage provided by these current reviews, no attempt will be made to systematically discuss or evaluate the liter-ature in this area. Rather, important findings will be summarized and some implications drawn.

Clearly, mental retardates do poorly on dis-crimination learning tasks compared to nor-mal persons. Some discussion has been de-voted to whether this represents an IQ or MA deficit. Although the various studies are not in complete agreement on this point, the evi-dence seems to warrant the conclusion that both MA and IQ deficits are involved. Ac-cordingly, retardates possibly not only suffer in rate of acquisition of a discrimination habit, but come to the experimental situation with less experience in the solution of such problems.

Intelligence and modality seem to interact with respect to this type of learning. Com-paratively speaking, tactile discrimination abil-ity is less impaired in mental retardates than is visual discrimination (O'Connor and Her-melin, 1963).

A number of conclusions can be made with some confidence regarding factors that influ-ence discrimination learning. In many in-stances the same factors that have been found to influence verbal learning are also implicated in the discrimination learning process. For in-stance, meaningfulness of the stimuli is related to learning rate in both situations.

In general, procedures that lead to increased distinctiveness of the stimuli to be discrimi-nated can enhance the rate of acquisition of the habit. One can promote distinctiveness, and thus decrease difficulty, by either increasing the number of relevant cues or by increasing the disparity between stimuli. Furthermore, this distinctiveness can either be inherent in the stimuli themselves or can be acquired through the use of special training techniques. More-over, retardates possibly may benefit more from such manipulations than normals, be-cause the latter have a superior ability to perceive distinctive qualities of the cues to be associated with a particular response. Incidentally, some evidence has suggested that this particular difference in abilities may be a partial result of experiential factors as opposed to intelligence per se.

Specifically, multidimensional stimulus displays produce better performance than unidimensional ones. Thus, for example, the subject learns faster if he can make the distinction on the basis of size and pattern, as opposed to pattern alone. Presenting the objects in their depth dimension of space also improves performance. Object discrimination is better than pattern, and pattern is slightly better than color as a cue. Novelty can, as a dimension, improve rate of learning. Discrimination concept tasks that emphasize a perceptual as opposed to a verbal mode of solution put retardates at less of a disadvantage (Milgram and Furth, 1963).

Another way to enhance the distinctiveness of the relevant functional cues is to use some special training technique. Usually this amounts to teaching the subject to verbally identify the stimuli that he must later learn to discriminate. Almost invariably studies along these lines have shown how efficacious verbal coding can be. In addition, the more ambiguous and meaningless the stimuli are initially, the more marked the benefits of pretraining seem to be, particularly for the retardate.

Language may not be a necessary precondition for the use of mediational responses in facilitating discriminating learning. Some evidence has indicated that cue distinctiveness can be achieved by requiring the subject to make a particular motor response in relation to each cue.

Previous experience in discrimination learning situations is an important factor related to rate of learning. Not surprisingly, the more practice a subject has on similar problems, the more rapidly he solves subsequent ones. This particular type of transfer is usually referred to as learning set or "learning-how-to-learn," seemingly indicating different psychological processes than those involved in the solution of individual problems.

Rate of discrimination learning set formation is related to both mental age and IQ (Harter, 1965). Learning set performance improves with MA to an upper limit of 8 or 9 years old and to an IQ of 100. Thus, if MA is taken as a measure of prior learning, additional practice would seem to be required for the retardate to reach the same level of performance as the normal.

Another factor related to the development of discrimination learning sets is the nature of the previous experience. Particularly important is the degree of success or failure that the mental defective has encountered, which could very well account for the finding that proceeding in an easy-to-hard sequence is better than going from one hard problem to another. Prolonged failure experience produces an inability to solve problems that used to be easy for the subject. Zeaman and House (1962) have termed this phenomenon "failure set." Others have noted that mental retardates have a generalized expectancy to fail and that this is, in turn, associated with an unnecessarily depressed level of performance (Cromwell, 1963).

MOTOR LEARNING

Obviously, measurement of any learning involves a motor response. In a sense all learning is "motor" to the extent that it requires an overt response on the part of the learner. Nevertheless, we can categorize certain behaviors with respect to (a) the relevance of the motor act to the psychological process under study, and (b) our interest in the actual movements themselves as the criterion of learning. Thus, for example, when the learning is reflected in the speed and accuracy of the overt movements, we are dealing with motor as opposed to, say, verbal learning.

Quite possibly the acquisition of motor skills has more relevance for a consideration of mental retardation than any other area of learning. One of the most obvious goals in the rehabilitation of the mental defective is to provide him with a vocational skill that will enable him to survive independently or semi-independently in the community. Usually, this means training him on some manual task such as operation of a drill press, sewing machine, lawn mower, and so on. Certainly, the useful acquisition of such vocational skill involves more than sheer motor dexterity, but it is certainly an important component of the learning process.

It is evident that defectives are less retarded

in motor learning than in other areas—possibly indicating that motor skills represent a lower-order process that is less affected by intellectual deficiency. Another explanation derives from the operations used in defining intelligence. The most frequently employed intelligence tests are highly loaded with verbal content. Consequently, these measures might correlate well with verbal learning and less so with performance measures.

Furthermore, when one considers severe and profound mental deficiency, where neurological and motor defects are more common, one finds a pronounced absence of many normal motor skills. Of course, this does not necessarily mean that motor skills are less easily learned by these individuals, but rather that they have not been learned. Possibly the environments for some individuals are inadequate for the acquisition of certain skills.

In general, then, correlations between mental status and motor proficiency tend to be significant, but low (Malpass, 1963) and probably result from the inclusion of extremely low-grade defectives in the samples under study. Moreover, the relationship between mental ability and tests of motor proficiency apparently is dependent on the particular motor ability involved. In other words, the deficiency in motor skills is specific to certain types of tasks or processes. Although there have been no direct studies on this point, an inter-experiment comparison suggests that the deficit is related to the requirement for precision of movement. The more gross the behavioral components, the less the retardate is disadvantaged. When there are initial differences between the performances of normals and retardates, additional training may help to reduce this discrepancy (Gordon, O'Connor, and Tizard, 1954; Holman, 1933).

The most frequently employed task for the study of motor learning in retardates is the pursuit rotor. Here the subject is given a stylus and asked to keep it on a revolving target. The measure of learning usually consists of time on target over trials. The relevant literature has been reviewed by Lipman (1963).

In general, comparisons of normals and retardates on the pursuit rotor show the latter group to be inferior. But, the inferiority is a relative matter, depending on such factors as degree of retardation, etiology, task difficulty, conditions of testing, and the particular pursuit phenomenon involved. Retardates demonstrate most of the same effects on this task as do normals. Thus, for example, they improve with practice. They perform better under distributed than under massed conditions (Barnett and Cantor, 1957). Their performance is facilitated by verbal reinforcement (Ellis and Distefano, 1959).

Evidence suggests an interaction between mental age and task difficulty (Lipman, 1963). In other words, the simpler the motor task, the less at a disadvantage is the retardate as compared with the normal. Ellis and Sloan (1957) found much poorer performance among their subjects with a 60 r.p.m. rotor than Barnett and Cantor using a 30 r.p.m. turntable. The best experimental evidence comes from a study by Annett (1957) who, although using a pegboard task instead of the rotary pursuit, found that performance curves for different IQ groups diverged as the task became more complex. Lower-level subjects were relatively more handicapped by increasing task difficulty. This observation has also been made by Cantor and Stacey (1951) and Sloan (1951).

Continued practice in motor learning seems to be of substantial benefit to retardates' learning. They appear to improve at a faster rate than normals or, at least, for a longer period. This is clearly demonstrated in a study of rotary pursuit performed by Baumeister, Hawkins, and Holland (1966). They have found that retardates, although initially well below normals, could, with sufficient practice, equal the performance of the normals. Although both groups improved with practice, the defectives' rate of learning was much sharper. A graph of this result is presented in Figure 1. This may be particularly so in the case of complex tasks. Initial level bears little relationship to trainability. Retardates also show substantial transfer effects between related motor tasks and seem to be especially responsive to the effects of verbal urging and reinforcement on these types of tasks. The presence of a concrete, reasonable goal also seems to be a potent motivator (Gordon, O'Connor, and Tizard, 1954, 1955). Clearly, with proper training methods, the moderately retarded individual can learn many complex and intricate motor skills.

Annett (1957) has suggested that various jobs for which mental defectives might be trained be analyzed in time-and-motion stud-

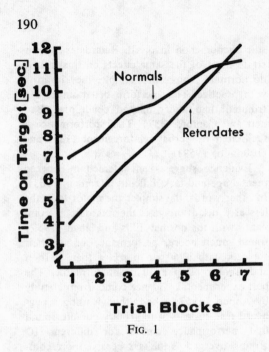

Trial Blocks

FIG. 1

ies to identify the specific motor components to be learned. The retardate, then, might be trained on each specific motor task before proceeding to the next. Furthermore, a job analysis may reveal that certain aspects of the task are more difficult than others. In fact, when a retardate fails to learn a motor skill, his deficiency is likely to be related to only certain portions of the task. Special training methods might then be initiated or a prosthetic device created to overcome the specific deficit. Wolfensberger (1964) has reported on the success of such devices in some European vocational training programs.

Related to the development of motor skills in retardates is the matter of reaction speed. In this regard, retardates have been shown to be inferior to normals (e.g., Baumeister, Urquhart, Beedle, and Smith, 1964; Berkson, 1961; Terrell and Ellis, 1964). However, more detailed examinations of the factors that underlie the reaction process have shown that certain variables interact with intelligence to affect response speed.

In a series of studies Berkson (1960a, 1960b, 1960c) has attempted to determine which factors are related to the relative response slowness of retardates. In brief, he has found that (a) stimulus duration thresholds are the same for normals and retardates, (b) variations in stimulus complexity do not produce differential effects for defectives as compared with normals, and (c) that response complexity is related to reaction-time deficit of the subnormals. Hawkins, Baumeister, Koenigsknecht, and Kellas (1965) have compared these groups in simple and discriminative reaction-time situations. They, also, report no interaction between stimulus complexity and intelligence. The important point is that retardates receive and process information, beyond some minimal value, about as rapidly as normal individuals. On the basis of these studies, one can conclude that in certain situations, where speed of movement is critical, reducing response alternatives is more crucial than reducing stimulus complexity.

As the result of his rather thorough analysis of the abilities and the trainability of severely retarded persons, Clarke (1958) has listed some reasonable and supported principles to be followed in training such individuals:

1. Suitable incentives and goals should be available.

2. The task should be broken down into its components, with each component learned separately, but in sequence.

3. Correct movements should be required before going on to the next stage in the sequence.

4. Practice should be distributed rather than massed.

5. The response should be thoroughly practiced until it is over-learned.

6. The learner should be encouraged to verbalize his behavior while he is in the process of making the response.

7. In the initial stages, accuracy rather than speed should be stressed.

8. The material to be learned should be well organized.

OPERANT CONDITIONING

Mental retardation cannot be considered an organismic condition in the same sense as can, say mongolism. The only way in which we can identify the condition of mental retardation is to observe the interaction between the organism and a normal or standard environment. The individual who cannot adjust in certain prescribed (although not necessarily formally stated) ways to the standard environment is adjudged to be retarded. This is not to imply that the maladaptive behavior must be permanent.

One approach to this problem is to "improve" the organism, which, in turn, may affect his behavior. Thus, we might act directly upon the individual by controlling his diet (as in the case of PKU), by operating upon him (as in the case of hydrocephalus), or by feeding him an "anti-imbecile pill" (as in the application of glutamic acid). Quite obviously, this represents the traditional approach of physical medicine. I do not doubt so much the validity of this approach, rather its generality. In most cases of mental retardation, effecting a treatment may be impossible without taking into account the environment in which we wish the individual to function.

Another view of the problem is that, for a given individual, the environment is "defective." We may conceive of behavior as a product of an interaction of organismic and environmental systems, such that one influences the other. Usually, this interaction results in a level of behavior that we term "average." According to this view, one might expect to improve the functioning of the defective individual by manipulating the environmental conditions that are related to the deficient behavior. Thus, for example, the child who has a hearing loss might be treated by rendering his auditory environment more intense through a hearing device.

Of course, efforts to create more favorable learning environments for the mentally retarded are not new. Indeed, much of the material of this book reflects an interest on the part of many researchers in altering features of the retardate's environment to produce better performance. Some have suggested, for example, that environmental distractions be reduced so that the relevant cues stand out better; that the materials to be learned be made more intense; that time intervals between events to be associated be shortened, and so on.

However, all these controls are essentially passive in that they merely make the conditions for learning more favorable. The environmental manipulation is only indirectly related to the learning outcome or, more precisely, to the frequency of the correct response. Moreover, we have to make the assumption that we have an actively participating subject with some understanding of the task before him. Verbal communication is usually an essential prerequisite to learning programs for the retarded. This is to say that we are then dealing with the higher grade defective. Almost completely ignored are the severely and profoundly retarded individuals who inhabit the back wards of many residential institutions. These individuals are usually regarded as incapable of learning much of anything and are sometimes referred to as "custodial."

Ellis (1963), however, has pointed out that many of these individuals have a potential for higher level adaptive behavior. Dokecki (1964) has reviewed the literature and arrived at a similar conclusion. Studies can be cited to support the contention that these severely retarded patients can learn. Thus, they can be classically conditioned (Grings, Lockhart, and Dameron, 1962). Their operant behavior can be controlled (Ellis, 1962; Fuller, 1949). They are capable of solving problems (Hollis, 1962). They can form learning sets or "learn-how-to-learn" (Girardeau, 1959) and transfer a response (Katz, 1964).

Operant conditioning, derived from the descriptive behaviorism of B. F. Skinner, his associates, and followers, is a technique that can be applied directly to the development of adaptive behavior. That is, the teacher not only provides a favorable learning environment, but he also arranges environmental factors to increase or decrease the frequency of certain responses. By applying principles of operant conditioning, behavior can be "shaped." Not only can one gain control over relatively simple responses, but the technique permits the development and control of complex behavioral sequences.

One important advantage of the technique is that it does not require the learner to possess language. In fact, the individual's behavior sometimes can be shaped without his "purposeful" participation. For this reason the techniques of operant conditioning should be particularly useful with severely defective or psychotic individuals whose abilities to communicate are extremely limited.

The basic principle of operant conditioning can be simply stated; the frequency of a response is subject to the consequences of that response. Thus, we can bring the response (actually, its frequency) under our control by identifying and arranging the reinforcement (consequences). Reinforcement is any stimulus event that can affect the frequency of the response under question. A negative reinforcement (as opposed to positive) is one that accompanies a decrease in the frequency of the operant that produces the reinforcement and an increase in responses that remove or terminate the reinforcement. These ideas are neither new nor particularly remarkable. Teachers have known for a long time that if a reward accompanies a behavior, the probability that the behavior will occur again is enhanced.

The studies by Skinner and others, however, have provided us with a great deal of information about the relationship between reward and response. For one thing, we know that the immediacy with which the reinforcement follows the response is crucial. We know also that in order to effectively and efficiently shape behavior we must reward successive approximations of the desired response. Furthermore, the "schedule" with which the reward follows the response has a great deal to do with how rapidly the response frequency develops and how long it can be maintained without reinforcement (i.e., extinction).

Only recently have the techniques of operant conditioning been applied to the practical problem of "shaping" more normal behavior in humans who are behaving abnormally. These techniques have been worked out using infrahuman organisms. Obviously, one can achieve much better control over the environments of animals than of humans. Thus, the study of the relationship between the environmental events and behavior has been undertaken with some precision. If nothing else, experimentation with animals has shown operant conditioning to be a powerful technique for generating behavior.

The application of operant conditioning procedures to the mentally retarded, particularly the severe cases, should be fruitful. As Lindsley (1964) has observed, persons who have a limited response repertoire and, therefore, less response competition, might prove more susceptible to operant conditioning than others, such as psychotics, who have a larger assortment of maladaptive responses. Lindsley even suggests that achieving higher-than-average performance on the part of some of these individuals may be possible.

OPERANT CONDITIONING STUDIES

Before going on to describe more specific applications of operant conditioning to mental retardation, let us review some of the formal research investigations of free operant conditioning in which retardates have been studied. These are important because they provide a great deal of information concerning the functioning of retardates under a variety of controlled environmental conditions, particularly reinforcement contingencies. The same manipulations that prove to be effective in shaping behavior in the laboratory should be effective in a practical, on-the-job, training program.

In the typical testing situation the subject is brought into a small room in which light and sound are under the control of the experimenter. Usually the only pieces of equipment in the room are a response lever and a reward trough. Sometimes lights are mounted on the wall or on a panel for use to study the discrimination abilities of the subject. The subject is usually told that by manipulating the response lever he can get rewards.

Several studies have been conducted in which response characteristics have been related to various types of reinforcement schedules (Bijou and Orlando, 1961; Ellis, 1962; Orlando and Bijou, 1960; Spradlin, 1962). There are several different kinds of reinforcement schedules. Basically, the schedules are either "fixed" or "variable." By a fixed schedule, we mean one in which the reward is forthcoming after a constant number of responses (fixed-ratio) or after a constant interval of time (fixed-interval). On the other hand, if the subject is rewarded on a variable basis we are dealing with either variable ratio or variable interval schedules. Obviously, the different schedules produce different response patterns.

The study of Orlando and Bijou (1960) on the effects of a variety of reinforcement schedules on the response rates of retarded children indicated that high response rates occur under several different reinforcement schedules. Variable reinforcement schedules appear to produce higher rates than do fixed schedules. With respect to fixed ratio schedules, the higher response rates are associated with lower ratios (i.e., more responses per reinforcement). This seems to agree with the results of a study by Ellis (1962). Orlando and Bijou have also found that multiple schedules produce more precise control over response rates than do simple schedules. Ellis, Barnett, and Pryer (1960) have shown that even profoundly retarded individuals, regarded as untestable, can respond differentially to changes in the reinforcement schedules. Certain types of schedule control are possibly more effective with retardates than with normals.

The high response rate under a fixed interval schedule displayed by some of the subjects in the Orlando and Bijou study is inefficient. That is, time rather than response rate determines reinforcement. In order to make use of this cue, however, the subject must be able to employ the temporal interval as a discriminative stimulus and, having done this, must then be able to withhold his response when cues associated with nonreinforcement are present. Timing of the operant is in itself a discriminative process. Data provided by Orlando (1961) suggest that some retarded subjects who display high rates of responding under fixed ratio schedules have deficiencies in discrimination of time intervals. Birnbrauer (1964) put retarded subjects on either a fixed ratio schedule or on a schedule in which he differentially reinforced low rates of responding. After this training, the subjects were then shifted to a combination of these two schedules. Discriminative stimulus control was achieved, indicating that low rates of responding can be reinforced, at least for some retardates.

The instructions and ambiguous initial reinforcement given the subject appear to affect the behavior that occurs under a fixed interval schedule (Headrick, 1963a). By giving definitive instructions together with exposing the subjects to other reinforcement schedules, Headrick produced high response rates in her subjects with little temporal discrimination. Ramsey (1963) has also concluded that the instructional procedures can have a marked effect upon response rates and discrimination. While this finding has more relevance from a methodological point of view, it points to the need to consider the "set" of the subject as well as his reinforcement history in similar situations.

Spradlin (1962) has studied the effects of partial schedules of reinforcement upon extinction (i.e., nonreward of the response). His results are, in general, typical of findings in this area: that 100 per cent reinforcement produces less resistance to extinction than partial reinforcement schedules. However, he did not find a difference between 50 per cent and 75 per cent schedules. In another phase of his investigation, Spradlin obtained no differences in spontaneous recovery of the response as a function of initial reinforcement conditions. Under some conditions, severely retarded subjects can continue to respond appropriately when shifted from a continuous reinforcement schedule to a variable one (House, Zeaman, and Fischer, 1957).

More data that bear upon the matter of response extinction in retardates is necessary. Some evidence indicates that IQ may be unrelated to resistance to extinction (Semler, 1965). Obviously, the success of any training program ultimately will be measured against the persistence of the behavior without reinforcement. Knowing which reinforcement schedules best produce greatest resistance to extinction in the retarded would be helpful. Of course, the research with animals gives us many indications.

The operant conditioning situation provides an excellent means of studying stimulus discrimination and response differentiation. However, few investigations have pursued this valuable line of inquiry. Such studies could shed light upon specific learning deficits of retarded children. One such investigation (Barrett and Lindsley, 1962), for instance, has shown retardates to have severe response differentiation deficits and relatively poor stimulus discrimination. Moreover, they do not use all the available functional stimuli in a discrimination situation (Orlando, 1961).

In another investigation, Barrett (1962) has found response differentiation and stimulus discrimination to be independent psychological processes. Either or both are vulnerable to deficit and spontaneous variations in the mentally retarded. Supposedly, also, these deficits would have to be treated independently. Age, psychometric status, length of institutionalization, verbal ability, and diagnosis are all virtually unrelated to individual performance, while school progress does bear a relationship to poor and adequate response differentiation and stimulus discrimination.

These studies point out a further implication of operant procedures for use with the mentally retarded. Conceivably, these techniques could be profitably applied to the diagnostic process. This application has already been made to psychotics (Lindsley, 1962). The ability of the subject to adjust to certain reinforcement schedules, to make discriminations, and to differentiate his responses could be subjected to close and rigorous scrutiny in a controlled setting and over a long period of time. Thus, not only would the severity of the behavioral deficit be assessed, but also systematically evaluated in terms of its reaction to various manipulations of the environment. Such studies might reveal, in behavioral terms, the specific kinds of learning deficits characteristic of the individual retardate. Once the defective behavior patterns have been identified and objectively measured, determining which environmental factors control the behaviors and what might be done about them should be possible. In this way, we may find, for instance, that vastly different training regimes are required for psychometrically similar individuals. Such an approach to the diagnosis of learning deficit certainly could have merit and may supplement or even supplant the current and largely ineffective global psychometric approach to the problem. Barrett (1964) has pointed out that functional descriptions of the individual's behavioral deficits should be of greater value to the teacher than a general psychometric assessment.

APPLICATIONS TO HUMAN PROBLEMS

Lindsley (1964b) has noted more than 100 applications of the operant method to pathological behavior in humans. Of special interest is the work of Ayllon and his associates (Ayllon, 1963; Ayllon and Azrin, 1964; Ayllon and Haughton, 1962; Ayllon and Michael, 1959). These psychologists have "shaped" the behavior of grossly disturbed psychiatric patients by the judicious application and withholding of reinforcement. For example, they have controlled hoarding, stealing, and undesirable verbal and eating behavior. In one study, Ayllon and Michael (1959) demonstrated the efficacy of employing psychiatric nurses as behavioral engineers. A group of nurses, trained in the operant method, were able to effectively and significantly modify problem behavior in disturbed patients. This could have great implications with respect to training and rehabilitation in residential institutions for the retarded.

Lindsley (1959) and Isaacs, Thomas, and Goldiamond (1960) have applied operant conditioning to shape speech in psychotics, and Flanagan, Goldiamond, and Azrin (1958) have controlled stuttering. Ferster and deMyer

(1961) shaped durable complex behavioral sequences in "inaccessible" autistic children with a concomitant reduction in autistic behavior.

Few applications of operant conditioning techniques have been attempted in the "treatment" of mental retardation. However, those efforts that have been reported are sufficient to demonstrate that the method has great potential.

One recent attempt (Girardeau and Spradlin, 1964) is particularly noteworthy. These workers instituted a program of positive reinforcement of desirable behaviors in a cottage of 28 adolescent girls whose IQs ranged from 20 to 50. A few examples of the behaviors that they attempted to "shape" include: dressing for a meal, washing hair, playing in a group, and working.

The reinforcements used in this project consisted of bronze tokens, approximately the size of a 50-cent piece. The patients were able to "spend" these tokens on a variety of things, including candy, clothes, and cosmetics, as well as certain privileges, such as watching television. The enthusiasm their subjects displayed for the tokens is encouraging, for one of the important benefits of secondary reinforcement is to make learning efficient.

Although the program is still in operation, the initial results are interesting. A checklist evaluation of behaviors, taken 22 weeks after the program began, revealed significant gains for the group as a whole. As might be expected, some individuals demonstrated remarkable progress while others displayed none.

Reinforcements were programmed for improvements in behavior, no matter how slight the improvement. Thus, each patient was reinforced on an individual basis with the particular response evaluated against her baseline. It should be noted that the "shaping" was done on an individual basis; Girardeau and Spradlin started with the behavior the individual displayed and proceeded from there. No group standards were established. Some patients had to "pay" to participate in the very activities for which others were "paid" (e.g., watching television).

As might be expected, some control is lost when the technique is transferred from the laboratory to the cottage setting. Moreover, when one proceeds from the control of a highly specific response to the control of complex patterns of living, a great deal of efficiency is going to be lost. Nevertheless, Girardeau and Spradlin have shown the technique can be effectively and economically applied on a group basis to a variety of behavioral anomalies.

Blackwood (1962) has described his attempts to apply reinforcement principles to the development and control of various behaviors in institutionalized retardates. He has found these techniques to be more beneficial if they are applied on an individual rather than a group basis. Thus, he was successful in reducing the frequency of regurgitating responses, avoidance behaviors, undesirable eating behaviors, etc., in individual cases.

In his group experiment with 45 subjects, Blackwood attempted to bring under control such behaviors as wetting, soiling, fighting, screaming, thumb sucking, etc. Compared with controls who did not receive the reinforcement treatment, the experimental subjects did not display significant improvement in these behaviors. When one considers the procedures Blackwood used and what he was attempting to accomplish, this outcome is not unexpected. The difficulty was not with the method but rather with the failure to control the sources of reinforcement that produced the behavior in the first place. Blackwood indicates that the two major problems encountered in an attempt to control the environmental contingencies for large groups of individuals in a ward setting are: (1) providing immediate reinforcement to the patients and (2) maintaining appropriate behavior on the part of the attendant personnel.

Birnbrauer and Lawler (1964) have attempted to establish social and academic behavior in a class of moderately to severely retarded children. They started with candy as the reinforcer and then gradually shifted to paper clips. The results of this program are particularly impressive. They were able to develop a number of social skills in these children and, in some cases, were working on pre-reading programs.

The operant conditioning method should prove particularly useful in the development of self-care skills such as self-feeding, dressing, toileting, and so on. Speech training might also be profitably approached with operant techniques. A recently established institutional program described by Pursley and Hamilton (1965) is an attempt to apply these methods to improve patient self-help abilities. Pursley and Hamilton point out that the key to the method is to require meaningful action on the part of the subject, to reward the behavior, and to gradually increase the complexity of the behavior. Spradlin (1964) has also found the technique to be successful in the development of self-feeding skills.

Gorton and Hollis (1965), in describing a cottage program for profoundly retarded girls based upon the application of reinforcement principles, report considerable progress with respect to the various self-help skills, as well as in the area of social development.

Another project that provides an excellent example of the effectiveness of behavior shaping techniques has been described by Bensberg, Colwell, and Cassel (1965). Six severely retarded patients were placed in a special training unit to develop self-help skills. All the training was conducted by attendant personnel. The experiment was continued for seven months. The improvement in behavior, at the end of this period, was quite remarkable. For example, all were toilet trained. They learned how to feed themselves; they allowed themselves to be bathed, and they became more responsive to verbal directions. This last result is important because it indicates that even severely retarded individuals can learn to associate verbal symbols with concrete stimuli and with specific behaviors.

A somewhat similar study reported by Hundziak, Maurer, and Watson (1965) indicated that (a) the operant conditioning method is superior to conventional toilet training, and (b) the behavior acquired through operant conditioning can be transferred to the regular living unit. However, the subjects in this experiment used the toilet only in a passive manner—when they were placed on the toilet. The program was not successful in developing a more complicated chain of associations including going into the bathroom, removing clothing, dressing, etc.

One other practical application of the principles of operant conditioning to retarded behavior has been attempted. Baumeister and Klosowski (1965) initiated a program to toilet train eleven severely retarded adolescents. These patients were isolated in a separate part of their cottage by day. All of their activities, including play and eating were confined to this area. Efforts were made to maintain consistent stimulus conditions. By observing each patient carefully, the attendants could determine when the subject had to urinate or defecate. If he urinated or defecated in the toilet, he was immediately reinforced by some object, usually food, known to have reward value for the particular subject. The attendants were instructed to reward immediately all adaptive behaviors associated with the process of elimination. Thus, for instance, the patient was reinforced for going into the bathroom, for removing his clothing, etc.

A great deal of variability was noted in the patient's response to the 70-day conditioning program. Some showed rapid and substantial improvement, while others demonstrated little gain. Interestingly enough, the improvements made by particular patients bore little relationship to predictions made by the attendants before the program began.

While the program could not be viewed as completely successful, it did indicate that control over these behaviors can be achieved, provided effective reinforcements can be identified for each subject.

PRINCIPLES OF OPERANT CONDITIONING

Regardless of the clinical type of retardation, of the retardate's level of ability, or of the response pattern to be shaped, the principles described below apply.

1. *The desired response must be potentially available.* The method does not lead to the formation of new responses, but rather brings old ones under control by changing response frequencies. An animal cannot be taught to do anything that is not already in his behavior repertory. Thus, one probably can never "shape" creative thinking in the planarian no matter how skillfully or diligently he controls the reinforcement schedule. In practical terms, this means that the subject should be carefully studied to determine whether the desired response pattern, or something similar to it, is available to him. A deaf retardate, for instance, will never learn to respond appropriately to a dinner bell or a fire whistle. This, of course, does not mean that the retardate must necessarily have displayed the association in question; it merely requires that he has the potential to make the response if the environmental contingencies are appropriate. Casual observa-

tion of the subject is unlikely to be enough for determining whether he has the potential for acquiring the desired behavior. Sometimes prolonged and diligent efforts to bring the behavior under control will fail. Even then, however, one should not automatically assume, by default, that the subject is incapable of acquiring the appropriate response sequence. The limitation may be in the teacher's failure to identify the environmental contingencies that are more potent in controlling the behavior than his own schedules.

2. *Desirable behaviors (i.e., improvements) should be reinforced and undesirable ones ignored.* What constitutes a reinforcement is an important consideration. Some objects are usually reinforcing to most people. Food should be a reinforcer for the hungry person. Various other rewards such as candy, toys, praise, and money will reinforce behaviors in most retarded individuals. Music has been found to be an effective reinforcer among profoundly and severely retarded children (Watson, Lawson, and Sanders, 1965). However, there are some, particularly profoundly retarded patients, who can tax the teacher's imagination in finding an object or activity that is rewarding.

The teacher should take a strictly operational attitude to the matter of reinforcement. A reinforcer is some stimulus that changes the probability of occurrence of a given response (i.e., if the subject is stimulated in some manner following a given response and, as a consequence, he makes the response more frequently, the stimulus is a reinforcer). What may be reinforcing to the teacher may not be to the subject and vice versa. Thus, one severely retarded patient who participated in the previously mentioned toilet training project (Baumeister and Klosowski, 1965) was more reinforced by an old shirt than anything else. Furthermore, what may reinforce one particular response, may not necessarily reinforce others; and what is reinforcing on one occasion, may not be effective on another. For each individual to be trained, the important reinforcers should be listed and ranked in the order of their effectiveness. Furthermore, the strength of a reinforcer on a given occasion depends partly upon how long the subject has been deprived of the reinforcer.

In short, careful attention should be given the matter of reinforcers. The project of Girardeau and Spradlin, described previously, is important from this standpoint. They have shown, in effect, the efficiency of secondary or generalized reinforcement with this population. (Perhaps the term "conditioned reinforcer" would be more accurate.) Secondary reinforcers have a greater generality than the primary reinforcers upon which they were initially founded. Moreover, the subject is not satiated on well-established conditioned reinforcers, which can usually be given without interfering with ongoing behavior as is frequently the case with primary reinforcers. Watson, Lawson, and Sanders (1965) have reported on the results of a study designed to determine whether conditioned reinforcers are effective with severely and profoundly retarded children. Their data clearly show that a previously neutral stimulus object (poker chips) can acquire reinforcement properties for such children. Furthermore, they found that the reinforcement value was quite stable. These findings agree nicely with the less formal observations of Girardeau and Spradlin (1964). One further implication is that many social stimuli (e.g., praise) that accompany administration of the primary reinforcers may also acquire reinforcing properties for the severely retarded. Support for this observation comes from the previously described study made by Bensberg, Colwell, and Cassel (1965).

On occasions, negative reinforcements may be administered. However, negative reinforcements may have the effect of only temporarily suppressing the undesirable response. Thus, administering negative reinforcement may bring more desirable behavior under control of the stimuli that are associated with the undesirable behavior. This, in effect, is to substitute a response. Under some conditions punishment is a rapid and thoroughly effective means for eliminating behavior (Solomon, 1964).

When an alternative response is available to the subject even mild punishment can be effective (Herman and Azrin, 1964). Various stereotyped behaviors might be particularly responsive to this type of treatment. In general, the effects of punishment are not as predictable as those that follow positive reinforcement. Another, probably more effective, means of eliminating undesirable responses is to allow them to occur without reinforcement. This, of course, is the process of extinction. Once

the rewarding contingencies are removed, the behavior will not be maintained. In fact, training programs for some retarded individuals may have to begin by extinguishing certain pervasive behaviors (e.g., hyperactivity). In attempting to extinguish undesirable behaviors, one should study the subject carefully to discover what is reinforcing the particular response. Often the reinforcer is not immediately apparent and extinction may have to proceed on a trial-and-error basis until the effective reinforcer is identified.

3. *Reinforcement should be immediate.* In order for a reinforcement to be maximally effective, it must immediately follow the appropriate behavior. There is abundant research to support these points: (1) the response temporally closest to the reward gains most in strength; (2) the response that is reinforced is the one that is learned, and (3) the greater the delay, the more likely irrelevant responses will occur and be reinforced.

One might expect that because of poor attention (Zeaman and House, 1963), inferior short-term memory, or dissociation of the verbal and motor signal systems (Luria, 1960), the retardate would be more handicapped by delay of reinforcement than the normal. Two studies involving discrimination learning that bear upon this issue (Hetherington, Ross, and Pick, 1964; Jacobs, 1950) do not indicate such an inferiority, although delays of reinforcement do impede learning in both normals and retardates. A third study, conducted by Schoelkopf and Orlando (1965), shows that delays of only five seconds can produce significant decrements in simultaneous discrimination learning of retardates.

Again, the importance of secondary reinforcement is indicated. While, quite frequently, the primary reinforcer must of necessity be delayed, a secondary reinforcer, such as a token or praise, can be given immediately.

4. *In establishing the behavior, the reinforcement should be administered on each occasion of the response. Then, as learning progresses, reinforcement should be delivered on an intermittent basis.* This principle has a great deal of research support that shows, in effect, that learning is fastest when the reinforcement is continuous, but that resistance to extinction is greater for subjects who have been trained on a partial schedule. In general, the strength of the response depends on the number of

times it has been reinforced in the past. A corollary to this principle is that magnitude of the reinforcement should be relatively great at first and then steadily decreased as learning progresses. However, abrupt decreases in magnitude should probably be avoided (Heber, 1959) since such alterations in reinforcement are followed by a substantial decrement in performance.

Of course, as indicated earlier, several different types of intermittent reinforcement can be employed. Ratio schedules tend to produce high rates of responding. However, a variable ratio schedule produces more resistance to extinction of the response than does a fixed ratio. Interval schedules generate more moderate and stable rates of responding than do ratio schedules. Possibly, in general, the best intermittent schedule would be a variable interval in which the intervals are gradually lengthened. However, the nature of the response and of the reinforcement should be an important consideration in the determination of which schedule will be the most effective. For instance, a fixed interval schedule might be the most desirable in those cases where it is advantageous to have the response tied closely to temporal stimuli.

5. *The desired behavior should be "shaped" by rewarding successive improvements in the components that constitute the behavior.* Most behavior in which we are interested actually consists of a complicated chain or sequence of responses. As a matter of fact, the fluency with which this sequence is carried out is frequently a measure of the learning itself. In shaping the desired behavior, one waits until a component of the response is emitted and then reinforces the subject. After this particular response is well established, the teacher waits until the next response in the sequence (i.e., improvement) makes its appearance, reinforcing the subject again, and so on. In this way, the entire complicated sequence can be constructed. No other aspect of the operant conditioning situation probably requires as much skill on the part of the teacher.

6. *The subject's environment during the initial stages of learning should be held as constant as possible.* Effective learning can only proceed as rapidly as the subject is able to discriminate the stimuli associated with making the response from those that are associated with withholding it. Learning difficulties in

many cases can be traced to failure to discriminate the relevant aspects of stimuli. The goal of the conditioning process is to develop discriminated operants. These are responses that occur in conjunction with discriminative stimuli that "tell" the subject that the response will be followed by a reinforcement. Operant stimulus generalization occurs when the learner fails to discriminate. Some retardates demonstrate poor stimulus discrimination (Barrett and Lindsley, 1962). Tempone (1965) has also found low MA subjects to demonstrate more stimulus generalization than higher MA subjects. Accordingly, the discriminative stimuli in any learning situation with such individuals should be emphasized and, perhaps, exaggerated. Furthermore, irrelevant sources of stimulation should be controlled. Baumeister and Klosowski (1965) found that some patients who had achieved some degree of toilet training completely regressed in this ability when they were abruptly shifted to a new environment.

On the other hand, after the response has been well established, deliberate environmental alterations should be slowly introduced to promote transfer to new situations. After all, in order to be functional, the behavior must usually be generalized to other and new contexts. For example, one wishes self-feeding behaviors to be maintained in environments other than where they were originally learned. If the alterations are deliberate and cautious, then the subject will continue to discriminate and attend to the relevant cues.

Sometimes improvements in behavior are only temporary and the individual reverts to his previous, less desirable, mode of responding. When this occurs, it is because the reinforcement contingencies have also reverted. In effect, the subject is returned to the very contingencies that produced the behavior initially. Indeed, one might be surprised if regression did not occur in this situation.

The methods and principles of operant conditioning at our present state of knowledge, seem to offer greater possibilities for radically controlling deviant behavior than any other system available. Of course, this is not to say that the method is infallible. It does not always succeed in bringing behavior under control, but the likelihood is high in such an event that the fault lies more with the teacher than with the method.

RECENT THEORETICAL DEVELOPMENTS

Very few attempts have been made to formulate theories of behavior to account specifically for the inadequacies characteristic of retarded individuals. This is not so surprising in view of the limitations of more general theories of behavior. Furthermore, one view, already alluded to, holds that no new set of laws is necessary to understand the behavior of mentally retarded individuals. In this case, one might expect the broader theoretical model to be extended to cover the mentally deficient. Actually, about the only widely known position that has been focused upon mental retardation, with some research backing, is field theory.

Another factor that must be mentioned regarding this problem is that mental retardation is still primarily viewed and defined in relation to intellective constructs. Thus, it has, in the past, seemed appropriate to construe mental retardation within the framework of one of the theories of intelligence. However, such theories usually have not been stated very explicitly nor have they been developed systematically to include mental retardation. The "low intelligence" concept of mental retardation does not really constitute a potent and productive explanatory or predictive system.

"Intelligence theory" is derived primarily from a mental testing or psychometric orientation. However, the development of a model of defective intelligence does not preclude other approaches and, indeed, ought to be rendered more complete and exact with the inclusion of the concepts and data from other theoretical and empirical vantage points. In fact, predictions about certain classes of adaptive behavior may not be possible without reference to such constructs. Further, differences between normal and retarded individuals are not entirely explicable on the basis of "intelligence," as evidenced by the apparent utility of defining mental retardation in relation to deficits in learning, maturation, or socialization (Heber, 1959a). For example, Kounin (1941a, 1941b), working within the framework of Lewinian field theory, postulated that mental retardation is directly associated with rigidity of the boundaries of physical systems. While the writer has no intention of reviewing the evidence for or against this particular theoretical concept (see Zigler, 1962), it is mentioned as an example of an alternative to the strictly psychometric approach.

Attention Theory. Zeaman and House, in a number of separate research reports, in reviews (Zeaman, 1959), and in a theoretical article (Zeaman and House, 1963), have attempted to analyze the learning deficits of mental retardates in terms of an attentional model of discrimination learning. Actually, they are dealing here with a form of stocastic or probability learning theory, similar in some respects to other statistical theories of learning.

Their basic notion is that a chain of two fundamental processes underlies discrimination learning: (1) observing the various stimulus dimensions, and (2) making the instrumental response. (By the term "dimensions," House and Zeaman are referring to broad classes of "cues" that have in common a stimulus property. Thus, color is a dimension while the specific colors are cues.) The consistent success of the latter is seen to depend upon the relevance of the former. The probability of each of a set of *observing* responses is a function of various factors and their interactions including intelligence, stimulus complexity, practice, reinforcement contingencies, past experience of the subject in similar situations, etc. The basic problem for the retardate is a low initial probability of attending to the relevant dimensions.

The retardate's capacity to acquire an instrumental response is not in question, but rather his ability to attend to the relevant and critical stimulus dimensions that lead to making the appropriate discriminations. House and Zeaman point out, rather convincingly, that slow discrimination learning is not characterized by a low rate of improvement in performance, but rather by the amount of time and practice needed for the learning to start (i.e., retardates experience relatively less difficulty in learning than in starting). Examination of individual learning curves in a two-choice discrimination situation indicates that learning, once it begins, proceeds rapidly, and in virtually the same form, for most subjects. Thus, these workers have focused upon the process that precedes instrumental approach to the relevant cues. This initial process consists of attending to the appropriate stimulus dimensions. The subject "learns" something only about those dimensions to which he is attending. Learning is confined to a single dimension at a time.

In any given discrimination problem, the subject can only attend to, at most, a few of the possible dimensions (e.g. color, form, size, texture) that characterize the discriminanda. Retarded subjects perceive fewer dimensions than normals (House and Zeaman point out that this could be an advantage in some very simple learning situations where there are only a few relevant and easily perceived dimensions). Moreover, the observing responses, depending upon the situation and the learner, have a high probability of occurrence and others low. Furthermore, the brighter subject is able to attend to those dimensions that have been relevant to the solution of other similar problems in the past. Thus, the two differences between the more intelligent and effective learner and the retarded one are: (a) the former attends to a larger set of dimensions, giving him a greater likelihood of identifying the relevant ones, and (b) he is better able to ignore those that are likely to be irrelevant.

The concept of "attention" as used here by House and Zeaman does not necessarily refer to the degree to which the subject perseveres in the task. Indeed, an individual may apply himself quite diligently to the solution of the problem and yet do poorly because of lack of attention or because of attention to the wrong dimensions.

Note that House and Zeaman are dealing here only with discrimination learning processes. While their conceptions may have value for explanatory and predictive purposes in other areas, the extension has yet to be made. Quite obviously, the theory will have to be modified to encompass phenomena in, say, verbal learning. Yet, the basic construct, that of attention, seemingly should be applicable to these other areas. For instance, inspection of the rotary pursuit learning curves given by Jones and Ellis (1962) indicates that, at least under some conditions, the rate of learning for the defective, once he has started to learn, is comparable to that of the normal subject. His difficulty, initially, may be that the appropriate attending responses have low probability of occurrence (Baumeister, Hawkins, and Holland, 1966).

Although Zeaman and House adopt mental retardation as a basis for their speculation, the theory extends to the discrimination learning of normal individuals as well. Nothing is special about their theory insofar as mental retardation is concerned. In fact, nothing is said about how or why the retarded individual suffers his defect in attention.

House and Zeaman have offered some suggestions, based on their theory and research, for improving retardates' performance on discrimination learning tasks. Since they regard as the retardate's fundamental difficulty his inability to attend to the relevant stimulus dimensions, the remedial procedure is to increase the probability that he will observe the relevant dimensions. Specific suggestions include (1) use of three-dimensional objects (e.g., cut-out letters), (2) use of easy-to-hard sequences, (3) emphasis upon relevant dimensions, such as form, by tracing, (4) increase of the novelty of either the negative or positive stimuli, (5) keeping the reward spatially or temporally contiguous with the cues, (6) avoidance of failure, and (7) establishment of a "set" to attend to relevant dimensions. All of these effects have been demonstrated empirically.

Stimulus Trace Theory. Another theoretical point of view that has been focused upon the learning and retention disabilities associated with mental retardation involves the stimulus trace concept (Ellis, 1963). Two major constructs are proposed to account specifically for short-term memory deficits in the retardate—stimulus trace (St) and central nervous system integrity (Ni).

Ellis's notion of stimulus trace is roughly analogous to the reverberatory circuit of neurophysiology. A stimulus, impinging upon a receptor organ, produces certain changes in the activity of the central nervous system. These electrical changes outlast the duration of the stimulus that initiated them, apparently by reverberating temporarily over various sequences of neurons. Electroencephalographic phenomena, such as alpha block duration, reflect these perseverative aftereffects. Such a process is presumed to subserve short-term memory (measured in terms of seconds). Ellis is concerned with molar behavior rather than with the more molecular physiological events described above. The neurophysiological mechanisms that are responsible for the neural phenomena after stimulation are presumed to be analogous to those processes that link a molar behavioral product with its stimulus antecessors. Among the various stimulus dimensions that affect the quality of St, in terms of amplitude and duration, are intensity, duration, and meaningfulness.

The construct of central nervous system integrity is less well defined by Ellis. Indeed, one wonders how it differs operationally from intelligence. By this concept, Ellis evidently is referring to the comparative ability of an organism to maintain the trace. Ni is affected by central nervous system pathology, which Ellis, incidentally, interprets quite broadly. Operationally, Ni is defined almost exclusively by an intelligence test score, although, logically, this is not the only index that might be used. Thus, the retardate, by fault of "neuropathology" suffers impairment in his ability to maintain an adequate trace with respect to duration or amplitude. To the extent that learning and long-term memory are dependent upon consolidation of the trace, the organism with a debilitated central nervous system will be impaired in these functions as well.

Ellis views the noncontinuity of events to be associated as crucial to an explanation of learning and retention deficits in the retarded (i.e., if A and B are to be associated but are temporally separated, then strictly speaking B is associated with the "trace" of A). It is interesting to note that Ellis, like House and Zeaman, does not question the retardate's ability, per se, to acquire and retain an instrumental response. In fact, Ellis makes it a special point to note the durability of an association in the retardate once it is formed. In the case of trace theory, however, experimentally separating the instrumental learning from short-term memory would be difficult. In fact, in actual learning experiments, the effect of different conditions of trace can only be inferred indirectly from differences in learning (e.g., Blue, 1963).

As already implied, the most obvious application of the St concept, as it relates to learning, is in those situations where the subject is required to associate two events that are separated in time. The theory predicts an interaction between such intervals and intelligence. That is, one is led to expect that the retardate would be more adversely affected by the delays than normals, the difference in performance becoming greater as the intervals are increased. Actually, the evidence for this hypothesis is equivocal (e.g., Baumeister, Beedle, and Urqu-

hart, 1964; Blue, 1963; Hawkins; 1964; Headrick and Ellis, 1964).

Many other situations arise in which the theory predicts differential effects for normal and retarded individuals. For instance, delay of reinforcement should be more deleterious to the performance of the defective. Intermittent reinforcement during learning might prove less effective for the retardate. He should be particularly handicapped in those situations that require him to temporarily "keep in mind" certain aspects of a problem.

If Ellis's analysis of mental deficiency in relation to short-term memory is correct, the best approach to training retarded individuals requires that effective measures be undertaken to improve their short-term memory. It does not seem too likely that one can act directly upon the retardate to improve his ability to maintain a trace (although this certainly does merit attention). Rather, the approach would be to "arrange" his environment to compensate for his inferior and impoverished trace. For instance, visual displays might be more effective than auditory. Simultaneous presentations in multiple modalities should be beneficial. Events to be associated should be presented simultaneously (or, at least, contiguously) rather than successively. The interval between presentation and reproduction of content should be as brief as possible. Reinforcement and performance feedback should be immediate. In situations where stimuli must be temporarily retained by the learner, making the initial stimulus more intense and of longer duration might prove helpful. Practice should be distributed. Meaningful materials should be used whenever possible. Mediators should be taught in order to help the retardate bridge gaps involving unfamiliar material.

Clearly, the stimulus trace theory applies only to that class of behaviors that involves short-term memory. (A careful analysis of most learning situations would show, however, that this ability is usually subtly involved). It is not intended to encompass the entire range of behavioral inadequacies characteristic of the mentally retarded. In time, the theory will almost certainly give way to a set of more inclusive principles. Nevertheless, I think that stimulus trace theory does offer some valuable suggestions for the training of mental defectives.

Verbal Dysfunction Theory (Luria). Russian theory of learning disability in the mentally retarded derives from notions of Pavlov and his classical conditioning model of learning. Luria (1960, 1963) is probably the best known exponent of this point of view in relation to mental retardation.

The Russian conception of mental retardation differs in some important respects from that of current American thinking. Among other things, in the Soviet view, mental retardation, or oligophrenia, is inevitably the consequence of nervous system pathology, although in many instances the nature of the lesion is, admittedly, difficult to specify. Luria is particularly disdainful of the notion that subnormality in the form of low intelligence is inheritable. He does not regard such an assertion as a "worthy contribution to science." While not wishing to enter into the nature-nurture controversy, I insist that the question of whether variations in heredity lead to variations in intelligent behavior is an empirical one.

According to Luria's theory, two primary signal systems subserve higher nervous activity. One of these systems is governed by direct signals from the environment and is characterized by its reflexive nature. The second signal system, possessing the properties of abstraction and conceptualization, involves language. This latter system develops to regulate responses to the direct signals. Thus, the human subordinates his behavior to his "verbally formulated intentions." Verbal behavior, in the normally functioning individual, is pre-eminent over motor behavior.

Higher nervous activity consists of two basic processes: excitation and inhibition. Stimulation reaching the cortex, spreads (irradiates) over the sensory area involved, but with diminishing intensity from the point of origin. This excitation effect is not unlike that of a stone dropped in a pool of water. However, the very process of excitation is said to produce an opposite effect—inhibition —in neighboring cortical regions. Learning, i.e. conditioning, occurs when the excitation established by a neutral stimulus temporally and spatially approximates that of the unconditioned stimulus. After the two stimuli are paired a sufficient number of times, the excitation of the former elicits the conditioned response.

The three main properties of the higher nervous processes are strength, equilibrium, and mobility. By "strength," Luria refers to the speed with which conditioning takes place, the amount of inhibition that develops to inappropriate responses, and the durability of the connection in the face of external inhibition or exhaustion. In speaking of "equilibrium," Luria is suggesting a balance between excitatory and inhibitory processes, such that one does not abnormally predominate over the other. "Mobility" refers to the capacity of the organism to rapidly adjust its mode of response to changing stimulus conditions.

Thus, the individual with a pathological weakness of the basic processes will acquire connections slowly, will respond inappropriately, and will be easily disrupted by extraneous stimuli and fatigue. If a disequilibrium between excitation and inhibition occurs, the effects depend upon which process predominates. If it is inhibition, the subject will require many trials to learn and will be "sluggish" in his higher thought processes. Should the excitatory processes prevail, the subject will respond erratically, impulsively, and inappropriately. Finally, when the faculty of mobility suffers, the subject no longer will adapt easily and readily to changing stimulus conditions. In this case, the outstanding symptom is perseveration.

Defects in these areas produce distinctive sets of symptoms. If the verbal system is left relatively intact, the syndrome of cerebro-asthenia ("cerebral weakness") results. This concept, incidentally, bears certain similarities to "exogenous" defects suggested some years ago by Strauss and his associates. Actually, the distinction between cerebro-asthenia and oligophrenia appears to lie in the pervasiveness of the cerebral lesion. Although persons with the latter condition also suffer derangements with respect to the strength and equilibrium of the nervous processes, their primary characteristic is the profoundly disturbed mobility of the higher nervous processes. Moreover, these defects extend to the second signalling system, resulting not only in a lack of development of these systems but also in dissociation between them. The regulatory function of the child's verbal behavior is diminished. Luria says, "Pathological inertia of once established verbal connections and the simultaneously arising pathological dissociation of the two signalling systems constitute a specific feature of the higher nervous activity in oligophrenic children" (1963, p. 383).

Luria is none too optimistic about what can be done to help the truly oligophrenic child. On the other hand, he contends that a great deal can be done to compensate for the defect of the child presenting the cerebro-asthenic syndrome. By Western criteria, many of these latter individuals would be identified as retarded.

In these children the verbal system remains intact. The treatment, then, is to compensate for the neurodynamic defects by bringing the motor reactions under the regulation of the verbal reactions. For instance, in the case where the principal defect is weakness of the inhibitory process within the first signaling system, the child will respond impulsively and erratically. But, when he is required to combine his motor reaction with the appropriate verbal reaction (i.e., the child says the word corresponding to his motor reaction), his performance should improve significantly. In those cases where the inhibitory factor is predominant, correct motor reactions can be reinforced and sustained by again combining the motor with the verbal reactions. In fact, regardless of the nature of the specific disability in the condition of cerebro-asthenia, the remedial procedure always seems to be to invoke the speech processes in order to compensate for the functional defect.

Regarding the more profoundly retarded (oligophrenic) youngster, Luria indicates that a great deal of emphasis will have to be placed upon language development and upon relating verbal behavior to motor behavior. While he does not suggest that an enlarged language system alone is sufficient to overcome the abnormality or inertness of mental function, he implies that it appears to be a necessary condition for cognitive development. In short, the mental defective has a reduced capacity to use symbols. When the retarded subjects are taught to verbally mediate their motor responses and when the task requires them to do so, their performance is greatly enhanced. Not only do retardates have a small vocabulary, but they are also reluctant to use what they do possess (O'Connor and Hermelin, 1963). However, not all the available evidence points to verbal-motor dissociation as the basic deficit in retarded processes. Rosen, Kivitz, and Rosen (1965) have failed to find any substantial dissociation between the verbal and motor systems of mental retardates.

In summary, according to Luria's notions, the key to educating the mentally retarded lies in (1) thorough diagnosis of the defect, (2) enlargement of vocabulary, and (3) forced verbal coding or mediation of motor responses. Indeed, a considerable amount of research, already discussed, indicates that when the mentally retarded individual is taught how to manipulate verbal symbols, his learning is greatly improved. Within the normal routine of the classroom, one could arrange many learning situations in such ways as to promote such verbal coding.

SUMMARY

An attempt has been made to discuss and evaluate some of the research literature as it provides directions for the effective training and education of mentally retarded persons. Specific areas of verbal, discrimination, and motor learning have been considered. The operant conditioning technique has been examined in some detail. A few implications have also been drawn from current theoretical formulations.

Clearly mental retardation cannot be considered a general and unitary behavioral deficit. Rather, the mental retardate is one whose interaction with his environment is impaired in specific and special ways. The research evidence suggests that learning disability associated with mental deficiency is specific to particular processes and tasks. Identification of such impairments, and the conditions under which they are variable, is necessary for the development of efficient and effective training methods.

Compared with normal individuals, mental retardates, as a group, are inferior in acquisition and comparable in retention. However, the nature and extent of deficits in acquisition are contingent upon a number of factors, including (a) meaningfulness of the material to be learned, (b) the way in which the materials are programmed, (c) the individual's previous experience with similar problems, and (d) the context in which the problem is presented.

With respect to verbal learning, we are

probably safe in concluding that mediation (i.e., assigning distinctive "labels" to cues) is a crucial aspect of efficient performance. Quite likely, mental retardates not only have a smaller reservoir of mediators than normals, but also less experience in the use of them. Measures that are taken to promote mediational responses are found to markedly facilitate verbal learning by retardates. The same holds true in discrimination learning. In general, procedures that enhance the distinctiveness of the stimuli to be discriminated and associated substantially benefit mental retardates' efforts to learn.

With the exception of those individuals whose retardation is severe, the mentally de-fective appear to have no special disability in motor learning. Differences in performance are more likely due to motivational factors than learning per se. Evidence is available to indicate that, with sufficient practice, the mental retardate performs a learned motor response quite as well as the normal.

Considerable attention was devoted to a description of operant conditioning techniques and their application to mental retardation. These techniques should prove particularly useful for working with severely retarded patients who have little or no language. Recent attempts to employ operant conditioning methods to "shaping" self-help skills have been generally successful.

REFERENCES

AKUTAGAWA, D., and BENOIT, E. P. The effect of age and relative brightness on associative learning in children. *Child Develpmt.*, 1959, *30*, 229–238.

ANNETT, J. The information capacity of young mental defectives in an assembly task. *J. Ment. Sci.*, 1957, *103*, 621–631.

AYLLON, T. Intensive treatment of psychotic behaviour by stimulus satiation and food reinforcement. *Behav. Res. Ther.*, 1963, *1*, 53–61.

———, and AZRIN, N. H. Reinforcement and instructions with mental patients. *J. exp. anal. Behav.*, 1964, *7*, 327–331.

———, and HAUGHTON, E. Control of the behavior of schizophrenic patients by food. *J. exp. anal. Behav.*, 1962, *5*, 343–352.

———, and MICHAEL, J. The psychiatric nurse as a behavioral engineer. *J. exper. anal. Behav.*, 1959, *2*, 323–334.

BARNETT, C. D., and CANTOR, G. N. Pursuit rotor performance in mental defectives as a function of distribution of practice. *Percept. mot. Skills*, 1957, *7*, 191–197.

———, ELLIS, N. R., and PRYER, M. W. Stimulus pretaining and delayed reaction in defectives. *Amer. J. ment. Defic.*, 1959, *64*, 104–111.

———, ———, and ———. Learning in familial and brain-injured defectives. *Amer. J. ment. Defic.*, 1960, *64*, 894–901. (a)

———, ———, and ———. Serial position effects in superior and retarded subjects. *Psychol., Rep.*, 1960, *7*, 111–113. (b)

BARRETT, B. H. Acquisition of operant differentiation and discrimination in institutionalized retarded children. Paper presented to the Eastern Psychological Association convention, Atlantic City, 1962.

———. Programmed instruction and retarded behavior. Paper read at American Association on Mental Deficiency, Portland, 1963.

———, and LINDSLEY, O. R. Deficits in acquisition of operant discrimination and differentiation shown by institutionalized retarded children. *Amer. J. Ment. Defic.*, 1962, *67*, 424–436.

BAUMEISTER, A. A. A comparison of normals and retardates with respect to incidental and intentional learning. *Amer. J. ment. Defic.*, 1963, *68*, 404–408. (a)

———. *Investigations of memory deficits in retardates.* Progress report, MH 07445-01, NIMH, 1963. (b)

————. Use of the WISC with mental retardates: a review. *Amer. J. ment. Defic.*, 1964, *69*, 183–194.

————, and BARTLETT, C. J. A comparison of the factor structure of normals and retardates on the WISC. *Amer. J. ment. Defic.*, 1962, *66*, 641–646.

————, ————, and HAWKINS, W. F. Stimulus trace as a predictor of performance. *Amer. J. ment. Defic.*, 1963, *67*, 726–729.

————, BEEDLE, R., and HAWKINS, W. F. Transposition in normals and retardates under varying conditions of training and test. *Amer. J. ment. Defic.*, 1964, *69*, 432–437.

————, ————, and URQUHART, D. GSR conditioning in normals and retardates. *Amer. J. ment. Defic.*, 1964, *69*, 114–120.

————, HAWKINS, W. F., and DAVIS, P. A. Stimulus-response durations in paired-associates learning of normals and retardates. *Amer. J. ment. Defic.*, 1966, *70*, 580–584.

————, ————, and HOLLAND, J. Motor learning and knowledge of results. *Amer. J. ment. Defic.*, 1966, *70*, 590–594.

————, ————, and KELLAS, G. The interactive effects of stimulus intensity and intelligence upon reaction time. *Amer. J. ment. Defic.*, 1965, *69*, 526–530.

————, and KLOSOWSKI, R. An attempt to group toilet train severely retarded patients. *Mental Retardation*, 1965, *3*, 24–26.

————, URQUHART, D., BEEDLE, R., and SMITH, T. Reaction times of normals and retardates under different stimulus intensity changes. *Amer. J. ment. Defic.*, 1964, *69*, 126–130.

BENSBERG, G. J., COLWELL, C. N., and CASSEL, R. H. Teaching the profoundly retarded self-help activities by behavior shaping techniques. *Amer. J. ment. Defic.*, 1965, *69*, 674–679.

BERKSON, G. An analysis of reaction time in normal and mentally deficient young men. I. Duration threshold experiment. *J. ment. Defic. Res.*, 1960, *4*, 51–58. (a)

————. An analysis of reaction time in normal and mentally deficient young men. II. Variation of complexity in reaction time tasks. *J. ment. Defic. Res.*, 1960, *4*, 59–67. (b)

————. An analysis of reaction time in normal and mentally deficient young men. III. Variation of stimulus and response complexity. *J. ment. Defic. Res.*, 1960, *4*, 69–77. (c)

————. Responsiveness of the mentally deficient. *Amer. J. ment. Defic.*, 1961, *66*, 277–286.

————, and CANTOR, G. N. A study of mediation in mentally retarded and normal school children. *J. educ. Psychol.*, 1960, *51*, 82–86.

BIJOU, S. W., and ORLANDO, R. Rapid development of multiple-schedule performances with retarded children. *J. exp. anal. Behav.*, 1961, *4*, 7–16.

BIRNBRAUER, J. S. Some multiple schedule effects in retarded adolescents. *J. exp. anal. Behav.*, 1964, *7*, 168 (Abstract).

————, and LAWLER, J., Token reinforcement for learning. *Mental Retardation*, 1964, *2*, 275–279.

BLACKWOOD, R. O. Operant conditioning as a method of training the mentally retarded. Unpublished doctoral dissertation, Ohio State University, 1962.

BLUE, C. M. Performance of normal and retarded subjects on a modified paired-associate task. *Amer. J. ment. Defic.*, 1963, *66*, 228–234.

BRENGELMANN, J. C., and HILLMAN, W. A., JR. Determinants of learning in the retardate: A pilot study. *Train. Sch. Bull.*, 1965, *61*, 156–162.

BURT, C. *The backward child.* London: University of London Press, 1958.

CANTOR, G. N., and HOTTEL, J. V. Psychomotor learning in defectives as a function of verbal pretraining. *Psychol. Rec.*, 1957, *7*, 79–85.

————, and RYAN, T. J. Retention of verbal paired-associates in normals and retardates. *Amer. J. ment. Defic.*, 1962, *66*, 861–865.

————, and STACEY, C. L. Manipulative dexterity in mental defectives. *Amer. J. ment. Defic.*, 1951, *56*, 401–410.

CASSEL, R. Serial verbal learning and retroactive inhibition in aments and children. *J. clin. Psychol.*, 1957, *13*, 369–372.

CLARKE, A. D. B. The abilities and trainability of imbeciles. In A. D. B. Clarke and A. M. Clarke (Eds.), *Mental deficiency; the changing outlook*. Glencoe, Ill.: The Free Press, 1958.

CROMWELL, R. L. A social learning approach to mental retardation. In N. R. Ellis (Ed.), *Handbook of mental deficiency: Psychological theory and research*. New York: McGraw-Hill, 1963.

DENNY, M. R. Research in learning and performance. In H. A. Stevens and R. Heber (Eds.), *Mental retardation*. Chicago: University of Chicago Press, 1964.

DENT, H. E., and JOHNSON, R. C. The effects of massed vs. distributed practice on the learning of organic and familial defectives. *Amer. J. ment. Defic.*, 1964, *68*, 533–536.

DICKERSON, D. J., GIRARDEAU, F. L., and SPRADLIN, J. E. Verbal pretraining and discrimination learning by the retardates. *Amer. J. ment. Defic.*, 1964, *68*, 476–484.

DOKECKI, P. R. Reviews of the literature relative to the behavior potential of the severely retarded. *Train. Schl. Bull.*, 1964, *61*, 65–75.

EISMAN, B. S. Paired-associate learning, generalization and retention as a function of intelligence. *Amer. J. ment. Defic.*, 1958, *63*, 481–489.

ELLIS, N. R. Amount of reward and operant behavior in mental defectives. *Amer. J. ment. Defic.*, 1962, *66*, 595–599.

————. The stimulus trace and behavioral inadequacy. In N. R. Ellis (Ed.), *Handbook of mental deficiency: Psychological theory and research*. New York: McGraw-Hill, 1963.

————. Toilet training the severely defective patient: an S-R reinforcement analysis. *Amer. J. ment. Defic.*, 1963, *68*, 98–103.

————, BARNETT, C. D., and PRYER, M. W. Operant behavior in mental defectives: exploratory studies, *J. exper. anal. Behav.*, 1960, *3*, 63–69.

————, ————, and ————. Performance of mental defectives on the mirror drawing task. *Percept. mot. Skills*, 1957, *7*, 271–274.

————, and DISTEFANO, M. K., JR. The effects of verbal urging and praise upon rotary pursuit performance in mental defectives. *Amer. J. ment. Defic.*, 1959, *64*, 486–490.

————, PRYER, M. W., and BARNETT, C. D. Motor learning and retention in normals and defectives. *Percept. mot. Skills*, 1960, *10*, 83–91. (a)

————, ————, and ————. Note on habit formation in normal and retarded subjects. *Psychol. Rep.*, 1960, *6*, 385–386. (b)

————, ————, DISTEFANO, M. K. JR., and PRYER, R. S. Learning in mentally defective, normal, and superior subjects. *Amer. J. ment. Defic.*, 1960, *64*, 725–734.

————, and SLOAN, W. Rotary pursuit performance as a function of mental age. *Percept. mot. Skills*, 1957, *7*, 267–270.

FERSTER, C. B., and DEMYER, M. K. The development of performance in autistic children in an automatically controlled environment. *J. chron. Dis.*, 1961, *13*, 312–345.

FLANAGAN, B., GOLDIAMOND, I., and AZRIN, N. H. Operant stuttering: The control of stuttering behavior through response-contingent consequences. *J. exp. anal. Behav.*, 1958, *1*, 173–177.

FORD, J. H. A comparison of the learning and forgetting rates of mentally retarded and normal school children. Unpublished doctoral dissertation, University of Oklahoma, 1962.

FULLER, P. R. Operant conditioning of a vegetative human organism. *Amer. J. Psychol.*, 1949, *62*, 587–589.

GALLAGHER, J. J., and LUCITO, L. J. Intellectual patterns of gifted compared with average and retarded. *Except. Children*, 1961, *27*, 479–482.

GIRARDEAU, F. L. The formation of discrimination learning sets in mongoloid and normal children. *J. comp. physiol. Psychol.*, 1959, *52*, 566–570.

———, and ELLIS, N. R. Rote verbal learning by normal and mentally retarded children. *Amer. J. ment. Defic.*, 1964, *68*, 525–532.

———, and SPRADLIN, J. E. Token rewards in a cottage program. *Mental Retardation*, 1964, *2*, 345–351.

GORDON, S., O'CONNOR, N., and TIZARD, J. Some effects of incentives on the performance of imbeciles. *Brit. J. Psychol.*, 1954, *45*, 277–287.

———, ———, and ———. Some effects of incentives on the performance of imbeciles on a repetitive task. *Amer. J. ment. Defic.*, 1955, *60*, 371–377.

GORTON, C. E., and HOLLIS, J. H. Redesigning a cottage unit for better programming and research for the severely retarded. *Mental Retardation*, 1965, *3*, 16–21.

GRINGS, W. W., LOCKHART, R. A., and DAMERON, L. E. Conditioning autonomic responses of mentally subnormal individuals. *Psychol. Monogr.*, 1962, *76*, (39), 1–35.

HARTER, S. Discrimination learning set in children as a function of IQ and MA. *J. exper. child Psychol.*, 1965, *2*, 31–43.

HAWKER, J. R., GEERTZ, U. W., and SHRAGO, M. Prompting and confirmation in sight vocabulary learning by retardates. *Amer. J. ment. Defic.*, 1964, *68*, 751–756.

HAWKINS, W. F. The effects of stimulus asynchronism in associative learning by normals and retardates. Unpublished doctoral dissertation, George Peabody College, 1964.

———, and BAUMEISTER, A. A. The effect of retroactive inhibition upon the digit span performance of normals and retardates. *Amer. J. ment. Defic.*, 1965, *69*, 871–876.

———, ———, KOENIGSKNECHT, R. A., and KELLAS, G. Simple and disjunctive reaction times of normals and retardates. *Amer. J. ment. Defic.*, 1965, *69*, 536–540.

HEADRICK, M. W. Effects of instructions and initial reinforcement on fixed-interval behavior in retardates. *Amer. J. ment. Defic.*, 1963, *68*, 425–432. (a)

———. Operant conditioning in mental deficiency. *Amer. J. ment. Defic.*, 1963, *67*, 924–929. (b)

———, and ELLIS, N. R. Short-term visual memory in normals and retardates. *J. exp. child Psych.*, 1964, *1*, 339–347.

HEBER, R. F. Motor task performance of high grade mentally retarded males as a function of the magnitude of incentive. *Amer. J. ment. Defic.*, 1958, *63*, 667–671.

———. A manual on terminology and classification in mental retardation. *Amer. J. ment. Defic. Monogr.*, 1959, *64*, No. 2.

HERMAN, R. L., and AZRIN, N. H. Punishment by noise in an alternate response situation. *J. exp. anal. Behav.*, 1964, *7*, 185–188.

HETHERINGTON, E. M., and BANTA, T. J., Incidental and intentional learning in normal and mentally retarded children, *J. comp. physiol. Psych.*, 1962, *55*, 402–404.

————, Ross, L. E., and PICK, H. L., JR. Delay of reward and learning in mentally retarded and normal children. *Child Developmt*, 1964, *35*, 653–659.

HOLLIS, J. H. Solution of bent-wire problems of severely retarded children. *Amer. J. ment. Defic.*, 1962, *67*, 463–472.

HOLMAN, P. The relationship between general mental development and manual dexterity. *Brit. J. Psychol.*, 1933, *23*, 279–283.

HOUSE, B. J. Discrimination learning without overt response or reward in retardates. *Amer. J. ment. Defic.*, 1964, *68*, 734–740. (a)

————. The effect of distinctive responses on discrimination reversals in retardates. *Amer. J. ment. Defic.*, 1964, *69*, 79–85. (b)

————, SMITH, M., and ZEAMAN, D. Verbal learning and retention as a function of number lists in retardates. *Amer. J. ment. Defic.*, 1964, *69*, 239–243.

————, and ZEAMAN, D. Miniature experiments in the discrimination learning of retardates. In L. P. Lipsitt and C. C. Spiker (Eds.), *Advances in child development and behavior*, Vol. I. New York: Academic Press, 1963.

————, ————, and FISCHER, W. *Learning and transfer in mental defectives.* Progress Report, M-1099, NIMH, 1957.

HUNDZIAK, M., MAURER, R. A., and WATSON, L. S., JR. Operant conditioning in toilet training of severely mentally retarded boys. *Amer. J. ment. Defic.*, 1965, *70*, 120–124.

ISAACS, W., THOMAS, J., and GOLDIAMOND, I. Applications of operant conditioning to reinstate verbal behavior in psychotics. *J. speech hear. Disorders*, 1960, *25*, 8–12.

ISCOE, I., and SEMLER, I. J. Paired-associate learning in normal and mentally retarded children as a function of four experimental conditions. *J. comp. physiol. Psychol.*, 1964, *57*, 387–392.

JACOBS, A. Performance of children in a discrimination problem as a function of symbolic guidance, delay of reward, and mental ability. Unpublished doctoral dissertation, University of Iowa, 1950.

JENSEN, A. Learning ability in retarded, average, and gifted children. *Merrill-Palmer Quart.*, 1963, *9*, 123–140.

JENSEN, A. R. Rote learning in retarded adults and normal children. *Amer. J. ment. Defic.*, 1965, *69*, 828–834.

————, and ROHWER, W. D., JR. The effect of verbal mediation on the learning and retention of paired-associates by retarded adults. *Amer. J. ment. Defic.*, 1963, *68*, 80–84. (a)

————, and ————. Verbal mediation in paired-associate and serial learning. *J. verb. learn. verb. Behav.*, 1963, *1*, 346–352. (b)

JOHNSON, D. M. *The psychology of thought and judgment.* New York: Harper, 1955.

JOHNSON, G. O., and BLAKE, K. A. *Learning performance of retarded and normal children.* Syracuse: Syracuse University Press, 1960.

JONES, W. R., and ELLIS, N. R. Inhibitory potential in rotary pursuit acquisition by normal and defective subjects. *J. exp. Psychol.*, 1962, *63*, 534–537.

KATZ, P. J. Another look at transfer of learning and mental retardation. *Mental Retardation*, 1964, *2*, 177–183.

KOUNIN, J. S. Experimental studies of rigidity. I. The measurement of rigidity in normal and feebleminded persons. *Charact. Pers.*, 1941, *9*, 251–273. (a)

————. Experimental studies of rigidity. II. The explanatory power of the concept of rigidity as applied to feeblemindedness. *Charact. Pers.,* 1941, *9,* 273–282. (b)

LINDSLEY, O. R. Reduction in rate of vocal psychotic symptoms by differential positive reinforcement. *J. exp. anal. Behav.,* 1959, *2,* 269.

———. Operant conditioning methods of diagnosis. In J. H. Nodine and J. H. Moyer (Eds.), *Psychosomatic medicine: The first Hehnemann symposium,* Philadelphia: Lea and Febiger, 1962, 41–54.

———. Direct measurement and prosthesis of retarded behavior. *J. Educ.,* 1964, *147,* 62–81. (a)

———. Geriatric behavioral prosthetics. In R. Kastenbaum (Ed.), *New thoughts on old age.* New York: Springer, 1964, 41–60. (b)

LIPMAN, R. S. Learning: Verbal, perceptual-motor, and classical conditioning. In N. R. Ellis (Ed.) *Handbook of mental deficiency: Psychological theory and research.* New York: McGraw-Hill, 1963.

LURIA, A. R. The role of speech in the regulation of normal and abnormal behavior. Washington, D.C.: U.S. Dept. of Health, Education, and Welfare, 1960.

———. Psychological studies of mental deficiency in the Soviet Union. In N. R. Ellis (Ed.) *Handbook of mental deficiency: Psychological theory and research.* New York: McGraw-Hill, 1963.

MADSEN, M. C. Distribution of practice and level of intelligence. *Psychol. Rep.,* 1963, *13,* 39–42.

MAGARET, A., and THOMPSON, C. W. Differential test responses of normal, superior, and mentally defective subjects. *J. abnorm. soc. Psychol.,* 1950, *45,* 163–167.

MALPASS, L. F. Motor skills in mental deficiency. In N. R. Ellis (Ed.), *Handbook of mental deficiency: Psychological theory and research.* New York: McGraw-Hill, 1963.

McPHERSON, M. W. A survey of experimental studies of learning in individuals who achieve subnormal ratings on standardized psychometric measures. *Amer. J. ment. Defic.,* 1948, *52,* 232–254.

———. Learning and mental deficiency. *Amer. J. ment. Defic.,* 1958, *62,* 870–877.

MILGRAM, N. A., and FURTH, H. G. The influence of language on concept attainment in educable retarded children. *Amer. J. ment. Defic.,* 1963, *67,* 733–739.

MITCHELL, W. C., JR. *Learning in undifferentiated and familial female mental defectives: a study to differentiate the bona fide mental defective from the so-called pseudo-defective.* Ann Arbor, Mich.: University Microfilms, 1952.

O'CONNOR, N., and HERMELIN, B. *Speech and thought in severe subnormality; An experimental study.* New York: The Macmillan Co., 1963.

ORLANDO, R. Component behaviors in free operant temporal discrimination. *Amer. J. ment. Defic.,* 1961, *65,* 615–619.

———. The functional role of discriminative stimuli in free operant performance of developmentally retarded children. *Psychol. Rec.,* 1961, *11,* 153–161.

———, and BIJOU, S. W. Single and multiple schedules of reinforcement in developmentally retarded children. *J. exper. anal. Behav.,* 1960, *3,* 339–348.

PRYER, R. S. Retroactive inhibition in normals and defectives as a function of temporal position of the interpolated task. *Amer. J. ment. Defic.,* 1960, *64,* 1004–1011.

PURSLEY, N. B., and HAMILTON, J. W. The development of a comprehensive cottage-life program. *Mental Retardation*, 1965, *3*, 26–29.

RAMSEY, O. E., JR. The effects of four instructional procedures on free operant discrimination and discrimination reversal in retardates. *Dissert. Abstracts*, 1963, *24*, 406.

RIEBER, M. Verbal mediation in normal and retarded children. *Amer. J. ment. Defic.*, 1964, *68*, 634–641.

RING, E. M., and PALERMO, D. S. Paired associate learning of retarded and normal children. *Amer. J. ment. Defic.*, 1961, *66*, 100–107.

ROSEN, M., KIVITZ, M., and ROSEN, B. S. Uni-modal and cross-modal "coding" in the mentally retarded. *Amer. J. ment. Defic.*, 1965, *69*, 716–722.

SANDERS, B., ROSS, L. E., and HEAL, L. W. Reversal and nonreversal shift learning in normal children and retardates of comparable mental age. *J. exp. Psychol.*, 1965, *69*, 84–88.

SCHEERENBERGER, R. C. Proactive inhibition among mentally retarded subjects. *Dissert. Abstracts*, 1964, *24*, 2367.

SCHOELKOPF, A. M., and ORLANDO, R. Delayed vs. immediate reinforcement in simultaneous discrimination problems with mentally retarded children. *Psychol. Rec.*, 1965, *15*, 15–23.

SEMLER, I. J. Selective learning in severely retarded children as a function of differential reaction to nonreward. *Child Developmt* 1965, *36*, 143–152.

SLOAN, W. Motor proficiency and intelligence. *Amer. J. ment. Defic.*, 1951, *55*, 394–406.

SMITH, M. P., and MEANS, J. R. Effects of type of stimulus pretraining on discrimination learning in mentally retarded. *Amer. J. ment. Defic.*, 1961, *66*, 259–265.

SPRADLIN, J. E. Effects of reinforcement schedules on extinction in severely mentally retarded children. *Amer. J. ment. Defic.*, 1962, *66*, 634–640.

———. The Premack hypothesis and self-feeding by profoundly retarded children. Working paper No. 79, Parsons Research Center, 1964.

SPRAGUE, R. L., and QUAY, H. C. A factor analytic study of the responses of mental retardates on the WAIS. Paper read at the American Association on Mental Deficiency convention, Miami Beach, 1965.

SOLOMON, R. L. Punishment. *Amer. Psychologist*, 1964, *19*, 239–253.

STEVENSON, H. W. Discrimination learning. In N. R. Ellis (Ed.), *Handbook of mental deficiency: Psychological theory and research*. New York: McGraw-Hill, 1963.

TEMPONE, V. J. Stimulus generalization as a function of mental age. *Child Developmt*, 1965, *36*, 229–235.

TERRELL, C. G., and ELLIS, N. R. Reaction time in normal and defective subjects following varied warning conditions. *J. abnorm. soc. Psychol.*, 1964, *69*, 449–452.

THOMPSON, C. W., and MAGARET, A. Differential test responses of normals and mental defectives. *J. abnorm. soc. Psychol.*, 1947, *42*, 285–293.

TILLMAN, M. H. Differential performance of normals and retardates on the WISC as predicted by stimulus trace theory. Unpublished masters thesis, University of Georgia, 1965.

VERGASON, G. A. Retention in retarded and normal subjects as a function of amount of original training. *Amer. J. ment. Defic.*, 1964, *68*, 623–629.

WALLACE, W. P., and UNDERWOOD, B. J. Implicit responses and the role of intralist similarity in verbal learning by normal and retarded subjects. *J. educ. Psychol.*, 1964, *55*, 362–370.

WALLIS, R. R. The learning of semi-concrete and abstract materials by bright and retarded students. Unpublished doctoral dissertation, University of Oklahoma, 1963.

WATSON, L. S., JR., LAWSON, R., and SANDERS, C. C. Generalized or token reinforcement with severely and profoundly retarded children. Paper presented to the annual meeting of the American Association on Mental Deficiency, Miami Beach, 1965.

WEIR, M. W., and STEVENSON, H. W. The effect of verbalization on children's learning as a function of chronological age. *Child Developmt,* 1959, *30,* 143–149.

WOLFENSBERGER, W. Teaching and training of the retarded in European countries. *Mental Retardation,* 1964, *2,* 331–337.

WOODROW, H. The ability to learn. *Psychol. Rev.,* 1946, *53,* 147–158.

ZEAMAN, D. Discrimination learning in retardates. *Train. Sch. Bull.,* 1959, *56,* 62–67.

———, and HOUSE, B. J. Approach and avoidance in the discrimination learning of retardates. *Child Developmt,* 1962, *33,* 355–372.

———, and ———. The role of attention in retardate discrimination learning. In N. R. Ellis (Ed.), *Handbook of mental deficiency: Psychological theory and research.* New York: McGraw-Hill, 1963.

ZIGLER, E. Rigidity in the feebleminded. In E. P. Trapp and P. Himelstein (Eds.), *Readings on the exceptional child.* New York: Appleton-Century-Crofts, 1962.

Programmed Instruction for Retarded Children

9

LESLIE F. MALPASS

SINCE 1960, interest in programmed instruction for the retarded has increased steadily. In part, this reflects the utilization of a special population by champions of research in programmed instruction; in part, it represents an adventure into a new educational arena by some teachers of the mentally retarded. Both groups recognize the potential advantages of educational efficiency and economy that programmed instruction offers. Informed teachers of retarded children, especially, see that programmed instruction can provide relief from repetitive drill-type instruction to help retardates acquire basic academic skills.

However, the majority of teachers and parents of retarded children know very little about this new educational technology, and much of the research with retarded children has not been widely publicized. Therefore, this chapter is devoted to a discussion of programmed instruction as an educational method, a description of the kinds of teaching machines and programmed textbooks available for use with retarded children, and an overview of research and applications of programmed instruction with the retarded.

PROGRAMMED INSTRUCTION

In a general sense, programmed instruction refers to any method of individualized instruction in which the learner progresses through a predetermined sequence of learning materials at his own rate of study. In this sense, a textbook represents one form of programmed instruction. Similarly, a teacher of the retarded can assign instructional units to individual children, encourage each to work at his own best pace, and then review the material with each child, correcting errors in performance as they are observed. Programmed instruction in this general sense is the aim of most educational procedures.

Such a state of affairs rarely exists in education of the retarded, however. Most teachers find it impossible to prepare, supervise, review, and correct each step in the learning process for every child. The ratio of children to teacher itself militates against this. Adding to the problem are inattention, distractibility, and variations in age, ability, and learning rate, particularly in classes for the educable mentally retarded (EMR). Consequently programmed instruction, defined in the broad sense, prevails only minimally in most EMR classrooms.

Dating from B. F. Skinner's work in the mid-1950s, programmed instruction has been defined more specifically. Skinner, an experimental psychologist, extrapolated his principles from controlled studies of infrahuman animals. Here the acquisition, reinforcement, and extinction of learned behavior was closely observed. He applied them to classroom situations, particularly those of normal children and college students. Subsequently, Skinner's concepts of programmed instruction (Skinner, 1958) have served as models for approximately 90 per cent of all efforts in this area. As far as I have been able to determine, linear programming (as Skinner's method is called) is the major type used with retarded children.

Authorities recognize that conditions for learning in most EMR classrooms often do not encourage much interest in or effective comprehension of the material to be learned. Consequently, relatively little effort is expended in learning by most retarded children in the typical classroom situation. By altering the presentation and reinforcement (or feedback) conditions, Skinner saw an opportunity to rectify these deficiencies. Perhaps a description of the rationale and major principles underlying programmed instruction by presenting them as a linear program would be useful at this point. The following 38 frames of J. L. Evans' program have been modified slightly for editorial convenience so the response, or answer, frames are in the margin beside the information frames. Before you begin each page, cover the outside margin with a piece of paper. After you read each information frame, uncover the accompanying response frame to check your response.

PRINCIPLES OF PROGRAMMED LEARNING

(James L. Evans, PhD) [1]

1. do not

1. Learning should be fun. However, in the early stages of learning a subject, students often make many errors. Most people (do/do not) like to make errors.

2. errors

2. When a student makes many errors in learning, he often decides that he does not like the subject. He would be more correct to decide that he does not like to make _____.

3. error

3. For a long time, educators, psychologists, and people in general thought that it was impossible to learn without making a large number of errors. In fact they even had a name for this kind of learning. They called it "trial-and-_____" learning.

4. Recent developments in the psychology of learning have cast serious doubts as to the necessity of "trial-and-error" learning. If the learning material is carefully prepared, or programmed, in a special way,

1. Copyright 1961 by Teaching Machines Inc., Albuquerque, New Mexico. Used by permission.

4. programmed

the student can master the subject while making very few errors. The material you are reading right now has been prepared, or _____ _____ in this special way.

5. is not

5. The basic idea of programmed learning is that the most efficient, pleasant, and permanent learning takes place when the student proceeds through a programmed course by a large number of small, easy-to-take steps. If each step the student takes is small, he (is/is not) likely to make errors. _____

6. programmed
course
few

6. A programmed course is made up of many small, easy-to-take steps. A student can proceed from knowing very little about a subject to mastery of the subject by going through a _____ _____ _____ . If the programmed course is carefully prepared, he should make (many/few) errors along the way.

7. steps

7. Programmed learning has many features that are different from conventional methods of learning. You have already learned one of these principles. This principle is that a student learns best if he proceeds by small _____ .

8. Steps

8. The features of programmed learning are applications of learning principles discovered in psychological laboratories. You have learned the first of these principles. You can guess that we call it the Principle of Small _____ .

9. psycho-
logical

9. The principles on which programmed learning is based were discovered in _____ laboratories. The first of these principles is the Principle of Small Steps.

10. Small Steps
11. The Principle of Small Steps

10. The first principle of programmed learning is *The Principle of* _____ _____ .

11. What is the first principle of programmed learning? _____ _____ _____ _____

12. Another finding from the psychological laboratories is that the student learns best if he is actively responding as he is learning.

The student who actually works out algebra problems will probably do (better/worse) on a test than the student who only reads the explanations and looks at the example.

12. better

13. Another way to say that people "learn by doing" is to say that they learn by active responding. You can guess that the second principle of Programmed Learning is the Principle of Active _____ .

13. Responding

14. Principles of programmed learning:
1) The Principle of Small Steps
2) The Principle of Active _____

14. Responding

15. Principles of programmed learning:
1) The Principle of _____
2) The Principle of _____

15. 1) Small Steps
2) Active Responding

16. Principles of programmed learning:
1)__ ___ __ ___ ___
2)__ _____ __ _____

16. 1) The Principle of Small Steps
2) The Principle of Active Responding

17. The third principle from the psychological laboratory: Students learn best when they can confirm their answers immediately. A student who must wait two weeks for test results probably (will/will not) learn as well as a student whose test is scored immediately.

17. will not

18. Third principle: A student learns best when he can confirm his answers immediately. This can be called the Principle of Immediate Confirmation. In the programmed course you are now using, you can confirm your answer immediately. So this programmed course (does/does not) use the Principle of Immediate _____ .

18. does Confirmation

19. When a student can immediately confirm his answer, the Principle of____ _____ is being applied

19. Immediate Confirmation

20. Three learning principles:
1) The Principle of *Small*

20. 1) Steps
2) Responding
3) Confirmation

_____ .
2) The Principle of *Active* _____ .
3) The Principle of *Immediate* _____

21. Three learning principles:
1) The Principle of _____
2) The Principle of _____ .
3) The Principle of _____ .

21. 1) Small Steps
2) Active Responding
3) Immediate Confirmation

22. When a subject matter, such as calculus, is broken down into parts so that the student can easily go from one item to the next, we are using the Principle of _____ _____ .

22. Small Steps

23. When the material from which the student is learning demands that he write his answer out, the Principle of_____ _____ is being used.

23. Active Responding

24. When the learning material is arranged so that the student can find out immediately if his answer is correct, the Principle of _____ _____ is being used.

24. Immediate Confirmation

25. Some people naturally learn more rapidly or more slowly than others. If the pace of a classroom is too fast or too slow for a child, he probably (will/will not) learn as well as he could at his own pace.

25. will not

26. In programmed learning, each student can work each step as slowly or as quickly as he chooses. This is called the Principle of Self-Pacing. Since you can spend as much or as little time as you wish on each step in this course, the Principle of Self-Pacing (is/is not) being used.

26. is

27. The Principle of programmed learning that allows each student to pace himself is called the Principle of _____ _____ .

27. Self-Pacing

28. When each student is allowed to learn at his own rate (as with a private tutor), the Principle of _____ _____ is being used.

28. Self-Pacing

29. You have now learned four of the five most important principles of pro-

grammed learning. Now we will review them.

1) Principle of _____ _____ (easy sequence of steps)

2) Principle of _____ _____ (student makes a definite response)

3) Principle of _____ _____ (Student learns immediately if he is right or wrong)

4) Principle of _____ _____ (student can choose his speed)

29. 1) Small Steps
   2) Active Responding
   3) Immediate Confirmation
   4) Self-Pacing

30. In programmed learning, the student makes a complete record of his learning experience. If he writes down his answer to each step, it (is/is not) possible to find out exactly where he made mistakes.

30. is

31. Suppose a student goes through 100 steps in a programmed course and writes down each answer. He makes four mistakes. From his record you (can/cannot) tell where each mistake was made.

31. can

32. Suppose you want to improve a programmed course by revising it. Suppose 10 students made a mistake on Step No. 37. This probably (would/would not) be a good frame to revise.

32. would

33. Students miss steps because they are too big, unclear, or have not been reviewed often enough. By looking over a programmed course, you (can/cannot) see exactly what steps came before a step on which a mistake was made.

33. can

34. Since accurate records of the learning experience of each student are available, revisions can be made on the basis of actual student responses. If the presentation of some point is not clear, this (will/will not) show up in the student's performance on the programmed course.

34. will

35. Revision of a programmed course on the basis of student performance is called the Principle of Program Testing. Since the course you are taking now has been developed on this basis, the Principle of _____ _____ has been used here.

35. Program Testing

36. Making revisions of programmed courses on the basis of the learning records of students is making use of the fifth Programming Principle: __ _____ __ _____ _____ .

36. The Principle of Program Testing

37. You have now learned five important programming principles. Now we will review them.

1) Principle of _____ _____ (easy progress from item to item)

2) Principle of _____ _____ (student actively records his responses)

3) Principle of _____ _____ (rapid knowledge of correctness)

4) Principle of _____ _____ (student chooses speed of progress)

5) Principle of _____ _____ (program revised on basis of student performance)

37. 1) Small Steps
   2) Active Responding
   3) Immediate Confirmation
   4) Self-Pacing
   5) Program Testing

38. Now see if you can list five programming principles without hints.
1)
2)
3)
4)
5)

38. 1) Principle of Small Steps
   2) Principle of Active Responding
   3) Principle of Immediate Confirmation
   4) Principle of Self-Pacing
   5) Principle of Program Testing

The regulation of learning is based on these five major principles, all of them confirmed in many laboratory studies (e.g., Green, 1962; Schramm, 1962; Stolurow, 1961). These in turn are subsumed by the more general principle that the teacher knows precisely what each student should learn. This is of crucial importance for those working with retarded children, since too often these teachers have ill-defined goals and presumptive methods. Principles of programmed instruction can bring both goals and methods into sharp focus. In particular, knowledge about controlled presentation and feedback or reinforcement of programmed instruction materials can be useful to the teacher of retarded children. It is well to examine these principles closely.

Controlled Presentation. The teacher, or programmer, must design his program so that it leads to a predetermined educational objective. The frames must be constructed so that communication to the learner is unambiguous. Every frame must be in his range of comprehension. To err on the side of repetition is better than to presume too much about the learner's state of knowledge as he progresses. Better still, as you already know, every program should be tested against the performance of representative subjects for whom the program is written.

As Evans' program suggests, frames must be arranged in small successive steps, each logically related to the other. This reduces the probability of error and maximizes the chance of success. Although some programs for normal children aim for no more than a 5 per cent error rate, my experience is that such a low error rate is difficult to achieve with retarded children. The length of each study period, the lower ability of retardates, and transient motivational considerations, such as room temperature and interest of the super-

visor, can greatly affect the error rate. However, a program that yields an average error rate higher than 15 per cent probably should be revised.

In programs for retarded children, repetition is particularly important for the presentation of information and concepts. In the pilot study of a word-recognition program for adolescent retardates, it was found that approximately 40 varied presentations of each word were necessary for effective acquisition and retention (Malpass, Gilmore, Hardy, and Williams, 1963). The number of repetitions will vary with the type and complexity of material to be learned, but the material must be presented in different contexts so it does not become boring.

Programmed instruction enables the teacher to emphasize major points and to exclude material that might be distracting. Since distractibility is characteristic of retarded children, the teacher's control over presentation conditions is a real asset.

Finally, controlled presentation suggests that the teacher can adapt the length of the study period for each individual (*viz.*, Principle of Self-Pacing). Thus, programmed instruction can be adapted to the convenience of the teacher as well as for the benefit of the retarded child. These advantages are rarely available under conventional EMR classroom conditions. Programmed instruction in this way can be used to help individualize the instruc-

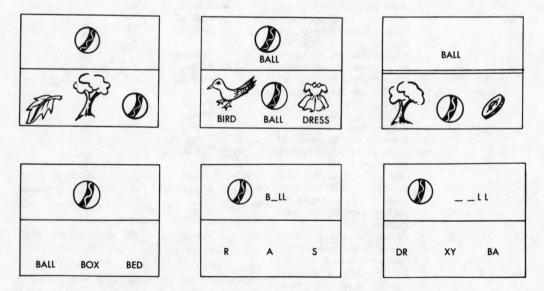

FIGURE 1. Sample Frames for Teaching Sight Vocabulary.

tional process. At the same time principles underlying the process can be exploited by the teacher for presentation of materials for which no program may be available.

Feedback. The requirement of active responding in programmed instruction insures attention to each frame as it is presented, particularly since the feedback is tied directly to the learner's response. In programmed instruction the child is informed immediately about the correctness of his answer, whereas in most classroom situations feedback is usually delayed for some hours or even days. For retarded children, this delay is often crucial and works against retention of the material to be learned.

The advantages of programmed instruction in this respect are obvious. Immediate confirmation facilitates efficiency in learning, a basic feature of programmed instruction. The kind of feedback that is provided will depend on the type of programmed instruction that is used. A teaching machine may provide both visual and auditory signals that inform the learner whether he is correct or not. A programmed textbook, on the other hand, relies on the type of confirmation you have encountered already.

TEACHING MACHINES

Teaching machines can be classified in at least three ways: (1) by the amount of control they exert over the learner's behavior, (2) by the type of power units used to activate the mechanism, and (3) by the type of response required.

The first category refers to whether the machine is fully automated or semi-automated. The second differentiates between machines that are actuated electronically or manually. Since both of these categories are typically included in the third type, machines requiring different response-types provide the most convenient way to describe most of the teaching machines available for use with retarded children. Selected responses are required by multiple-choice machines; constructed responses are demanded by completion devices using paper rolls or typewriter-like mechanisms.

Selected Response Teaching Machines. A variety of teaching machines are based on Pressey's early model (Figure 2).

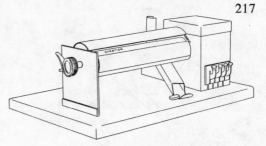

FIGURE 2. Pressey Drum Tutor.[2]

2. Figures 2, 3, and 6 were supplied by Dr. Lawrence Stolurow and were originally used in his monograph, *Teaching by Machine,* published by the Cooperative Research Program, U.S. Office of Education, 1961.

Information frames are presented in a display window by means of a roller unit. Alternative answers are shown simultaneously. The learner presses one of four keys (see response unit). The correct choice enables the roller unit to move; an incorrect response prevents forward movement of the program. A counter unit records all responses.

This system underlies most other multiple-choice machines, two of which are illustrated in Figure 3. The Rheem DIDAK 101 machine is automated. With the TEACHALL, frames on individual cards are inserted into the depository. The learner pushes a lever so that an information frame and alternative responses are shown in the display unit. After selecting his response and depressing the appropriate response key, visual and auditory signals yield feedback about the correctness of his choice. The learner then manually operates a lever to obtain the next frame in the program. No counters are included in these machines. They are relatively inexpensive and the TEACHALL has been found to be as effective for teaching word-recognition and spelling to retarded children as a fully automated constructed response machine described below.

Constructed Response Machines. Some teaching machines require that the learner write out or otherwise construct a response in order to progress through the program. A variety of such techniques have been used with retarded children.

Perhaps the best-known automated teaching method was developed by O. K. Moore. Originally, Moore used an electric typewriter in conjunction with a filmstrip projector. The child's fingernails were painted the same colors as the typewriter keys that they were to de-

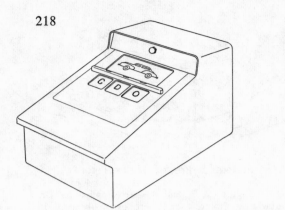

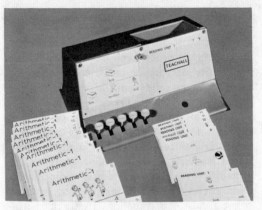

FIGURE 3. *Left,* The Rheem DIDAK 101; and *right,* the TEACHALL.*

* Used by permission of Rheem Manufacturing Corp., South Gate, California, and Publishers Company, Washington, D.C.

press in order to facilitate visual-motor co-ordination for "typing."

As information frames were presented (by means of the film projector on a small screen above the machine), the child learned to de-press the appropriate keys and thus actuated the projector for the next frame. Wrong presses would not activate the electronic mech-anism. Subsequently, the child learned to type correctly, as well as to spell and read.

Moore's original teaching machine has been expanded and now he uses it as a part of a total "autotelic learning environment." The room in which learning takes place is free from distractions and is used for one child at a time. Phonics are included in his spelling and reading programs by having tape record-ings present correct pronunciations at the same time the word is presented visually. The child says the word aloud, in addition to typing it. Computers continually record many aspects of the child's response to the program. Moore (1963) contends that bright 2-year-old young-sters, as well as older normal and retarded children, have learned to read efficiently and well by these means.

Moore's machines are not readily available to teachers of the retarded. However, a variant of his early machine was developed by Wyck-off (1960) and has been used successfully with retarded adolescents (Figure 4), although it is no longer commercially available. The Filmtutor's program is on 8mm filmstrips. The projector is actuated electronically when the correct typewriter key is depressed. Like Moore's machine, feedback occurs when the child sees his correct answer typed out in the display unit. The projector then automatically presents the next frame of the program.

Another fully automated constructed re-sponse teaching machine has been developed by Mast (1962). Utilizing a projector and filmstrip cartridges, this machine requires the child to copy a symbol representing the cor-rect alternative or to copy the letter, word, picture, or number on recording paper. By pressing a button, the correct answer is re-

FIGURE 4. The Wyckoff Film Tutor.*

* Used by permission of Teaching Machines, Inc., a division of Grolier, Inc., New York.

vealed as the child's response is simultaneously moved under a transparent plastic plate. This makes a comparison possible but prevents "fudging" on the wrong answers. The MAST machine has been found to be a reliable teach-ing device and is relatively free from me-chanical flaws. In addition (and possibly of greatest interest), there is a wide variety of programs available for use in this machine.

Several kinds of semi-automated constructed response teaching machines are commercially available. Most of them are based on Skinner's original designs. The Skinner Disk Machine presents and records verbal information. The program is printed on a disk, with space available for a written response either on the same program rolls or on a separate program tape. The Disk Machine, shown in Figure 6, is like the MAST machine, in that both require the learner to write down his response after presentation of an information frame. Depressing a button or rotating a lever causes the correct answer to be shown at the same time that the constructed response is moved under a transparent window.

The chief advantage of constructed response machines for use with retarded children is that they necessitate complex motor responses used in everyday educational activities —either writing, printing, or typing. Unless the program is built in very small steps, however, this proves to be a disadvantage for use with retarded children. Most reading and spelling programs available for constructed-response machines are not appropriate for the retarded. They tend to be geared to average students and thus the steps in the program are too large for retarded children to follow. In addition, the fully automated machines tend to be more expensive and relatively less available than either selected-response machines or semi-automated machines. The MAST machine, however, provides flexibility and reliability of operation and many programs are available for use in it, including one developed under a grant by the U.S. Office of Education by my colleagues and myself (1966).

The teaching machines described in this section are merely representative of the vast array available. Hendershot (1964) publishes a manual that reviews all commercially available machines by type and manufacturer. Information is kept current by means of annual supplements.

Considerations in Using Teaching Machines with Retarded Children. I pointed out earlier that teaching machines possess obvious advantages for helping retarded children to learn various academic skills: (1) they individualize instruction; (2) they focus attention on learning by reducing distractions; (3) they permit self-pacing, making possible variations in the length of instructional periods, and (4) they contribute to motivation to learn.

Effective utilization of automated instruction depends on several considerations: the availability of programs, the purchase and maintenance costs for the machine, the amount

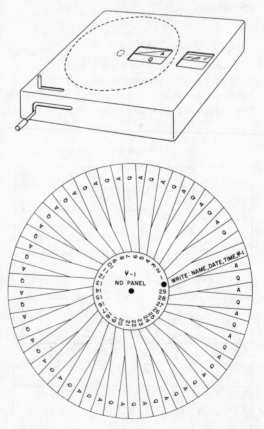

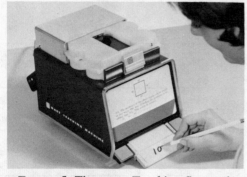

FIGURE 5. The MAST Teaching System.*

* Used by permission of **Keystone View Co.**, Meadville, Pennsylvania.

FIGURE 6. Skinner Disk Machine (*top*) and Program Disk (*bottom*).

of adult supervision required, and the willingness of the teacher to use programmed instruction as a pedagogical tool.

Finally, a teaching machine is only as useful as the program that goes in it. If the program is not relevant and well-written, and if consecutive programs are not available for the achievement levels of concern to the teacher, the automated device itself has relatively little value. Similarly, the cost and mechanical complexity of the machine cannot be so great as to make it unfeasible for class or home use. Since the development of Pressey's and Skinner's early machines, the engineering and cost aspects of automated instructions have improved to the point where a school, an institution, and even most individual parents of retarded children can afford the initial cost and upkeep on one or more machines and a library of programs. Moreover, schools could loan programs to each other in the same way that lending libraries operate.

PROGRAMMED TEXTBOOKS

Programmed textbooks are supposed to perform the same presentation and feedback functions as teaching machines. Their chief advantages are that no "hardware" is neces-

sary. The learner carries his program with him in book form, rather than having to go to a specified location to use a machine. Programmed textbooks are also cheaper than teaching machines.

Homme and Glaser (1959) describe some early programmed textbooks and compare them with teaching machines. Such books have been used with retarded as well as normal children. One of the several formats for such programs is to place information frames on one page of a pair, with room to record the response. The facing page contains feedback information. Representative page pairs from an arithetic program are given in Figure 7. Each frame (A^1, A^2 . . . A^6) can be presented on individual pages or they can be combined on one page.

Most linear-programmed textbooks are now printed so that information frames follow consecutively down the page, as in the program given earlier in the chapter. A cardboard or paper mask is used to cover the response frames. When the information frame is completed, the mask is slid down the page so that comparison is possible. This, of course, points up one of the difficulties of programmed textbooks, i.e., no external control over feedback. Consequently, children must be taught the value of observing the rules of

Page 1		Page 2
A^1 $\quad$ $1 + 1 =$		2
A^2 $\quad$ $1 + 2 =$		3
A^3 $\quad$ $2 + 1 =$		3
A^4 $\quad$ $3 + 1 =$		4
A^5 $\quad$ $2 + 3 =$		5
A^6 $\quad$ $1 + 3 =$		4

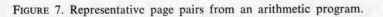

FIGURE 7. Representative page pairs from an arithmetic program.

Page 1

> This is a scrambled book.
> You do not read the pages
> in their numerical order.
> Turn to page 3 for your
> first problem.

Page 2

> 14 − 7 does <u>not</u> equal 20
>
> 14 + 6 = 20
>
> Go back to page 3

Page 3

> 14 − 7 =
>
> | Choose one: | Address: |
> |---|---|
> | 20 | p. 2 |
> | 5 | p. 4 |
> | 7 | p. 5 |
> | 2 | p. 6 |

Page 4

> 14 − 7 = 5 is <u>wrong</u>
>
> Go back to page 3

Page 5

> You are right
> 14 − 7 = 7
>
> Now do this one.
> 19 − 5 =
>
> | Choose one: | Address: |
> |---|---|
> | 24 | p. 7 |
> | 14 | p. 8 |
> | 6 | p. 9 |

Page 6

> 14 − 7 = 7
>
> 14 ÷ 7 = 2
>
> Go back to page 3

Page 7

> 19 − 5 = 14
>
> 19 + 5 = 24
>
> Go back to page 5

Page 8

> Good: 19 − 5 = 14
> Now do this:
>   29 − 12 =
>
> | Choose one: | Address: |
> |---|---|
> | 18 | p. 13 |
> | 7 | p. 10 |
> | 17 | p. 11 |

FIGURE 8. Representative sequence of items from a scrambled textbook.

the procedure. Otherwise, cheating (and subsequent devaluation of learning) is a typical result.

A well-known type of programmed textbook is Crowder's "scrambled text" (Crowder, 1958). In such texts, the branching technique is used in the program. The reader begins on the first page but rapidly is directed to sequences that vary in many ways. Rate of progress depends on the selection of alternatives. A representative sequence of items is given in Figure 8, where each block of items represents a page. Each page contains information, a question about it, and some alternative responses to which "page addresses" are attached. If a correct answer is selected (see "page 3" in Figure 8), the reader is told he is correct, and why the answer is right, then he is given a new problem with additional responses and addresses. If the answer is incorrect, the reader is so informed and told why. He is then directed back to the original information page and told to select another answer.

The scrambled textbook presumably provides for greater individuation in learning than does a linear program. The reader who responds correctly most of the time "branches" quite rapidly and progresses through the book with a minimum of repetition. On the other hand, the reader who merely guesses soon finds out that it does him little good. The guesser, along with the learner who simply does not comprehend the information frame, is given an explanation at each step. This supposedly adds to his comprehension about the reason for his error and reduces the probability of its recurrence. Studies of normal subjects offer some support for this contention, but very little research using scrambled textbooks has been done with the retarded. This may be because a third-grade reading achievement level is required to follow even the simplest directions. The costs in publishing scrambled textbooks are higher than those for linear programs.

In summary, programmed textbooks offer efficiency in progress, economy in cost, and portability as their chief advantages over teaching machines. These are obtained at the possible expense of control over presentation and feedback conditions. Goldstein and Gotkin (1963) summarized eight studies, including two of their own, that compared teaching machines with programmed textbooks. No significant differences in mastery of subject matter were reported between the two conditions in any of these investigations. However, time was included as a variable in five of the studies. Four of these, including two investigations of spelling for fourth-grade children, yielded significant differences in favor of the programmed textbooks (i.e., children completed more textbook pages than machine frames in a given length of time).

Observing another variable of general interest, McNeil (1963) reported that boys in primary grades demonstrated superiority over girls in programmed instruction. However, girls demonstrated significantly higher grades under conventional female-teacher clasroom conditions. This suggests that sex of the teacher may be an extremely important variable in determining motivation for learning in young children. Such sex differences have not been widely studied for older groups of normal or for retarded children.

Regarding variations among teaching methods, Warburton's (1962) review of educational methods says, in part, "one gains the impression from a perusal of the literature that differences in technique and organization tend to be swamped by teacher differences" (p. 386). While this observation was directed to equivocal studies of teachers, it might also apply to variations of programmed instruction. That this educational tool is effective for many children is well substantiated. But the parameters of the method have not been well defined and, consequently, many specific aspects of programmed instruction for retarded children have yet to be explored.

RESEARCH WITH RETARDED CHILDREN

The results of research leave little doubt that retarded children can acquire and retain basic academic skills by means of programmed instruction. Indeed, several children, in a study conducted by my colleagues and myself (1963, 1967), retained a high level of vocabulary-recognition and reading skills for more than two years. In addition to these word skills, programmed instruction of spelling and cursive writing and a variety of arithmetic skills have been investigated. Some psychologist-educators have even constructed total classroom environments that focus on programmed instruction.

This is not to suggest that programmed instruction can be used to replace the teacher. It is useful as a supplement to, not a surrogate for, the classroom instructor. Used properly, both teaching machines and programmed textbooks can decrease the teacher's burden and increase the pupil's interest in learning. At least, the majority of studies clearly suggest this.

Word Skills. Stolurow (1961) was among the first to report that programmed instruction can be effective for teaching sight vocabulary to retarded children. He devised a linear program for use in his own selected-response machine. At about the same time, Moore reported case studies that suggested that retardates could learn to read and type common words. Several other major investigations of word skills began in the early 1960s, most of them sponsored by the U.S. Office of Education.

Ellson (1962) reiterated earlier observations that institutionalized retardates can learn word skills by means of automated instruction. He reported a maximum average learning rate of nineteen words per hour. High interest on the part of children was noticed, along with a significant increase in word-recognition for words not practiced on the machine. Ellson also pointed out a problem in programming vocabulary words for retardates. Only 20 per cent of the Gates Word List was presented pictorially; articles, prepositions, adjectives, and similar words were not introduced in this manner. This increased the amount of prompting required by an attending teacher. This problem is of interest to several investigators and words of the type mentioned are being presented in programs by means of contextual and form prompts.

Birnbrauer and his colleagues at the Rainier, Washington, State School (1964a) also have reported remarkable word-acquisition rates by retarded children. They found that some moderately retarded children can assimilate up to six new words per learning session, under both multiple-choice and constructed response modes of programmed instruction. Birnbrauer's team developed a phonics program

to accompany sight-vocabulary presentation and used trinkets, gold stars, and other tangible rewards to motivate children initially. A later report (1964b) suggests that even though the motivational effects of such reinforcements may wear off, as with normal children, high word-acquisition rates can be expected from exposure to programmed instruction.

The aforementioned studies strongly confirm the idea that retarded children can learn simple word skills by means of programmed instruction. But what about contextual reading, a more complex skill? And do retarded children retain what they acquire by this method? Does programmed instruction compare favorably with conventional classroom instruction? Can programmed textbooks be used with retarded children? The following studies provide at least partial answers to these questions.

Blackman and Smith (1964) constructed word-recognition programs for institutionalized retarded children that resulted in the children's learning to read phrases and sentences. Increases in these skills were reflected in standardized and specially constructed reading achievement tests. Although Blackman and Smith reported no significant differences in the progress of retardates taught by machine compared with those taught by traditional methods, their study clearly indicates that institutionalized retarded children can learn to read complex material by means of programmed instruction.

On the other hand, my colleagues and I (1963, 1966) found two types of automated instruction superior to conventional classroom teaching, although not to individual human tutoring. This was true for both public school and institutionalized educable mentally retarded children. The study dealt with acquisition and retention of word-recognition, reading and spelling skills. Individual words were learned first; then they were presented in phrases and sentences. Finally, subjects were required to read a paragraph composed of words taught in the program. Acquisition rates varied extensively, with retardates in the 65-to-70 IQ range showing most progress. Probably the most striking finding of this study was that retention rates were very high. Practically all of the subjects taught by programmed instruction retained from 75 to 92 per cent of their post-program knowledge three months later. As mentioned earlier, some children retained their gains two years after completing the program.

These results were confirmed in part by a study by Lawson and Watson (1964). They found that a group of institutionalized EMR children retained approximately 85 per cent of the new words they learned from teaching machines over a three-month period. Such results underscore the potential value of programmed instruction and give some answers to questions about effectiveness of teaching machines for retarded children.

The utility of programmed textbooks for retarded children has been investigated in part by Woolman and Davy (1963). Woolman had developed a special reading program over several years that was then programmed by Davy. They found that both educable and trainable retardates taught with these textbooks were superior in reading achievement to those taught in conventional patterns.

Regarding spelling, my colleagues and I (1963) found that educable retarded children can learn to spell common words by means of programmed instruction. T. F. Naumann (1962) supplemented sight words with phonics by means of a tape recorder. Most teachers would agree with these investigators that it is desirable to have the children write out whole words every time they meet them in the program. (In most programs, parts of words are sometimes provided as prompts to vary the presentation conditions).

Naumann, Porter, and Wensley (1964) also have taught articulatory skills to retardates by means of programmed instruction techniques. Parsons (1963) has applied programming principles to the teaching of cursive writing. She contends that, working on an average of half an hour per day, any child who can hold a pencil in his hand can learn to print his name and write legibly, meaningfully, and in context by means of programmed instruction.

The data from these studies are convincing. Retarded children can acquire highly complex word skills by means of programmed instruction. They can also retain these skills for significant periods of time so that "true learning" rather than temporary acquisition occurs.

Number Skills. Fewer programs exist for teaching simple number skills to retarded children than word-skill programs. From available studies, however, there is little doubt that programmed instruction can help retardates to learn basic arithmetic processes and concepts, particularly addition and subtraction.

Smith and Quackenbush (1960) used multiple-choice machines at the Devereaux Schools to teach elementary mathematics to retarded adolescents (mean IQ 71). They contend that programmed instruction is useful as a method for promoting such academic achievement, particularly since it seems to increase motivation for other classroom learning as well.

The same kind of results were reported by Blackman and Smith (1964). As with their word-skill programs, Blackman and Smith found that retardates acquired arithmetic skills efficiently and consistently under programmed instruction. In addition, they found significant differences in favor of programmed instruction over conventional classroom instruction on one arithmetic post-test, although not on two others. Retention of arithmetic skills was very high after three months. These studies confirm earlier reports by Stolurow (1960) about effectiveness of programming instruction for teaching number skills and suggest that abstract number concepts can be learned by retarded children if presented appropriately.

Programmed Classrooms. By their very nature, special education classrooms require somewhat different facilities, equipment, and utilization than those for normal children. Within this framework, some unique classroom plans have been suggested for optimum use of programmed instruction. Birnbrauer, Bijou, Wolf, Kidder, and Tague (1964a) have constructed the model shown in Figure 9.

The classroom is subdivided into individual study cells, each equipped with a teaching machine and related materials. Programs are obtained from the teacher. After preliminary instruction, the child can fit the programs into the machines and operate them without help. The curriculum includes word drill, reading, and arithmetic.

The teacher serves a more generous purpose than program-dispenser, however. She records each child's progress, supplements programmed instruction with other types (focusing on concept-development rather than skill-drill), and encourages attainment of social skills through a variety of group activities.

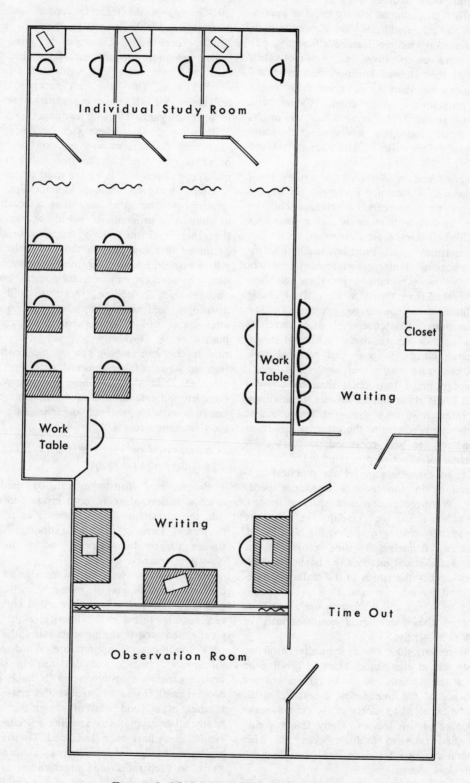

FIGURE 9. Model of programmed classroom.

After more than a year's experimentation with this programmed classroom, the investigators and school officials were pleased to find: (1) retarded children learned efficiently; (2) they were co-operative and well-motivated, and (3) they showed improvements in school activities other than the academic skills taught by programmed instruction. Cruickshank (1964) reported the same kinds of results for special classrooms developed at Syracuse University for work with brain-damaged children.

Implications of Research in Programmed Instruction for Retarded Children. The experience of most teachers of retarded children agrees closely with research that reports that the children learn more slowly and retain less than normals under ordinary teaching-learning situations. Unfortunately, many teachers develop low expectations for these children and, rather than trying to alter the learning conditions, continue to be governed by low expectations. Consequently, such teachers often operate in relatively inefficient ways. Research clearly suggests that retarded children can learn more, and better and faster, by programmed instruction than by conventional EMR classroom techniques. In addition, this research suggests that such improvement in learning is related to the presentation, repetition, and feedback conditions that are characteristic of effective programming.

Let us examine some of the practical considerations in conventional classroom pedagogy. Word-recognition and spelling lessons, for example, can be presented in a variety of ways: by writing words on the blackboard, by using flannelgraph, slide projection, or other audio-visual methods, by having the students identify the words in the textbook material, and by other means. It is probably too much to expect any teacher to use all or even most of these techniques simultaneously or even consistently.

Moreover, since classes typically enroll between ten to eighteen children, depending on age of the students and the enlightenment and affluence of the community, a teacher hardly can be expected to supervise each child's progress through his lessons. Many teachers cannot find time to evaluate even the daily general progress for each child, let alone his individual lessons.

In group situations, a teacher finds it diffi-cult to keep each child attending to every specific step in the learning process and almost impossible to supply feedback to each child at each stage. Consequently, most retarded children sooner or later become distracted and many lose significant aspects of the lesson. Thus, the very nature of the conventional EMR classroom situation seems to operate against efficient learning.

Possibly, good teachers can be differentiated from mediocre or poor ones on the basis of whether they individualize instruction maximally and effectively. Even the most dedicated teachers, however, cannot individualize instruction in the same way that a teaching machine or a programmed workbook can. On the other hand, no teaching machine or programmed text can provide the variety of ancillary reinforcements to learning that humans can. A teacher can simultaneously smile, change voice inflections, touch a child reassuringly, and merely represent the normal size, shape, and other physical features of a human being. Obviously, however, if the human teacher can employ programmed instruction as a part of her tuitional repertory, the retarded child should benefit greatly. More complete individualization of instruction would be thus possible without dehumanizing the total learning process.

UTILIZATION OF PROGRAMMED INSTRUCTION WITHIN THE CLASSROOM

Programmed instruction can be used to teach a variety of skills, both inside and outside the classroom. Most research is related to formal learning activities, although some studies suggest less obvious benefits to the classroom teacher.

Acquisition of Academic skills. One of the insistent implications of research with programmed instruction is that retarded children can acquire verbal and numerical skills efficiently and well if the presentation and feedback conditions are appropriate. Word-recognition and phonics, complex reading skills, and a variety of arithmetic skills have been programmed. These can relieve the classroom teacher of a good deal of repetitious drill. Many other programs concerning cognate curricular areas have been developed. Their availability will allow the teacher to concentrate more on preparation and organization of the curriculum, the development of the children's personal-social skills, and the investigation of new ways to help her students acquire the host of attributes necessary to meet the demands of the outside world. Hendershot (1965) maintains a current bibliography of self-instructional programs, presentation devices, and supply sources. Revised every year and available at low cost, it is a practical handbook for administrators and teachers who need to know what programs are available and how to obtain them.

Retention of Learning. One of the most striking research findings with retarded children is that they can retain effectively presented academic material about as well as normal children do. In this regard, programmed instruction has provided information about retention of learning that is at variance with some popular conceptions and even with the experience of many teachers of the conventional EMR classes.

Dunn (1963) has suggested that many teachers subscribe to the "leaky bucket" theory of retention. That is, they believe that EMR children forget even more rapidly than they learn and that a teacher must expect the child to make extremely slow progress in academic work because he quickly loses whatever he learns from daily drill. Typically, Dunn observes, no explanation is offered for this common observation other than vague generalizations.

Ellis (1963) agrees that attention declines with degree of retardation, and presumes that this decline is a function of central nervous sysem dysfunction, possibly of a biochemical nature. His "stimulus trace" theory is intriguing and some significant empirical evidence has been reported to support it. However, Ellis points out that once a retarded child has thoroughly learned a particular activity, he tends to retain it as well as normals, even on a long-term basis.

This is precisely the conclusion that has been arrived at on the basis of programmed instruction research. If the child learns something thoroughly (i.e., operationally, when his error rates are low, particularly in the latter stages of the program), and he can transfer his learned skills immediately to material outside the program itself, then he tends to retain the skill over long periods of time. This is particularly true if he has continued to practice the skill.

One study showed that retarded children had a much higher tolerance for repetitive material than did normal children of the same IQ but younger (Ellis, 1963). Retarded children seem to be able to react more positively to repetition than do normals—and it is precisely this requirement in the teaching process to which many teachers object. Programmed instruction, by reducing dreary drill for the teacher, can serve to reduce teacher boredom while increasing the retarded child's academic skill and interest in further learning.

Development of Better Work Habits. Another potential advantage is that programmed instruction seems to motivate retarded children to be more self-dependent. Retardates who become responsible for obtaining their daily program lessons, placing them in the proper automated device, operating a fairly complex instrument, and acquiring a whole new set of information in the process might well be expected to become more satisfied with their own ability to perform independently. Consequently, they may be expected to be susceptible to suggestions that would improve their work habits and their autonomy of behavior in other areas of activity.

Benefits to the Teacher. Reduction of monotonous drill and more freedom to perform other teaching functions are not the only advantages offered to teachers by programmed instruction. One of the prime benefits is that she can generalize these principles to other areas of her teaching activity. Dunn (1963, p. 113), among others, specifically recommends that EMR teachers should not use traditional textbooks and workbooks for instructional purposes. Although he does not propose principles of programmed instruction directly, he describes almost step by step the same procedures this chapter has outlined. Nothing can substitute for careful preparation of material, systematic presentation in small-step intervals, repetition of it in appropriate amounts and ways, a constant feedback to the child of the results of his activity, and, finally, offering some kind of explicit or implicit reward to the child for having learned. These are the principles of programmed instruction and every really effective teacher utilizes them most of the time. Programmed instructional devices use them all the time.

Finally, and as stated earlier, the individual teacher can develop programs of her own, if the cost burden of commercial programs becomes significantly high or no programs are available for her special area of interest. Most universities now offer courses or seminars in programming techniques, so that almost anyone can learn how to construct programs. Unless drastically different results are obtained in regular classroom use from those observed in empirical studies, a substantial increase in academic use of programmed instruction can be expected for retarded children, to the point that teaching machines and programs may become as common as any other audio-visual device in classes for the educable mentally retarded.

UTILIZATION OF PROGRAMMED INSTRUCTION
OUTSIDE THE CLASSROOM

While primary emphasis has been in the development of programs for academic improvement, many practical uses exist for this technique in skills needed outside the classroom: (1) personal care and grooming, proper health practices, and the demonstration of social skills, especially important to retarded adolescents and adults, (2) vocational preparation and information about specific job skills, and (3) the training of professional and volunteer workers to deal with retarded children.

Development of Personal Social Skills. A study conducted at the MacDonald Training Center (Hilliard, 1965) showed that most adolescents in the EMR range were extremely naive in their knowledge and application of common personal social skills. Most of the subjects in the study were commuters to the center; a small minority were enrolled in a residential program. All of them showed little knowledge about proper grooming, dating practices, health routines, and basic biological (particularly sexual) processes. Such information can be presented effectively by means of programmed instruction supplemented by discussion groups and individual interviews. Similarly, since many retarded adolescents and adults operate motor vehicles—and many more could do so with appropriate instruction—a pictorial-verbal program teaching the elements of automobile operation and safety has potential value.

For the severely retarded, interesting programs are available that teach common signals and signs (even "His" and "Hers" are not recognized by many trainable retardates) and how to tell time. In particular, the Grolier TMI programs for telling time have been found to be very useful for trainable retarded children (Bradley and Hundziak, 1965). Hendershot (1965) lists others that can be of immense help in making these children more conversant with their everyday environment.

Vocational Skills. Fraenkel (1961) reviewed the literature on vocational rehabilitation of the retarded and presented a rather pessimistic picture about job opportunities for them in the future. He suggested that automation would cause a decrease in work possibilities generally and that normal persons may compete vigorously for jobs that many retarded adults now fill (e.g., domestic and low-skill service jobs).

Paradoxically, automation may well open up more opportunities for the retarded, since this group characteristically can tolerate monotonous and routine industrial tasks at least as successfully as normals can (Tizard and O'Connor, 1950). In these instances, programmed instruction can be employed, for example, to teach the elements of machine structure and operation and related information. This kind of instruction already has been used successfully with normal persons for a variety of tasks (Schramm, 1964), and the technology is readily adaptable for training retarded adults in a variety of occupational tasks.

Training of Volunteer Workers. An interesting instructional program has been prepared by Gilmore, Rich, and Williams (1965) to help volunteers become acquainted with the characteristics of retarded children. It introduces the reader to basic concepts about mental deficiency and describes typical activities in which retardates can participate. In a unique and highly imaginative way, this program captures some of the exciting possibilities that volunteer work holds, without being either patronizing or unrealistic. The authors report a warm response on the part of many volunteers who have used it in a number of public and private agencies.

Retrospectively, the applications of research in programmed instruction for retarded children extend almost as far as the initiative of the programmer permits, within the limitations of the procedure. While it is probably not true that "anything that can be described can be programmed," the possibilities are enormous for wider and more effective use with retarded children of this new educational technology.

PROGRESS AND PROSPECT

Research with programmed instruction attests to its ability for teaching word and number skills to retarded children. Whether it is more effective than other types of instruction for these purposes is still somewhat equivocal, although several studies strongly favor it over conventional classroom teaching. Certainly it presents some clear advantages for teachers who can obtain materials and space for programmed instruction. It can reduce the drudgery of repetitive drill; it enables truly individualized instruction; children can work at their own pace; and it encourages motivation for learning.

Although many publishers have brought a variety of programs to the open market, few of them have been designed specifically for retarded children. As with conventional textbooks, however, many of them can be adapted for retardates, particularly at the lower grade levels. Many investigators who have developed special programs make them available at cost to teachers and parents of the retarded.

The problems of programmed instruction for the retarded seem to be more in terms of development and dissemination of programs than in establishing the validity and utility of the method. This is true, also, for computer-assisted instruction, which uses principles developed for teaching machines but whose cost so far has inhibited classroom use for the retarded. From research reported so far, programmed instruction is likely to become an increasingly significant educational tool for helping retarded children acquire and retain academic and personal-social skills necessary for self-subsistence in our complex society.

REFERENCES

BIRNBRAUER, J. S., BIJOU, S. W., WOLF, M. M., KIDDER, J. D., and TAGUE, C. M. A programed instruction classroom for educable retardates. (Mimeographed report) Seattle: University of Washington, 1964. (a)

———, KIDDER, J. D., and TAGUE, C. Programing reading for the teacher's point of view. *Programed Instruction*, 1964, *3*, 1–2. (b)

BLACKMAN, L., and SMITH, M. P. *The development and evaluation of a curriculum for educable mental retardates utilizing self-instructor devices or teaching machines.* Bordentown, N.J.: Johnstone Training and Research Center, 1964.

BLATT, B. Educating intelligence: A study in the prevention of mental retardation. (Mimeographed report) Boston: Boston University, 1964.

BRADLEY, B. H., and HUNDZIAK, M. TMI-Grolier time telling program for the mentally retarded. *Exceptional Child.*, 1965, *32*, 17–20.

CARTRIGHT, G. P. Two types of programed instruction for mentally retarded adolescents. Unpublished master's thesis, University of Illinois, 1962.

CROWDER, N. A. *An automatic tutoring book on number systems,* Vols. I, II, and III. Arlington, Va.: Psychological Research Associates, 1958.

CRUICKSHANK, W. Personal communication, 1964.

DUNN, L. M. *Exceptional children in the schools,* Educable mentally retarded children. New York: Holt, Rinehart and Winston, 1963, Chap. 2.

ELLIS, N. R. *The stimulus trace and behavioral inadequacy.* In N. R. Ellis (Ed.), *Handbook of mental deficiency.* New York: McGraw-Hill, 1963, Chap. 4.

ELLSON, D. G. Feasibility of machine testing of reading vocabulary to mentally retarded children. (Mimeographed report) Bloomington: Indiana University, 1962.

EVANS, J. L. *Principles of programed learning.* New York: Teaching Materials Inc., Grolier, Inc., 1962.

FINN, J. D., and PERRIN, D. G. *Teaching machines and programed learning: A survey of the industry—1962.* Washington, D.C.: U.S. Office of Education, 1962.

FRAENKEL, W. A. *The mentally retarded and their vocational rehabilitation: A resource handbook.* New York: National Association for Retarded Children, 1961.

FRY, E. B., and ROSENOFF, W. E. *Lessons for self instruction in basic skills manual for teachers.* Monterey: California Test Bureau, 1963.

GILMORE, A. S., RICH, T., and WILLIAMS, C. F. *Mental retardation: A programed manual for volunteer workers.* Tampa, Fla.: MacDonald Training Center, 1965.

GOLDSTEIN, L. S., and GOTKIN, L. G. A review of research: Teaching machines vs. programed textbooks as presentation modes. *Journal of Programed Instruction,* 1963, *1,* 29–36.

GREEN, E. *The learning process and programed instruction.* New York: Holt, Rinehart, and Winston, 1962.

HENDERSHOT, C. *Programed learning: A bibliography of programs and presentation devices.* (3d ed.) Bay City, Mich., 1964; Supplements, 1965.

HILLIARD, T. Unpublished report. Tampa, Fla.: MacDonald Training Center, 1965.

HOMME, L., and GLASER, R. Relationships between programed textbooks and teaching machines. In E. Galanter (Ed.), *Automatic teaching: The state of the art.* New York: John Wiley and Sons, 1959, 103–108.

LAWSON, R., and WATSON, L. J. Transfer of training from a machine program by mentally retarded children. (Mimeographed report) Columbus: Ohio State University, College of Education, 1964.

LUMSDAINE, A. A., and GLASER, R. (Eds.). *Teaching machines and programed learning: A source book.* Washington, D.C.: National Education Association, 1960.

McNEIL, J. D. Superior reading achievement of boys through programed instruction versus inferior progress under formal teachers. Los Angeles: University of California, Undated (1963?).

MALPASS, L., GILMORE, A. S., HARDY, M. W., and WILLIAMS, C. A comparison of two automated teaching procedures for retarded children. (Technical report) Washington, D.C.: U.S. Office of Education, 1963.

———, HARDY, M. W., GILMORE, A. S., and WILLIAMS, C. F. Automated instruction for retarded children. *Amer. J. ment. Defic.,* 1964, *69,* 405–412.

———, WILLIAMS, C. F., and GILMORE, A. S. Further development of automated instruction for retarded children. (Technical report) Washington, D.C.: U.S. Office of Education, 1967.

Mast Teaching System. Distributed by Keystone View Company, Meadville, Pa., 1962.

MOORE, O. K. Autotelic responsive environments and exceptional children. Hamden, Conn.: Responsive Environments Foundation, Inc., 1963.

———. Early reading and writing. Part I: Skills. Part II: Teaching Methods. (Motion pictures) Hamden, Conn.: Responsive Environments Foundation, Inc., 1963.

NAUMANN, T. F. The development of an automated basic spelling program for EMR children. (Mimeographed report) Ellensburg, Wash.: Central Washington State College, 1962.

———, PORTER, L. A., and WENSLEY, O. W. Principles of learning applied in automated instruction of handicapped pupils. Mimeographed paper read at University of Washington research meeting, 1962.

———, ———, ———. Development of an automated program to teach auditory discrimination. (Mimeographed report) Ellensburg, Wash.: Central Washington State College, 1964.

ODELL, W. *How teachers can evaluate teaching machines.* New York: Teaching Materials, Inc., Grolier, Inc., 1964.

PARSONS, BOBBIE. Developing basic cursive writing skills. *NSPI Journal,* 1963, *2,* 4.

PLATT, H. Teaching machine working well with retarded students. *Rehabilitation Records,* 1965, *6,* 25–27.

PRESSEY, S. L. Development and appraisal of devices providing immediate automatic scoring of subjective tests and concomitant self-instruction. *J. Psychol.,* 1950, *29,* 417–447.

PRICE, J. E. Automated teaching programs with mentally retarded students. *Amer. J. ment. Defic.,* 1963, *68,* 69–72.

Publishers Company. *The TEACHALL.* Washington, D.C.: Author, 1963.

Rheem Manufacturing Co. *The Didak 101 Teaching Machine.* South Gate, Calif.: Author, 1959.

SCHRAMM, W. *The research on programed instruction: An annotated bibliography* Washington, D.C.: U.S. Office of Education, 1964.

———. *Programed instruction—today and tomorrow.* New York: Fund for the Advancement of Education, 1962.

SKINNER, B. F. Teaching machines. *Science,* 1958, *128,* 969–977.

SMITH, E. A., and QUACKENBUSH, J. Devereaux teaching aids employed in presenting elementary mathematics in a special education setting. *Psychol. Rep.,* 1960, *7,* 333–336.

STOLUROW, L. Teaching machines and special education. *Educ. & Psych. Meas.,* 1960, *20,* 429–448.

———. *Teaching by machine.* Washington, D.C.: U.S. Office of Education, 1961.

———. Programed instruction for the mentally retarded. *Review educ. Research.,* 1963, *33,* 126–136.

TIZARD, J., and O'CONNOR, N. The employability of high-grade mental defectives. *Amer. J. ment. Defic.,* 1950, *54,* 563–575; *55,* 144–157.

WARBURTON, F. W. Educational psychology. *Ann. rev. Psychol.,* 1962, *13,* 371–414.

WILLIAMS, J. P. Effectiveness of constructed-response and multiple-choice programing modes as a function of test mode. *J. educ. Psy.,* 1965, *56,* 111–117.

WOOLMAN, M., and DAVY, R. A. *Developing symbolic skills in the mentally retarded.* Washington, D.C.: Institute of Educational Research, 1963.

WYCKOFF, B. *The film tutor.* Produced by TMI-Grolier, Inc., New York, 1960. (Not available commercially)

Vocational Preparation and Occupation[1]   10

WOLF WOLFENSBERGER

THE emphasis in this chapter will be on the vocational preparation and occupation of those retardates who live in the community before, during, and probably after vocational training. While some of the material covered may be relevant to institutional training as well, to cover such programming adequately would have required almost a chapter by itself.

The scope of this chapter does not permit an extensive review of the vast amount of material available in the area. In order to keep the chapter at a reasonable length while still communicating a substantial body of information, the reader is referred to certain basic works by Clarke (1958), Fraenkel (1961), Gunzburg (1958, 1960), Heber (1964), O'Connor (1957), O'Connor and Tizard (1956), and the U.S. Department of Health, Education, and Welfare (HEW, 1961), and to reviews by Engel (1950, 1952), Goldstein (1964), Kolstoe (1961), Shafter (1957), Tizard (1958), Tizard and O'Connor 1950a, 1950b), and Windle (1962). The special emphasis in this chapter will be on points and issues that hitherto have been neglected, that have assumed new importance in the recent past, or that, in my opinion, need further analysis and interpretation. An attempt has been made to cover relevant material that appeared before autumn, 1964. Some later material was subsequently included, but was not based on an equally intensive search.

1. The preparation of this chapter was supported in part by Grant HD-00370 from the National Institute of Child Health and Human Development.

A VOCATIONAL CREED

The oft-quoted motto of the Vineland Training School is "Happiness first—all else follows." I would propose that for the adult retardate with work potential, the motto should be "a full day of work—happiness usually will follow."

Through the process of evolution, different species have developed modes of activity most suitable for their survival and well-being. If this mode of activity is denied to them, they often fail to thrive and may even die. In man, the optimal activity seems to be work, in the broader sense. Historically, when peoples with varying outlooks on work have clashed, those with more industrious habits and attitudes seem to have usually triumphed even if they were technologically and intellectually less advanced, and numerically inferior.

Our culture is highly work-oriented. The highest status is conferred not by appearance and stature, not by descent and tradition, and not by income and wealth, although all these may play a role. The most significant status recognition comes from what one does or accomplishes in the way of work.

A program aimed at solving social problems must be sensitive to the existing cultural values. It is much more likely to be successful if it reflects these values, and more likely to fail if it develops in contradiction to them. I propose a creed of vocational training and occupation of retardates that I believe to be consistent with the predominant cultural values of American society, as well as the principles advanced by some of the leaders in the field of habilitation of the retarded.

1. A working retardate is generally a happier person. Work gives self-esteem and a feeling of accomplishment and worth.

2. Work lends adult status to a retardate, and thus adds to his dignity in the sight of others.

3. In our work-oriented society, positive attitudes will generally be expressed toward the worker, and negative ones toward the drone. Thus, the retardate's adjustment will be enhanced by the community attitudes he encounters.

4. The family of the working retardate is, generally, a better adjusted family. Since work tends to make the retardate more acceptable, it engenders positive attitudes in the family benefiting the retardate indirectly.

5. A retardate capable of working will be less likely to become an economic burden to his family or society.

6. A working retardate contributes to the economic welfare of society.

7. He earns an income that is likely to give him more of the material benefits enjoyed by the majority of our citizens.

8. Idleness can lead to nonadaptive or maladaptive behavior.

The question may be raised as to which retardates are capable of productive and meaningful work. The following answers are proposed:

1. A retardate who is capable of basic self-care is almost certainly capable of at least sheltered work.

2. A retardate who can profit from arts and crafts activities or who is capable of purposeful play is very likely to be capable of at least sheltered work.

3. Inability to walk, lack of speech or language, and even incontinence are not necessarily indicators that a retardate is incapable of at least sheltered work.

In economic terms, habilitation of the retardate is easy to justify. According to the President's Panel Report (1963a, p. 2), the nation is deprived of "several billion dollars" of economic output because of the incapacitating effects of retardation. From the literature (e.g., Bobroff, 1956; Goodwill Industries, 1961, p. 73, 74; Office of Vocational Rehabilitation [OVR], Southern Methodist University [SMU] and National Association for Retarded

Children [NARC], 1961, p. 96; Phelps, 1956) and current wage trends, it appears that a young retardate with a work life of 30 years ahead of him may expect to earn about $100,-000. A successfully placed retardate has been found to return between $7 (OVR, 1961) to $10 (President's Committee on Employment of the Handicapped, 1963) in income taxes for every $1 spent in his habilitation. Analyzing earning data for retardates rehabilitated by state rehabilitation agencies between 1958 and 1963 (HEW, 1964b), it was found that only 8 per cent of the group were wage earners before the initiation of services. Of these 8 per cent, half were earning less than $10 per per week. At closure, however, only 7 per cent had no earnings, and the weekly wage was $35. In a nonretarded comparison group, 28 per cent had earnings at intake and their mean wage at closure was $43 a week. However, 17 per cent had no earnings at all at closure. Thus, retardates were earning less, but more of them were employed. The overall average direct cost to rehabilitate a retardate was $453, while a comparable figure for a nonretardate was $480. The figures were even more favorable for those clients whose mental retardation was considered a secondary rather than a primary problem. Phelps (1965, p. 3) reports that the average cost per retardate habilitated in West Virginia in 1961-62 was an even lower $242.

Sheltered employment of lower functioning retardates may prevent or postpone institutionalization, thus saving considerable expenses since judging from current average daily costs alone, a 30-year period of institutionalization would require well over $50,000.

While we have relatively little knowledge regarding the operating costs of well-functioning, broad service programs for retardates, we have good reason to believe that such programs will, in the long run, be more economical than the alternative wastage of human resources, institutionalization, and charity. The more intangible humane benefits of such programs are, of course, immeasurable.

SOME HISTORICAL BACKGROUND

Workshops probably had their antecedents in the sixteenth-century hospices of the St. Vincent de Paul Society and in the unsavory workhouses for the poor developing in England about the same time. In the United States, workshops apparently were first introduced by the Perkins School for the Blind in 1840. U.S. workshops for the retarded probably had their beginnings in 1919 when the city of New York opened a shop that served mostly retarded girls and that assisted them in finding jobs in the community (Davies, 1959, p. 193 ff.). Shortly thereafter, Rome State School started a workshop solely for retarded girls at one of its industrial colonies at Oriskany Falls, New York, in which the girls engaged in hand-sewing of baseballs. The first full-fledged community rehabilitation center and workshop for retardates was established by the Association for the Help of Retarded Children in New York City in 1953. This workshop, aided by federal grants, has been a model for many others. The Opportunity Workshop of Minneapolis must also be given credit as a pioneer. Although it became operational in late 1953, it was initiated in 1952.

Since 1954, the Vocational Rehabilitation Administration (VRA, formerly the Office of Vocational Rehabilitation), has funded 38 special demonstration projects establishing sheltered workshops. An additional 25 occupational and special education-vocational training projects were scheduled to be funded by VRA during fiscal year 1964 (HEW, 1964a). By 1961, there were about 75 workshops primarily serving the retarded, and at present more than 200 vocational rehabilitation agencies and sheltered workshops are engaged in this work (President's Committee on Employment of the Handicapped, 1963). The directory of sheltered workshops for the retarded compiled by the National Association for Retarded Children (NARC, 1964) lists 320 shops serving at least some retardates although only 231 provided directory information.

To date, most workshops have been operated by private agencies and initiative. Public agencies other than schools have been involved mostly in granting financial support or in assisting in the job placement process. With increasing emphasis on publicly operated comprehensive services, we can expect to see a significant shift of sheltered workshop administration from private into public hands. An interesting example is in Tennessee where the state parent association started a network of workshops, in part supported by proceeds from bubble-gum machines. The network subsequently was taken over by the state.

In 1943, the Barden-LaFollette Amendments to the 1920 Vocational Rehabilitation Act were passed, opening the door for the use of federal vocational rehabilitation funds for the retarded. Federal participation in the rehabilitation of the retarded was further expanded by Public Law 565 (the Vocational Rehabilitation Amendments) in 1954, and most recently in 1965, In 1945, 106 retardates were known to have been habilitated by state-federal agencies. Between 1950 and 1954, the retarded constituted 1 per cent of all cases of habilitation. Between 1955 and 1963, the number of habilitations increased from 531 to 5,909, and was expected to reach 7,500 in 1964. In terms of proportions, the retarded habilitations increased to 4.4 per cent. Although retardates outnumber blind persons 15 to 1 in this country, only recently have there been more habilitations among the retarded than the blind.

SCOPE AND PREVALENCE OF THE PROBLEM

Severe intellectual impairment can affect an individual to the degree that he would be unlikely to survive, or survive without extensive care, even in a simple and undemanding environment. However, as Kanner (1949) has pointed out, most cases of subaverage intellectual functioning would not be considered a problem unless the environment, particularly the social environment, were complex and demanding. Gruenberg (1964) indicates that mental retardation can be viewed as a defect in the functional relationship between an individual and his immediate social environment. Thus, the number of inadequately functioning individuals will depend not only upon individual task performance ability, but also upon the tasks that the environment sets. Within this framework, it is perfectly natural that prevalence of mental retardation should be lowest in the youngest age groups, and highest in the mid-teen group where the school makes heavy demands. "As our society becomes more complex, there will be more and more people who can't cope with it" (Mead, 1959, p. 256). "The more intricate the mechanization and automation in industry becomes, the higher will be the number of people falling by the roadside of economic and cultural competition" (Kratter, 1958, p. 529). Kratter further points out that a substantial number of retardates could, in effect, be "cured" by abandoning education, while, on the other hand, an increase in technology may make dullards out of individuals with IQs of 90 or even 100. Thus," the community create[s] its own mental deficiency problem" (Perry, 1954, p. 68).

In a sense, then, the definition of retardation is a social one, and the prevalence of retardation depends upon the social structure of a certain place and time. Thus, self-service laundries and elevators, automats, even traffic cloverleafs are, in a social and habilitational sense, causes of mental retardation as surely as the proverbial fall on the head or the kick of the mule. Individuals displaced by automated equipment from their long-held repetitive, manual jobs may become unemployed and problem cases. When they come to the attention of the authorities, such as rehabilitation agencies, they may be tested and found to be of low IQ and suddenly, for the first time in their lives, be identified as retarded. "For all practical purposes, then, retardation for the vocational rehabilitation counselor is principally a sociological phenomenon" (Rogers, 1962, p. 5).

That retardation is ultimately defined socially and not medically or even psychometrically has been rather well established in fact, though often ignored. Prevalence surveys tend to find peak rates between the ages of about 10 to 14, with sharply declining rates on either side. Few people would argue seriously that the prevalence drop in the late teens is a result of a substantial decline in the number of indivduals with IQ scores in the retarded range.

Just what the prevalence of work-age retardates is, is difficult, if not futile to answer. A strictly psychometric criterion would be simple to formulate and would, almost by definition, yield a close estimate. However, such a criterion would probably not be very helpful in predicting the social problem and the programming needs.

Ginzberg and Bray (1953), in analyzing World War II draft rejection patterns, found that, for the period from the beginning of selective service to December, 1944, about 14 per cent of draft registrants were rejected because of mental deficiency. Striking differences among regions, states, counties, and races were noted. For example, South Carolina had a retardation rejection rate of 27.7 per cent for Negroes, while for whites the mean rejection rate was 4.3 per cent. The highest white rejection rate was in Tennessee and Kentucky (6.4 per cent), the lowest in the District of Columbia (0.4 per cent) and Washington and Oregon (0.5 per cent).

According to surveys reviewed in the Manpower Report (1964), about 220,000 young men turning 18 in 1964 failed the Armed Forces mental tests, and a good proportion of these failures were mentally retarded. The 220,000 "can be expected to lack many of the qualities needed to lead self-sufficient lives in the civilian economy." This dire pronouncement was supported by the fact that 28 per cent of the sample were unemployed, and 5 per cent were not even looking for a job.

Prevalence of work-age retardates in a given locality probably varies according to a large number of factors, including: (1) the nature of the local industrial pattern; (2) nationwide economic conditions; (3) the local social pattern, including the distribution of underprivileged or minority groups; (4) the local age distribution, and (5) the local sex distribution. Thus, a slum location in an economically depressed area where young adult males are disproportionally heavily represented is likely to yield ten- and even a hundred-fold the rate of work-age retardates as compared to a town of middle- and upper-class character that has become a retirement haven for older people.

That startling local and regional differences can exist is well documented. Such differences were indicated by Thorndike and Woodyard (1942), and were sharply underlined by the findings emerging from the armed forces draft selection process (Manpower Report, 1964). For example, even when comparing such crude geographical areas as states, recent "mental" rejections varied from 3 to 55 per cent. The majority of these rejectees were characterized as "products of poverty." Gruenberg (1964) points out that in 1929 Lewis found considerable differences in the prevalence of retardation between different areas in England. Lewis noted an atypically high prevalence of reported adult mental retardation in one of the areas; this was felt to be a result of an economic depression in the main industry of that area, since no ethnological factors seemed to account for the difference. A study of retardation in the Chicago schools (Mullen and Nee, 1952) showed how great the differences in mental retardation prevalence can be even between districts within one city. Even at the time this study was conducted, recommendations for placement in educable classes varied from zero in some of the districts to 30.03 per thousand in others. The more severely retarded were often "excused" from school, and excuse cases varied from 0 to 20.96 per 4,000.

In a very noteworthy study, Kennedy, Van De Riet, and White (1963) investigated intelligence and achievement trends in a large Negro sample in the Southeast. Upon school entry, Negro children were found to have an average IQ of 86, with scores progressively falling to an average of 65 at age 13. A similar, but not as drastic progressive separation of groups was demonstrated in a longitudinal study by Osborn (1960). While the Negroes' mean IQ did not fall with age, the overlap between groups vanished almost completely in four years because of range constriction.

In the Onondaga study (New York State Department of Mental Hygiene, 1955) further evidence was provided for the operation of socio-cultural factors in the genesis of mental retardation. In the age group below five years, retardation was more than twice as prevalent among the white than the nonwhite population in Syracuse. However, this relationship was reversed in the 5-to-9 and 10-to-14 age ranges. Both groups displayed a dramatic drop in prevalence in the age range of 15 to 17, but the ratio between the white and the nonwhite population increased to almost four nonwhite retardates for every white one.

Gruenberg (1964, p. 269) plotted the results of various prevalence studies, pointing out the great discrepancies not only in numbers but even in trends and ratios. He pointed out that community uniqueness should be expected, and that epidemiological data from one community may not necessarily be applicable to another, even if they have many similar characteristics. Thus, great caution is indicated in estimating rates of local retardation prevalence and distribution.

Lately, the prevalence estimate of 3 per cent has achieved great publicity and popularity. This may be a fairly accurate estimate of the national prevalence of retardation at this time according to a psychometric criterion (IQ of 70 or less). However, many forget that: (1) even by this criterion, the rate of individuals falling below IQ 70 at one time in their lives is much greater than 3 per cent; and (2) many individuals may have IQs above 70, yet will be retarded at some time in their lives in the sense of the definition of the American Association on Mental Deficiency (i.e., impaired adaptive behavior associated with subaverage intellectual functioning originating at an early age) and certainly in a broad social sense.

In long-term comprehensive program planning for retardates, one's estimates of service needs must be based on considerations of local age and sex distribution, population mobility, differences in retardates' severity grouping, socio-economic status distribution, and industrial and other conditions. However, too many individuals and agencies suddenly cast into the role of program planners have ignored these factors and have blindly multiplied population-age estimates by .03.

For reasons touched upon above it is obviously impossible here to give an estimate of the prevalence of work-age retardates in a specific locality. As risky as it is, the most practical steps to take in program planning would probably be to look at local draft rejection patterns and at prevalence studies of areas most like the area being planned for, allowing for some of the conditions described above. Good reviews of prevalence studies or other contributions that may be useful are found in Gruenberg (1964), Levinson (1962), Ministry of Health (1962), O'Connor (1958), O'Connor and Tizard (1956), and Tizard (1964). The survey data of Jastack, MacPhee, and Whiteman (1962) may also be of use. However, their criteria were rather unusual, and their conclusions, especially in regard to age distributions, were not always in accord with the raw data presented.

Service development is often preceded by expensive and time-consuming surveys of needs, which is proper in cases where comprehensive planning is underway, or where planners hope to satisfy the demand for a particular service. But it is utterly wasted when it is obvious from the start that the service will not satisfy the need. In such cases, planning money would be better spent on service development. Gruenberg (1964) also points out that surveys, though expensive, are cheaper than services and may be used by those opposed to extension of services as a delaying tactic in the political arena.

While numerous studies have indicated that the majority of retardates can make an adequate economic adjustment after leaving school, estimates of the number who need help in vocational placement or in further training vary considerably. Snyder (1964) reports that 25 per cent of educable school dropouts aged 17 to 21 in New York City need protracted counseling and placement assistance. A similar estimate is given by Davies (quoted by Rogers, 1962), while DiMichael (1955) gives a figure of 40 per cent, adding that even those who find jobs more quickly often do so with the help of employment services, teachers, and vocational counselors. Rogers (1962, p. 18) also quotes Fraenkel as stating that most of the marginally independent retardates (i.e., about 2.5 per cent of the population) "can utilize some vocational guidance and training," and need "counseling in periods of stress and crisis."

Estimates of workshop needs also vary. Pense (1960, 1961) quotes an estimate of 1 workshop place per 2,000 population, based on British experience. Jacobs and Weingold (1958) give an estimate of 1 per 1,000, and in the Goodwill Industries report (1961, p. 44) a figure of 1.4 per 1,000 is mentioned. DiMichael sees a need for 10% of retarded youths, or about 100,000 workshop places in the country (HEW, 1961, p. 17), while the NARC (1959) recognizes a need for 250,000 retarded individuals.

Three good reasons why increasing consideration will probably be given to the vocational preparation and occupation of retardates are:

1. The rapid increase in the complexity of our society will probably result in a sizable increase in the number of individuals who will be identified as retarded. These are the individuals who, because of subaverage intelligence, will require considerable supervision, guidance, tuition, and assistance from the rest of society.

2. Our Protestant ethic places great value on work. Even if our society could sustain an unemployment rate of 20 per cent, such a situation seems hardly likely to be tolerated. Already, one can cite examples where the cost of employment is higher than the cost of unemployment.

3. As our society becomes more affluent, it will be more willing to channel some of its wealth to the fuller development of the potentials of its citizens, and to risk the high initial investments often necessary before the long-range benefits of the cultivation of human resources can be reaped.

MANPOWER TRENDS AND AUTOMATION

Industrial processes utilizing large numbers of people in repetitive and relatively simple tasks have, for over 50 years, offered the means of maximizing the economic productivity of the retardate. One of the ironies of history is that we recognize this possibility only when the industrial pattern is being revolutionized; when machines increasingly substitute for men on those tasks unskilled individuals previously performed successfully (Killingsworth, 1966); and now when the struggle for the retardate's place in the economy is likely to be a "cliff-hanger."

The contemporary young adult retardate faces a formidable challenge when he sets out to find a job. His problem is not merely a lower skill level and learning potential; he also faces competition for jobs from young, unemployed, unskilled, but nonretarded youths. The rate of unemployment in the 16-to-21 age group is more than double that of the total labor force, and, among Negro youths, it is double that of white youths (President's Committee on Youth Employment, 1963). Much like the retarded, a major proportion of nonretarded unemployed youths have no skills to offer and thus tend to compete for the same unskilled jobs. Because of these conditions, as well as the persisting trends toward automation, dire forecasts are sometimes heard regarding the long-range employment prospects of the retarded. Indeed, some people go as far as to question the justifiability of developing extensive vocational services for the retarded.

While automation, in conjunction with increases in complexity of societal demands, may well result in an increase in retardation, retardates' employability itself may not necessarily be affected. As Goldstein and Heber (HEW, 1961, p. 35) point out, predicting all the implications of the ongoing technological revolution is difficult. They believe that neither of the extremes of optimism or pessimism concerning the occupational market for the mentally retarded is warranted (HEW, 1961, p. 36). Instead, flexibility in patterns of planning and training is needed. Thus, Kruger (1963) feels that changing conditions may be handled by changes in special education and in job training.

Significant recent advances in legislation also have greatly improved the prospects for the retarded. Among the provisions of the 1961 Area Redevelopment Act, which is aimed at economic development of distressed areas, is the retraining or relocation of unemployed or underemployed persons. By May, 1963, 400 projects in 44 states had resulted in training for over 20,000 individuals. The 1962 Manpower Development and Training Act and its amendments provides for training or the upgrading of skills regardless of location and has clauses specifically emphasizing training of youths ages 16 to 21 with inadequate education. The 1962 Trade Expansion Act provides funds to relocate workers displaced because of importation of certain goods resulting in changes in local industrial conditions. The 1963 Vocational Education Act permits expansion of vocational services, especially to the young. The Economic Opportunities Act of 1964 and other legislation passed and likely to be passed in connection with the "war on poverty" is also relevant to manpower and retardation problems. In summary, these various pieces of legislation are likely to have a profound impact on manpower trends. Many of the provisions conducive to employment, relocation, training, retraining, and education are not only aimed directly at the lower intelligence groups, but are also likely to result in indirect benefits to them by upgrading workers at all levels. Other recent legislation (e.g., the National Defense Education Act and its amendments, the Elementary and Secondary Education Act, amendments to the Social Security and Vocational Rehabilitation Act, the Health Professions Educational Assistance Act, and the Higher Education Facilities Act, as well as scattered educational provisions such as the one contained in the Mental Retardation Facilities and Community

Mental Health Centers Construction Act) may profit retardates directly or indirectly by contributing heavily to the general upgrading.

Manpower for skilled occupations is scarce, and large numbers of jobs at higher levels could be filled or created if enough skilled personnel were available. For example, the National Institutes of Health estimated that between 1960 and 1970, 45,000 new professional research workers will be required for health-related research alone (Manpower Report, 1964). The President's Panel Report, Task Force on Education and Rehabilitation (1963b) estimated that the shortage of teachers of the retarded alone is 55,000, and 63,000 school counselors are needed right now (Manpower Report, 1966). The list of skilled manpower shortages and future requirements is long and wide-ranging.

For a substantial number of higher level jobs, skill and training are more important than high intelligence. There thus exists a problem of upgrading large segments of the labor market, especially of those workers who, though of average intelligence, are engaged in simple, repetitive, routine, and basically manual tasks—tasks that should be reserved in large measure for the retarded. As long as the worker of normal potential is upgraded faster than or as fast as automation develops, work should be available for retardates.

Already indications have appeared that upgrading is proceeding apace. The proportion of high school graduates has increased steadily since 1952, as has the proportion of those finishing at least five years of schooling, or college. Between 1960 and 1964 alone, there has been a 30 per cent increase in students at the college and professional school level (U.S. Bureau of Census, 1965). The Manpower Report (1964) estimates that in 1975, 73 per cent of workers between ages of 25 to 34 will have at least a high school education and 19 per cent a college education. While jobs in the 1960s will increase by 40 per cent at the professional and technical levels, and 20 per cent for sales and business personnel, the President's Committee on Youth Employment (1963) estimates that the number of semi-skilled jobs will increase at two-thirds the rate of total employment and that the number of unskilled jobs will remain the same, although, of course, this means that the proportion of those jobs will drop.

While productivity in industry has increased steadily at rates of 2.5 to 3.5 per cent, the service industries have increased their productivity at a much lower rate resulting in continued rise of demand for such labor. Increases in leisure time activities also are expected to add to the demand for personal services. Semiskilled personal services are particularly expected to offer increasing opportunities.

In some respects, factory employment may be more advantageous to retardates than service and other kinds of work. O'Connor and Tizard (1956) found that over twice as many retardates failed in nonindustrial as in industrial jobs. They felt (Tizard and O'Connor, 1952) that in large industrial firms, the quality of supervisory personnel may be higher. Service work usually requires more flexibility and diversity than factory work, and some service employments are more likely to bring out the retardate's interpersonal shortcomings. However, if a counselor or agency believes that service occupations are optimal placements for retardates, there will be an increased likelihood that such placements are sought (e.g., Kolstoe, 1961b, p. 51) and obtained, and stronger encouragement may be given to the retardate to take and hold such jobs. Thus, placement statistics may be very misleading regarding potential occupational placements. Whether retardates will be placed and persevere in industrial work will, in part, depend on counselor and agency attitudes.

However, since the trend is for increase of opportunity in services, this area should receive heavy training emphasis. The U.S. government has set an example in reorienting employers to the need to hire retardates for jobs they can do. The Civil Service Commission (Anonymous, 1964; Baker, 1962) has ruled that jobs can be "re-engineered" on an experimental basis to fit the abilities of retarded workers, and written requirements for a job can be waived. Agreements can be drawn up between government and rehabilitation agencies regarding conditions of the retardates' employment. Further study is being given to the matter (HEW, 1964a), and possibly the federal government may become a significant employment source for retardates. Already over 800 individuals have been hired under this program and appear to be doing well (Manpower Report, 1966).

Even as certain unskilled or semiskilled industrial jobs are eliminated by automation, the new jobs created in conjunction with automated processes are not always skilled ones. In many instances, feeding into and removing from a automated process is a simple, tedious, and repetitive job, as is the monitoring of panels of lights and the pushing of buttons in response to signals. Nor is it true that automation always eliminates the jobs that are likely to be held by retardates. For example, the recently introduced cash register that automatically calculates the amount of change a customer is to be given and then dispenses the small coin change should tend to make more feasible employing retardates as checkers in supermarkets and similar establishments.

While the vast majority of retardates will be found in unskilled or semi-skilled jobs and earning modest wages, a number of follow-up studies (e.g., Engel, 1950, 1952 [2]; Krishef and Hall, 1955) have found that retardates can, on occasion, gain entry into skilled and unusual occupations, and can earn very good salaries. Some retardates find work in occupations that might be unexpected in light of their IQs. One study found truck drivers, parachute sewers, and sawing machine operators with IQs between 50 and 69. Bartenders and carpenters were found in the 70 to 79 IQ range (Rynbrandt, 1947), and were also encountered in Bobroff's (1956) follow-up study. Generally, people do not realize how little intelligence it takes to perform a large number of jobs. Individuals once only rarely considered "feasible" (Hegge, 1950) for training can be placed not only in sheltered, but also open employment (Fraenkel, 1961b).

Davies (1959, p. 212) estimated that half of the restaurant industry jobs in New York City were within the ability scope of the retarded. He also pointed out that textile mills were once operated by children and that similar machine operations should, therefore, be within the range of child-like intelligence. Kruger (1963) analyzed the 1960 occupational distribution of women in Michigan and concluded that 45 per cent were working in occupations for which retardates might be

2. The reviews of outcome studies by Engel turned up several interesting but rarely quoted references which deserve wider attention. These studies seemed to have been "lost" because they were published in relatively inaccessible sources.

trained. This is a very high estimate, but is encouraging even if it may be somewhat over-optimistic. Delp (1957) identified a wide range of tasks in which retardates with IQs in the 20s, 30s, and 40s were found to engage, and Wolfensberger and Tizard (1964) documented some remarkable accomplishments by low functioning retardates working in a factory in England. Unger and Burr (Engel, 1950) performed a series of job analyses that showed that a wide variety of industrial tasks could be done on an MA level of 9 to 10. Even sales girls could manage with an MA of 9.5. Over 30 years ago, Beckham (1930) found that MAs of 7 to 8 were sufficient for a variety of laundry tasks, and Tizard and O'Connor (1950a) pointed out that persons of even lower MAs could perform such work. Krishef and Hall (1955) reported that 15 per cent of the retardates under county supervision in Hennepin County, Minnesota, were earning $3,000 or more, a very respectable figure at that time. Finally Saenger (1957), in his classic study of the adjustment of severely retarded adults in New York City, found that 27 per cent of his community sample was employed, and a total of 36 per cent had been employed at some time after leaving school. Even among the mongoloids, 6 per cent were employed at the time of the study.

Numerous other accounts of the vocational success of retardates could be cited. Reviews of follow-up and community adjustment studies have been published by Engel (1950, 1952), Goldstein (1964), O'Connor (1957), Reynolds and Stunkard (1960), and Tizard (1958). More recent studies have usually confirmed the conclusions of those reviewed above. One of the best controlled follow-up studies (Kennedy, 1966) also yielded the most encouraging conclusions.

In sum, then, there is no justification in discrediting vocational training of retardates on the ground that they are or soon will be unemployable. While some unskilled and semi-skilled jobs will be lost to automation, an expansion of service jobs, a movement of non-retarded workers into more skilled occupations and, perhaps, more sheltered employment for retardates should leave enough openings to accommodate the majority of retarded individuals with work potential. Indeed, in attempting to safeguard the retardate's place in the economy, we may conceivably impose economic

slavery upon him. Tizard (1958, 1964) has pointed out that this is a danger that may not be as remote as may appear at first. One should recall that sheltered workshops have, at times, degenerated into unsavory sweatshops.

FARM EMPLOYMENT OF THE RETARDED

One area in which the employment picture for retardates is very bleak is agriculture. Since many misconceptions exist regarding the retardate's prospects in this line of work, the topic will be explored in further detail.

One still hears the traditional contention that farm work is a good activity for the retardate and one for which he is well suited. This misconception is usually held by those ignorant of the contemporary farm situation and those who have difficult-to-discard commitments to agricultural or horticultural training.

The picture drawn by the Manpower Reports (1964, 1966) is a grim one for the farmer, not to mention the rural retardate. Farm employment is the only major employment sector in the nation that has for some time not only declined proportionately, but also in terms of actual numbers. Since World War II, farm employment has dropped by about 200,000 individuals a year, or a total of about 45 per cent, and is projected to decline another 35 per cent between 1964 and 1980. Out-migration is currently about 5.7 per cent a year, and most of the migrants have been young people, as only about 10 per cent of the boys now growing up on farms can expect to make an adequate living in agriculture (President's Committee on Youth Employment, 1963). In West Virginia, between 50 and 55 per cent of rural youths aged 10 to 17 in 1950 had moved out of rural areas by 1960. Apparently, the migration was highest both among the best and the least educated —a significant datum as regards the rural prospects of retardates. Far from presenting employment possibilities, the training programs under the Manpower Development and Training Act have even had to be denied to certain rural areas because the "reasonable expectation of employment" required by the act was lacking. The Manpower Reports (1964, 1966) even state that out-migration will continue to be necessary in many areas. The government is trying to expedite this process with programs under the Area Redevelopment Act. By December, 1963, almost 27,000 individuals with predominantly rural backgrounds received training, but about 92 per cent were trained for industry and commerce, and only 8 per cent for agriculture.

Patterson and Speck (1963) described the operation of a relatively recent vocational training program for retardates in a rural area. They found that very little work could be found for women, and that employment for men was mostly seasonal.

In the light of these trends, and the fact that massive expenditure is being directed toward getting rural youths off the farms, recommending that retardates be trained for rural work makes little sense, especially if nonrural retardates or public funds are involved. Exceptions may be justified in two kinds of instances: (1) where specific unexploited local conditions hold definite promises of long-range employment and (2) where agriculture is run on an industrial basis. For example, in large dairy and chicken farms, operations much resemble the production line, and many tasks can be performed efficiently by retardates.

Aside from poor farm employment in general, contemporary farming holds three dangers for the retardate: First, contrary to popular conception, the tasks required are often numerous and diversified, and the risk of failure is high. In many types of farming, if not most, a person who cannot respond to the challenge of diverse requirements is not very useful and can easily be replaced by someone more adaptive. Secondly, farming is the third most hazardous occupation, behind mining and construction. Third, the retardate may easily be caught up in the plight of seasonal and migratory workers who toil long hours for short wages a few months during the year (Manpower Report, 1966) and who may live on welfare the rest of the time.

VOCATIONAL SUCCESS PREDICTION

A standard practice of vocational programs all over the country is to run candidates for training through a series of evaluation examinations, including medical and psychological assessment, and perhaps sensory testing and social history. Moreover, the programs often have a period of four to twelve weeks during which work evaluation or work sampling is carried out. Usually this necessitates the rotating of the trainee between work tasks that are often of a make-believe nature, and ordinarily he may spend about a week on any one of the sample tasks. The notion that this entire evaluative process is absolutely essential has become one of the "sacred cows" of our vocational training programs despite the fact that the evidence is lacking or, at best, highly tenuous.

Studies reaching into the hundreds have attempted to identify predictors of outcome in retardates. The work more specifically concerned with job success prediction has suffered from five serious shortcomings:

Poor Design and Control. One of the more common errors here is failure to consider selection factors. In one typical study, retardates who succeeded on work placement were compared with those who stayed in the sheltered workshop, with the implicit idea that differences might be predictive of success. However, the authors indicated that the majority of the nonemployed workers were, in fact, never given a chance at employment. While group differences may thus be predictive of the staff's willingness to permit placement, such a design cannot reveal uncontaminated job success factors. Similarly, in another study the outcome of habilitation efforts of a sample of retardates in New York City between 1953 and 1955 were investigated. Again, many retardates were, on an *a priori* basis, ruled unfeasible because of low IQ or lack of academic skills. Thus, unfeasibility and service outcome were confounded, together with factors such as reading level.

The practice of validating a predictive technique against workshop performance instead of competitive employment is also encountered over and over in the research literature. This practice appears only permissible if workshop performance is all that is to be predicted. However, researchers characteristically and inappropriately imply that workshop performance is an adequate criterion of later competitive employment performance. Tobias (1964) has indicated some of the reasons why predictors of workshop productivity may very well be quite different from predictors of competitive employment.

Lack of Cross-Validation. Apparently only

one good and at least partly cross-validated study exists (O'Connor and Tizard, 1956), and the lesson to be learned from it is most instructive. A wide range of intelligence, psychophysiological, personality, motor and other tests were administered to a group of 104 retardates. A few tests, primarily with motor content, predicted employment success. Part of the battery was then cross-validated on a second sample of about equal size, whereupon the original multiple correlations of .5 to .6 dropped to .25. The authors concluded that the exclusion of retardates on the basis of unstable criteria would be unwise, as it would lead to hardship and injustice.

Lack of Confirmation across Studies. At one time or other almost every variable investigated has been found to be predictive. However, contradictory results or lack of follow-up by others have then left doubt about the validity of any claim involving that variable.

Emphasis on Variables Associated with the Retardate. Hardly any studies have concentrated on, or even taken into account, the variables inherent in the training and placement process, or those associated with the placement situation. For example, a counselor may have failed to work out problems such as the trainee's transportation to a new job in a situation where even a normal person without a car may have found it impossible to hold the job for any length of time. The same can be said about some of the placement situations. For example, counselors in the past have occasionally placed retardates as orderlies in nursing homes. Some of these nursing homes were operated strictly for profit, the residents received inadequate and unkind treatment, and the employes were worked a double shift for six or even seven days a week for wages consisting of pocket money, room and board. If a retardate failed in such a situation, the blame was laid to personal variables and scarcely ever to placement or employer variables.

Kolstoe and Shafter (1961) have drawn attention to the importance of relating the predictors to the job to be predicted, pointing out that those variables that make for success in one situation may make for failure in another. They indicated the possibility that job success prediction may need to be tied to job description. Peterson and Jones (1964) compiled a large number of descriptions of jobs that reportedly are and have been held by retardates, but the utility of this approach awaits demonstration. Kolstoe (1964), drawing attention to the importance of factors outside the retardate, pointed out that their scope is so large that it is a wonder that prediction is attempted at all. In one of the few studies relevant to the assessment of placement variables, Phelps (1965) surveyed the attitudes of potential employers toward mentally retarded workers and found that exactly in those service occupations where retardates are often placed, attitudes toward them were the least favorable. Unfortunately, research studies virtually never randomize or control for the important placement variables.

Weakness of Some Predictors. Potential predictors can probably be arranged along a continuum from "softness" to "hardness." The soft predictors are those that are rather inherently unstable and subject to modification, such as initial motor performance scores. Hard predictors are those with a promise of stability. Macmillan (1962) feels that unstable characteristics that are modified in the process of habilitation have been seized upon most readily as potential predictors, instead of the more stable ones.

Perhaps the most basic fallacy of numerous shotgun-type searches for employment predictors is the assumption that the criteria for successful employment are fairly homogeneous for a heterogeneous range of jobs likely to be held by retardates.

Because of the considerable attention they have drawn, the McDonald Training Center reports of dragnet-type research should receive special mention. Ferguson (1959, Part II) collected a wide range of test data on a group of workshop clients and computed correlations with various measures of success, including competitive employment. While other studies counted themselves fortunate to achieve good prediction of workshop behavior, Ferguson's data predicted competitive employment even better than it did workshop behavior. Indeed, some of his coefficients approached the test-retest reliabilities of the instruments he used. Patterson (1964), in a review, felt that "these results are so unusual that one suspects that there must be some serious error or defect in this study." In a later report (Pinkard, Gilmore, Ricker, and Williams, 1963), no attempt was made to explain Ferguson's results. Instead, the subjects used in Ferguson's study appeared to be incorporated in a second, larger study. Over 46 scales were investigated, and the more promising ones were, apparently on a *post hoc* basis, designated for inclusion in a Vocational Capacity Scale. However, this scale does not seem to have been cross-validated. Also, there were a number of problems in the study that would have to be overcome in any cross-validation. In short, the McDonald Training Center studies are suggestive, but the Vocational Capacity Scale, based mostly on psychometric tests, should be used with considerable skepticism until it is cross-validated. In another noteworthy project at the Johnstone Center, a state residential facility specifically operated for the purpose of training young adult retardates for employment, a four-year study was conducted that assessed the utility of over 40 evaluation measures. None predicted off-campus day work ratings even though many motor measures and work samples were included (Parnicky and Kahn, 1963).

Partly as a consequence of the shortcomings reviewed above, none of the measures usually derived from psychological tests and other data have been adequately proven to be useful in prediction. Only a few variables have emerged as strongly suggestive, one of these being motor performance. In his review, Windle (1962) considers the studies of motor performance of retardates to be perhaps the most predictive ones to date. Also, in a more recent factor analysis of a wide array of tests and scales, Taylor (1964) identified eleven factors of abilities, only one of which, general dexterity, correlated with work competence.

However, even the utility of motor tests can be regarded with some skepticism in view of contradictory studies (e.g., Meadow and Greenspan, 1961) and others that indicate that initial scores on motor tasks or tests are not predictors of performance after practice or learning. When first tested on these tasks, retardates tend to score lower, often very much lower, than normal individuals, but with practice the difference between these groups can diminish (Reynolds and Stacey, 1955), vanish (Carrier, Malpass, and Orton, 1961; Holman, 1933), or even reverse (Baumeister, Hawkins, and Holland, 1966). O'Connor (1957), in reporting the thesis study of Gordon, pointed out that within an "imbecile"

group, no relationship between initial and final levels was noted. In fact, per cent improvement tended to be higher for the initially low scorers. Improvement rate was also found unrelated to IQ by Tobias and Gorelick (1960). O'Connor and Tizard (1956, p. 102 ff.) report a number of studies that indicate that motor performance can be greatly affected by situational and motivational factors and, again, that initial ability has little relationship with level achieved with training. For example, trainable retardates who had reached an apparent plateau on a motor performance task improved by over 300 per cent during a period of eleven weeks during which incentive schemes and work conditions were manipulated. At the end of the eleven weeks, this group (IQ 28 to 41) performed faster than a mildly retarded one with an average IQ of 71 (Loos and Tizard, 1955). O'Connor (1957) relates how some retardates in an institutional workshop achieved a level of output of about 50 per cent of normal, staying at this apparently maximal level for months. Yet, after factory placement, they might achieve a 100 per cent output within a few days. A team of six "typical imbeciles" with a mean IQ of 33 worked together for years eventually producing 30,000 to 40,000 cardboard boxes each week (Clarke and Hermelin, 1955). Even after 42 one-hour trials, the majority of a group of trainable retardates were still improving on a simple repetitive manual task (Gordon, O'Connor, and Tizard, 1955). On a test of spatial relations and visual-motor co-ordination, a month after the conclusion of a series of 32 spaced practice trials, a group of "imbeciles" performed at an average equivalent to the 37th percentile of normal adults (Tizard and Loos, 1954). Significantly, the first few practice trials brought about the most rapid improvements, raising grave doubts as to the validity of one-shot tests of retardates' visual-motor abilities. Tobias (1964) feels that those evaluative techniques that assess initial performance are not very appropriate for retardates. In occupations in which retardates can hope to find employment, ultimate efficiency is often a more significant factor than initial performance or speed of acquisition.

Although the experimental evidence is not unanimous (e.g., Tobias and Gorelick, 1963), the status of our knowledge of certain aspects of retardates' industrial performances can be summarized, to echo Clarke and Hermelin (1955), as follows:

1. The initial ability of retardates on industrial tasks tends to be low, and, at times, exceedingly low.

2. Initial ability is not a good predictor of final ability.

3. The main distinction between the performance of normals and retardates on simple tasks is not so much the end-level as the time and the conditions needed to achieve it (see also President's Panel, 1964, p. 6).

The importance of academic skills for job success is not clear, and a number of studies have even found inverse relationships (Kolstoe, 1961). However, this may be the result of confounding of variables because of selection. For example, the high achievers in a training program may be the behavior problems. Common sense would appear to indicate that when other things are equal, the ability to read, write, and do simple arithmetic could not possibly be a drawback. To the contrary, lack of these skills is almost certain to be frustrating, and at the very least a limiting factor to employment level and income. Young (1958) analyzed 118 types of jobs held by retardates, and found that some academic skills were required by most of them. On the other hand, Dubrow (1962) and Tobias (1964) state that "illiteracy is not an insuperable handicap to employment," although Tobias found this to be truer for male than female retardates. Dinger (1961) found that 33 per cent of jobs held by retardates required no reading, the rest requiring only some word recognition or very simple word-combination-type reading. Failure of some studies to find a relationship between reading and employment success may be because no standardized achievement test currently in use adequately measures what might be called social or vocational reading vocabulary.

Guralnick (1964) found arithmetic skill to be more important than reading in job prediction. Dinger also found that arithmetic was required on more jobs held by retardates than was reading. A study of the extent to which arithmetic skills correlate with telling time, management of time problems, and punctuality would be interesting.

Since interest tests have proven the only or most significant predictors of success in a number of vocational endeavors pursued by normals, the hope has sometimes been expressed that similar success might be achieved with the retarded if only a suitable interest test for them would be developed. Indeed, research on such instruments is now underway (e.g., Burg and Barrett, 1965; Parnicky, Kahn, and Burdett, 1965). However, preliminary findings suggest that the relevant interests of retardates are easily affected by experience. If that should be the case, training should probably aim at shaping interest, rather than be based upon it.

Although the intelligence test has been one of the mainstays of the vocational evaluation, it has been one of the least predictive. The IQ group between about 55 to 85 tends to be more successful than the 25 to 55 group, but even here the evidence is not conclusive. Gunzburg (National Society for Mentally Handicapped Children, 1963) mentions one study in which a 35-to-49 group had an employment rate as good as a borderline group. Within broad IQ groupings, intelligence tests have not tended to be useful. Some of the studies that did find intelligence differences between success and failure groups have probably been affected by chance factors, and numerous others have suffered design shortcomings. As Windle (1962) has pointed out, the personnel in retardation may be so much impressed by IQ scores and similar variables that one can predict *their* decision (e.g., decision to release, place, train, or terminate), but that prediction of the retardate's later behavior and performance is not, as yet, possible.

One of the reasons why intelligence tests have failed to predict may be that the types of learning and of intelligence are so varied, and that some types of intelligenec are more predictive of some types of learning than others. Whereas the intelligence tests ordinarily used have been global or verbal in nature, many types of learning required of the retarded have been narrow, specific, and nonverbal. It is also conceivable that intelligence becomes less predictive as more training can be offered, consistent with the findings that, on simple tasks, individuals at the higher intelligence levels may start higher or learn faster, but that those on the lower levels learn longer and may eventually catch up.

One of the many types of learning seems to be more unitary and does not seem to differentiate between groups of normals and re-tardates. This is the type of learning acquired through classical conditioning. A provocative study was conducted by Franks and Franks (1962), who reasoned that those retardates who condition fastest are the ones who can profit most from experience and who there-fore learn to get along on community place-ments. Consistent with this hypothesis, suc-cessful community workers conditioned and extinguished fastest. An institutional work group performed second best, and an institu-tional group with chronic work adjustment problems did worst. All groups were approxi-mately equal in regard to age, IQ, and other characteristics. These results, derived from a relatively well controlled study, deserve close attention.

Disenchantment with intelligence tests and other nonpredictive measures was probably one of the reasons why work sample observa-tions came into vogue. Basically, the idea was commendable. The rationale was that the trainee would engage over a longer period in a series of test tasks that would be rather spe-cific and that would be similar to industrial tasks. Thus, relative ability on different tasks should be disclosed and prediction improved. But, as DiMichael (1963) has pointed out, of hundreds of work samples devised, only few were studied scientifically, and little of value has emerged.

A number of behavioral characteristics of retardates, as well as practical considerations, have combined to render the technique rather doubtful. For example, it is time-consuming. In some workshops, trainees spend up to three months on work sample tasks. Usually, per-haps a week is spent on one sample. Further-more, work sampling can deaden motivation. Ordinarily, the work is contrived and no pay is given, both facts not being conducive to optimum performance in retardates. Some of the samples measure things that should be taught for a long period before being evalu-ated. Thus, a sample may involve use of pliers and screwdrivers in combination—an utterly novel skill for many trainees. By constantly shifting trainees from task to task, as is usu-ally done, the trainee may not stay long enough on one activity to reach an asymptote of performance. This then deprives him of the opportunity to experience success, and may do so week after week. Also, as has been empha-sized repeatedly by the British studies, often it is the rate of improvement and not the ulti-mate performance that differentiates normals from retardates.

Ladas (1961) found a significant correla-tion between work sample learning and later production rate, but concluded that the rela-tionship was still too low to be useful. Tobias (1964) also found that his work sample evaluation was a fairly good predictor of work-shop productiveness, but apparently did not extend his prediction to independent employ-ment. Patterson (1964) even goes as far as to say that current preoccupation with work samples is something of a fad unsupported by evidence. Work sampling, he asserts, is viewed as if it were a criterion itself and not in need of validation.

If work sampling takes so much time, in-volves contrived tasks, and is, at best, only marginally predictive, the question can be raised whether it may not be more economical to commence training without evaluation, as is done very effectively in the outstanding Middlesex program in England (Wolfensberger and Tizard, 1964). The supervisors in that program repeatedly told me that nothing pre-dicted work like work itself and that they never dared to predict later performance from earlier behavior because of a number of spec-tacularly wrong attempts at such prediction. In a conference sponsored by OVR, SMU, and NARC (1961, p. 71) even 50 practice sessions on a work sample failed to produce a per-formance asymptote, and reduced evaluation and increased training were recommended.

Windle's (1962) study constituted a monu-mental review of the work regarding long-term adjustment and success of previously institutionalized retardates. He concluded that the vast majority of these studies suffered from serious methodological flaws. "Integration of these imperfect studies has revealed the con-flicts due to unreliability and specificity. . . . The most that can be accepted from the previous literature is a number of suggestions, best estimates, and reasonable hypotheses" (Windle, 1962, p. 133, 134). Virtually the same could be said about similar studies with community retardates.

The practice of basing vocational training and placement policies on unvalidated evalua-tion procedures is very costly. For example, I know of one instance in which an expenditure of $15,000 and six months' time was planned for obtaining testing and work sample evaluation from agencies that only occasionally were involved with retardates, all in order to screen 100 potential trainees for a workshop. This was in an area where candidates for workshops abounded, and where most of them had already been through a series of diagnostic services and processes. In its survey of retardates habilitated between 1958 and 1963, the U.S. Department of Health, Education, and Welfare (1964b) found that the average diagnostic expenditure, apparently exclusive of work evaluation, was $88. Interestingly, the comparable cost for nonretarded clients was $41.

Despite the low utility and the high cost of diagnosis and evaluation data, only a few voices have been raised against this practice, and even then only in ambivalent and self-contradictory fashion. For example, Dubrow (1961) describes an expensive and demanding seven-week evaluation including work sampling, testing, and history compilation, and then adds: "Although we still lack the skill to predict outcomes from the Evaluation experience except for a small number of cases, we do utilize this procedure to identify trainees' problems, to establish interim goals, and to outline a training program designed to overcome their particular deficiencies." Klebanoff (1961) cites an example where lengthy, formal, and structured evaluation was felt important in order to influence staff attitudes and biases—a curious reason, but at least a legitimate one. Gunzburg (1964a) suggests that once a person has been diagnosed as a retardate, it may be best to forget about his specific IQ and MA. He (1963b) pretty well summarizes the state of the science: "By and large, the full scope of a subnormal's work ability can only be gauged by a sensitive trial-and-error approach in the actual work situation."

DiMichael (1960) refers to the process of first collecting and tabulating IQs, and then pointing out their uselessness, as "the schizophrenia of the IQ." This schizophrenia is strikingly exemplified, to cite only one instance, throughout the Goodwill Industries' (1961) conference report on work evaluation and employment preparation for retarded adults. The report abounds with statements to the effect that intelligence scores are not very

useful but that they are, nevertheless, very important, and must be obtained.

The vast expenditure that goes into evaluation of the retardate for training or placement purposes seems to be justified only under three circumstances:

1. If the agency is willing to collect and record these data: (a) according to some rationale; (b) in a way that renders them amenable to research; and (c) in an operation that is conducted so that meaningful questions can be answered by analyzing such data. Scores and figures alone are utterly useless if the operation does not permit them to be cast into a meaningful design.

2. If it has already been established by previous research that under local conditions certain predictors seem to work. Even then, the predictors should be used within the framework of a researchable design as above in order to cross-valdiate the findings.

3. If prediction has been clearly cross-validated.

Even after conditions two and three are fulfilled, administrators should ask themselves further whether the cost of prediction is justifiable, both financially and in terms of human values. A predictor may be significant statistically, but a slight percentage increase in predictiveness over base rate may not be worth the expense involved, nor the cost of misery engendered in the "false negative" and his family.

SOME POSSIBILITIES FOR FURTHER RESEARCH

Considering that the task of a vocational preparation program is to teach and improve skills, one wonders why scores particularly subject to modification, such as motor test scores, are seized upon so eagerly as predictors. If such scores are used at all, it would appear much more logical to attempt to use improvement rate or level attained after a specified amount of training under good incentive conditions, instead of initial level as usually measured, or improvement rate in the absence of incentives. Conceivably, the work sample procedure may become a very promising tool, if only it would take into account the findings of experimental work to date. In order to be predictively effective, work sample performance, instead of being divorced from the potentially substantial incentives offered on the work floor, should be intimately and strongly tied to a highly meaningful reward system, probably primarily money. Also, using fewer samples and exploring the upper limit of performance on at least one task may be more fruitful than chasing clients from one work sample to another.

Psychological testing is costly whereas social, background, and observational data can usually be obtained more easily by extensive questionnaires answered by the family or by observation ratings in the workshop. While such data have been used in the search for predictors, much more could be done here. Thus, previous behavior (Windle, 1962) and emotional stability (O'Connor and Tizard, 1956) could be very significant. Certain types of delinquent behavior, arson, and unaccepted sexual habits may prove highly discriminating, at least as long-range community success is concerned.[3] Studies that emphasize public behavior rather than inferred personality traits are more successful. For example, behavior in school seemed to be a significant variable in predicting later employment outcome (Guralnick, 1964; Voelker, 1963). Data on previous work history, both in and out of the home, can be collected relatively easily and may prove very useful (Kolstoe, 1961b). Other variables that have looked promising in past studies (Kolstoe, 1961a; Phelps, 1956; Shafter, 1957; Warren, 1961 [4]) are those that reflect the old-fashioned personal-social virtues that can be publicly observed, such as obedience, grooming, punctuality, conformity with safety rules, completion of assigned tasks, etc. Conceivably, some of the less clearly defined items might be anchored to more specific observable behavior, thereby increasing their reliability. This behavior could be rated by supervisors who are working with the trainee, thus taking little time. A recently developed employability scale for handicapped persons (Gellman, Stern and Soloff, 1963) may hold

3. Many studies have used contrast groups in which the success criterion was an extremely generous one (e.g., one month of employment), not very consonant with a common-sense view of vocational success.

4. Warren's study suffers from a very common selection flaw. His success group not only contained *bona fide* placements, but also those Ss still in training who were believed to be future successes. As so often in this type of research, outcome and selection were thus confounded.

some promise because it incorporates a wide range of socio-historical background, although many of the items could be further anchored. Linde (1964) has devised a rating scale that assigns weights to attendance, perseverance, productivity, quality of work, grooming, generalization of work habits, and trainee's relationship to supervisor and co-workers. This scale correlated .75 with employment, using job-holding for 31 days as the criterion.

Whereas various handicaps *per se* (aside from general poor health) have usually not been found to have significant effects on employability, multiple handicaps may very well result in a multiplicative rather than additive decrease in success. Besides chronic health problems, such handicaps would most likely include speech impediments, seizures, and sensory, motor, and aesthetic defects. While Guralnick (1956) analyzed for the effects of multiple handicaps in rehabilitation outcome of retardates in New York City, the before-mentioned confounding of outcome and feasibility criteria precludes a meaningful interpretation of the results. However, later Guralnick (1964) reported a highly significant relationship between secondary disability and employment outcome. Kolstoe (1961a) found that handicaps affecting co-ordination were significant, and Saenger (1957) reported less employment among multiple-handicapped retardates. Other recently published data (HEW, 1964b) indicate that the cost of rehabilitating retardates increases sharply when associated disabilities such as blindness or heart disease are present. This may well reflect the difficulty of placing such clients. Pinkard, Gilmore, Ricker, and Williams (1963) investigated the problem, but their data is only suggestive because they used handicap labels such as "CP," "mongolism," "intracranial pathology," etc., which do not reveal anything about the public deficit associated with them. The studies of some of these aspects in regard to institutional release (Windle, 1962) are not very relevant to employability of community retardates. One problem would be faced in devising an adequate quantification of handicaps and their combinations.

Very little evidence is available regarding the importance of appearance and aesthetic handicaps, and the few studies that are available do not always make this distinction. Warren (1961) and Kolstoe (1961a; 1961b) have found appearance to be important, Kolstoe concluding that the appearance of a handicap (e.g., a hearing aid) can be more detrimental than the handicap itself. Saenger (1957) found that appearance was more important than ability for getting a job, and he implied that more mongoloids could have found employment had they not been stigmatized by their relatively conspicuous features. This problem deserves considerably more attention.

The majority of retardates apparently integrate into the labor market with little or no assistance by public agencies. A study of the characteristics of this group might be fruitful, comparing them with those retardates who need further vocational training, and with those who, even after such training, find only sheltered employment if any (Tobias, in Training School, 1962; also President's Panel, 1964).

The problem of controls has been one of the most vexing ones in vocational prediction research. One way to overcome this would be for a number of shops or programs to enter into a joint experimental endeavor wherein all participants would adopt a design that keeps most relevant variables constant while manipulating only one or a small number. Since uniformity of local conditions and procedures would be very difficult to attain, this could probably only be done effectively in an area-wide metropolitan program that has administrative control over several shops. To date, this condition does probably not exist in the United States, but it does in the English program described by Wolfensberger and Tizard (1964). However, as program planning is proceeding apace, such an opportunity may present itself in the future. Not only predictor variables, but staff patterning, training, administration, scheduling, and many other issues of interest could be studied in this fashion.

Virtually no work has been done on trainer or counselor attitudes and their effect upon placement. For example, counselors with contrasting views on retardation and retardates' job success potentials could be assigned equated groups of counselees. We take too much for granted that rehabilitation skills or experience, rather than attitudes, are important in this work.

More work is needed to identify the type of job that, in the long run, may be held more successfully by a person of retarded rather than normal intelligence.

As mentioned previously, almost no work has been done regarding placement variables, and such factors are much in need of study. Also, job analysis in relation to a factorial approach to ability assessment may be fruitful. Tobias (1964) suggests that retardates may fall into certain factor types of intelligence presently inadequately assessed by Wechsler and similar scales. Persons strong in certain factors might be more suited for some types of employment than others. Some of his findings indicate that strong perceptual organization ability is required for many types of factory employment, while a verbal comprehension factor is closely related to success in messenger work.

THE TRAINING MILIEU

As long ago as 1952, Tizard and O'Connor formulated six criticisms of traditional training methods in retardation: (1) training more likely to promote occupation instead of employment; (2) too little relationship between the work done in the training situation and that done on those jobs likely to be obtained in the community; (3) too little or obsolete machinery in workshops and not enough emphasis on the tempo of production; (4) not enough contact with commercial firms; (5) not enough use of incentive schemes; and (6) too little supervision of placements.

In 1958, Gunzburg repeated the same points, adding a seventh: too little emphasis on selection and training of supervisors. And yet today, in this country, even some of our best programs are still subject to the same criticisms. Indeed, one sometimes can become discouraged observing the inertness of the field.

One basic principle for a vocational program in retardation is that it must be primarily educational in the wider sense, and not therapeutic in nature. Sometimes training or supervisory personnel come into the field with a psychiatric or mental health orientation, and they may need some time before they appreciate, and can adopt, a different approach. In the meantime, much harm can be done in mismanaging trainees. Behavior usually considered therapeutic in other settings or with other groups can be maladaptive in work training. On the other hand, many therapeutic benefits flow naturally from educative measures, such as changes in self-concept as a result of increased skill with tools.

In order to do their educational job, supervisors must know their business. This sounds self-evident but nevertheless needs emphasis, because sometimes supervisors seem to think that they only need to know more than the trainees. However, more is not enough. Supervisors need to be well versed in industrial methods, procedures, materials, and tools. In addition, every program should have at the very least one and preferably several persons intimately familiar with local economic, industrial, and market conditions. These qualifications are probably better met by individuals with an industrial rather than a mental health or even a rehabilitation background.[5] Some workshop managers "cannot adapt to the environment in which they are working. They try to operate a workshop as if it were an occupational therapy center, social casework agency, an individual or group psychotherapy program, a vocational guidance agency, a school, or whatever they worked in before they came to the workshop" (Nelson, 1965).

I have visited numerous retardation programs of various types in the United States and several European countries (Wolfensberger, 1964a, 1964b, 1965; Wolfensberger and Tizard, 1964), and formed the strong impression during these visits that good retardation programming requires not only technical know-how, but also a strong commitment by the workers to the cause of retardation (Kruger, 1963, p. 172). Except perhaps in the case of programs for the educable, I have never seen an effective and efficient retardation service that was not headed and staffed by individuals who were enthusiastic about their work and who had strong faith in the growth potential of the retardate. Vocational programs should be headed by such people. While programs permeated by doubt, indifference, or pessimism rarely appear to be successful, programs manned by enthusiastic, dedicated staff seem much less likely to fail. An example of how adversity can be over-

come by strong commitment has been described (Wolfensberger, 1964b; Sykes, 1965).

Another principle is that the training setting should simulate—as much as feasible—conditions typically encountered in industry. This can be done in innumerable ways such as use of time clock and numbered time cards, mode of payment, of eating lunch, etc. However, to put this principle into practice requires constant vigilance. For example, air-conditioned workshops are no longer uncommon. If the trainee is later likely to work in a setting that is not air-conditioned or outdoors, is it appropriate to train him in and for comfort?

A common violation of the "simulation principle" is a part-time operation. Too many shops start the day late, close early, or otherwise work on a short schedule. Surprisingly, the rationale may not be lack of funds but the argument that the trainees are too distractable, poorly motivated, or "something-or-other" to work 40 hours a week.

Workshops run a risk in basing training on a 9 A.M.-to-3:30-P.M. day and assuming that the trainee can easily transfer to a 8 A.M.-to-5 P.M. schedule in that he may not be properly prepared for rush-hour commuting, different sleeping and eating schedules, etc., in addition to the sudden change in stamina required after job placement. O'Connor (1957, p. 469) has reported an illustrative and, unfortunately, not atypical example. Boys who had received workshop training were placed on a construction job where the hours were long and considerable physical stamina was required. In the first month, 20 of the 60 placements failed, most of them because of the sudden increase in work hours and demands for which the workshop had not adequately prepared them. While numerous studies have found undesirable habits and social actions to be the main causes of job failures, such unacceptable behavior may very likely be triggered by physical and emotional fatigue associated with exposure to unaccustomed demands and hours. Both Kolstoe (1961a, 1961b) and Cohen (1960) found that lack of physical strength may be a factor contributing to failure.

Some programs close down in inclement weather when travel is difficult, thus following school practice. Program directors should ask themselves whether business and industry close on these days. Humane and school-like as such practices may appear, will they prepare

---

5. Material relevant to the personnel problem of training and workshop programs can be found in Ferguson (1959), Jacobs and Weingold (1958), President's Panel (1963c), Wolfensberger and Tizard (1964), and the interesting "Scott," or Ministry of Health (1962), report from England.

the trainee for the day he must brave the weather or lose his job?

A recent NARC (1964) directory of sheltered workshops servicing the retarded lists 231 shops that submitted information regarding their operation. Of these, 228 give information about their schedules. Only 43 shops work a full day or longer, and of these, 36 are not primarily retardation shops. Most of them are Goodwill centers. Modal operation (45 shops) is six hours per day, *including lunch break!* Of these 45 shops, 20 do not work a full week or a full year. Generally, the shorter the work day, the shorter is also the work year. Of the 29 shops operating less than six hours per day, seventeen do not operate a full week or year. Of the 43 that operate for at least eight hours, only two do not work a full year. A nationwide NARC (1959) survey of 56 shops primarily for the retarded found that few operated an eight-hour day; a large number emphasized recreation, social activities, and arts and crafts; only slightly more than half of them engaged in light industrial work; and less than a third engaged in placement of their graduates.

Another violation of the "simulation principle" is a poorly rationalized emphasis on recreational activities. Such activities have a place in the training of retardates, but if offered within the context of a vocational program, they should be carefully structured and based on sound rationales. Recreation, in this context, should not be primarily for "fun" but for learning. It should be a medium for socialization, self-concept formation, and development of constructive leisure-time utilization. Since associations to recreational activities may interfere with those to be developed to the work and training situation, distinction between recreational and other training activities appears highly desirable. This can be accomplished by holding recreational activities at night (Dybwad, 1961, 1964), by holding them at a different locality, or by having different personnel conduct them (Walshe, 1964). In the latter case, workshops may find volunteers or youth groups willing to organize recreation programs. If none of these are feasible, recreation periods may be temporally set off to some degree by scheduling them first thing in the morning, or last thing in the afternoon. Also, they could be gradually phased out, from heavier emphasis

in early stages of training to elimination during the latter. The question of whether retardates on their own will use the recreational skills they acquire in such training is by no means settled. Thus, Peterson and Smith (1960) found in a follow-up study that former educable students tend to make little use of recreational facilities and activities available in the community.

Personal adjustment training (PAT) is important, but can also be distorted. PAT activities should be concentrated during the initial training phase, and later should be conducted mostly informally and "on the floor," (i.e., as part of the work supervision instead of in distinct groupings).

Overemphasis on social and recreational activities is often rationalized as consistent with findings that retardates' job failures are more likely to result from personal-social than industrial shortcomings. Such findings, however, do not imply that training should have no industrial substance. As competition for unskilled and semiskilled jobs increases, stamina, energy and simple skills such as hand-tool facility will become even more important than before. Peckham (1951) showed that even when retardates fail for reasons that can be later classified as social, such social failures may, nevertheless, be secondary to antecedent failure in non-social achievement such as commuting, telling time, etc. The basic point emphasized here is not that social and non-industrial activities are unimportant, but that the trainee should also have become hardened before placement by exposure to workaday demands and to substantial periods of sustained work, uncontaminated by activities that would not also be encountered in industry. He should have come to know what an industrial atmosphere is like, what he can expect, and what constitutes inappropriate behavior in a job situation.

Training that is too specific and too oriented to one trade or occupation is widely believed to be no longer appropriate for retarded persons for two reasons. Firstly, narrow specialty training resulting in a saleable skill is too demanding for most retardates. Secondly, in today's rapidly changing world, a specific skill can quickly become obsolescent. Already, many of the traditional handcrafts are in little demand. Nevertheless, one occasionally still encounters programs of training in tailoring, upholstery, barbering and shoe repair, even though non-retarded and skilled shoe repairman have difficulty making a living, and barbering often requires a high school diploma. Boys who are lucky to get jobs on the gas pump or washing cars are trained as mechanics. Printing is popular even in the best workshops—usually because of gifts of obsolete presses no longer used in industry. By nearly every criterion, printers' training for retardates is unrealistic. It begins with a none-too-literate trainee, requires a high teacher-learner ratio for a long period, and generally produces a not-too-skilled operator who is unlikely to find employment, especially if he was, as is very likely, trained on obsolete equipment. One of the most highly acclaimed workshops in the country runs a big farm operation and gives training in printing. Even though these activities take up a significant portion of the training effort, only 8 per cent of their recent placements were in horticulture, 3 per cent in farming, and none in graphic arts.

At the other extreme, training is occasionally stripped of relevant content (e.g., Rothberg, Cicenia, and Bogatz, 1965), perhaps on the ground that specific training has been shown to be inappropriate. Some such programs may even have a strong occupational therapy flavor (e.g., needle and leather work, weaving, woodcarving, etc.). Ceramics may be taught, even though a retardate is extremely unlikely to earn his living with ceramics, or even use it as a hobby. In a modern habilitational or industrial workshop, there is no place for such "old-fashioned despised basket-rug-mat-making of the Colony days" (Gunzburg, in National Society for Mentally Handicapped Children, 1963). This sort of training makes about as much sense today as preparing retardates to be armor polishers, moat cleaners, or court jesters.

Workshop overspecialization, which may result when work revolves around one contract or one contractor, should be avoided. It could lead to a restriction of training opportunity, or even sudden financial disaster (e.g., Blue, 1964). Walshe (1964) and Gunzburg (1963b) have pointed out that as desirable as light industrial contract work is, it can be overemphasized once its profitability is recognized and exploited. While not many of our workshops have developed far enough to have to worry about that danger, the need to develop the physical strength and endurance of the retardate must be recognized and met. Pre- or post-work calisthenics may be desirable for training purposes. Also, a variety of jobs requiring hand tools are desirable as facility with hand tools has been found to be useful in a number of studies (e.g., Kolstoe, 1961a, 1961b). For girls, experience in practical garment mending is important. The advantages and disadvantages of manufacturing, salvaging, and contracting work have been tabulated and compared by Jacobs and Weingold (1958, pp. 70–71).

Habilitation is not a passive process and requires the intense participation of the trainee. Candidates often come with poor motivation and high expectancy for failure. Therefore, instructors should pay great attention to the construction of a flexible incentive and reward scheme (IRS). The following points warrant consideration:

1. Needs vary, and so should incentives. A repertoire of incentives should be devised to satisfy monetary needs as well as those for prestige, power, social recognition, and approval from the family. Interesting IRSs are described by Gunzburg (1958), Linde (1962), and others. Dubrow (1961), for example, relates how successful termination from a program can be associated with a number of rewards. Thus, the trainees' graduation can be celebrated at a party at which he is lionized, and he can become eligible for an alumni club. Gordon, O'Connor and Tizard (1955) found that of four incentive conditions, self-competition (where trainees try to better their own previous performance) resulted in the greatest improvement.

2. To whet the appetite of the trainees, a minimal token payment should be provided for mere attendance alone. This can serve to establish positive association to the training situation.

3. Except for the base pay for attendance, the IRS should be tied intimately to performance and to feedback. The monthly rating commonly encountered is not sufficient as retardates will then not ordinarily associate the reinforcement with the relevant behavior. Consistent with learning principles, reward and punishment or nonreward should be clearly associated with the relevant behavior. Some IRSs can be activated daily and even several times during the day. Monetary rewards should

be paid out weekly and tied to an evaluation *for that week* if at all possible, not the one previous. One way to accomplish this would be to operate on a Friday through Thursday "fiscal week." The weekly evaluation should be based on ratings of the various supervisors, integrated by one person, and *interpreted to the trainee.* Basing pay on two major and completely separately considered evaluation areas seems highly desirable (i.e., 50 per cent of the pay might be determined by work performance, the other 50 per cent by conduct and attitude).

Rating scales to evaluate retardates' work behavior abound, but little has been done to evaluate their reliability and validity. Most of these scales are probably best used as indicators of change with the same rater reporting (Gunzburg, 1963a), rather than as measures of an absolute level. Some scales that may be useful in initial assessment, assessment of change, promotion or placement decision, and follow-up ratings are found in Doll (1953, pp. 30–33), Gunzburg (1958, p. 343, 1963a, 1964b), Jacobs and Weingold (1958, pp. 52–55), Kennedy (1948, p. 111), Kokaska (1964), Kolstoe (1961a), Michal-Smith (1951), Pinkard, Gilmore, Ricker, and Williams (1963, pp. 20–22, 49–52) and Warren (1961). In using or adapting these scales, one should keep in mind that those items based on observable behavior acts will probably prove to be the most reliable. Probably more evaluaators will agree on "others in the same work ask to work with him," than on "gets along well with others." A good example of a rating scale closely tied to observable and quantifiable behavior, and usable in PAT, is the Willmar Rating Scale for Shaving (Mertens and Fuller, 1963). The Vineland Social Maturity Scale is sometimes used to evaluate PAT, but the customary comparisons of SQ changes over time without conversion to standard score equivalents are invalid (Wolfensberger, 1962).

The application of learning principles to workshop practice constitutes a fertile field for research. The use of verbal urging and praise, new ways to encourage competition or work toward goals, the translation of external rewards into internal ones, and many other possibilities need to be studied. Even a modest number of industrial psychologists could make a major contribution if their skills could be brought to bear upon this problem. Thus,

Carter and Margolin (1964) point out that the management of the retarded is a vital industry and that the talent of industrial psychologists long employed to increase the efficiency of other industrial operations should now begin to be applied to the habilitation of the retarded as well.

QUASI-ACADEMIC EDUCATION

As indicated before, the relation between retardates' academic skills and their job success is not clear. However, it stands to reason that academic skills increase adequacy and reduce frustration, rather than vice versa. Also, many academic programs may not have emphasized those academic skills most useful on the job (e.g. Neuhaus, 1965; Rothberg, Cicenia, and Bogatz, 1965).

Even individuals who cannot read sequentially can be taught word recognition, and, whether an instructor prefers to teach by phonics or by sight, he should help such individuals to recognize certain basic words on sight. A number of lists of such basic words have been compiled; programs for the retarded might well teach a selection of them. Ideally, this should be done in the schools, but any time may be better than not at all. Dolch (1936) gives a list of 220 words considered basic for children in general. Borreca, Burger, Goldstein, and Simches (1953) offer a functional core vocabulary more specifically for retardates, plus some references to other general lists. Goldstein and Mann (1949) and Young (1958) provide occupational vocabularies for retardates, both lists categorizing words by job area (e.g., food preparation, laundry and cleaning work, etc.). Gunzburg (1960) gives a "social sight vocabulary" with many industrial words, but some British terms need to be stricken from the list for use in the United States. Mastery of such basic sight and vocational vocabulary may well be as important as a reading achievement score on a standardized achievement test.

Even the severely retarded can acquire some reading skills. However, O'Connor and Hermelin (1963) have demonstrated that reading skill depends significantly upon spoken vocabulary. Words with a high frequency of occurrence in the retardate's speech are learned faster than rarely used words. Consequently, if vocational vocabulary is first introduced into the spoken language of trainees, they should later have less difficulty in learning to read them.

Borreca, Burger, Goldstein, Mann, Simches, and Simches (1950) present some lessons, exercises, and problems that appear of value in an academic program stressing vocational preparation. Sniff (1962) presents a complete and very good curriculum for young retarded adults, listing many films and other resources. The curriculum is entirely centered around practical units, experiences, and needs, and could become a major resource for teaching personnel in both schools and workshops. The "Guide to Jobs for the Mentally Retarded" by Peterson and Jones (1964) contains descriptions of job requirements on three levels of specificity. The outline of the requirements on the more general levels could also serve as a curriculum and training guide. Similar material is presented in a syllabus of occupational information for mildly retarded students (Barnum, 1965). DiMichael (1964) suggests a four-track approach to the vocational training of retardates, at least three of these tracks to be provided by the schools. If a school cannot provide all tracks, different units could be built corresponding to the difficulty levels of each. Other curriculum and program ideas are described by Moore (Goodwill Industries, 1961, pp. 19–34), Deno, Henze, Krantz, and Barklind (1965), and Kolstoe and Frey (1965).

Since poor hygiene, habits, or attitudes in the area of sex can lead very quickly to job or community failure (e.g., Saenger, 1960), education on these problems is greatly needed by the retarded. Instead, this problem is commonly ignored even by such excellent and practical texts as Sniff (1962). Typically, if the topic is broached at all, crucial teaching areas are simply not covered. The most useful reference that I could find was by Selznick (1962), and training personnel may find it worthwhile. Close liaison with other services, parents, and the churches is particularly important in seeing to it that adequate, proper, and effective education is given.

One of the obstacles faced by schools is the unfeasibility (Deno, 1960) of setting up training situations simulating industrial work conditions. School systems may be severely hampered by legal restrictions on activities of a nature readily engaged in by nongovern-

metal workshops, such as buying and selling. A possible way to circumvent such restrictions would be for school systems to contract for training with workshops, similar to a work-study program. This could also have the advantage of providing PAT and other training at the school while removing all nonwork connotations and associations from the workshop. situation. One Midwestern school system provides a sequence of social-educational instruction, sheltered work experience, on-the-job training, and placement and follow-up. Since the operation of a sheltered workshop would have been too costly for the school, the students are sent to an already existing workshop on a half-day basis, and tuition is paid to the shop by the school district. This work experience begins early, in the first year of a four-year high school program, and is replaced by part-time, on-the-job training in the second and third year. In the fourth year the student works full-time, but continues to receive supervision and assistance from the school's special education staff.

OTHER ISSUES

In training as in evaluation, the practice of rotating work assignments is common and has several advantages in: (1) providing trainees with a range of experiences that may be beneficial to them in later work situations, (2) inducing an attitude of receptiveness toward the kind of changes and shifts they may be asked to undergo at work, and (3) giving the trainer an opportunity to observe behavior under a variety of realistic conditions, basing further training and placement decisions on this observation. However, frequent shifts may fail to permit retardates the long learning periods necessary to achieve high output in some areas, thus depriving them of an important or even crucial success experience and giving an insufficient picture of what they can do. Relationships with supervisors, which can be important media for learning, may be disrupted by constantly moving trainees about. The practice of automatically shifting trainees after predetermined intervals must therefore be questioned.

Another practice is the exclusion of trainees from a program after an adminstratively set period of training. Dybwad (1961, 1964) criticizes this practice, pointing out that "the thrifty and efficient Dutch think nothing of having the training of the mentally retarded in the workshop (we are not talking here about school) extend to four and even six years. Compare this with our own impatience, our tendency to stampede the failures after a far too short training and trial period." Some workshops will exclude trainees after as little as eight to nine months. While this practice may be efficient in increasing turnover and habilitating the largest number of trainees in the shortest time, it should not persist as more training programs are established. Individuals may enter training with a short lifetime of maladaptive behavior behind them, and nine months is not long enough to change such strongly established patterns. Indeed, some retardates who have not received the appropriate antecedent management may never be habilitated, much as even some normals remain inadequate for life. However, some retardates, especially when parallel services such as parent counseling are available, may overcome poor habits of even long standing with extended training lasting for several years.

Counseling is usually viewed as part of the vocational training process. With retardates, such counseling often is, and probably should be, tied in with concrete occurrences and problems. Goldstein and Heber (HEW, 1961) stress the importance of taking advantage of incidental opportunities that deal with a variety of personal, social, academic, or vocational problems. Such informal counseling, often being tied to specific problems and situations, may be more effective than the more formal counseling often conducted with nonretarded clients.

In concluding the discussion of the training milieu, perhaps the most important principle to remember is that programs for the vocational preparation of the retarded should make maximal use of available and relevant research data (Goldstein and Heber, in HEW, 1961).

WORKSHOP OPERATION

A list of recommended readings on workshops for the retarded might include: Cohen (1961), Ferguson (1959), Fraenkel (1962), Jacobs and Weingold (1958), Massie (1961), NARC (1959), Nelson (1964), Pense (1960, 1961), Speijer (1959), Walshe (1964), Weingold (1961), and Wolfensberger and Tizard (1964).

WORKSHOP TYPES

One can conceive of three broad types of workshops, namely (1) the "habilitational workshop" for the preparation of trainees for ultimate employment on the open labor market, (2) the "terminal workshop" for sheltered employment of retardates who can engage in productive work, but only under protective conditions, and (3) the "occupational workshop," which is, in effect, a day care center for adult retardates, except that many of its clients could be engaged in some adult activity such as light and very simple work for at least part of the day.

Dybwad (1964) suggests that the nontransitional or terminal workshop that offers sheltered employment for an indefinite period should become largely self-supporting by means of subcontracts. On the other hand, the more transitional the workshop, the more subsidy it may require. While distinct types of shops can be operated under one roof, maximum physical separation is desirable (Gunzburg, 1963b), as otherwise standards and management methods may have and will tend to be aimed at the lowest level. In practice, however, only larger programs will be able to achieve the optimal degree of separation. Therefore, in the subsequent discussion, the term "workshop" will usually be employed in a broad and inclusive sense.

Another distinction can be made between single (or single major) disability workshops, and combination- or omnibus-type shops. Sentiment seems to be growing in favor of combining disability types, since the handicapped workers can thus compensate for each other's difficulties and can consequently operate more profitably by diversifying the work (Pennsylvania Department of Public Welfare, 1961, p. 8). However, the more handicap types to be served, the more the staff has to learn and to know. Different handicaps tend to engender different types of more typical emotional reactions and behavior patterns. A greater knowledge of restorative technology would have to be mastered if appreciable numbers of trainees require a wide range of orthopedic devices, hearing aids, microscopic and telescopic lenses, etc. Furthermore, more intensive supervision of drugs may be necessary, since anticonvulsants, tranquilizers, muscle relaxants, energizers, and many other medications may be part of habilitational regimens. Laws regarding various handicaps differ greatly, and for each handicap, there is a different continuum of services with which the personnel should be familiar. The diversity of handicaps may thus become more of a hindrance than a help. Counselors who already have a difficult time mastering one major handicap area may become pedestrian jacks-of-all-trades, and the quality of service may suffer. Finally, the danger exists that, as in the past, "high glamor" handicaps will be given favorite treatment over "low glamor" handicaps such as retardation. To date not enough omnibus shops have included retardates and have studied their own operations adequately to render a judgment on the relative merits of the two types of approaches. Program planners should consider the pros and cons of both types. Rural and small communities that cannot afford specialty shops may see an upsurge in omnibus services and thereby provide natural laboratories.

WORKSHOP PLANNING AND OPERATION

Ground plans for vocational training facilities that may be useful in building design are found in Caswell Rehabilitation Center (1961), Ferguson (1959, Part I), Fraenkel (1962), Jacobs and Weingold (1958), and Joint Committee of the PHS and the VRA (1963). Architectural comments are also found in Goodwill (1961) and Gunzburg (1963b). Fraenkel (1962) compiled guidelines for setting up a workshop, covering: (1) pros and cons of mixed- versus single-handicap shops, (2) organizing steps, (3) location, (4) products and services reportedly turned out by shops, as well as suggestions for some yet untried, (5) basic equipment, (6) building and space requirements, (7) staffing and administrative structure, (8) funding, (9) insurance, and (10) legal requirements. Initial planning considerations are also discussed by Massie (1961) and NARC (1963). Wolfensberger and Tizard (1964) have documented the operation of an area-wide occupation and training center program. Other ideas and guidelines can be found in Dolnick (1963) and Nelson (1964). Information regarding legal aspects of workshop operations is obtainable from the U.S. Department of Labor and includes copies of the Fair Labor Standards Act, interpretive guides to it, and regulations concerning sheltered workshops, subcontracting, employment of handicapped workers, required records, and child labor. State minimum wage laws can also be obtained from the U.S. Department of Labor, as well as from the appropriate state departments. The Advisory Committee on Sheltered Workshops of the Wage and Hour and Public Contracts Division of the department also publishes a concise and useful "Statement of Principles Respecting the Policies, Organization, Operation, and Service Activities of Sheltered Workshops and Homebound Programs." Further important requirements may be learned from the local U.S. Employment Service, and from state and local departments of health, welfare, safety, rehabilitation, labor, industry, building, and taxation. A booklet on standards for sheltered workshops can be purchased for $1 from the National Association of Sheltered Workshops and Homebound Programs.

As Dubrow (1961) has pointed out, "programming for the mentally retarded in sheltered workshops calls for the utmost in creativity of all kinds of personnel." Creativity does not usually flourish in a highly structured and rigid environment, and, for this and other reasons, vocational programs should be structured and run as informally as possible. This does not mean that trainee supervision should be *laissez-faire* (Tizard, 1953), but that emphasis be placed on providing the needed service instead of satisfying paper rules. For example, some centers, even those aimed at lower ability groups, impose so many restrictions on eligibility that a large number of individuals with potential for sheltered employment and great need for such services are excluded. Thus, one center requires the following: CA 21 to 30; IQ 30 to 50; retardation as primary disability; functional psychomotor ability; ability for self-care; potential ability for self-transportation; absence of chronic emotional disturbance or other serious personality defects; absence of severe speech impediment; absence of prosthetic or wheelchair condition; and control of seizures if epileptic. These criteria probably exclude a substantial proportion if not the majority of retardates in that age and IQ range. While some centers would not be able to function

if too many trainees were multiply handicapped, admission should be determined more
by whether the center can render a real service
than by blind application of categoric criteria.
Within a broad definition of retardation, the
question should be asked: does the applicant
need our service, and are we the best or even
only service which can satisfy his need? The
main emphasis should be on the human problem, and not on the administrative process
for its own sake.

Another problem is the danger of prolifera-
tion of rules and regulations, paper work, red
tape, and concern with staff problems. Too
much time can be spent on decision making
via endless staff meetings. Such meetings
should be held to a minimum. A really good
and well-informed director can make many
decisions ordinarily rendered by screening, promotion, and placement conferences, thereby
saving much staff time. Processing schedules
should not be followed only because they exist.
Thus, some centers channel trainees along according to a preconceived scheme, regardless of
demonstrated need. Much paper work can be
eliminated by use of forms for recording (e.g.,
Dolnick, 1963) and correspondence, but form-
filling should be kept to the minimum consistent with adequate record-keeping and
training.

Above all, jealous guarding of privileges,
rivalry, and self-centeredness *vis-à-vis* other
retardation services should be avoided. Relationships with these, as well as with other
exceptionality services, should be flexible, and
the vocational program should be viewed as
a continuity of other programs. If a training
agency becomes too concerned with its boundaries, it is a sign that the staff or administration has become centered on itself instead of
the problem of retardation.

Many services in retardation are enmeshed
in ritualism as regards the administrative processing of their clients. The degree of ritualism
seems to be inversely related to the confidence
and competence of the people rendering the
service. The less the service accomplishment,
the more rigid the insistence upon referral
procedures, diagnostics, admission requirements, staffing, etc. All this is in contrast to
the informality of some highly successful services. Much of this seems to be paralleling
what has happened in mental health, or, for
that matter, in gambling: the more the out-

come seems to be determined by chance or
forces beyond our control or ken, the more
"superstitious" ritualism arises in connection
with efforts to control the outcome.

Broad principles of workshop training of
retardates have innumerable specific implications in practice. This chapter cannot hope
to cover all of these specifics. Some contributions specific to training and trainee management problems are found in Dubrow (1961),
Gunzburg (1960, 1963b), Linde (1962),
Lytle (1963), O'Connor and Tizard (1956),
Tizard (1953), and Yepsen (in DiMichael,
1958).

WORK PROCUREMENT

Workshop programs need to anchor their
operations strongly in the community, and an
excellent discussion on how to get community
support and constructive publicity is presented
by Margolis (1965). Indeed, Niehm (1958),
after a survey of sheltered workshops for the
retarded, concluded that the success of workshop programs seemed to depend in good
degree upon the amount of community interest and support.

Two major community anchors consist in
work procurement on the one hand, and placement procurement and supervision on the
other. The ingenuity and flexibility of the program director is by far a more limiting factor
to work procurement than the retardates' abilities. Repeated demonstrations have shown that,
with proper adaptations and the exercise of
ingenuity, there are few jobs that cannot be
modified so that nearly all handicapped persons can work at them (Dolnick, 1963, p. 51).
If procurement of profitable work is a problem, one person in the program should be
designated to spend a major share or even all
of his time on the problem. He should go out
and observe a wide range of industrial processes, alert to the possibility of developing the
same process in the workshop.

In many instances, a process may not lend
itself to workshop operation directly, but could
be adapted by breakdown of steps or construction of jigs, fixtures, devices, etc. (Wolfensberger, 1964b). Walshe (1964) points out
that some shops have invented such clever
devices as to surpass even factory performance. Also, a work procurer should never be
discouraged by statements of industrial per-

sonnel that an operation cannot be performed by retardates. Such personnel may have only vague ideas what retardates can do, responding more to a stereotype than a reality. The technically skilled work procurer should convince himself personally whether or not the operation can be adapted.

What is, in effect, an excellent text on contract procurement has been written by Dolnick (1963). His monograph should be found in every workshop. He covers such topics as industrial purchasing and contracting practices, contract solicitation, record keeping, pricing, bidding, lucrativeness of contracts, and time study procedures. The results of an instructive survey of contractors' opinions on sheltered workshops are also presented (Dolnick, 1963, 1964). There is thus no point in duplicating this excellent work here. However, I will point out again that trying to save on the "anchoring" positions is a poor practice. A good procurement man will repay his salary many times over. Dolnick found that there seemed to be a relationship between workshop income and having a full-time procurement position. Also, the number of bids that were submitted depended on whether the shop had no, part-time, or full-time procurement man.

A good example of a series of industrial contracts that turned out to be very lucrative and appropriate for lower functioning retardates (mean IQ = 43) is contained in a report by the Occupational Training Center for the Mentally Retarded Young Adults of Rhode Island (1960). With a strong emphasis on industrial contracts, this center had no difficulties finding an abundance of lucrative jobs to perform even within a relatively short time after getting started. Korn (1964) gave examples of two workshops almost identical in all respects and type of client, yet one was able to pay double the wages of the other even though it was located in a less favorable area. Concluding that the higher paying workshop was more efficient and more adept at obtaining good contracts than the other, he pointed out that the difficulties of some workshops cannot always be rationalized as being due to external factors. Other relevant coverage is found in Dubrow (1958), Jacobs and Weingold (1958), and Nelson (1964).

Small workshops may find it advantageous to pool procurement staff. However, in doing so, the precautions described by Dolnick should be observed. The formation of a regional or even national procurement and merchandising organization for retardation workshops has been proposed (Siebring, 1964).

SAFETY

The question of retardates' safety and accident rates keeps coming up in many contexts and is sometimes posed by potential employers possessed by misconceptions regarding workman's compensation insurance rates. First of all, the evidence regarding retardates' accident proneness, while meager, was felt to be encouraging by Tizard and O'Connor (1950b). Phelps (1956) found, in a follow-up study, that 92 per cent of employed retardates were rated as average or superior in their safety habits, while only 6 per cent were rated as careless. Walshe (1964) reported that retardates had the same or lower accident rates than normals. Wolfensberger and Tizard (1964) presented further evidence of good records by industrially occupied retardates, and a study done for DuPont (President's Committee on Employment of the Handicapped, 1962, p. 19) disclosed that handicapped workers, including the retarded, had better safety records than those normals who suffered handicaps after coming to work for DuPont.

HABILITATION IN THE PROGRAMMING CONTINUUM

While a respectable body of publications are concerned with vocational training, little has been written on the programmatic aspects of such services. A service can be said to become programmatic if it (1) aims at satisfying the need for its particular service on an area-wide basis (principles that should guide the planning of area-wide rehabilitation services are stated by the Joint Committee of the Public Health Service and the Vocational Rehabilitation Administration, 1963, pp. 7-12) or (2) if it is administratively integrated with other parallel or contiguous services. With the new emphasis on continuous and comprehensive services, concern with the more narrow aspects of a particular service will have to be supplemented with concern about antecedent, concurrent and subsequent services, integration of those services into a program, and, ultimately, with concern about the problem of mental retardation as a whole. Thus, a program for retardates will be only fractionally efficient if it is not integrated into a broader program of services for the retarded, and perhaps for exceptionality groups in general. A habilitational workshop in retardation, perhaps even more than other services, will be very ineffective if it operates in a vacuum.

On the "input" side, a habilitation program needs antecedents such as educable and trainable classes in public schools, home visiting and truancy services, minimal health provisions, etc. In a proper service continuum, a habilitational program should not be confronted with young adult clients who need training in the use of glasses and hearing aids, who do not know the basics of grooming, who have never had to work, fulfill any demands, or commune acceptably with peers, who cannot obey, who are ignorant of basic conventions of courtesy, etc. However, only too many vocational programs are confronted with exactly this type of youngster (e.g., Cortazzo, 1964), and must direct a major part of their effort to PAT. This not only subtracts from the time that could be spent on establishing or strengthening industrial habits and skills, but also it is sometimes too late to reshape these youngsters. Personal habits strongly established during the first 16 to 18 years of life are very hard to change. Kolstoe (1961b) found that responsibility and independence were important elements making for job success, but that these were virtues that could, in his success group, be traced to the early home environment of the trainee.

On the "output" side of the program, a vigorous placement service is essential. Ideally, one person should devote full time to the locating of jobs and the guidance of trainees placed into them. Even a relatively small program should strive to fill such a full-time position, as crises may come up that must be handled without delay and at all hours. Walshe (1964) advocates that shop personnel conduct at least the initial placement supervision, rather than handing this job to outsiders. He recommends that one staff member be assigned to this type of duty.

Some vocational programs for the retarded plan to use state rehabilitation services for placement of their graduates. This may or may not be adequate, and often is not. State vocational rehabilitation workers have traditionally handled the physically disabled worker and are only beginning to reconcile themselves to working with psychiatric cases, not even to mention retardates. They may have difficulty in emancipating themselves from a historical emphasis on medical aspects, and, when presented with a retarded client, they may give inordinate attention to sight and hearing, speech, physical restoration by means of surgery, braces, prostheses, etc., and wonder why these efforts do not seem to improve the job-holding behavior of the client. Many state vocational rehabilitation workers lack both knowledge of retardation and the proper attitude toward it, and have no confidence that they can be effective in placing retardates. As Kruger (1963) points out, vocational rehabilitation personnel need to have a commitment to the idea that the retardate should and can be placed, and have to be willing to respond to crises around the clock (Caswell Rehabilition Center, 1961, p. 5). Regrettably, appointment of vocational rehabilitation personnel in some states is controlled by political patronage. Such personnel may be very inadequate although, if possessed by positive attitudes, they can become more effective than trained personnel with poor attitudes.

State services may be inclined to give up hope on retarded clients later found to be employable by an agency specializing in retardation (Kolstoe, 1961b; Goodwill Industries, 1961, p. 59). Rogers, (1962, pp. 52–53) has pointed out additional reasons why state placement services are often of little help to retardates, even if they do have selective placement specialists. Olshansky (1960) scathingly criticized state-federal rehabilitation agencies for a number of practices and shortcomings that jeopardize the chances of mental patients for rehabilitation. Many of his points appear valid in the field of retardation. While in some areas or services, retardates receive competent and intensive attention, inability of state vocational rehabilitation agencies to find adequate placement opportunities for retardates at this time should, by no means, be interpreted to indicate that they cannot be found. Saenger's (1957) study is somewhat illustrative of the situation. Among his sample of employed severely retarded adults in New

York City, only 6 per cent of placements were a result of the efforts of public employment agencies. Most jobs were found through friends, relatives, or on the retardates' own initiative. Similarly, Rogers and Murphy (HEW, 1961) report an experience in one locality where the schools found that the teachers themselves had to engage in job placement through personal contacts with prospective employers as other agencies were of little help. Ferguson (1959) reported that 60 per cent of his workshop trainees found jobs through their own efforts or those of their family, 12 per cent were placed through state employment agencies, and 35 per cent through the district office of vocational rehabilitation. However, while 45 per cent of the trainees who found a job privately still held their position, only 13 per cent of those who were placed through the rehabilitation office were successful.

The highly effective placement officer probably has four attributes: (1) he understands the human problem associated with retardation, (2) he strongly believes that retardates can be vocationally successful, (3) he feels that he can be successful in placing them, and (4) he is capable of exploiting all the flexibility permitted him. Traditional placement identification may not always be effective in retardation, and agencies should be willing not only to permit, but even encourage unorthodox and creative approaches by their counselors. An interesting example of a then relatively untried and creative habilitation program has been documented by Potts (1950). By serving virtually 24 hours a day for a period of 18 months as vocational counselor, personal adviser, probation officer, teacher, and placement supervisor, 19 of 22 previously institutionalized young retardates were successfully established in the community as ascertained by a three-year follow-up. A traditional and bureaucratic program would not have been able to handle the problems that arose.

A number of techniques can be utilized to improve placement procurement and success.

Apprenticeship-type Arrangement. In this case, the counselor reaches an agreement with an employer to the effect that the trainee is not to be paid any wages until a certain level of competence is reached (e.g., Kolstoe, 1961b, p. 52). The counselor may even offer to pay a training fee or tuition if the employer agrees to furnish intensive initial training and supervision. Such arrangements may prove an entry to a firm that appears likely to provide further placements in the future.

On-the-Job Training. The training or rehabilitation agency offers to provide the initial on-the-job training and supervision. For a week or two, a counselor may play the role of a "co-employee" with the trainee, filling the job together, learning about plant routine, etc., with the counselor gradually fading out of the picture.

The two techniques described above should be explored much more fully than they have been. They would add greatly to the flexibility of a program and have the advantage of, in effect, accomplishing training without using workshop facilities and overhead. In small and rural communities, these two techniques may prove much more economical than the establishment and operation of a sheltered workshop.

Meticulous Care in Introducing a Trainee to a New Job. An ill-trained but well-placed retardate may make a better adjustment than one who is well-trained but ill-placed (Parnicky, 1964). A trainee's fears and apprehensions may be more of an obstacle to success, especially on a first job, than incompetence. Common errors include:

1. Precipitous placement where the trainee is not emotionally prepared for the impending change.

2. Inadequate briefing on and training for a particular placement. For example, a trainee prepared for horticultural work may be placed in an opening on a factory assembly line. The trainee's expectation may have been built up for an entirely different line of work, and his rigidity may cost him his job.

3. Inadequate communication with and preparation of the employer or supervisor. Employers sometimes develop curious beliefs or attitudes toward the employment of the handicapped. For example, potential employers are sometimes reluctant to hire the handicapped because they fear an increase in their workmen's compensation rates. In fact, these rates depend on the inherent hazards of the job and on the firm's long-range accident record, not on the personal characteristics of the worker. A good pamphlet for the prospective employer or supervisor of a retardate is available (HEW, 1964c). Often employers are re-

luctant to inform the counselor of early and minor problems, and blandly assert that all is well. Suddenly, the trainee is discharged with the explanation that he just never was any good. The employer needs to be sensitized to the desirability of communicating sources of difficulties well before they become crises.

4. Inadequate attention to small but important details. Transportation is a typical example. The job may be inaccessible without a car; the trip may be too long; an alternate arrangement may be impossible to make if the planned transportation does not realize or breaks down, etc. The placement check-off list by Pinkard, Gilmore, Ricker, and Williams (1963, p. 58) is a device that counselors may find helpful during the placement process.

5. Premature close-out. Some rehabilitation agencies have a schizophrenia of the close-out, which requires a definite final termination of involvement in a case. Theoretically, after close-out, the case is not supposed to be serviced any further. One of the practices associated with this schizophrenia is the pressure for terminations. In some rehabilitation-hungry agencies and states, a counselor is required to fulfill a quota of placements to hold his job or to gain advancement. Even when no official quota is set up, an unofficial expectancy for close-outs may be just as threatening. Sometimes the agency, and not the counselor, is under close-out pressure, and, as the end of the business year approaches, it engages in a frantic screening of the records to see if a few more close-outs can be squeezed from the caseload prior to the deadline.

As Olshansky (1960) pointed out, rehabilitation agencies that overemphasize quantity of output are likely to be more selective in their choice of clients and may turn away those most in need of help. More understandable and humane, but still questionable, is the practice of closing out a case as a success, only to have it re-entered elsewhere or later as a new case. In this fashion, one case may enter our national statistics several times as a successful rehabilitation or referral. Practices like these have been occasionally prevalent in various rehabilitation fields and are by no means unique to retardation. In fact, they may be even less common with retarded than nonretarded clients (HEW, 1964b).

In the past, services to the retarded have tended to be on an all-or-nothing basis. However, present sentiment favors providing continued and lifelong supervision as needed. Goldstein and Heber (HEW, 1961) and Heber (1964) urge that job placement should include definite plans for follow-up to achieve optimal adjustment. They emphasize that providing post-placement services that will handle problems as they develop is more economical than offering these services after problems have become pervasive and embedded in the retarded client's total adjustment. Even more strongly, the Task Force on Education and Rehabilitation of the President's Panel (1963b) recommended as essential "supportive services and facilities, such as supervised residential facilities, day-by-day counseling services, legal services, and special recreational activities" (p. 54). Many retardates would be capable of leading productive lives in the community but need occasional tuition, help, and guidance with difficult problems, or at times of crisis. The need for such supervision would, of course, vary greatly. Some retardates would require it only a few times in their lives, others may need it several times a month. If flexible supervision were available, many major problems could be averted, and the social and financial cost of such supervision would be less expensive than its alternatives. Perhaps one should think about viewing the long-range goal of vocational training of most retardates as a "free but guided life in the economy," rather than as a definitely discontinous terminus after a short period of successful work.

Templeton (1961), an employer of retarded workers, offers an interesting discussion of the daily problems of retardates closed out on community placements. From her experience, she strongly advocates continued supervision, and suggests cottage-type residence as a possible solution.

The hostel or half-way house has been neglected as a means of providing the "just noticeable difference" in guidance that may mean the difference between success and failure. Such a facility can function both parallel to a training program and on its output side. A hostel for perhaps four to twelve residents can be run relatively inexpensively. An older, large residence may be ideally suited. Since the retardates would be working during the day except in case of sickness or between jobs, the house parents may work at least part-time, too. Girls may be easier to accommodate than the same number of boys, as the former would be more likely to render effective assistance in housekeeping.

In addition to general housekeeping, the tasks of the house parents could include provision of: (1) an emotional tie that would give some security to a retardate with few, if any, family connections; (2) occasional help with difficult problems such as budgeting, taxes, arrangement of new transportation routes, etc.; (3) an atmosphere conducive to constructive leisure time use; and (4) mediation between the residents and agencies. On the one hand, no more paternalistic tuition should be provided than is necessary, but on on the other hand, if trouble should be brewing, timely mediation may avert a "community failure."

A hostel not only provides a degree of structure and supervision, but also an emotional atmosphere more conducive to many retardates' adjustment. Thus, Tizard and O'Connor (1950a) cite several studies that indicate that "group placements" enhance the likelihood of community adjustment of retardates, the hostel being one version of such a placement. Arguments in favor of group placements are also presented by Harmes (1949) and Wardell (1946). Cate and Gengenheimer (1950), arguing in favor of group placement, give an example of five boys living in a boarding house with a couple while working for a nearby hospital. Encouraging experiences of a variety of group home projects were reviewed in the spring 1966 issue of the NARC residential newsletter *(The Record).* On the other hand, Chandler and Shafter (1955) take a more pessimistic view of group placement. They feel that assimilation into the community is retarded, that stronger group members may lead others astray, that the likelihood of individualized handling is reduced, and that one poor adjustment may reflect upon the adjustment of the entire group.

Boarding houses have been proposed in lieu of hostels. However, even when formal arrangements are made with boarding houses, the basic orientation and motivation of the typical landlord is such as to require more independence and self-direction from the boarder than the hostel resident.

Residential units can be attached to a workshop and serve either primarily as a home for out-of-town trainees or as a training experience for independent or hostel living.

Work programs for the homebound are sometimes mentioned as desirable. However, there should be very little need for such a program as long as workshops exercise flexibility in their eligibility requirements. Most retardates capable of work are ambulatory. Even those who are not ambulatory ordinarily can be brought to the shop to work there. Since homebound programs for the retarded can be vexed by many problems, they should be avoided unless no other alternative exists.

Counseling the family of the retarded may not only be important but sometimes even essential. DiMichael (HEW, 1961) states that, in his experience, the progress of retarded clients in sheltered workshops is very intimately related to the management of the rest of the family. Counseling should not only be provided during a later phase of training or placement, but even preventively during the childhood of the retarded. Patterson (1964) feels that the parental attitude toward work and employment may be a very significant and hitherto neglected predictive datum. One of the most pathetic recurring situations arises when a parent brings in an oafish, indolent, and perhaps even physically very strong young man with the request to "teach him a trade or something because we can't handle him anymore." Upon interview it may turn out that the boy has been overprotected and indulged all his life, that no consistent limits were ever enforced, that he has spent years sitting around the house idle, and that now the parents are worried because their health is failing or he is actually abusing them physically. The agency is expected to take him in and, reversing the habits of a small lifetime, quickly prepare him for independent living, if possible in something where he does not get his hands dirty. Perhaps all this happened because years ago, after an intensive team evaluation, the parents were called in for a hurried "feedback" session where they were told their boy was retarded, that they should "accept" it, and, not at all unlikely, that his case was "hopeless."

One of the most serious service gaps in the vocational preparation of the retardate exists between the early high school years and the time the youngster reaches 16. To many school systems, even the retardate with work potential is an embarrassment as they do not provide any or enough services for him. Instead, the youngster may be subtly squeezed out of school, as "leaving behavior" is rewarded, and "staying behavior" is punished or ignored. Once the youngster takes the hint or is actually excluded, he will find in most states that he can neither work nor be serviced by state rehabilitation agencies until he is 16, at which time he may only be able to work by permit and on a limited basis until he is 18. Even where vocational rehabilitation counselors may be assigned to work with the schools, and where teachers are assigned to rehabilitation agencies (Goodwill Industries, 1961, p. 71), such arrangements are not likely to be of much benefit to the below-16 group. This situation is a very undesirable one, unconducive to good habit and attitude formation, and is one of the more pressing ones calling for attention by state and local authorities.

In order to smooth the transition from school to work, work-study programs have increasingly developed. In such programs, the student spends part of his day in classes, and part at a work assignment on the school grounds or at a job in the community. Some probably typical work-study programs have been described recently by Kokaska (1964) and Shawn (1964), and Kolstoe and Frey (1965) detail an outstanding one. However, Goldstein and Heber (HEW, 1961) caution school-work programs administrators to ascertain the reality of the work experience offered to the pupil, to stay alert to the implications of changing employment opportunities and labor needs, and to pattern work experiences accordingly. On the other hand, they also warn of the error of becoming overly specific in training. In teaching retarded girls to cook, sew, and keep house, the schools have probably served them better than they often have the boys, who may be trained in areas in which they cannot find employment later on.

Closely related to the work-study programs are arrangements in which the student may be given a supervised work experience for two consecutive summers (Kennedy, 1962). If properly conducted, such programs can give the school more options in preparing retarded youngsters for their life in the world of work.

Even in states where the public schools are quite willing and capable of preparing retardates for employment and in helping them to obtain jobs, they may encounter limitations that may greatly reduce their effectiveness. Thus, in Barnett's survey (HEW, 1961), he found that the schools' effectiveness was impaired by problems with work permits, curricular restrictions, legality of work-school programs, parental attitudes, employer resistance and even opposition from vocational rehabilitation agencies.

A current trend is for extension of habilitation services to disadvantaged groups who are more likely to generate a disproportionate number of retardates. In 1963, only 11.3 per cent of rehabilitated retardates were Negro (HEW, 1964b), even though the statistics clearly indicate that this group not only suffers from a higher prevalence of retardation, but also a disproportionate amount of unemployment.

SHELTERED WORKSHOPS AND LABOR UNIONS

A persistent notion is widely encountered among both laymen and special education and rehabilitation personnel that labor unions are strongly opposed to sheltered workshops. Such notions are often supported by hearsay evidence only, and rarely does one encounter individuals with first-hand experience of unresolved union opposition. The unions' concerns, especially in times or areas of depressed economics, are to be appreciated. One union concern has been with exploitation of handicapped individuals who are vigorous and capable of work, but have difficulties finding a job. As one labor representative stated: "While we lend our support to the principles and objectives of nonprofit sheltered workshops, this does not mean that labor should support anything and everything that has been called a sheltered workshop. Too many times disabled workers have been exploited to undercut the market for goods and services in which the workshop functions." Rothman (1964) presented a noteworthy viewpoint on sheltered workshops as seen through the eyes of organized labor. Korn (1964) and Redkey (1964) replied with a critique and discussion of some of the points raised by Rothman, and together the three articles provide an interesting insight into the problem of union-workshop relationships.

In order to maximize co-operation, labor representatives should be asked to become members of the supervising body of the shop or program, or the advisory or equivalent body in case of public programs. Labor groups should be invited for tours of the facilities to see it in operation, and the alternatives to workshop programs, and the likely cost of such alternatives, should be pointed out. The World Health Organization Report (1954) recommends that parents of the retarded who also belong to trade unions may provide the bridge by which other trade union members can be educated regarding the vocational training and employment needs of the retarded.

In order to gain a better perspective on the union issue, I contacted the office of the Wayne County (Detroit) AFL-CIO, and was furnished with the recently adopted (Fifth Constitutional Convention) AFL-CIO Resolution (No. 64) on sheltered workshops for the handicapped:

WHEREAS, Sheltered workshops provide a means for training and employment of handicapped persons who cannot fit into ordinary competitive employment, and as such are recognized as a part of the process of rehabilitation of handicapped persons by organized labor; and

WHEREAS, Sheltered workshops should provide under effective medical and vocational supervision, not only useful and remunerative work but opportunities for vocational adjustment and advancement with, whenever possible, transfer to open employment; and

WHEREAS, Organized labor has supported the development of programs of sheltered employment as an effective medium for helping handicapped workers gain reasonable and satisfying employment opportunities; and

WHEREAS, Although wage standards of sheltered workshops are covered by the federal minimum wage law, this law permits payment of subminimum wages when the Wage-Hour division of the U.S. Department of Labor grants permission to do so. Such permission has been widely sought and readily granted, resulting in undesirably low wages for sheltered shopworkers; and

WHEREAS, Sheltered workshops have a responsibility to the handicapped to give them more than work alone. They must provide work with wages consistent with self-respect and self-support. Moreover, sheltered workshops are important in shaping community attitudes towards the handicapped. Where shopworkers' wages are a mere pittance, the community will hold the abilities of sheltered shopworkers in low regard at the same time giving the workshops an unhealthy reputation as sweatshops; therefore, be it

RESOLVED, That organized labor continue to support the sheltered workshop program wherever workshops meet the following standards:

1. Sheltered workshops should adhere to federal and state wage and hour regulations, where applicable, and maintain wage standards comparable to prevailing wage piece rate standards for similar work in private employment.

2. The workshop should conform to national, state, and local codes and standards covering safety, health, sanitation, lighting, heating, and ventilation.

3. The right of workers in sheltered workshops to organize into unions of their own choosing for purpose of collective bargaining should be recognized by the boards and administrators of sheltered workshops.

4. Sheltered workshops should not seek to deprive workers in competitive industry of their jobs by bidding for work, usually performed through normal industrial channels, on the basis of substandard wages paid to sheltered workers.

5. The policy-making boards of sheltered workshops should be representative of all community interests related to the workshops, including representatives of organized labor.

Generally, the resolution is a reasonable one and can largely be complied with by workshops. The item presenting some difficulties is the one concerned with the certification of sheltered workshops so as to permit subminimum wages. This apprehension seems to be aimed primarily at instances where nonretarded workers are employed, and where they may, at times, have been exploited.

I was informed that some of the beliefs regarding union opposition to sheltered workshops have arisen out of misunderstandings, poor public relations, or actions based upon a prejudiced rationale. For example, employers may ward off workshop procurement by claiming labor opposition when, in fact, their labor contract contains no relevant clause and when no negotiations on this issue have been conducted.

In one of the few informative treatises on the union issue, Dolnick (1963) found in a survey that only few workshops considered unions a major problem. Often, unions were not so much concerned with workshops at all as with the general practice of contracting work to outsiders. A number of the incidents quoted by Dolnick were illustrative of poor communication and public relations. He also recounted examples that illustrated how difficulties were and should be overcome.

CONCLUSIONS

From the preceding sections, the following broad conclusions are abstracted.

1. A productive work life can be viewed as

one of the main goals of developmental, educational, and habilitational programming for the retarded.

2. The prevalence of work-age retardates is probably tied to the degree of societal complexity. As regards habilitation, this prevalence is likely to increase appreciably in the future.

3. The work future of the retarded is difficult to assess. Factors that lead to a pessimistic forecast are offset by trends permitting a guarded optimism. However, only creative and flexible programming is likely to safeguard the retardate's place in a productive economy.

4. While habilitation of the retarded has generally been viewed as a short-term, discontinuous process, changing conditions will demand long-range guidance and supervision.

5. In the United States, vocational training practices in the field of mental retardation have not been harmonious with the body of empirical knowledge available. Where good information has been available, it has often been ignored as in the area of training. Where no conclusive information exists, it has frequently been assumed to exist as in the area of selection and evaluation.

6. The search for outcome predictors has been based, almost overwhelmingly, on the naive assumption that outcome is largely or almost exclusively determined by subject variables. Outcome studies, to be fruitful, need to take into account training, placement process, and placement situation variables.

7. While researchers have not neglected the field of vocational training, the quality of research has been low. What is needed is not more research, but better research. The time for ill-controlled, shotgun type studies seems passed, as such work seems unlikely to add convincing evidence to the already confusing and contradictory body of such studies.

REFERENCES

Anonymous. President receives progress report on federal employment of retarded. *Ment. Retard.*, 1964, *2*, 243, 246.

APPELL, M. J., WILLIAMS, C. M., and FISHELL, K. N. Significant factors in placing mental retardates from a workshop situation. *Personnel Guid. J.*, 1962, *41*, 260–265.

BAKER, G. R. Employment of the mentally retarded in the United States government. *Ment. Retard.*, 1962, *2*, 121–126.

BARNUM, LILLIAN GENTRY. *Syllabus of occupational information for mentally retarded senior high school boys.* Carson City, Nev.: Division of Vocational Rehabilitation, State Dept. of Education, 1965.

BAUMEISTER, A. A., HAWKINS, W. F., and HOLLAND, JEAN. Motor learning and knowledge of results. *Amer. J. ment. Defic.*, 1966, *70*, 590–594.

BECKHAM, A. S. Minimum intelligence levels for several occupations. *Personnel J.*, 1930, *9*, 309–313.

BLUE, M. Trainable mentally retarded in sheltered workshops. *Ment. Retard.*, 1964, *2*, 97–104.

BOBROFF, A. Economic adjustment of 121 adults, formerly students in classes for the mental retardates. *Amer. J. ment. Defic.*, 1956, *60*, 525–535.

BORRECA, F., BURGER, R., GOLDSTEIN, I., MANN, H., SIMCHES, G., and SIMCHES, R. A workshop in developing lessons for retarded adolescents in a program of occupational education. *Amer. J. ment. Defic.*, 1950, *55*, 23–59.

———, ———, ———, and SIMCHES, R. A functional core vocabulary for slow learners. *Amer. J. ment. Defic.*, 1953, *58*, 273–300.

BURG, BILLIE W., and BARRETT, A. M. Interest testing with the mentally retarded: a bi-sensory approach. *Amer. J. ment. Defic.*, 1965, *69*, 548–552.

CARRIER, N. A., MALPASS, L. F., and ORTON, K. D. *Responses of bright, normal, and retarded children to learning tasks.* Carbondale, Ill., 1961. (Cooperative Research Project No. 578).

CARTER, L. F., and MARGOLIN, J. B. Psychology in the states. (An approach to retardation.) *Amer. Psychologist,* 1964, *19,* 358–360.

Caswell Rehabilitation Center. *Progress Report, 1960–61.* Kinston, N.C.: Author, 1961.

CATE, HILDA, and GENGENHEIMER, RUTH A. The community supervisor looks at parole. *Amer. J. ment. Defic.,* 1950, *55,* 275–278.

CHANDLER, C. S., and SHAFTER, A. J. A critique of the group placement concept. *Amer. J. ment. Defic.,* 1955, *59,* 517–521.

CLARKE, A. D. B. The abilities and trainability of imbeciles. In Ann M. Clarke and A. D. B. Clarke (Eds.), *Mental deficiency: The changing outlook.* Glencoe, Ill.: The Free Press, 1958, Chap. 13.

———, and HERMELIN, BEATE F. Adult imbeciles, their abilities and trainability. *Lancet,* 1955, *269,* 337–339.

CLARKE, ANN M., and CLARKE, A. D. B. (Eds.). *Mental deficiency: The changing outlook.* Glencoe, Ill.: The Free Press, 1958.

COHEN, J. S. An analysis of vocational failures of mental retardates placed in the community after a period of institutionalization. *Amer. J. ment Defic.,* 1960, *65,* 371–375.

———. A workshop operation within the framework of a state institution. *Amer. J. ment. Defic.,* 1961, *66,* 51–56.

CORTAZZO, A. D. Increasing sociability for the retarded through activity programs. *J. Rehabilit.,* 1964, *30* (2), 13–14.

DAVIES, S. P. *The mentally retarded in society.* New York: Columbia University Press, 1959.

DELP, H. A. Criteria for vocational training of the mentally retarded: a revised concept of the necessary mental level. *Train. Sch. Bull.,* 1957, *54,* 14–20.

DENO, EVELYN. Community coordinated effort in vocational training for the retarded. Paper presented at CEC convention, Los Angeles, 1960.

———, HENZE, R., KRANTZ, G., and BARKLIND, K. *Retarded youth: Their school-rehabilitation needs.* Minneapolis: Minneapolis Public Schools, 1965.

DIMICHAEL, S. G. The problem of post-adolescence. In *The exceptional child faces adulthood.* Woods School Proceedings. Langhorne, Pa.: The Woods Schools, 1955, 24–38.

———. Vocational diagnosis and counseling of the retarded in sheltered workshops. *Amer. J. ment. Defic.,* 1960, *64,* 652–657.

———. The low IQ problem. *Rehabilit. Rec.,* 1963, No. 3, 3–6.

———. Providing full vocational opportunities for retarded adolescents and adults. *J. Rehabilit.,* 1964, *30* (4), 10–12; 30–31.

DINGER, J. C. Post-school adjustment of former educable retarded pupils. *Except. Child.,* 1961, *27,* 353–356.

DOLCH, E. W. A basic sight vocabulary. *Elem. Sch. J.,* 1936, *36,* 456–460.

DOLL, A. E. *The measurement of social competence.* Washington, D.C.: Educational Test Bureau, 1953.

DOLNICK, M. *Contract procurement practices of sheltered workshops.* Chicago: National Society for Crippled Children and Adults, 1963.

———. Contractor opinions of sheltered workshops. *J. Rehabilit.,* 1964, *30* (2), 23–25.

DUBROW, M. Work procurement and job production. *Amer. J. ment. Defic.,* 1958, *63,* 355–359.

————. Patterns of programming. In Pennsylvania Dept. of Public Welfare, *Sheltered workshop programming for the mentally retarded in Pennsylvania*, 1961, 15–21.

————. *Working for maturity: specialized rehabilitation training for mentally retarded young adults*. New York: AHRC, 1962.

DYBWAD, G. Rehabilitation for the adult retardate. *Amer. J. Publ. Hlth..* 1961, *51*, 998–1004.

————. *Challenges in mental retardation*. New York: Columbia University Press, 1964.

ENGEL, ANNA M. Employment of the mentally retarded. In S. G. DiMichael (Ed.), *Vocational rehabilitation of the mentally retarded*. Washington, D.C.: U.S. Office of Vocational Rehabilitation, 1950.

————. Employment of the mentally retarded. *Amer. J. ment. Defic.*, 1952, *57*, 243–267.

FERGUSON, R. G. Part I: *Manual of operations for a sheltered workshop to serve mentally retarded youths*. Part II: *Evaluation of the potential for vocational habilitation of mentally retarded youth*. Tampa, Fla.: Sertoma Sheltered Workshop (MacDonald Training Center). 1959.

FRAENKEL, W. A. *The mentally retarded and their vocational rehabilitation: a resource handbook*. New York: National Association for Retarded Children, 1961. (a)

————. The role of the workshop in relation to special education. In Goodwill Industries of America. *A report on the institute on sheltered workshop services for the mentally retarded*. Washington, D.C.: Author, 1961. (b)

————. *Fundamentals in organizing a sheltered workshop for the mentally retarded*. New York: National Association for Retarded Children, 1962.

FRANKS, VIOLET, and FRANKS, C. M. Classical conditioning procedures as an index of vocational adjustment among mental defectives. *Percept. mot. Skills*, 1962, *14*, 241–242.

GELLMAN, W., STERN, D. J., and SOLOFF, A. *A scale of employability for handicapped persons*. Chicago: Jewish Vocational Service, 1963 (Monograph No. 4).

GINZBERG, E., and BRAY, D. W. *The uneducated*. New York: Columbia Univer. Press, 1953.

GOLDSTEIN, H. Social and occupational adjustment. In H. A. Stevens and R. Heber (Eds.), *Mental retardation: A review of research*. Chicago: University of Chicago Press, 1964, 214–258.

GOLDSTEIN, I., and MANN, H. An occupational vocabulary for retarded adolescents. *Amer. J. ment. Defic.*, 1949, *54*, 38–72.

Goodwill Industries of America. *A report on the institute on sheltered workshop services for the mentally retarded*. Washington, D.C.: Author, 1961.

GORDON, S., O'CONNOR, N., and TIZARD, J. Some effects of incentives on the performance of imbeciles on a repetitive task. *Amer. J. ment. Defic.*, 1955, *60*, 371–377.

GRUENBERG, E. M. Epidemiology. In H. A. Stevens and R. Heber (Eds.), *Mental retardation: a review of research*. Chicago: University of Chicago Press, 1964, 259–306.

GUNZBURG, H. C. Vocational and social rehabilitation of the feeble-minded. In Ann M. Clarke and A. D. B. Clarke (Eds.), *Mental deficiency: The changing outlook*. Glencoe, Ill.: The Free Press, 1958, 334–364.

————. *Social rehabilitation of the subnormal*. London: Bailliere, Tindall and Cox, 1960.

————. *Progress Assessment Chart (PAC)*. (2nd ed.) London: National Association of Mental Health, 1963. (a)

————. *Senior training centers: An outline of the principles and practices of social education and training for older mentally subnormal people.* London: National Association of Mental Health, 1963. (b)

————. Mental subnormality: Some thoughts for the future. *Teach. & Train.,* 1964, *2,* 102–108. (a)

————. A new method of charting social skills progress. *Ment. Retard.,* 1964, *2,* 370–373. (b)

GURALNICK, D. Vocational rehabilitation services in New York City for the mentally retarded: An analysis of 248 cases, 1953–1955. *Amer. J. ment. Defic.,* 1956, *61,* 368–377.

————. The relationship of personal characteristics and educational experience of mentally retarded persons to their successful utilization of a vocational rehabilitation program. *Dissert. Abstr.,* 1964, *24,* 2782.

HARMES, MARY. Casework in the social adjustment of adult defectives. *Amer. J. ment. Defic.,* 1949, *54,* 238.

HEBER, R. (Ed.) *Vocational rehabilitation of the mentally retarded.* Washington, D.C.: U.S. Government Printing Office, 1964.

HEGGE, T. G. Psychological aspects of mental retardation. In S. G. DiMichael (Ed.), *Vocational rehabilitation of the mentally retarded.* Washington, D.C.: U.S. Office of Vocational Rehabilitation, 1950, 18–35.

HOLMAN, PORTIA. The relationship between general mental development and manual dexterity. *Brit. J. Psychol.,* 1933, *23,* 279–283.

JACOBS, A., and WEINGOLD, J. T. *The sheltered workshop, a community rehabilitation resource for the mentally retarded.* New York: Teachers College Bureau of Publications, 1958.

JASTAK, J. F., MACPHEE, M. M., and WHITEMAN, M. *Mental retardation: Its nature and incidence; a population survey of the State of Delaware.* Newark: University of Delaware Press, 1962. (Distributed by University Publishers, New York 10003)

Joint Committee of the Public Health Service and the V.R.A. *Areawide planning of facilities for rehabilitation services.* Washington, D.C.: U.S. Government Printing Office, 1963.

KANNER, L. Feeblemindedness: Absolute, relative, and apparent. *Nerv. Child,* 1949, *7,* 365–397.

KENNEDY, RUBY J. R. *The social adjustment of morons in a Connecticut city.* Hartford: State of Connecticut, 1948.

————. Social adjustment of the mentally retarded. *Rehabilit. Rec.,* 1962, No. 6, 15–18.

————. *A Connecticut community revisited: A study of the social adjustment of a group of mentally deficient adults in 1948 and 1960.* Hartford: Connecticut State Dept. of Health, 1966.

KENNEDY, W. A., VAN DERIET, V., and WHITE, J. C. A normative sample of intelligence and achievement of Negro elementary school children in the southeastern United States. *Monogr. Soc. Res. Child Develpm.,* 1963, *28,* 1–112.

KILLINGSWORTH, C. C. *Structural unemployment in the United States.* (Seminar on Manpower Policy and Program, December, 1965.) Washington, D.C.: U.S. Government Printing Office, 1966.

KLEBANOFF, L. B. Varieties of the mentally retarded and their potential. In Pennsylvania Dept. of Public Welfare, *Sheltered workshop programming for the mentally retarded in Pennsylvania,* 1961, 21–26.

KOKASKA, C. In-school work experience: A tool for community adjustment. *Ment. Retard.,* 1964, *2,* 365–369.

KOLSTOE, O. P. An examination of some characteristics which discriminate between employed and not-employed mentally retarded males. *Amer. J. ment. Defic.*, 1961, *66*, 472–482. (a)

———. The employment evaluation of the mentally retarded. In Goodwill Industries of America, Inc., *A report on the institute on sheltered workshop services for the mentally retarded*. Washington, D.C.: Author, 1961, 47–53. (b)

———. *Static and dynamic characteristics of retardates for predicting employability*. Paper read at the American Psychological Association convention, Los Angeles, 1964.

———, and FREY, R. M. *A high school work-study program for mentally subnormal students*. Carbondale: Southern Illinois University Press, 1965.

———, and SHAFTER, A. J. Employability prediction for mentally retarded adults: A methodological note. *Amer. J. ment. Defic.*, 1961, *66*, 287–289.

KORN, A. Fair labor standards and workshops. *Rehab. Rec.*, 1964, *5* (6), 30–31.

KRATTER, F. E. Research into the causes of mental deficiency. *N. Carolina Med. J.*, 1958, *19*, 528–534.

KRISHEF, C., and HALL, M. Employment of the mentally retarded in Hennepin County, Minnesota. *Amer. J. ment. Defic.*, 1955, *60*, 182–189.

KRUGER, D. H. Trends in service employment: Implications for the educable mentally retarded. *Except. Children*, 1963, *30*, 167–172.

LADAS, P. G. Work sample learning rates of the mentally retarded trainee as indicators of production in a work-training center. *Personnel Guid. J.*, 1961, *39*, 396–402.

LEVINSON, E. J. *Retarded children in Maine: A survey and analysis*. Maine Studies, 1962, 2nd Series, No. 77.

LINDE, T. Techniques for establishing motivation through operant conditioning. *Amer. J. ment. Defic.*, 1962, *67*, 437–440.

———. A clinical vocational performance index for rehabilitation workshops. Paper read at the American Psychological Association convention, Los Angeles, 1964.

LIVINGSTON, S. *Living with epileptic seizures*. Springfield, Ill.: Charles C Thomas, 1963.

LOOS, F. M., and TIZARD, J. The employment of adult imbeciles in a hospital workshop. *Amer. J. ment. Defic.*, 1955, *59*, 395–403.

LYTLE, H. G. Pre-shop ground work for retarded: Ten prerequisites to facilitate private employment. *Rehabilit. Rec.*, 1963, (5), 28–29.

MACMILLAN, M. B. Adjustment and process: A neglected feature of follow-up studies of retarded people. *Amer. J. ment. Defic.*, 1962, *67*, 418–423.

Manpower report of the President, and a report on manpower requirements, resources, utilization, and training by the U.S. Department of Labor. Washington, D.C.: U.S. Government Printing Office, 1964.

———. Washington, D.C.: U.S. Government Printing Office, 1966.

MARGOLIS, DORIS. Effective public relations for the sheltered workshop. *J. Rehabilit.*, 1965, *31* (1), 28–29.

MASSIE, W. A. Community planning for a workshop. In Pennsylvania Dept. of Public Welfare, *Sheltered workshop programming for the mentally retarded in Pennsylvania*, 1961, 10–14.

MEAD, MARGARET. Research: Cult or cure? *Amer. J. ment. Defic.*, 1959, *64*, 253–264.

MEADOW, L., and GREENSPAN, E. Employability of lower level mental retardates. *Amer. J. ment. Defic.*, 1961, *65*, 623–628.

MERTENS, G. C., and FULLER, G. B. Conditioning of molar behavior in "regressed" psychotics: 1. An objective measure of personal habit training with "regressed" psychotics. *J. clin. Psychol.,* 1963, *19,* 333–337.

MICHAL-SMITH, H. Personality training in vocational education for the retarded child. *J. except. Child.,* 1951, *17,* 108–110.

Ministry of Health. *The training of staff of the training centers for the mentally subnormal.* London: Her Majesty's Stationery Office, 1962.

MULLEN, FRANCES A., and NEE, MARY M. Distribution of mental retardation in an urban school population. *Amer. J. ment. Defic.,* 1952, *58,* 777–790.

National Association for Retarded Children. *A summary of "Sheltered Workshop Questionnaire." New York:* Author, 1959.

———. *Nine basic steps in setting up a workshop.* New York: Author, 1963.

———. *Directory of sheltered workshops serving the mentally retarded.* New York, Author, 1964.

National Society for Mentally Handicapped Children. *Training and employment of the mentally handicapped.* Southampton, England: Millbrook Press, 1963.

NELSON, N. The economics of a sub-contract and manufacturing workshop. *J. Rehabilit.,* 1964, *30* (4), 18–19, 45.

———. Industrial operation of the sheltered workshop. *J. Rehabilit.,* 1965, *31,* (1), 38–41.

NEUHAUS, E. C. A unique pre-vocational program for educable retardates. *Ment. Retard.,* 1965, *3* (4), 19–21.

New York State Department of Mental Hygiene. A special census of suspected referred mental retardation, Onondaga County, New York. In Technical Report of the Mental Health Research Unit. Syracuse: Syracuse University Press, 1955.

NIEHM, B. F. Study of sheltered workshops for the mentally retarded. *Train. Sch. Bull.,* 1958, *54,* 67–71.

Occupational Training Center for the Mentally Retarded Young Adults of Rhode Island. *Request for continuation grant and first annual report.* Providence: Author, 1960.

O'CONNOR, N. The successful employment of the mentally handicapped. In L. T. Hilliard and B. H. Kirman (Eds.), *Mental deficiency.* Boston: Little, Brown, 1957, 448–480.

———. The prevalence of mental defect. In Ann M. Clarke and A. D. B. Clarke (Eds.), *Mental deficiency: The changing outlook.* Glencoe, Ill.: The Free Press, 1958, 21–39.

———, and HERMELIN, BEATE. *Speech and thought in severe subnormality.* New York: Macmillan, 1963.

———, and TIZARD, J. *The social problem of mental deficiency.* London: Pergamon Press, 1956.

Office of Vocational Rehabilitation. *Vocational rehabilitation for the mentally disabled: 1961 fact sheet.* Washington, D.C.: Author, 1961.

Office of Vocational Rehabilitation, Southern Methodist University, and National Association for Retarded Children. *Rehabilitation and research in retardation: A conference on the vocational rehabilitation of the mentally retarded.* Washington, D.C.: Office of Vocational Rehabilitation, 1961.

OLSHANSKY, S. S. Vocational rehabilitation and the ex-mental patient. *J. Rehabilit.,* 1960, *26* (6), 17–19, 40–45.

Opportunity Workshop, Inc. *Opportunity Workshop.* (OWS Series No. 1) Minneapolis: Author, 1964.

OSBORN, R. T. Racial differences in mental growth and school achievement: A longitudinal study. *Psychol. Rep.,* 1960, *7,* 233–239.

PARNICKY, J. J. The newly graduated retardate. *Rehabilit. Rec.*, 1964, *5* (3), 26–29.

———, BLACKMAN, L. S., COHEN, J. S., and KAHN, H. Johnstone's 5-phase training. *Rehabilit. Rec.*, July-August, 1961. (Seen in reprint.)

———, and KAHN, H. *Evaluating and developing vocational potential of institutionalized retarded adolescents.* Bordentown, N. J.: E. R. Johnstone Training and Research Center, 1963.

———, ———, and BURDETT, A. Preliminary efforts at determining the significance of retardates' vocational interests. *Amer. J. ment. Defic.*, 1965, *70*, 393–398.

PATTERSON, C. H. Methods of assessing the vocational adjustment potential of the mentally handicapped. *Train. Sch. Bull.*, 1964, *61*, 129–152.

PATTERSON, M., and SPECK, MIRIAM PARTRIDGE. *The vocational rehabilitation of retarded, brain-injured youth in a rural regional center.* Gainesville, Va.: The Partridge Schools, 1963.

PECKHAM, R. Problems in job adjustment of the mentally retarded. *Amer. J. ment. Defic.*, 1951, *56*, 448–453.

Pennsylvania Dept. of Public Welfare. *Sheltered workshop programming for the mentally retarded in Pennsylvania.* Author, 1961.

PENSE, A. W. Community programs for the mentally retarded in England. *Ment. Hyg., N. Y.*, 1960, *31*, 6–8.

———. Community programs for the mentally retarded in England. *Canad. Ment. Hlth. Suppl.*, 1961, No. 23.

PERRY, S. H. Some theoretic problems of mental deficiency and their action implications. *Psychiatry*, 1954, *17*, 45–73.

PETERSON, L., and SMITH, L. L. A comparison of the post-school adjustment of educable mentally retarded adults with that of adults of normal intelligence. *Except. Children*, 1960, *26*, 404–408.

PETERSON, R. O., and JONES, EDNA M. *Guide to jobs for the mentally retarded.* (Rev. ed.) Pittsburgh: American Institute for Research, 1964.

PHELPS, H. R. Postschool adjustment of mentally retarded children in selected Ohio cities. *Except. Children*, 1956, *23*, 58–62, 91.

PHELPS, W. R. Attitudes related to the employment of the mentally retarded. *Amer. J. ment. Defic.*, 1965, *69*, 575–585.

PINKARD, C. M., GILMORE, A. S., RICKER, L. H., and WILLIAMS, C. F. *Predicting vocational capacity of retarded adults.* Tampa, Fla.: MacDonald Training Center Foundation, 1963.

POTTS, JANE M. Vocational rehabilitation for the mentally retarded in Michigan. In S. G. DiMichael (Ed.), *Vocational rehabilitation of the mentally retarded.* Washington, D.C.: U.S. Office of Vocational Rehabilitation, 1950.

President's Committee on Employment of the Handicapped. *Employment of the mentally handicapped: A group discussion.* Washington, D.C.: U.S. Government Printing Office, 1962.

———. *Guide to job placement of the mentally retarded.* Washington, D.C.: U.S. Government Printing Office, 1963.

President's Committee on Youth Employment. *The challenge of jobless youth.* Washington, D.C.: U.S. Government Printing Office, 1963.

President's Panel on Mental Retardation. *A proposed program for national action to combat mental retardation.* Washington, D.C.: U.S. Government Printing Office, 1963. (a)

———. *Report of the task force on education and rehabilitation.* Washington, D.C.: U.S. Government Printing Office, 1963. (b)

————. *Report of the mission to the Netherlands*. Washington, D.C.: U.S. Government Printing Office, 1963. (c)

————. *Report of the task force on behavioral and social research*. Washington, D.C.: U.S. Government Printing Office, 1964.

REDKEY, H. Wages and productivity. *Rehab. Rec.*, 1964, *5* (6), 31.

REYNOLDS, M. C., and STUNKARD, C. L. *A comparative study of day-class versus institutionalized educable retardates*. Minneapolis: University of Minnesota College of Education, 1960. (Co-operative Research Project No. 192)

REYNOLDS, W. F., and STACEY, C. L. A comparison of normals and subnormals in mirror drawing. *J. genet. Psychol.*, 1955, *87*, 301–308.

ROGERS, D. P. *Development of a state-wide program for the vocational rehabilitation of the mentally retarded*. Charleston, W. Va.: Biggs-Johnstone-Withrow, Beckley, 1962.

ROTHBERG, J., CICENIA, E. F., and BOGATZ, B. E. A residential school program preparing educable retardates for on-the-job training. *Ment. Retard.*, 1965, *3* (5), 10–15.

ROTHMAN, J. F. Organized labor and sheltered workshops. *Rehab. Rec.*, 1964, *5*(6), 28–29.

RYNBRANDT, DOROTHY M. A study of the socio-economic adjustment of people who have attended the auxiliary and ungraded classes of the Grand Rapids public schools. Unpublished dissertation, Wayne State University, 1947.

SAENGER, G. *The adjustment of severely retarded adults in the community*. Albany: New York State Interdepartmental Health Resources Board, 1957.

————. *Factors influencing the institutionalization of mentally retarded individuals in New York City: A study of the effect of services, personal characteristics, and family background on the decision to institutionalize*. Albany: Interdepartmental Health Resources Board, 1960.

SELZNICK, H. M. Sex education and the mentally retarded. *Johnstone Bull.*, 1962, *5*, 23–30.

SHAFTER, A. J. Criteria for selecting institutionalized mental defectives for vocational placement. *Amer. J. ment. Defic.*, 1957, *61*, 599–616.

SHAWN, B. Review of a work-experience program. *Ment. Retard.*, 1964, *2*, 360–364.

SIEBRING, G. Your place on the team. Symposium, North Central Region of the American Association on Mental Deficiency, Omaha, Neb., 1964.

SNIFF, W. F. *A curriculum for the mentally retarded young adult*. Springfield, Ill.: Charles C Thomas, 1962.

SNYDER, E. E. The role of psychology in the vocational rehabilitation of the mentally retarded. Paper presented at the annual convention of the American Association on Mental Deficients, Kansas City, Mo., 1964.

SPEIJER, N. Some views on sheltered workshops for the mentally handicapped. *Int. J. soc. Psychiat.*, 1959, *5*, 142–145.

SYKES, P. Practical problems of rehabilitation in Scotland. *J. ment. Subnorm.*, 1965, *11*, 37–42.

TAYLOR, J. B. The structure of ability in the lower intellectual range. *Amer. J. ment. Defic.*, 1964, *68*, 766–774.

TEMPLETON, W. C. An employer's view. *Rehabilit. Rec.*, 1961, *2*(4), 25–26.

THORNDIKE, E. L., and WOODYARD, E. Differences within and between communities in the intelligence of the children. *J. educ. Psychol.*, 1942, *33*, 641–656.

THORNE, G. B. Sex education of mentally retarded girls. *Amer. J. ment. Defic.,* 1957, *62,* 460–463.

TIZARD, J. The effects of different types of supervision on the behavior of mental defectives in a sheltered workshop. *Amer. J. ment. Defic.,* 1953, *58,* 143–161.

————. Longitudinal and follow-up studies. In Ann M. and A. D. B. Clarke (Eds.), *Mental deficiency: The changing outlook.* Glencoe, Ill.: Free Press, 1958, 442–449.

————. Research in mental deficiency. *Med. World (London),* 1958, *89,* 41–45.

————. *Community services for the mentally handicapped.* London: Oxford University Press, 1964.

————, and LOOS, F. M. The learning of a spatial relations test by adult imbeciles. *Amer. J. ment. Defic.,* 1954, *59,* 85–90.

————, and O'CONNOR, N. The employability of high-grade mental defectives. I. *Amer. J. ment. Defic.,* 1950, *54,* 563–576. (a)

————, and ————. The employability of high-grade mental defectives. II. *Amer. J. ment. Defic.,* 1950, *55,* 144–157. (b)

————, and ————. The occupational adaptation of high-grade mental defectives. *Lancet,* 1952, *263* (2), 620–623.

TOBIAS, J. Evaluating the vocational potential of retarded adults through psychological tests. Paper read at the American Psychological Association Convention, Los Angeles, 1964.

————, and GORELICK, J. The effectiveness of the Purdue pegboard in evaluating work potential of retarded adults. *Train. Sch. Bull.,* 1960, *57,* 94–104.

————, and ————. Work characteristics of retarded adults at trainable levels. *Ment. Retard.,* 1963, *1,* 338–344.

Training School. *1961 conference on psychological problems in the habilitation of the mentally retarded.* Vineland, N. J.: Author, 1962.

U.S. Bureau of the Census. Current population reports: Population characteristics. Series P-20, No. 133, Feb. 18, 1965.

U.S. Department of Health, Education, and Welfare. *Preparation of mentally retarded youth for gainful employment.* Washington, D.C.: U.S. Government Printing Office, 1961.

————. *Response to the recommendations of the President's Panel Report.* Washington, D.C.: U.S. Government Printing Office, 1964. (a)

————. *Selected characteristics of the mentally retarded clients rehabilitated by state vocational rehabilitation agencies in fiscal years 1958 and 1963.* Washington, D.C.: U.S. Government Printing Office, 1964. (b)

————. *So you are going to supervise a mentally retarded employee.* Washington, D.C.: U.S. Government Printing Office, 1964. (c)

VOELKER, P. H. The value of certain selected factors in predicting early post-school employment for white educable mentally retarded males. *Dissert. Abstr.,* 1963, *23,* 3243.

WALSHE, P. Modern trends in the development of adult training centers. *Teaching & Train.,* 1964, *2,* 70–76.

WARDELL, WINIFRED R. The adjustment of moron males in a group placement. *Amer. J. ment. Defic.,* 1946, *50,* 425–433.

WARREN, F. G. Ratings of employed and unemployed mentally handicapped males on personality and work factors. *Amer. J. ment. Defic.,* 1961, *65,* 629–633.

WEINGOLD, J. T. Guidelines for program evaluations of sheltered workshops for the mentally retarded. In Pennsylvania Dept. of Public Welfare,

Sheltered workshop programming for the mentally retarded in Pennsylvania. Author, 1961, 34–38.

WINDLE, C. Prognosis of mental subnormals. *Amer. J. ment. Defic., Monogr. Suppl.,* 1962, *66*(5).

WOLFENSBERGER, W. Age variations in Vineland SQ scores for the four levels of adaptive behavior of the 1959 AAMD behavioral classification. *Amer. J. ment. Defic.,* 1962, *67*, 452–454.

————. Some observations on European programs for the mentally retarded. *Ment. Retard.,* 1964, *2*, 280–285. (a)

————. Teaching and training of the retarded in European countries. *Ment. Retard.,* 1964, *2*, 331–337. (b)

————. General observations on European programs. *Ment. Retard.,* 1965, *3*, 8–11.

————, and TIZARD, J. Survey of an areawide industrial training program for adult retardates in England. Unpublished manuscript, 1964. (Available from the first-listed author.)

World Health Organization. *The mentally subnormal child.* Geneva: Author, 1954.

YOUNG, M. A. Academic requirements of jobs held by the educable mentally retarded in the state of Connecticut. *Amer. J. ment. Defic.,* 1958, *62*, 792–802.

Public School Programs for the Mentally Retarded

WALTER C. FITZGIBBON

AT the outset, I must admit a bias in favor of the view that, with an adequate program in the schools, many mentally retarded children can become contributing members of the community. To be adequate, a program for learning basic skills should have organized instructional groups and use special teaching techniques and materials (Barnett, 1962). An adequate program also should attempt to ameliorate the psychological and sociological problems associated with retardation.

The purpose of this chapter is to present recommendations for the organization of public school programs for the educable mentally retarded and the trainable mentally retarded. An organization plan is important because:

(a) Programs operating within the schools and involving the use of numerous personnel and plant facilities need co-ordination (Voelker and Mullen, 1963).

(b) The implementation and continuation of content and methodology require such a plan (Charters, 1964).

(c) Continuity of a program is facilitated by providing scope and sequence (Lonsdale, 1964).

(d) More retardates are now in school than not, but often no special provisions are being made for them (President's Panel on Mental Retardation, 1962). The presence of retardates in regular classes indicates that we are not providing as many special classes as are needed and that some retardates can function adequately in school with minimal special provisions.

(e) The reversibility of retardation (Heber, 1961) makes it imperative that a special-class pupil be prepared to re-enter a regular education class without undue administrative delay. Organization could permit a transitional stage in which a pupil could be phased into the regular class.

(f) The wide variations in the needs of pupils demand that the school maximumly utilize its facilities. Organization would permit an administrator to extend or improve services for the retarded as the need arose (Charters, 1964).

Choice of the terms "educable" and "trainable" and the educational differentiation between the two groups appears to be related to the concept of educability that was popular in the early 1900's. At that time, education was concerned with developing literate and socially responsible retardates who would exercise good judgment regarding their own welfare and for the good of society (Capobianco, 1958). Depending upon his capability to benefit from education, a retarded child was labeled "educable" or "uneducable." The essence of the differentiation was in the child's being able to learn to read (Williams and Wallin, 1959).

Through the years, the purpose of education was broadened to that of helping a retarded individual to fully develop his capacities even within a limited environment (Capobianco, 1958). With this development, programs for the educable mentally retarded became a part of school organization.

The educable mentally retarded make up about 85 per cent of the retardate school population (President's Panel, 1962). They tend to be most frequently found in low socio-economic cultural groups (Sarason, 1959). Their physical stature and motor co-ordination appear to be close to, but somewhat below, that of the normal child of the same CA (Johnson, 1963). Educable retarded children tend to learn in the same way as normal children do, but more slowly (Kirk, 1964). The highest academic achievement of educable retarded children has been suggested to be equal to that of a child in the fourth, fifth, or sixth grade (Goldstein and Seigle, 1958; Kirk and Johnson, 1951).

The biggest difficulty for educable retardates during their school years may be in trying to gain social acceptance. Johnson (1963) attributed the social rejection of retardates in regular classes to unacceptable behavior rather than low academic ability. Retarded children in special classes, however, were found to be more socially mature and emotionally stable than those in regular classes (Blatt, 1958). In adulthood, educable retardates may become social problems, but they are often engaged, on the other hand, in unskilled or semiskilled occupations (Charles, 1953; Kruger, 1963; Mackie, 1960).

The above generalized characteristics must be modified by the differences in capabilities that appear within individuals as well as within the classification (Butterfield, 1961; Cain and Levine, 1961; Kirk and McCarthy, 1961). Such differences include the presence of organic and emotional involvement (Gallagher, 1960; Lyons and Powers, 1963; Strauss and Kephart, 1955). Environmental factors also appear to have considerable influence upon the functioning level of the retardate and his social adaptability (Della-Dora, 1963; Kirk, 1964; Kolstoe, 1961; Larson and Olson, 1963).

Neither "educable" nor "uneducable" were appropriate terms for the more severely retarded. Therefore the term "trainable" developed (Williams and Wallin, 1959). Hill (1953) explains training as conditioning of the retarded by experiences that do not involve insight or mastery of basic academic skills. Thus, to Hill, training is primarily habit formation. Distinctions made between educable and trainable programs are currently based upon the child's potential to benefit from instruction in academic subjects or other traditional school offerings and his potential to participate in community life (Blessing, 1959; Goldberg and Cruickshank, 1958; Tisdall and Moss, 1962). The basic goal for the educable retarded is the attainment of personal, social, and economic security without supervision (Capobianco, 1958). It is hoped that the trainable will improve their mental, physical, and social behavior after training and will learn to protect themselves from common dangers. The basic goal for the trainable is that they will become socially co-operative and economically useful in their homes or in sheltered conditions (Capobianco, 1958; Hill, 1953).

Accounting for only about .4 per cent of the school population (Gardner and Nisonger, 1962), trainable children are only now receiving attention in the public schools. Trainable children most frequently have normal parents and siblings and come from all socio-economic levels. Physical abnormalities and medical problems are frequently present; disorders in communication, motor and visual co-ordination, and behavior are also common (Heber, 1961). Usually they are not a social threat to the community although their preference to play with younger children may cause concern. However, as noted by Davies and Ecob (1959), their childish behavior in unsupervised situations may more often be irritating to a community and result in actions that are detrimental to their own health and safety.

At present, programs tend to include only the minimal academic skills necessary for health and safety and to emphasize self-help and adjustment skills (Hill, 1953; Peck and Sexton, 1960). Current programs also attempt to prepare the trainable retarded to make a limited contribution toward their own economic support through participation in simple household tasks or through sheltered work situations (Perry, 1960; Rosenzweig and Long, 1960). However, a more favorable prognosis for their social adaptability appears to be emerging (Windle, 1962).

PUBLIC SCHOOL PROGRAMS FOR THE EDUCABLE MENTALLY RETARDED

Wallace and Starr (1960) have reported the results of a survey of the educational provisions made for the retarded by school systems of 106 large cities in the United States. Each city had a population of 100,000 or more according to the 1950 census. The 98 systems that responded to the questionnaire all had services for retarded children. The authors concluded that large cities tended to provide special day classes for the educable retarded more frequently than any other type of special educational placement, although the types of programs appeared to vary considerably.

The U.S. Office of Education (Mackie, Williams, and Hunter, 1963) made a national survey of the educational provisions for exceptional children in 1958. The results indicated that all of the states and 83 per cent of the 3,641 local public school systems that responded to the questionnaire had special facilities for the retarded. In the number of exceptional pupils enrolled, the retarded were surpassed only by the speech-impaired. While school placement practices varied widely, most of the retarded attended full-time special classes or special schools. A summary of housing practices showed that 66 per cent of the programs were located in elementary school buildings, 25 per cent were in secondary school buildings and the remaining programs were in other community facilities. The survey also indicated that preschool programs for the retarded were growing. Kindergarten classes were the most common, followed by combined nursery-kindergarten classes, while nursery classes alone were least common.

Perhaps most noteworthy in the U.S. Office of Education survey was the rapid growth within the decade in the number of systems reporting programs for the retarded. From 729 school systems in 1948, the number rose to 3,005 in 1958 for an increase of 312 per cent. The significance of the growth appears not to be in the number of systems making provisions for the retarded but in the expansion of the programs to small towns, and to rural and sparsely settled areas.

The variability of the types and content of school programs for the educable retarded appears to be influenced by the nature and degree of the retardation, and by CA and the needs of the retardate. Other influences on the program are the organization, geographical location, economic and population characteristics of the school district, and the educational philosophy that exists in the particular district offering the program.

The ability to provide multiple programs, each designed to meet the needs of a more homogeneous group, resides largely within densely populated school districts (Wallace

and Starr, 1960). In smaller towns and in rural areas, programs tend to be developed for children having a wider range in CA, ability, and type and degree of impairment (Travelstead, 1960). However, most of the programs commonly found for the educable retarded in any geographical area may be found within the organizational plans that follow. These organizational plans, and much of the discussion about them, were taken from the writings of Connor and Talbot (1964), Cruickshank (1958a), Dunn (1963), Kirk and Johnson (1951), and Wallin (1955), and from curriculum guides.

REGULAR CLASS WITH NO SPECIAL PROVISIONS

As indicated by the Report on Mental Retardation (President's Panel, 1962), only one out of four retardates is receiving adequate educational services. Certainly the greatest number of educables is now in a regular class without special provisions being made for them.

Opposition to special classes is most often based upon their costs or upon the disadvantages of separating retarded and normal children (Cruickshank, 1958b; Doll, 1962; Horn, 1924; Wallin, 1955). Special classes for the retarded, however, are not as expensive for a local school system as some persons might expect (Fitzgibbon, 1964). The advisability of educating the retarded apart from normal children is not as easily determined. Opponents to the separation of children argue that separate education is unsound since all individuals, including the retarded, must function in a competitive society consisting of individuals with varying degrees of ability. The essence of their argument is that educating the retarded in a protected environment is not realistic because they will be ill prepared to meet the demands of life after their schooling is completed.

Extreme objections to educating the retarded apart from normal children appear to be refuted by the abundant current literature concerned wtih the total problem of retardation. Moderate objections to the separation of the retarded, though, appear to be supported by professional educators as reflected in curriculum guides and in the emphasis placed upon the need for the retarded child to have association with normal children (Krugman, 1962; Levine, 1961; Reynolds, 1962).

REGULAR CLASS WITH CONSULTATORY SERVICES

In this plan, the child is enrolled in and receives instruction in the regular class. A teacher with training for and experience with the retarded serves as a consultant for the regular teacher of the class that the child attends. The consultant usually works with the teacher, although he may work with an individual child or with small groups of children for short periods of time. The consultant suggests and provides materials for unique experiences for the retarded within the classroom. Usually, though, an attempt is made to provide counsel and materials that will enable the retarded child to participate in the regular classroom activities without undue deviation from the regular curriculum. This plan has been found helpful for small districts in which retarded children are too few or too widely scattered to form a class. The plan has also been gaining popularity for the more academically and socially able retarded.

REGULAR CLASS WITH ITINERANT SERVICES

This plan is similar to the consultant plan in that the child is enrolled in a regular class, but differs from consultative services in that the itinerant teacher has the prime responsibility for working with an individual child or with small groups of children. The itinerant teacher may teach a program that is entirely independent of the regular class. However, an attempt is usually made to work closely with the classroom teacher. This plan has been rejected for the retarded by Cruickshank (1958b) and by Kirk (1962) because it is based on a premise that tutoring in an academic subject will alleviate the mental retardation.

SPECIAL CLASS

The special class for the educable retarded is most frequently located in a regular school building and is usually composed of 12 to 15 children at the primary and intermediate levels or of 18 to 25 adolescents at the advanced level. The rationale most often presented for the special class is that it allows the retarded child to continue relationships with normal children and, at the same time, makes available to them the necessary special experiences materials, and methods.

Among the several types of educable special classes are the "self-contained," the "segregated," and the "integrated." A self-contained class is one in which the special teacher has primary responsibility for the instructional program for the child; the children, however, usually do have contact with intellectually normal children. This type of class is most common at the primary and intermediate program levels. In a segregated class the retarded have no contact with other children. An integrated class is one in which the children may attend a special class for as little as one instructional period and the remainder of the school day be with the rest of the student body. Thus, the self-contained class could be thought of as partially integrated. In self-contained classes, the special teacher provides abstract and intellectual educational experiences and for the development of many social-civic skills. The children are integrated with normal children for subjects such as physical education, music, of school activities. In some partially integrated programs, individual children may be integrated into a regular class for a subject area such as arthmetic, science, or social studies.

As advanced programs are often in a high school that is departmentalized, they are generally integrated programs.

PROGRAM LEVELS

Special education programs are organized according to levels of development into groups, with each three years being termed a program or a program level. A complete educational program would consist of preschool, primary, intermediate, advanced, and postschool program levels.

The Preschool Program. The preschool program is a fairly recent addition to the public school and grew out of interest in the effects of cultural deprivation (Connor and Talbot, 1964; Hosley, 1963). It is for children with a CA of 4 to 6 years who have a MA of 2 to 4 years. Emphasis is placed upon language development, perceptual and conceptual development, self-help skills, and social living.

At present, preschool programs tend to be experimental. Judging from current views about retardation and the results of the Office of Education survey, it appears that their number will increase rapidly.

The Primary Program The primary program is for children with CA of 6 to 9 years and a MA of about 3 to 7 years. Much of the content is similar to that found at kindergarten level. Most often the emphasis is placed upon the development of socially acceptable standards of behavior, work habits, and readiness for academic instruction. Since some of the children in this program will have been transferred from a regular class, readiness for arithmetic and reading may be a proper emphasis for the primary program, but formal arithmetic and reading experiences may also be appropriate for some children.

The Intermediate Program. This is the most frequently found program and is for the children with a CA of 10 to 12 years and a MA of 5 to 9 years. The emphasis at this level is most often upon the development of skills in basic subject areas (arithmetic, health, oral and written communication, reading, and science) and upon developing the abilities necessary for living in society. The intermediate program is generally conceded as being the most appropriate level for the retarded child to make the most progress in academic skills. Therefore, some teachers conduct a rather formal program. Others, believing that social living skills are more important, emphasize the unit method of teaching presented by Descoeudres (1928), Ingram (1953), Martens (1950), and Thorsell (1961).

The Advanced Program. The advanced program is for youths with a CA from 13 to 18 years having a MA of 7 to 12 years. Dunn (1963) indicates that these youths range in ability levels from two to seven years in grade capacity. In addition, extensive differences exist in their previous educational experiences. Smaller schools may have a single advanced class with a CA range as great as six years. Larger school districts, however, tend to separate the advanced programs into a junior high group for 13- to 15-year-old students and a senior high group for 16- to 18-year-olds.

As advanced programs terminate the public school education for most of the retarded, they tend to provide utilitarian school experiences. They are usually organized around a core plan as discussed by Saylor and Alexander (1959). The core may primarily consist of a combination of academic subject matter and the social-occupational skills that retardates need to function in society; or, the core may consist primarily of work experiences. While not precise, "core" will be used here to designate the former plan, and "work experience program" will be used to designate the latter.

In junior high core programs, the youth usually attends a special class for half a school day. Activities in the special class may consist of developing and making functional use of basic academic skills, tutoring in the work assigned in other classes, developing units centered around teen-agers' interests, or a combination of these activities. During the remainder of the day, the pupils usually take non-academic courses in the regular school program. Junior high pupils are frequently assigned work within the school for one period.

In a three-year junior high work experience program, an attempt is made to make maximum use of the facilities of the school to permit the retarded to orient himself to society and to the work world. The pupil's school day may consist of the core plan. However, the academic skills taught by the special teacher may use unit teaching, and the topic is of such a nature that the content can be specifically related to preparatory attitudes and skills necessary for work.

Senior high core programs usually extend junior high experiences. They differ in the types and degree of abstractness of the concepts presented, and with stress placed upon the social requirements of young adulthood. There is also a replacement of time spent in classes with some supervised work experiences within the school or community.

In the three-year senior high work experience program, the pupils' school day is often organized similarly to that of the junior high. However, beginning with perhaps one period of work during the first year, the length of the work experiences are increased in the second and third years. The trend in some schools is to place pupils into full-time work experiences in the third year with satisfactory employment for two or three years being a prerequisite for graduation (Eskridge and

Partridge, 1963; Rich and Beekman, 1954).

Another popular trend is the use of a "track plan" in order to provide more adequately for the needs of retarded children with varying degrees of ability (Kelly, 1955; Wallin, 1955; Wrightstone, 1959). It emerged as a result of differential goals that the educable students could reasonably be expected to attain. Track programs usually consist of a core program for those having the ability for further academic progress and a work experience program for pupils with minimal skills for or little interest in an academic program (Stanton and Cassidy, 1964; Syden, 1962).

The Postschool Program. Since the postschool program has the function of extending help to the retarded after their school experiences, it provides services for the drop-out as well as adults. Hence, the CA of those in the program may range from approximately 16 up. Services offered include vocational assessment and training, job placement and supervision, and counseling of both a personal and a vocational nature. School work concentrates upon functional application of basic skills and upon problems encountered in working. The length of work experiences vary, but frequently the retarded work part of the day and return to school for several hours. In some cases he may work a full day and attend school one evening a week.

Formerly, the postschool program was not a part of the school. Instead, the retarded became members of adult education groups, vocational schools, or vocational rehabilitation programs. However, the work experience programs of the last decade Eskridge and Partridge, 1963; Rich and Beekman, 1954) indicate the feasibility of and need for coordination between the school and other agencies that will assume primary responsibility for the retarded after the school years.

PUBLIC SCHOOL PROGRAMS FOR THE TRAINABLE MENTALLY RETARDED

Programs for the trainable have only recently become a part of the public schools. Kirk (1957) found that eighteen states had legislation permitting public education of trainable children in 1956. However, classes were just beginning to be organized. He found that the few preschool classes that existed were most often sponsored and managed by parents of retarded children. The preschool classes tended to be heterogeneous in composition, containing children too young for public school classes as well as school-aged children with low intelligence and with other behavioral problems. Classes for the trainable within the public school have rapidly expanded during the last ten years (NARC, 1961; Voelker and Mullen, 1963). Even though Farber (1959) found that approximately half of the 7- to 16-year-old exceptional children in Illinois who were not enrolled in school could be classified as trainable, the trend appears to be that trainable classes will continue to grow in number and in diversification. This expected growth is based upon increasing interest of professional persons in the trainable retardate (Blessing, 1959) as reflected in the number of experimental programs being conducted and the activities of organized local, state, and national agencies (Gershenson and Schreiber, 1963; Kurren, 1962; Williams and Wallin, 1959). Current estimates indicate that a community should plan classes for one to two severely retarded persons per 1,000 school-aged children (Kirk, 1957). Based upon the result of a census of the severely retarded living in New York State, Bienenstok and Coxe (1957) estimated that eight to twelve children might be expected for enrollment in classes for trainable children in a community having a population of 10,000 school children. Kirk (1957) suggested that public schools should provide programs for trainable children between the ages of 6 to 16 years. Kirk recommended that a more appropriate program be provided for youths past the age of 16, such as sheltered-work situations.

The recency of the entry of the trainable into the school and the complex network of agencies that are partially responsible for the retarded make it difficult to isolate and describe the educational programs. The difficulty is compounded by the overlap in CA and degree of impairment within a program. The descriptions of the following programs, were principally taken from Gardner and Nisonger (1962), Kirk (1957), Kirk, Karns, and Kirk (1955), Niehm (1958), and Williams and Wallin (1959).

NURSERY SCHOOL PROGRAMS

These programs are for retarded children who are either too young or are too immature to attend a special education class. At this level, an attempt is made to develop basic self-help skills, speech, and language, and to provide successful social experiences for the child. In addition to diagnostic services for the child, counseling services are often provided for the parents. The nursery program also provides temporary relief for mothers from continuous care of the child.

THE SPECIAL CLASS

The special class is the most common program for the trainable in the public schools. These classes tend to consist of children having wider variation in abilities, CA, and etiology than classes for the educable retarded. The CA range within a special class for the trainable children is frequently stated as being from 6 to 16 years old. In practice, the upper limit may be 14 years old since some programs exclude children at this age or send them to sheltered workshops or to day centers. In rural areas, the age limit for trainable class attendance may be extended up to the early 20s. The program content is concerned most with basic communication, interpersonal skills, self-help, and sensory and perceptual development. Some teen-agers and the more capable young trainable retarded children may attain a second-grade academic level. Instruction, though, tends to be restricted to the functional use of rudimentary skills. The rationale for such restriction rests upon the notion that the achievement level of trainable retardates is too low to warrant the time and energy used to teach them. Semi-dependency only requires minimal skills necessary for health and safety. However, some evidence indicates that the expected work and behavioral level of trainable children may be too low (Cain and Levine, 1961; Capobianco and Cole, 1960; Peck and Sexton, 1960; Reynolds, 1963; Tisdall, 1960).

DAY CARE CENTERS

Day care centers are not actually a part of school systems. However, their preschool and postschool programs justify day care centers being presented as an example of a co-operative program that may be developed between the school and other agencies.

Day care centers tend to be in a transitional stage. Formerly they were organized by parents and other lay groups or by non-educational agencies to meet the needs of young school-age children and early teen-age youths who were excluded from school. Children excluded from school, of course, included the trainable as well as the more profoundly retarded. Thus, there existed a wide range in abilities and CA of the children in attendance. The centers were a terminal community service for the retarded. They served the needs of the children as best they could and as long as they could. Then the children were returned to their parents or institutionalized.

Before trainable classes were established by the schools, many day care centers conducted programs that were the forerunners of the current trainable classes. Some centers are still operating classes for children who would be eligible for trainable programs, but these children are rapidly being absorbed by the schools. Other day care centers now have preschool classes and the children are enrolled in public school trainable classes when they meet the school requirements.

The primary function of day care centers at present appears to be the provision of services for retarded children who are not enrolled in school because of the severity of their retardation or of physical or behavioral problems. The programs extend from services needed by very young to immature children to sheltered workshops and adult recreation. Thus, the school is apparently incapable of adequately meeting the needs of children in day care centers but may co-operate with their programs. A co-operative program could, for example, have the school provide instructional materials and, perhaps, a classroom and a teacher; parents could provide lunches, transportation and some funds; other agencies could provide health services and family counseling; and others, sheltered workshops and recreational facilities.

SHELTERED WORKSHOPS

The school places emphasis upon adjustment by the trainable child to the community and his family, his performance of simple routine tasks, and his acquisition of skills and attitudes for these roles. However, school programs for the trainable are frequently terminated prematurely. The care and support of the young adult often becomes the responsibility of the parents. A fortunate few of the more capable children receive vocational training services, some receive the aid of social service agencies, some are institutionalized, a few are sent to private schools, but the majority remain at home without help.

To provide a continuous program for the trainable persons to become less dependent upon others, parent and private groups established sheltered workshops. However, as workshops require a fairly large population from which to draw eligible members, are expensive to operate, and are complex in organization and structure, they have been developed most often in large cities. However, an increasing growth in the number of workshops has been noted (Niehm, 1958).

Workshops might best be a responsibility of an agency other than the school. They have been presented here to demonstrate a complete program and as an example of the responsibility of the school to provide cooperative services with other agencies. The school, then, should actively encourage sheltered workshops but should not assume primary responsibility for organizing and conducting them.

ORGANIZATIONAL PROBLEMS

Special programs for the mentally retarded are growing in number, in variation, and in complexity. Empirical evaluation of specialized programs for the retarded is needed. Investigators have frequently attempted to compare retarded children enrolled in special education classes with those enrolled in regular public school classes or in institutional classes. As indicated by Cain and Levine (1963) and by Kirk (1964), these studies have not provided an acceptable evaluation of the effectiveness of programs. Among the problems encountered in the studies were inadequate control over environmental and teacher variables, variations in curricula and classroom placement, and the questionable reliability and validity of the measuring instruments used.

Most of the studies cited in this section, however, are evaluations of the effectiveness of special classes. In addition, the studies were selected so as to derive some organizational implications from problems encountered in educating the retarded. The studies to be reviewed are not necessarily the most significant nor the most comprehensive. More comprehensive reviews of the literature are presented by Cain and Levine (1963), Charney (1963), Goldstein (1964), Heber (1963a), Johnson (1962), and Kirk (1964).

Mullen and Itkin (1961a) compared the effectiveness of instruction used in educable special classes with that of the regular grades with respect to the retarded children's academic performance and adjustment. The sample consisted of 681 children who ranged in CA from 7 to 13 years old and in IQ from 50 to 74. Matched on nine variables, the resulting pairs had a mean CA of 11.35 years, a mean MA of 7.70 years, and a median IQ of 69.78. Of the sample group, 56 per cent of the children were males and 44 per cent were females. Mullen and Itken retested 140 matched pairs of retarded children at a one-year interval and 64 pairs at a two-year interval. The major hypothesis tested was that mentally handicapped children would profit more from instruction in a special class than in a regular class.

The data were obtained from standardized achievement tests, a test of general information and comprehension that pertained specifically to the curriculum for the mentally retarded, and various psychological and sociometric devices. By means of statistical controls, the data were evaluated throughout the two years of the study. The major findings were:

1. The median gain in reading and arithmetic was less than .5 year for those children with a MA of 6 years and above. The authors noted, though, that those in the upper quarter of the sample with respect to MA gained almost .9 year but those in the lower quarter made little or no gain.

2. The regular class group made a significantly larger gain in arithmetic over a one-year period than the special class group. However, no differences were found in the second year.

3. A significant decrease in hostility and superiority on a sociometric rating scale was found for the special class children.

4. Selective factors such as low socio-economic status, inadequate housing, contact with social agencies, extreme overcrowding, and family instability were associated with rapid placement in special classes.

Because of the difficulties encountered in matching the children, Mullen and Itken cautioned that their findings have limited applicability for other than lower socio-economic retarded children. They also indicated that, in both special classes and regular classes, the average academic achievement was not consistent with measured ability. The authors concluded that special class placement had been demonstrated to be superior to regular class for the more severely handicapped, for children with emotional problems, and for those from lower socio-economic levels.

Thurstone (1960) compared the intellectual growth, academic achievement, social development, and gross motor skills of educable mentally retarded children. The sample consisted of 1,273 children with an IQ range of 50 to 79; 769 children were in special classes and 504 were in regular grades. The Stanford-Binet, the Primary Mental Abilities Test, a test of gross motor skills, and various sociometric devices were administered at one- and two-year intervals. The results were:

1. On the first administration of the achievement test, the regular class retardates had a significantly higher achievement score than the special-class children in all areas except arithmetic computation.

2. No significant differences occurred between the placement groups on the second administration of the test. However, except in arithmetic computation, the gain scores were significantly higher in favor of the special-class children within the 50 to 59 IQ range.

3. Special-class children appeared to be better adjusted in school and to have more friends than the regular-class retarded. The mentally retarded in the regular grades were found to be rejected and to be social isolates.

Stanton and Cassidy (1964) compared the achievement and adjustment of educable mentally retarded children in regular classes with those in special classes and a third group of children from a state residential school. The students were divided into subgroups according to three IQ levels: 50 to 59, 60 to 69, and 70 to 75. In addition to finding that referrals for special classes were most frequently made

for children with low IQs and social maladjustment, the authors noted that, for the regular classrooms, the teacher was unable to divide his time among children with varying abilities and that the retarded were in competition with every other child in the class. Special classes differed from regular classes in that competition was minimized and the teacher's attention was on the retarded child.

Significant differences that emerged in academic gains were in favor of the regular-class group. The gains of both special- and regular-class students did not approximate what would be expected from their MA, except for children within the 50 to 59 IQ range, who achieved better than expected. The significant differences in social adjustment were in favor of the special-class group. However, as noted by the authors, the better social adjustment occurred in the protected environment of the special classroom. Stanton and Cassidy concluded that programs with a more limited range must be provided for the retarded. Current practices appear more adequate for the less capable retarded child and no equivalent program exists for the more capable. They suggest that special education must provide a situation that will approximate the competition of the regular classroom for the higher-IQ retardate but also reduce the competition so as to be stimulating rather than frustrating.

Goldstein, Jordan, and Moss (1962) reasoned that an "ideal" program would be necessary to evaluate the appropriateness of placing the retarded in special classes. The "ideal" program was defined as "an activated educational program under the leadership of well-trained, closely supervised teachers in a class that is relatively homogeneous in terms of abilities and ages of children" (Goldstein, Jordan, and Moss, 1962, p. 8). It would consist of a well-defined curriculum and precise teaching methods for children who meet the current criteria for classification as educable mentally retarded. In addition, children in an ideal program would not have been in regular class prior to placement. The authors also hypothesized that children would need to be in special classes for at least four years before positive changes could be expected.

They began a four-year study in 1962 of a sample consisting of incoming first-graders who obtained an IQ between 60 and 85 on the Stanford-Binet. Teacher competency, curriculum content, and teaching methods were controlled. The teachers selected for the study were those who had all been trained in special education. The "Curriculum Guide for Teachers of the Educable Mentally Handicapped" (Goldstein and Seigle. 1958) was revised and the "discovery method" was selected for use in the special classes. The discovery method is one "wherein the teacher arranges and manages conditions for learning so that the children participate actively in arriving at insightful solutions."

During the first two years of the study, the data were primarily individual intelligence and achievement test results. The home environment was evaluated by a sociologist, and an investigation of productive thinking was completed by Tisdall (1962). The results indicated that the regular-class retarded children were in the first quartile in testing even though the achievement of the classes in which they were enrolled was low. Further, about half of them were failed at the end of the first year. It was found that the average IQ for both the special and regular classes increased about seven points between the first and second testing. Little change in group averages occurred after the first year. The special classes were superior to the regular ones in arithmetic, in paragraph reading, and word knowledge, but were inferior in word discrimination. Tisdall also found that the special class children were more fluent in their speech, more original in their concepts, and more flexible in their thinking.

The authors concluded that the regular class retardates are low achievers; however, judgment must be withheld about the effectiveness of special classes. The regular-class retardates demonstrated more hostility and frustration than did the special-class retardates as the former became less capable of meeting the achievement expectancies of the regular grades.

Peck and Sexton (1960) compared the progress of trainable mentally retarded children over a two-year period in a public school class, a segregated class in a community center, and a class in a residential institution. At the initiation of the study, nine children were in class at each facility and a control group of nine children at home and in no organized program. The groups had an approximate CA range of 6 to 12 years, a MA of below 6 years, and an IQ range of 22 to 50.

At the end of the project, there were nine subjects in the public school class, six in the community center class, eight in the institutional class, and seven in the control group. A curriculum, lesson plans, and methods of instruction were developed for each teacher to follow to equalize teacher influence. The curriculum consisted of social adjustment, self-care, language development, physical development, music, arts and crafts, and economic usefulness. Progress in the seven areas of the curriculum was determined by ratings. Psychological and medical data and home background information was used to supplement the classroom observations.

The authors suggested that the following results should only be considered as trends: (1) The average performance of the subjects in classes was significantly above that of the control group; (2) The three classes did not differ significantly; and (3) None of the four groups showed significant changes in IQ or SQ. Peck and Sexton also found that all classes tended to make the greatest progress in the first half of the first year.

In comparing trainable children who attended school in the community or in an institution with those who lived in the community or institution but did not attend school, Cain and Levine (1961) were seeking ways of developing social competence in the trainable. Competence, defined as the attainment of skills that would permit the child to achieve self-sufficiency and increased social responsibility, was measured by a scale involving five areas: self-help, initiative, responsibility, social skills, and communication. Growth in competency was determined by the differences between the initial and final ratings on the scale. Community children were rated by their mothers and institutionalized children were rated by attendants. In addition, classroom procedures that contributed to social competence were rated by two project members.

Analyses indicated that social competence increased significantly for both the school and non-school groups in the community, while significant decrease in social competence appeared in both institutional groups. Approximately 11 per cent of the community class time (180 minutes a day) was directed toward social competency, the 11 per cent about equally divided between high- and low-quality instruction. Within the institution, approximately 9 per cent of the instruction, all of it of low quality (150 minutes a day) was directed toward social competency. Further, Cain and Levine found that the low behavioral ratings of the children were not observable to the teachers.

The authors concluded: (1) little time was given to the development of social competence in the present school programs; (2) the large amount of time in which the activities are unorganized or the activities are not directed toward increasing the child's social competence was mainly a result of the teacher's expectations about the children's abilities; (3) teachers accepted deviant behavior and performance below the level of the childrens' abilities and falsely assumed that there was little variation among the children; and (4) the residential institution provided little opportunity for the development of social competence. Despite the variety of services that must have been available in an institution, it might have been better to keep the trainable child at home.

The study of Mullen and Itkin (1961b), who evaluated four months of reading instruction for the educable mentally handicapped, is important in its attempt to control the teacher variable. Each teacher was assigned to one of the following methods: (1) a free reading program based upon the pupil's interest; (2) correlated units that centered around topics of social, and personal importance to the children and cut across subject lines; (3) instruction in each of the basic school subjects; and (4) phonics emphasis.

Close contact was maintained with each teacher in order to provide uniformity among the various method groups. Data were gathered through the use of an achievement battery, reading tests, and personality and behavior evaluations. Comparison of the progress of the groups at semester intervals indicated no general superiority for any of the four methods of teaching reading. The "interest method" was found to be superior to the "units method" for retarded members of the advanced classes in general information and comprehension. The "subjects method" was superior to the "units method" for the better, but not the poorer, readers of the primary classes. The data were rendered tentative by a disconcerting teacher attrition, attributed to illness and to the inability of some of the teachers to adequately carry out the experimental conditions.

As indicated by the authors, the study exemplifies the difficulties encountered by teachers in using and applying materials and concepts appropriate to the various methods of reading instruction. The difficulties occurred even under close supervision, indicating that more study is needed of teacher personality and effectiveness.

Cruickshank and Haring (1957) developed a project to demonstrate that the use of lay persons in special education programs would make more individualized instruction in the classroom possible and would increase the quality of education of exceptional children.

Eleven women who volunteered their services as teacher assistants were employed. All high-school graduates, they ranged in age from 28 to 65 years old and were motivated by an expressed interest in exceptional children. The women were required to serve for not less than four hours per day for five days a week throughout the academic year. Evaluation of the project was made by periodic observation of the classroom, reports from teachers, assistants, and parents of the children, and a final report by the teachers. All of the teachers were found to be favorable toward the use of assistants. Each teacher reported that she was able to do more planning, to provide more materials, to give more individual attention to the children, and to increase her quality of instruction. Parents unanimously indicated that their children gained from the teacher assistant plan. To improve the plan, a workshop was recommended for the assistants before their placement in a classroom. The purpose of the workshop was to provide specific training in the kinds of duties appropriate to each type of exceptionality.

The authors concluded that teacher assistants did not take over any of the regular teacher's duties but that they were important in the adjustment of children who were being integrated into regular classrooms. In addition to being a plan to help meet the shortage of trained teachers, Cruickshank and Haring indicated that teacher assistants may be a necessary part of educational programs for exceptional children.

RECENT TRENDS IN ELEMENTARY SCHOOL ORGANIZATION

Within the last decade, studies of grouping practices for instructional purposes have increased (Floyd, 1954; Harris, 1960; Hillson, 1965a; Stoddard, 1958). Out of these studies has emerged an indication of dissatisfaction with the traditional grade-school organization. An awareness also has developed for the need to improve the educational attainment of the child and, at the same time, to provide for the variation that exists within children grouped together in a particular grade (Hillson, 1965b).

The foremost interest in elementary education at the present time is in individualized instruction (Henry, 1962), which is an attempt to provide for the individual differences of pupils (Shane, 1962; Wilhelms, 1962). Incorporating all aspects of education, including curricular content, methods, objectives, and organization, individualized instruction places heavy emphasis on upgrading the student to higher achievement. This emphasis might well be carefully considered when examining the adequacy of current elementary programs for the mentally retarded.

Two of the organizational plans in elementary education that appear to be receiving the most attention are the nongraded program and team teaching. Much of the discussion of the nongraded program is found in Goodlad and Anderson (1963) and Hillson (1965b) Anderson, Hagstrom, and Robinson (1960), Brownell (1963), Dean and Witherspoon (1962), and Shaplin and Olds (1964) supplied the basis for the discussion of team teaching.

THE NONGRADED PROGRAM

The nongraded program is concerned with the vertical organization of the school (i.e., the progression of the pupil from entry in school until he graduates). Vertical organization differs from horizontal organization in that the latter is concerned with grouping children by ability for instructional purposes (Goodlad and Rehage, 1962; Shane, 1962). The nongraded program and attempts to implement it appear to have aroused a considerable controversy. In general, it is an organi-zational plan that consists of three-year blocks of time. The purposes of the plan are to eliminate grade levels, to incorporate the principles of child development into the school situation, and to provide continuous progress for the child (Hillson, 1965b).

The nongraded plan is thought of as part of a larger function of the school. Concepts. skills and values are developed over a period of several years of schooling. Each child attempts to attain as many of them as possible but at his own speed, regardless of the time it may take him. The child's reading level is generally used for advancing him through the nongraded plan. The nongraded plan does not alter the teacher-pupil ratio, which remains about 1 to 25. However, the nongraded plan does necessitate a wide range of materials to meet the needs of the children, even though the range of a particular group of children may be reduced. In addition, traditional report cards are eliminated, progress reports, conferences, and evaluative letters are used instead. Fundamental changes also are needed in curriculum and instructional practices (Goodlad and Anderson, 1963). Schools appear to experience considerable difficulty in making the necessary changes. In a study of 89 communities claiming to have nongraded schools, Goodlad and Anderson (1962) found that the teachers and parents had considerable difficulty in eliminating the expectations of graded classrooms. The investigators also found that most of the schools tended to make horizontal modifications in their school organization and gave practically no consideration to the critical aspects necessary for a nongraded program. According to Hillson's extensive review (1965a), the positive aspects of nongraded elementary programs for mentally retarded children are:

1. Children compete with their own record rather than with each other.

2. Children are happier without worry about promotion.

3. Pressure to achieve end-of-term goals are reduced or eliminated.

4. Some slow learners achieve more through additional time to assimilate new concepts.

5. No gaps exist in instruction nor does repetition of materials occur since a child begins a new school year where he left off.

6. The program is adaptable to lags and spurts in growth.

7. The emotional needs of the children are better met.

8. Flexibility in grouping reduces the discipline problems and permits a child to complete the program without failure experiences.

9. Nongrading provides an increased awareness by teachers of pupil individuality.

Disadvantages included in Hillson's list of nongraded programs for the mentally retarded include:

1. Nongrading without curriculum reform does not remove the problems existing in graded organization.

2. Since curricula are organized around grades and graded textbooks, basic changes in the school must be made, or curricular pattern and school organization will be incompatible.

3. Some difficulty is encountered by the child when making the transition from nongraded to graded programs.

4. Teachers show tendency to retain grade concepts and grade expectancies.

5. Teaching is more challenging and difficult.

6. Extensive records must be kept for each child.

7. Nongrading alone does not improve achievement. Significant differences in instructional practices is necessary.

8. New parent reporting procedures need to be planned, because the traditional marking system is inappropriate.

TEAM TEACHING

Team teaching is an attempt to adapt the school to the population increase and to organize pupils into instructional groups so as to take advantage of research findings and of recent developments in education. Team teaching attempts to provide better instruction through the use of lay persons and the more effective use of teaching personnel. Further, it is a plan to attract and hold competent teachers by developing a hierarchy of teaching with increasing responsibilities and financial remuneration for better trained and more competent teachers (Anderson, 1961; Dean and Witherspoon, 1962).

Many different team patterns exist. A team may consist of two teachers working together at a grade level or within a subject area, or may extend to a complex eight- to ten-member team that cuts across grade and subject levels (Brownell, 1963; Shaplin, 1961). As a horizontal organizational plan, a team may be developed within many vertical organizational plans, which is particularly recommended by Goodlad and Anderson (1963) for the nongraded program.

Basically, the team consists of a group of teachers who have joint responsibility for a large group of students. The number of students for whom the team is responsible varies with the number of team members. The teacher-pupil ratio usually is equal to the approximate 1 to 25 of traditional classrooms although instructional groups may vary from one child to 200 children (Anderson, Hagstrom, and Robinson, 1960). Thus, team teaching is a refinement of the role and duties of teachers into a co-operative unit, not a plan to reduce the number of teachers (Dean and Witherspoon, 1962). The team forms a distinct unit within the school (Brownell, 1963). Teachers are responsible for all subjects, so the team is not a departmentalized program. The students for which the team is responsible are treated as a complete unit. For instructional purposes, the grouping is based on the need of the pupils and is very flexible. For example, remedial work and work required by the special needs of individual pupils can be given by a team member.

Advantages of team teaching listed by Hillson (1965a) that appear pertinent for the retarded are:

1. The ability of the team to provide for a wide range and depth of competencies needed for curricular areas and instructional methods.

2. The basic group is so large that small groups can be formed for almost any purpose.

3. During large-group teaching periods, other teachers are free to work with small groups, to plan, or to engage in other activities.

4. The team is adaptable to the use of educational television, programmed instruction, and visual aids, as well as to improve the use of more conventional methods and materials.

5. Team members are not isolated and have the advantage of a mutual exchange of information and viewpoints.

6. Evaluation is the combined effort of several persons.

7. The team will provide stability to a program through a nucleus of upper-echelon personnel even with a fairly frequent change of teachers.

Some of the disadvantages noted by critics of team teaching with the retarded have also been enumerated by Hillson (1965a):

1. Because of the recency of most of the programs placed into operation, the value of team teaching has not yet been established.

2. Appropriate criteria for transferring a child from one group to another is difficult to establish.

3. Contact with a large group of team members leads to complex human relations.

4. Opportunities for pupil leadership may be lost because of the complexities of the program and the size of the group.

5. Noise may be a problem in a large group or when small groups are working in one room.

6. Instruction may tend to become lecture-type and formal.

7. Teachers with the special competencies and qualifications necessary for team leaders and senior teachers will be difficult to find.

8. Specific qualifications and functions of the team members are lacking.

9. Team teaching will probably cost more because the team leaders and senior teachers will be paid more, secretarial help will be necessary, and new buildings with adjustable space will be needed.

RECOMMENDATIONS

The five recommendations that follow are proposed to meet the complexity of school organization for the mentally retarded, of the difficulties encountered in teaching them and evaluating programs for them, and of current trends in elementary school organization. The recommendations are conceived as applicable to both the educable and the trainable. They are made with reference to large- and medium-size school districts. However, they also take cognizance of the administrative requirements and unique problems associated with smaller schools. The basic recommendations may be implemented in these schools with only minor modifications. The willingness of a school district to investigate organizational change is more at issue than the inappropriateness of the organizational suggestions that follow.

RECOMMENDATION NO. 1

A comprehensive program for the mentally retarded requires that the school clearly define the extent and limitations of its role and services to the retarded and provide adequately those services for which it is responsible. Educational programs for the mentally retarded are part of a total educational institution and are directly influenced by its purposes. Current concepts of the central purpose of education must be understood by those responsible for the retarded.

The Educational Policies Commission of the National Educational Association (1961) declared that the central purpose is the development of the student's rational powers. The meaning of the term "rational powers" as used by the commission is not clear (Brameld, 1961), but it appears to emphasize the use of logic and available evidence to bring about critical thinking. Attainment of this purpose is currently advocated through mastery of the knowledge contained in subject matter, especially that contained in foreign languages, mathematics, and science (Forshay, 1961; Phenix, 1962). As indicated in a recent poll of elementary and secondary principals (NEA, 1962), the emphasis on subject matter is increasing and is moving down to the lower grades. These principals also indicated that the trend is to organize the content into broad fields based on problems of living and to increase the use of teacher aids and technological media. An increasing pressure for more academic work and achievement was also indicated.

The current emphasis upon academics and the limited concept of the purpose of education have not been unchallenged. Perkinson (1963), for example, objected to children being referred to as "natural resources." He suggested that the school be pluralistic and be concerned with the expressive as well as the cognitive domain. Brameld (1961, 1962) advocated a radical redefinition of the purpose. He stresses that the school should be an active leader and participant in bringing about social change for a world civilization. World civilization, to Brameld, is directed toward the attainment of the "widest and deepest aspirations of the greatest number of human beings everywhere on earth."

Opposing views as to the purpose of education indicate that school districts might do well to examine their programs and their goals with respect to the retarded. Some suggestions for the education of the retarded may come from the research related to the educational implications of socio-economic class. The work of Coleman (1961), Havighurst (1962), Kaplan (1963), and Vontress (1963) demonstrates that some of the problems associated with retardation may also be found among the economically deprived. Thus, the purposes of education for both groups may be similar because of the commonality in their educational needs. A project now being conducted (North Carolina State Department of Public Instruction, 1965) with respect to the education of lower socio-economic children may become especially significant for the retarded.

Mental retardation has educational, medical, psychological, and social components (Begab, 1963). A comprehensive program for the retarded involves some services that are outside the function of the school (Appell, 1963; Tisdall and Moss, 1962). The educational institution should note the trend toward national, state, and local co--operation in meeting these needs (Kurtz, 1964; Mooring and Currie, 1964; Nisonger, 1963) and assess its contributory and co-operative role as a member of the team. The school may assume primary responsibility for the children during one segment of their life. However, this segment of the child's life should not be introduced suddenly and terminated abruptly (Connor and Talbot, 1964; Wolinsky, 1961). The school's primary responsibility for the children should be accomplished through preschool and postschool programs. In addition, since no single agency is capable of providing all of the services related to retardation, the school should co-ordinate its services with other agencies even during the school years (Goldstein, 1963).

The varied and extended services needed by the retarded make it necessary that school buildings do not remain idle for long periods of time. Maximum efficiency should be ob-

tained from community buildings. The school may provide facilities for non-school personnel to offer services such as recreational programs, diagnostic services, and parent counseling. These services however, can and should be scheduled so as not to interfere with the educational program.

In addition, the program content, as well as continuity, should be uniform if adequate school services are to be provided. Simches and Bohn (1963) concluded that special curricula for the retarded did not exist. The implication that a curriculum for the retarded would need to be unique and not be found in the regular class is difficult to accept. However, their suggestion that curricula need to be developed by professional organizations that have the knowledge and skills of many disciplines rather than by scattered individuals and groups has merit.

Johnson (1962) supports the need for some curricular uniformity. He believes that special education, which is supposed to be of benefit to the retarded, has not resulted in better learning by special-class pupils as compared to regular-class retardates. Steigman (1964) has opposed Johnson's conclusion that the incentive for learning has been removed by concentrating too much on success. However, Johnson's conclusion and the frequent problems encountered by teachers working with the retarded suggest that curricular uniformity that includes guides for levels of attainment may be desirable.

Curricular guides developed at the state level tend to be flexible in content. Some flexibility in curricular content is desirable because of the diversity of community and individual needs but requirements for uniformity also exist (Begab, 1963; Bruner, 1963). State personnel should not develop curricula and impose them upon local school systems, but the timidity to propose content sometimes found in state programs tends to reduce uniformity.

Developing such uniformity through committees may be possible at the national, state and local levels. As visualized at the national level, the committee would represent a wide range of geographical regions, disciplines, and subject areas. This committee would be responsible for broad curricular content. Representative groups at the state level would add the unique requirements of the state to the basic curriculum developed at the national level. The local school system would then add its contribution. Thus the curricula in each local district would contain the uniformity of needs developed at the national level, the state level, and the local community. All must be designed to meet the unique needs of a specific group of retarded persons. The curricula should be highly specific, being developed by the universality of the subject or curricular area, not necessarily by the geographical level. For example, reading and oral communication content could be specifically developed at the national level and minor adjustments could be made at the local level. Content related to adjustment within the community, however, could be broadly outlined at the national and state levels and be specifically developed at the local level. Changes in these curricula would be made as needed but most changes ought to be made by the appropriate committee. A local school system could make a few minor changes in the national and state curricula but frequent revisions would be inadvisable, since any changes by a local school system would tend to negate the attempt to provide uniformity in the curricula.

The flexibility required by the unique needs of the individual may be attained through three ways: (1) the content would be in sequential order thus permitting continuous progress; (2) the content developed by the local system would be directed to the needs of children within each community; and (3) the teacher would still have considerable freedom in the class for meeting individual differences. A uniform curriculum does not need to violate the necessity of providing for the diverse needs of the retarded nor need it regiment classroom procedure.

RECOMMENDATION NO. 2

Programs should reflect an expectancy of greater achievement from retardates, especially in the academic area.

The present expectations for the academic attainment and social adjustment of educable and trainable retarded children in special classes appear to be unduly influenced by the less capable children in each classification (Mullen and Itken, 1961a). Differences in tests were also found to influence achievement

results (Smith and Stroud, 1960); however, the lower-IQ trainable and educable retarded made the most gains. The larger gains made by the less able retarded children seems to be associated with the teacher being most concerned with these children (Cain and Levine, 1961; Goldstein, Jordan, and Moss, 1962; Stanton and Cassidy, 1964). The capabilities of the retarded seem to be underestimated by the special-class teacher, and in many cases, she becomes engulfed in efforts to provide for the more severely retarded child. Blue (1964) noted that assumptions and generalizations regarding the capabilities of trainable children were commonly unfounded and led to inappropriately low expectations for workshop participants. Blatt (1960) found that, in textbooks, many popular views about retardation often were not supported by the literature.

One generalization that probably most influences teachers is the use of the MA for curriculum development. In fairness, the MA is most frequently suggested as a guide for curriculum content and expected achievement, but teachers tend to rely upon it as an ultimate criterion. Apparently they transpose the IQ to an MA and assign unwarranted stability to it. Teachers may allow for some change in MA due to maturational processes, but they do not make sufficient allowance for the difficulties encountered in intelligence testing or changes in the IQ which may occur. Most teachers of the retarded would agree that, under normal environmental conditions, intelligence, as measured on intelligence tests, may only shift approximately 3 to 5 points. Many, in fact, might agree with Clarke (1961), Husen (1961), Leahy (1935), and Wheeler (1942) that major changes in adverse environments characterized by cruelty, neglect, and educational isolation may result in IQ shifts as great as 20 points. However, teachers' expectancy of too little achievement from the retarded appears to be most related to the teachers' use of goals that are congruous with the concept of intelligence obtaining maturity by the age of 16. Expected goals established by acceptance of the above concept has major limitations. Terman and Merrill (1960) now conceive that intelligence may continue to grow to at least 18 years of age, and Bayley (1955) has demonstrated that some 25-year-old adults with an MA of 12 still improve. Thurstone (1926) has shown that an adult with an

MA of 12 and a normal child with a CA of 12 are not the same because of variations in the test items and the experiences of the individuals. Teachers appear to accept MA units as equal and as uniform in magnitude from year to year, contrary to the fact that they are adjusted to permit the computation of IQs. Mental test scores also may fluctuate widely for individual children although they appear to be useful for prediction purposes over short periods of time. These fluctuations may be related to the age of testing and interval between tests, or variations within the test, the individual, or his environment (Honzik, MacFarlane, and Allen, 1948; McCandless, 1964; Vernon, 1961). In addition, the importance of general intelligence appears to decrease as children grow older, while dependency upon specific factors appears to increase (Garrett, Bryan, and Perl, 1961). General intelligence also may be a manifestation of the whole personality as indicated by Wechsler (1950) and not be restricted to intellectual ability.

Some authors have recommended that a child be assessed by a battery of devices and by means of multidisciplinary team for placement in a class (Kirk, 1957; Wallace and Starr, 1960), Gallagher and Moss (1963) suggest that a profile of test results are more useful than a single score. In addition, the work by Kirk and McCarthy (1961) and Mueller and Weaver (1964) indicates that a profile of psycholinguistic abilities can be much more significant for programming for a child than a simple MA. Thus, the achievement expectancies for a child should be based upon a profile of his performance and an analysis of his educational needs rather than on a global concept such as MA.

The greater gains in social adjustment made by special-class children (Mullen and Itkin, 1961a; Stanton and Cassidy, 1964) and the tendency for the difference in academic achievement between special- and regular-class retardates to disappear during the second year (Goldstein, Jordan, and Moss, 1962) indicates that teachers are being successful with children with severe handicaps. These studies also indicate that teachers of the retarded must cope with severe behavioral problems that demand immediate attention. However, teachers may place too much stress for classroom practicalities, resulting in a lack of em-

phasis upon academic success. Bruner's (1963) suggestion that attention be paid to the learning process might alleviate some of the teachers' problems of discipline and instructional techniques, and increase the academic achievement of the retarded. In Bruner's view, the fundamental concepts of the subject matter to be learned should be presented for the child's intuitive understanding. In this process, fundamental ideas or concepts are those that have wide and powerful applicability for learning how things or ideas are related. Intuition refers to grasping the meaning of a problem or a situation without dependence upon analytic thinking. After a child has intuitively grasped a basic understanding of simple concepts, more complex applications of them should be developed through instruction. Such an approach appears to be advantageous for the development of the systematic step-by-step instruction generally recommended for the retarded. Repetition would also occur as the fundamental concepts and ideas are applied in accordance with the child's ability to understand and use them in increasingly complex situations.

The finding that retarded children were able to engage in productive thinking (Tisdall, 1962) and that the social adjustment of special class children improves supports the suggestion by Goldstein, Jordan, and Moss (1962) that special education classes may be accomplishing more than is evident in a one- or two-year study period. For this reason, special-class organization should not be abandoned, but it should be upgraded primarily through more emphasis upon the academic areas.

The primary and intermediate special class should consist of a balanced program with approximately half its time devoted to academically related instruction and the remaining time devoted to social and personal adjustment skills. At the advanced level, academics should comprise about one-fourth of the time and the remaining three-fourths time should consist of work or work-preparatory skills development. The retarded should not be expected to achieve as normal children do, nor should emphasis upon academic attainment be at the expense of the necessary concern for the social and emotional growth of the pupils. However, all retardates, including the older and more capable trainable, should have exposure to and the opportunity to develop basic academic skills. Such skills obviously should be adjusted to the child's capabilities.

RECOMMENDATION NO. 3

The school must provide a comprehensive program that is more compatible with the differences within mental retardation and the concepts of "educable" and "trainable."

A review of the complexity of school organization for the mentally retarded reveals that the term "special class" or "special education" is about as meaningful and descriptive as the term "mental retardation." Many types of retardates including familial retarded, neurologically impaired, and multiple-handicapped children are all frequently included in the same program (Krugman, 1962). A finer educational differentiation must be made. This means that with the current concept of retardation including children with IQs of 85 or less (Goldstein, Jordan, and Moss, 1962; Heber, 1961) a comprehensive organizational plan must be developed with ranges from nearly regular education to that which is appropriate for children who are barely trainable.

The emphasis should reflect the current trend of a close integration of the programs for the retarded with the total school curricula (Voelker and Mullen, 1963).

The comprehensive plan can be developed by combining the nongraded program and the track plan with an adaptation of the hierarchy of special education developed by Reynolds (1962). His plan is based on the number of children needing specialized services and the kinds that a school may provide, varying from those that are given in the regular classroom to those obtained in hospitals and treatment centers. The plan can be used to differentiate children—the more capable or better socially adjusted children being placed in regular class, and other retarded children being integrated in special class for much of the day. Other special-class children may have minimal integration, while others, may be the responsibility of the preschool and postschool or work experience programs. In still another group, exemplified by workshops, the school would provide co-operative services only.

The track plan suggested by Kelly (1955) involved placing children over 12 years old into three groups. As suggested, the CA range within each of the three groups would be about three years. The first group would contain children with a CA range of 12 to 15 years old, having IQs of 50 to 79; the second group, a CA range of 15 to 18 years old, having an IQ range of 50 to 64; and the third group, a CA range of about 15 to 18 years old, having IQs of 65 to 79. The first group in Kelly's plan is commonly found in junior high school classes. Her suggestion that the 15- to 18-year-old group be subdivided into two groups having a smaller IQ range than the frequently found 50-to-80 spread is of special interest. Also of interest is the necessity of developing specific curricula that are commensurate with the abilities of each group.

Track programs can be viewed as continuous guides, paralleling each other and providing a commonality of experiences, but with distinct variations in the goals and objectives of each track. The power of each program should be in its flexibility to serve the individual student. In some cases, the goals for an individual may need to be shortened; in other cases, they may need to be extended. An individual should never be bound to any one track but be assigned to another as his needs change. In addition, as new knowledge about retardation is gained, the goals and objectives of a program will change as well.

Individualized education required by the complexities of retardation could be met by extending track plans down to beginning school programs, which could operate within the framework of the modified organizational plan of Reynolds (1962). Each track would have a distinct plan, function as a nongraded program, and involve the total education of the retarded from entrance into school until he takes his place in the community.

The child would be placed in a track program according to his estimated potential for independent adjustment in the community. In addition to being carefully assessed for placement in a track, each child should be continuously evaluated. The latter procedure is expensive, but a question may be raised: how expensive is it to adequately educate a child?

The number of track programs and their emphasis will vary with the number of needs of the mentally retarded children in a particular school district. In general, at least two tracks should be developed within each of the present educable and trainable groups. Some tracks may include: (1) children enrolled in regular class but also receiving special services; (2) special-class children with fairly high academic and social potentiality who need, at least temporarily, more individual attention; (3) children with low academic potential but having fairly high potential for work adjustment; (4) multihandicapped children needing considerable services of various specialized personnel; (5) more capable trainable children with a fairly high potentiality for community adjustment, and (6) barely trainable children with a potential for minimal community adjustment.

RECOMMENDATION NO. 4

With the exception of those retardates having severe behavioral disturbances, team teaching should be used for the instruction of the mentally retarded.

Review of nongraded programs revealed that special classes for the retarded have been organized along nongraded lines. Team teaching has been recommended for nongraded programs (Goodlad and Anderson, 1963) and also for the retarded (Taylor and Olsen, 1964), although the team usually suggested is a multidisciplinary one concerned with the total care of the retarded (Wolinsky, 1961). Team teaching appears to be compatible with the suggested hierarchy of special services that the school may provide. The track program could serve as a guide for the development of services; team teaching could be used for the organization of instructional groups.

The problems encountered in teaching the retarded may be too complex for a single teacher. The effect upon the teacher laboring alone and being unappreciated professionally was clearly presented in the study by Cain and Levine (1961). Apparently, special-class teachers need help in the classroom to relieve some of the isolation they feel. Much of evidence from working with teachers in the retarded field supports the conclusion of Cruickshank and Haring (1957) that they would welcome any help they can get. The advantages of team teaching (Hillson, 1965; Stanford Institute for Communication Research, 1962) may be instrumental in relieving some

of these problems in teaching retarded children. This is true whether team teaching is used in regular or in special classes.

The following suggestions are pertinent to practice of team teaching:

(1) Many retarded are now in regular classes and those who can benefit from the regular class should remain there.

(2) A teacher trained in working with the retarded should be a member of the regular school team. In addition to serving the retarded child, the teacher could provide valuable counsel to other members of the team.

(3) Team teaching for special classes can take two directions—comprehensive or specific. In the former case, the special class becomes part of a more comprehensive team functioning for the entire school population, and the special class children participate in all activities from which they can profit. The emphasis is on what the retarded can do, not on what they cannot. If a teacher doubts their ability to perform a task or to profit from a group experience, he should let them try anyway. The special teacher in a class that is a part of a more comprehensive team should be primarily responsible for working with the retarded in small-group learning. However, he should accept other duties as a team member, including responsibility for some large-group instruction. Likewise, teachers trained in regular school subject areas should also work with the retarded. The second direction team teaching can take is to function as a separate and distinct unit within the school. The team that serves only retarded children may be used where the school does not engage in comprehensive team teaching or when the children are severely retarded. This plan may be better used, for example, with trainable children. For this reason, enlisting only those persons trained in various areas of exceptionality seems best for a team for the retarded.

RECOMMENDATION NO. 5

The complexities of mental retardation require a program of continuous expansion of the professional competencies of the teacher of the retarded. This program should involve a hierarchy of preparation that connotes the co-operation of the teaching institution, the school system, and the professional initiative of the teacher.

Critics of teacher education contend that too much emphasis is placed upon dispensing information and unrelated theory (Bruner, 1963; Heathers, 1964). While research in the preparation of teachers has increased (Gage, 1963; Klohr, 1962), more study should be directed toward the teacher's activities in the classroom (Warburton, 1962). Heathers (1964) suggested that teacher education should be organized around operational definitions of learning goals and the teaching-learning process. The need for certification reciprocity and for some uniformity in teacher preparation is also apparent (Conant, 1963).

Conant (1963), Keppel (1961), and Sarason, Davidson, and Blatt (1962) agree that to improve teaching competency, professional education should occur after the student has attained a firm background in general education and in content areas. However, they disagree on when professional education should be initiated and how general competency may best be attained. Keppel (1961) and Sarason, Davidson, and Blatt (1962) agree that professional education should be provided in the last year of a five-year program. Conant (1963), however, believes that teachers can be prepared in four years. The five-year work-study plan by Trump (1958) and the use of undergraduate seminars (Sarason, Davidson, and Blatt, 1962) represent the emphasis being placed upon the need for practical experience by potential teachers.

The Ford Foundation reports (1960, 1962) indicated that attempts to improve teaching: (1) have led to the recruiting of teachers from the ranks of liberal arts graduates, (2) have strengthened teachers' liberal arts background, (3) have increased the use of five- and six-year programs for professional education, (4) have raised standards for teacher certification, and (5) have increased the use of seminars and internships. In addition, an increased emphasis on in-service training and summer institutes has been noted by Conant (1963) and Trump (1961).

In regard to certification, Krause (1963) found that requirements for teachers of the retarded were similar in all 50 states. Nevertheless, he recommended that there be nationally uniform certification requirements that would permit trained teachers of the retarded

to change their professional location without being hindered by the necessity of fulfilling some particular requirement of a state.

Heber (1963b) appears to imply that certification at the undergraduate level in both mental retardation and regular education may not be advisable where the meeting of the present general education requirements may result in dual certification. He reports that prior experience in regular-class teaching was not recommended as a requirement for admission to graduate training in mental retardation.

An upgrading of teachers' proficiency to work with the retarded and to broaden the teachers' exposure to various types of exceptional children also is recommended (Cain, 1964; Heber, 1963b). The problems encountered by teachers of the retarded can be seen clearly in the teaching of reading in the Mullen and Itkin study (1961b). They indicated that teachers of the retarded need a more adequate preparation than they are now getting. Moreover, teachers have reported a feeling of inadequate preparation to meet their complex responsibilities (Cain and Levine, 1961; Mackie, Dunn, and Cain, 1960). As noted by Sparks and Blackman (1965), an investigation appears to be needed urgently for the hypothesis that special preparation does result in a special approach to teaching the retarded child. Mackie, Dunn, and Cain (1960) found that teachers of the retarded restricted their interests in teaching methods to those applicable for the retarded. Cain (1964) suggested that interdisciplinary training is necessary and that teachers need more training in broad concepts rather than the specializations now used. Heber (1963b), citing recommendations of a national conference for standards for the preparation of teachers of the retarded, stated that an emphasis was placed upon the need for more depth in the biological and behavioral sciences. Cain (1964) and Heber (1963b) suggest that teacher candidates need direct contact with children while training.

While many organizational plans have been developed that have implications for the preparation of teachers (Hillson, 1965), team teaching appears to be receiving considerable attention in institutions of higher education (Shaplin and Olds, 1964). Team teaching for the preparation of teachers of the retarded appears to be a way of providing necessary depth and breadth in the training program, and it may also better prepare teachers to function in recent organizational patterns within the schools.

The team should consist of a multidisciplinary unit when preparing teachers of the retarded. One individual should co-ordinate the unit with each member of the team having status equivalent to the amount of responsibility he has for the students. Teachers responsible for working with the students during their practical experiences should be full members of the team. The team may be composed of members from the fields of biology, education, medicine, psychology, social work, and sociology. It should also contain personnel associated with other areas of exceptionality such as the emotionally disturbed, the physically handicapped, and the speech-impaired. The team members would, in most cases, have other institutional duties but would be able to become involved in the program as much as desirable. Students would be assigned to the team in, perhaps, the junior year, since the team, or parts of it, should function as a unit for two years with a given group of students. To strengthen the work of the team, staff members should be assigned who could work with the students on an individual basis and in small groups while they are in supervised teaching or in an internship.

The suggested team plan could permit the use of large- and small-group instruction, the use of seminars, and lecture periods. The plan would tend to permit the exposure of the students to the greatest variety of ideas and current research. Instruction about the use of instructional techniques and materials for the retarded also could be made more meaningful. Most of all, the plan can provide the necessary flexibility and yet demand the depth and discipline of scholarship. Many students preparing to teach the retarded would welcome a plan such as the team teaching and could demonstrate their ability to meet the demands of scholarship.

Track programs for the preparation of teachers to work with the retarded at various levels should be developed for regular class teachers, special education teachers, and master teachers of the retarded. Preparation at each of these levels is possible in the present structure of higher education.

Regular Class Teachers. Many retarded children are now in regular classes (President's Panel, 1962). Therefore, all teachers should have some preparation for helping these children. A program for the preparation of teachers of the intellectually normal to also work with the retarded in regular classes may be considered as the first-level track program. It might consist of an introductory course to exceptional children, a seminar, and practical experience with the retarded. The introductory course on exceptional children should be at the sophomore level, because it can be argued that a course at this level can be justified as part of general education requirements. In addition, a seminar concerned with the problems of educating exceptional children is suggested as part of the professional education sequence. The seminar may best be conducted after the student has had some professional education, probably in the senior year. When possible, practical experience with the retarded should be associated with the seminar (Sarason, Davidson, and Blatt, 1962).

Special Education Teachers. The second-level track program should prepare teachers with special competencies for teaching the retarded. Special teachers of the retarded should receive within a four-year period the basic preparation and certification to permit them to function in a classroom. This recommendation is made only if there is a hierarchy of preparation that includes an additional level of preparation (master teachers). The practicalities of the shortage of teachers and the costs to the student of longer preparation also are important.

Potential teachers of the retarded might be recruited as early as the freshman year of college. As indicated by Meyers (1964), freshmen who have exposure to retarded children prove to be a valuable source of teachers. Instead of course work related to mental retardation at the freshman level, the student needs practical experience with retardates by having the opportunity to perform simple service tasks within a class for the retarded or in a service clinic (Heber, 1963b). Practical exposure to classrooms and clinics for retardates should continue throughout the student's program. If team organization exists within a nearby school, participation within the team would be highly desirable. Further, future teachers should have a broad exposure to the field of exceptional children (Cain,

1964)). Therefore, the practical classroom experience ought to be extended to encompass experience with several types of handicapped children.

Supervised teaching experiences should be completed at least one term before the student graduates. Implementation of this would permit the student to return to the campus for a seminar and additional study. While students now have seminars while doing their supervised teaching, they have agreed almost unanimously that they wished to return to the campus after supervised teaching for clarification of many points of confusion and concern.

The teacher in a four-year program should be prepared and certified as a teacher of the mentally retarded so as to occupy a position in the team hierarchy presented by Anderson, Hagstrom, and Robinson (1960). The present policy of certifying a teacher in mental retardation and in elementary or secondary education (Heber, 1963b) is not recommended. Dual certification is sometimes justified on the basis that a student may not wish to teach the retarded after his preparation. Another reason given for dual certification is that students meet the requirements for special and regular education certificates, therefore they should obtain both of them. A further reason offered is that some states demand standard certification in order to teach the retarded. All of the reasons for dual certification are questionable. In the first place, preparation for dual certification is, at best, weak in both areas. Second, the present ambivalence toward entering the field of mental retardation could be reduced through the student's early experience with the retarded, the continuity of the program, and the excellence of it. Third, the emphasis of the teacher-of-the-retarded program is entirely different from that of regular teachers although the organizational plan is similar. Thus dual certification is not feasible.

Master Teachers. The third track in a special education program should prepare master teachers. Although it would consist of a fifth and sixth year of preparation, it should not be equated with obtaining a master's degree; that degree may be conferred, however. The program may be viewed as an extension of the four-year plan, adding depth to one's understanding of mental retardation and by extending the student's competency to assume more complex assignments. Students in the master teacher program should receive the benefits of the multidisciplinary team just as the four-year program. Institutions enrolling sufficient numbers of students in the fifth year may provide some group instruction and seminars. In institutions having smaller enrollments and in the sixth year, the programs would be individualized.

The master teacher program should be clearly differentiated from a program preparing administrative personnel. Emphasis in the fifth year should be placed upon seminars, individual work, and practical experiences for understanding the process of education. The sixth year should primarily be an internship. Students in the fifth and sixth year also should receive some instruction and supervised experience in the broader field of exceptional children. The students should have the opportunity to work in comprehensive organizational patterns where the retarded are in special classes and in regular classes.

A final recommendation for the master teacher program is that the fifth year emphasize experimental teaching and the development of methods and materials. A major emphasis should be placed on what methods and materials are appropriate or inappropriate and under what conditions are they successful or unsuccessful. The emphasis in the sixth year should be upon program development, interdisciplinary communication, personnel relationships, leadership responsibilities, and on research.

The continuous preparation required for teaching the mentally retarded makes it mandatory that the school system participate in the preparation of teachers. Teachers are not fully prepared in four years. Only basic preparation can be gained in such a short time. Thus, the school has the responsibility to help its teachers be familiar with recent developments. Schools should develop and conduct workshops, send teachers to college or university institutes, and retain professional personnel as consultants. One of the school's most important roles is to conduct experimental programs. A team leader, or his equivalent if the team organization is not in operation within a school, should assume responsibility for the experimental programs. In addition, experimental programs should not be restricted to that which occurs in the classroom. They should also involve experimentation with teacher preparation and organizational plans.

The most crucial aspect of teaching the retarded is the responsibility of the teacher to develop and maintain his professional competence. The training institution and the school system only provide an organizational structure to aid him. A competent teacher of the retarded is committed to his children and is interested in applying new theories and research findings. Such a teacher finds the retarded challenging and is always questioning his point of view, his methods, and his successes and failures. He is a perennial student, as the study of mental retardation is too dynamic to permit him to be fully satisfied with his approach. The teacher must recognize this fact and accept the responsibility for his continued education.

SUMMARY

The evaluation of special education programs appear to be at best difficult by standardized achievement tests (Smith and Stroud, 1960). Still, academic achievement has been one of the primary criteria used to evaluate the effectiveness of special classes. The academic achievement of both regular-class and special-class retardates has been found to be below their measured potential in all of the comparative studies reviewed. Further, as compared to regular-class retardates, special-class children achieved less. Yet differences between the achievement of special-class and regular-class retarded children tended to disappear during, or after, the second year (Mullen and Itkin, 1961b; Thurstone, 1960; Smith and Stroud, 1960). The disappearance of the difference in achievement appears to support the hypothesis of Goldstein, Jordan, and Moss (1962) that children need to be in special classes for at least four years before expected results can be attained.

Separation of mentally retarded children into smaller IQ ranges indicates that the higher-IQ retardate may not have an adequate program in either special or regular classes. Further, the special class may more adequately meet the needs of lower-IQ retarded children (Stanton and Cassidy, 1964; Thurstone, 1960).

Selection factors apparently influence the composition of the special class and the results of the program. Special-class children tend to come from lower socio-economic homes, to have emotional problems, and to be more quickly referred for special-class placement since they are a social problem in the regular classroom (Mullen and Itkin, 1961a; Stanton and Cassidy, 1964).

The reduction of hostility and better social adjustment of special-class retardates may be biased by the protected environment of the class (Stanton and Cassidy, 1964). However, the increasing social and emotional difficulties encountered by regular-class retardates (Goldstein, Jordan, and Moss, 1962) suggests that special-class placement may be appropriate to improve their social and emotional behavior (Mullen and Itkin, 1961a).

Special class retardates frequently attend regular class before being placed in a special class. Placement of educable retarded children in special class upon entering school may be beneficial in academic achievement and social adjustment (Goldstein, Jordan, and Moss, 1962). In addition, early placement was found to contribute to the retarded child's ability to do productive thinking (Tisdall, 1962).

The effectiveness of programs for the educable mentally retarded may be more related to the teacher's personal characteristics, flexibility, and creativeness than to a specific teaching method. Problems associated with teaching in a special classroom may be partially solved by the use of lay persons as assistants. As indicated by Cruickshank and Haring (1957), teaching assistants performed functional and routine duties that permitted more time for instruction by the teacher. Further, teacher assistants were found to be a welcome addition to the classroom.

The inferior academic achievement of the special-class educable mentally retarded appears to provide support for discontinuing special classes for these children. However, control of the curricular content, instructional methods, and research design has not been adequate. When more control is maintained over these variables, special classes appear to be, at least tentatively, more justified (Goldstein, Jordan, and Moss, 1962).

The study by Cain and Levine (1961), which found a lack of classroom application for the activities and curricular emphasis commonly suggested for trainable children, indicates that teachers experience difficulty in implementing curricula directed toward social competence. Part of the difficulty has been attributed to poor organization of time within the classes, lack of understanding by the teacher of the curricular objectives, and a willingness to accept undue and inappropriate behavior.

The difficulties encountered by teachers of the trainable may be related to inadequate teacher education programs. The difficulties also appear to be related to the teachers' feeling a lack of professional worth due to want of acceptance of the trainable child by administrators.

Educational planning for the broad classifications of "educable" and "trainable" is inappropriate. Provisions must be made for the differences in the potential educational attainment and social adjustment of individuals who are retarded. The necessary provisions may be made through the development of track programs, which function as nongraded programs. The central purpose of track programs should be a concern with the expected social competency of the retarded. To attain the central purpose of track programs, a specific curriculum must be developed for each track. However, the two organizational plans currently receiving the most attention are the nongraded program and team teaching. The nongraded plan is the basic organizational one for the retarded in special classes. Team teaching, as viewed in elementary schools, appears to be an interesting organizational plan that may be useful for the retarded. However, caution will need to be taken to avoid some of the disadvantages of team teaching. In addition, the costs of educating the retarded in this manner may be increased, but not to the extent that some may imagine.

REFERENCES

ANDERSON, R., HAGSTROM, E. A., and ROBINSON, W. M. Team teaching in an elementary school. *Sch. Rev.*, 1960, *68*, 71–84.

ANDERSON, R. H. Team teaching. *NEA J.*, 1961, *50*, 52–54.

APPELL, M. J. One community's approach—planning for the mentally retarded. *Ment. Retard.*, 1963, *1*, 268–275.

BARNETT, W. K. *Services for exceptional children: A guide for program development.* Richmond, Va.: State Dept. of Education, 1962.

BAYLEY, NANCY. On the growth of intelligence. *Amer. Psychologist*, 1955, *10*, 805–818.

BEGAB, M. J. Some elements and principles in community planning. *Ment. Retard.*, 1963, *1*, 262–266.

BIENENSTOK, T., and COXE, W. W. Census of severely retarded children in New York. Cited by S. Kirk, *Public school provisions for severely retarded: A survey of practices in the United States.* Albany, N. Y.: Interdepartmental Health Resources Board, 1957, 16.

BLATT, B. The physical, personal and academic status of children who are mentally retarded attending special classes as compared with children who are mentally retarded attending regular classes. *Amer. J. ment Defic.*, 1958, *62*, 810–818.

————. Some persistently recurring assumptions concerning the mentally subnormal. *Train. Sch. Bull.*, 1960, *57*, 48–59.

BLESSING, K. B. A survey of public school administrators' attitudes regarding services for trainable retarded children. *Amer. J. ment. Defic.*, 1959, *64*, 509–519.

BLUE, C. M Trainable mentally retarded in sheltered workshops. *Ment. Retard.*, 1964, *2*, 97–104

BRAMELD, T. What is the central purpose of American education? *Phi Delta Kappan*, 1961, *43*, 9–14.

————. World civilization: The galvanizing purpose of public education. *Phi Delta Kappan*, 1962, *44*, 58–65.

BROWNELL, J. A. (Ed.). *Annual report of the teaching team program, 1961-1962.* Claremont, Calif.: Claremont Graduate School, 1963.

BRUNER, J. S. *The process of education.* Cambridge: Harvard University Press, 1963.

BUTTERFIELD, E. C. A provocative case of over-achievement by a mongoloid. *Amer. J. ment. Defic.,* 1961, *66,* 444–448.

CAIN, L. F. Special education moves ahead: A comment on the education of teachers. *Except. Child.,* 1964, *30,* 211–217.

——, and LEVINE. S. *A study of the effects of community and institutional school classes for trainable mentally retarded children.* San Francisco: San Francisco State College, 1961.

——, and ——. The mentally retarded. *Rev. educ. Res.,* 1963, *33,* 67–82.

CAPOBIANCO, R. J. The training of mentally deficient children. In W. M. Cruickshank and G. O. Johnson (Eds.), *Education of exceptional children and youth.* Englewood Cliff, N.J.: Prentice-Hall, 1958, Chapt. 6.

——, and COLE, DOROTHY A. Social behavior of mentally retarded children. *Amer. J. ment. Defic.,* 1960, *64,* 638–651.

CHARLES, D. C. Ability and accomplishment of persons earlier judged mentally deficient. *Genet. Psychol. Monogr.,* 1953, *47,* 3–71.

CHARNEY, L. The trainable mentally retarded. In S. A. Kirk and Bluma A. Weiner (Eds.), *Behavioral research on exceptional children.* Washington, D.C.: Council for Exceptional Children, 1963, Chap. 3.

CHARTERS, W. W., JR. An approach to the formal organization of the school. In D. E. Griffiths (Ed.), *Behavioral science and educational administration.* New York: Yearbook of National Society for the Study of Education, 1964, Part 2.

CLARKE, A. D. B. Genetic and environmental studies of intelligence. In Ann M. Clarke and A. D. B. Clarke (Eds.), *Mental deficiency: The changing outlook.* Glencoe, Ill.: The Free Press, 1961, Chap. 5.

COLEMAN, J. S. *The adolescent society: The social life of the teenager and its impact on education.* New York: Free Press of Glencoe, 1961.

CONANT, J. B. *The education of American teachers.* New York: McGraw-Hill, 1963.

CONNOR, FRANCIS P., and TALBOT, MABEL E. *An experimental curriculum for young mentally retarded children.* New York: Teachers College, Columbia University, Bureau of Publications, 1964.

CRUICKSHANK, W. M. Current educational practices with exceptional children. In M. W. Cruickshank and G. O. Johnson (Eds.), *Education of exceptional children and youth.* Englewood Cliffs, N. J.: Prentice-Hall, 1958, Chap. 2. (a)

——. The development of education for exceptional children. In M. W. Cruickshank and G. O. Johnson (Eds.), *Education of exceptional children and youth.* Englewood Cliffs, N. J.: Prentice-Hall, 1958, Chap. 1 (b)

——, and HARING, N. C. *A demonstration: Assistants for teachers of exceptional children.* Syracuse: Syracuse University Press, 1957.

DAVIES, S. P., and ECOB, KATHERINE G. *The mentally retarded in society.* New York: Columbia University Press, 1959.

DEAN, S. E., and WITHERSPOON, CLINETTE F. Team teaching in the elementary school. *Educ. Briefs,* 1962, No. 38.

DELLA-DORA, D. The culturally disadvantaged: Further observations. *Except. Child,* 1963, *29,* 226–236.

DESCOEUDRES, ALICE. *The education of mentally defective children.* (Trans. by E. F. Rowe) New York: Heath, 1928.

DOLL, E. E. A historical survey of research and management of mental retardation in the United States. In E. P. Trapp and P. Himmelstein (Eds.), *Readings on the exceptional child.* New York: Appleton-Century-Crofts, 1962, 21–68.

DUNN, L. M. Educable mentally retarded children. In L. M. Dunn (Ed.), *Exceptional children in the schools.* New York: Holt, Rinehart, Winston, 1963, Chap. 2.

Educational Policies Commission. *The central purpose of American education.* Washington, D.C.: National Education Association, 1961.

ESKRIDGE, C. S., and PARTRIDGE, D. L. Vocational rehabilitation for exceptional children through special education. *Except. Child.,* 1963, *29,* 452–458.

FARBER, B. *The prevalence of children in Illinois in 1958.* Springfield, Ill.: Superintendent of Public Instruction, 1959.

FITZGIBBON, W. C. Money for the retarded. *Mich. Educ. J.,* 1964, 24, 51.

FLOYD, C. Meeting children's reading needs in the middle grades: A preliminary report. *Elem. Sch. J.,* 1954, *55,* 99–103.

The Ford Foundation. *Time, talent and teachers.* New York: Author, 1960.

——. *The new teacher.* New York: Author, 1962.

FORSHAY, A. W. A modest proposal. *Educ. Leadership,* 1961, *18,* 506–516, 528.

GAGE, N. L. (Ed.). *Handbook of research on teaching.* Chicago: Rand McNally, 1963.

GALLAGHER, J. J. *The tutoring of brain-injured mentally retarded children.* Springfield, Ill.: Charles C Thomas, 1960.

——, and Moss, J. W. New concepts of intelligence and their effect on exceptional children. *Except. Child.,* 1963, *30,* 1–5.

GARDNER, W. I., and NISONGER, H. W. A manual on program development in mental retardation. *Amer. J. ment. Defic., Monogr. Suppl.,* 1962, *66*(1).

GARRETT, H. E., BRYAN, ALICE J., and PERL, RUTH E. The age factor in mental organization. In J. J. Jenkins and D. G. Paterson (Eds.), *Studies in individual differences: The search for intelligence.* New York: Appleton-Century-Crofts, 1961, 396–413.

GERSHENSON, S., and SCHREIBER, M. Mentally retarded teenagers in a social group. *Children,* 1963, *10,* 104–108.

GOLDBERG, I. I., and CRUICKSHANK, W. M. The trainable but non-educable: Whose responsibility? *NEA J.,* 1958, *47,* 622–623.

GOLDSTEIN, H. Issues in the education of the educable mentally retarded. *Ment. Retard.,* 1963, *1,* 10–12, 52–53.

——. Social and occupational adjustment. In H. A. Stevens and R. Heber (Eds.), *Mental retardation: A review of research.* Chicago: University of Chicago Press, 1964, 214–258.

——, JORDAN, LAURA J., and MOSS, J. W. *Early school development of low IQ children: A study of special class placement.* Urbana: University of Illinois, 1962.

——, and SEIGLE, DOROTHY. *Curriculum guide for teachers of the educable mentally handicapped.* Springfield, Ill.: Dept. of Public Instruction, 1958.

GOODLAD, J. I., and ANDERSON, R. H. Educational practices in nongraded schools: A survey of perceptions. *Elem. Sch. J.,* 1962, *63,* 33–40.

——, and ——. *The nongraded elementary school.* (Rev. ed.) New York: Harcourt, Brace, and World, 1963.

——, and REHAGE, K. Unscrambling the vocabulary of school organization. *NEA J.,* 1962, *51,* 34–36.

HARRIS, C. W. (Ed.). *Encyclopedia of educational research.* New York: Macmillan, 1960.

HAVIGHURST, R. J., BOWMAN, P. H., LIDDLE, G. P., MATTHEWS, C. U., and PIERCE, J. U. *Growing up in River City*. New York: John Wiley, 1962.

HEATHERS, G. Team teaching and the educational reform movement. In J. T. Shaplin and H. F. Olds (Eds.), *Team teaching*. New York: Harper and Row, 1964, Chap. 11.

HEBER, R. (Ed.) A manual on terminology and classification in mental retardation. *Amer. J. ment. Defic., Monogr. Suppl.*, 1961, *66* (2).

HEBER, R. F. The educable mentally retarded. In S. A. Kirk and Bluma B. Weiner (Eds.), *Behavioral research on exceptional children*. Washington, D.C.: Council for Exceptional Children, 1963, Chap. 2. (a)

————. Standards for the preparation and certification of teachers of the mentally retarded. *Ment. Retard.*, 1963, *1*, 35–37, 60–62. (b)

HENRY, N. B. (Ed.) *Individualizing instruction*. New York: Yearbook of the National Society for the Study of Education, 1962, Part I.

HILL, A. S. *The forward look: The severely retarded child goes to school*. Washington, D.C.: U.S. Government Printing Office, 1953.

HILLSON, MAURIE (Ed.). *Change and innovation in elementary school organization: selected readings*. New York: Holt, Rinehart, and Winston, 1965. (a)

————. Nongraded schools: Organizational design for elementary education. In Maurie Hillson (Ed.), *Change and innovation in elementary school organization: Selected readings*. New York: Holt, Rinehart, and Winston, 1965, 309–323. (b)

HONZIK, M. P., MACFARLANE, JEAN W., and ALLEN, L. The stability of mental test performance between two and eighteen years. *J. exp. Educ.*, 1948, *17*, 309–324.

HORN, J. L. *Education of exceptional children*. New York: Appleton-Century-Crofts, 1924.

HOSLEY, ELEANOR. Culturally deprived children in day-care programs. *Children*, 1963, *10*, 175–179.

HUSEN, T. The influence of schooling upon IQ. In J. J. Jenkins and D. G. Paterson (Eds.), *Studies in individual differences: The search for intelligence*. New York: Appleton-Century-Crofts, 1961, 677–693.

INGRAM, CHRISTINE. *Education of the slow learning child*. (2nd ed.) New York: Ronald Press, 1953.

JOHNSON, G. O. Special education for the mentally handicapped—a paradox. *Except. Child.*, 1962, *29*, 62–69.

————. Psychological characteristics of the mentally retarded. In W. M. Cruickshank (Ed.), *Psychology of exceptional children and youth*. (2nd ed.) Englewood Cliffs, N. J.: Prentice-Hall, 1963, Chap. 9.

KAPLAN, B. A. Issues in educating the culturally disadvantaged. *Phi Delta Kappan*, 1963, *45*, 70–76.

KELLY, ELIZABETH M. Are we providing opportunities for the older mentally retarded? *Except. Child.*, 1955, *21*, 297–309.

KEPPEL, F. Master of arts in teaching. *Sat. Rev.*, 1961, *44*, 63–65.

KIRK, S. A. *Public school provisions for severely retarded: A survey of practices in the United States*. Albany, N. Y.: Interdepartmental Health Resources Board, 1957.

————. *Educating exceptional children*. Boston: Houghton Mifflin, 1962.

————. Research in education. In H. A. Stevens and R. Heber (Eds.), *Mental retardation: A review of research*. Chicago: University of Chicago Press, 1964, 57–99.

————, and JOHNSON, G. O. *Educating the retarded child*. Cambridge: Houghton Mifflin, 1951.

————, KARNES, M. B., and KIRK, WINIFRED D. *You and your retarded child.* New York: Macmillan, 1955.

————, and McCARTHY, J. J. The Illinois test of psycholinguistic abilities span approach to differential diagnosis. *Amer. J. ment. Defic.,* 1961, *66,* 399–412.

KLOHR, P. R. Studies of the teaching act: What progress? *Educ. Leadership,* 1962, *20,* 93–96.

KOLSTOE, O. P. An examination of some characteristics which discriminate between employed and not employed mentally retarded males. *Amer. J. ment. Defic.,* 1961, *66,* 472–482.

KRAUSE, I. B., JR., Requirements for teachers of mentally retarded children in the fifty states. *Ment. Retard.,* 1963, *1,* 38–40, 62–64.

KRUGER, D. H. Trends in service employment: Implications for the educable mentally retarded. *Except. Child.,* 1963, *30,* 167–172.

KRUGMAN, M. An administrator speaks on current trends in special education in New York City. *Except. Child.,* 1962, *28,* 245–248.

KURREN, O. Inter-agency joint planning and collaboration—fact and fiction. *Except. Child.,* 1962, *29,* 143–148.

KURTZ, R. A. Implications of recent sociological research in mental retardation. *Amer. J. ment. Defic.,* 1964, *69,* 16–20.

LARSON, R., and OLSON, J. L. A method of identifying culturally deprived kindergarten children. *Except. Child.,* 1963, *30,* 130–134.

LEAHY, ALICE M. Nature-nurture and intelligence. *Gent. Psychol. Monogr.,* 1935, *17,* 241–305.

LEVINE, S. A proposed conceptual framework for special education. *Except. Child.,* 1961, *28,* 83–90.

LONSDALE, R. C. Maintaining the organization in dynamic equilibrium. In D. E. Griffiths (Ed.), *Behavioral science and educational administration.* New York: Yearbook of the National Society for the Study of Education, 1964, Part II, Chap. 7.

LYONS, DOROTHY J., and POWERS, VIRGINIA. Follow-up study of elementary school children exempted from Los Angeles City schools during 1960–1961. *Except. Child.,* 1963, *30,* 155–162.

MACKIE, R. Preparation of mentally retarded youth for gainful employment. Washington, D.C.: U.S. Government Printing Office, 1960.

————, DUNN, L. M., and CAIN, L. F. *Professional preparation for teachers of exceptional children: An overview.* Washington, D.C.: U.S. Government Printing Office. 1960.

————, WILLIAMS, H., and HUNTER, PATRICIA. *Statistics of special education for exceptional children and youth, 1957–1958.* Washington, D.C.: U.S. Government Printing Office, 1963.

MARTENS, ELISE. *Curriculum adjustments for the mentally retarded.* Washington, D.C.: U.S. Government Printing Office, 1950.

McCANDLESS, B. R. Relation of environmental factors to intellectual functioning. In H. A. Stevens and R. Heber (Eds.), *Mental retardation: A review of research.* Chicago: University of Chicago Press, 1964, 175–213.

MEYERS, C. E. Realities in teacher recruitment. *Ment. Retard.,* 1964, *2,* 42–46.

MOORING, I. P., and CURRIE, R. F. A conceptual model for community services for the mentally retarded. *Except. Child.,* 1964, *30,* 202–205.

MULLEN, FRANCES, and ITKIN, W. *Achievement and adjustment of educable mentally handicapped children in special classes and in regular grades.* Chicago: Board of Education, 1961. (a)

————, and ————. *Teaching the educable mentally handicapped child: A comparison of four methods of instruction.* Chicago: Board of Education, 1961. (b)

MUELLER, M. W., and WEAVER, S. J. Psycholinguistic abilities of institutionalized trainable mental retardates. *Amer. J. ment. Defic.,* 1964, *68,* 775–783.

National Association for Retarded Children. *Summary of statistics of state level support of programs of special education in the public schools for children classified as "trainable" mentally retarded or equivalent.* New York: Author, 1961.

National Education Association. *The principals look at the schools: A status study of selected instructional practices.* Washington, D.C.: Author, 1962.

NIEHM, B. F. Study of sheltered workshops for the mentally retarded. *Train. Sch. Bull.,* 1958, *54,* 67–71.

NISONGER, H. W. Report of the President's panel: A blueprint for action in mental retardation. *Ment. Retard.,* 1963, *1,* 224–229.

North Carolina State Department of Public Instruction. *Comprehensive school improvement project.* Raleigh: Author, 1965.

PECK, J. R., and SEXTON, LUCILLE C. *A comparative investigation of the learning and social adjustment of trainable children in public school facilities, segregated community centers, and state residential centers.* Austin: University of Texas, 1960.

PERKINSON, H. J. American education: Icons and images. *Educ. Forum,* 1963, *27,* 233–245.

PERRY, NATALIE. *Teaching the mentally retarded child.* New York: Columbia University Press, 1960.

PHENIX, P. H. The disciplines as curriculum content. In A. H. Passow (Ed.), *Curriculum crossroads.* New York: Teachers College, Columbia University, Bureau of Publications, 1962, 57–65.

President's Panel on Mental Retardation. *A proposed program for national action to combat mental retardation.* Washington, D.C.: U.S. Government Printing Office, 1962.

REYNOLDS, M. C. A framework for considering some issues in special education. *Except. Child.,* 1962, *28,* 367–370.

————. A strategy for research. *Except. Child.,* 1963, *29,* 213–219.

RICH, D. H., and BEEKMAN, M. E. *Program for mentally handicapped children in high school.* Lansing, Mich.: Lansing Public Schools, 1954.

ROSENZWEIG, E., and LONG, JULIA. *Understanding and teaching the dependent retarded child.* Darien, Conn.: Educational Publications Corp., 1960.

SARASON, S. B. *Psychological problems in mental deficiency.* (3rd ed.) New York: Harper and Row, 1959.

————, DAVIDSON, K., and BLATT, B. *The preparation of teachers: An unstudied problem in education.* New York: John Wiley, 1962.

SAYLOR, J. G., and ALEXANDER, W. M. *Curriculum planning for better teaching and learning.* New York: Rinehart, 1959.

SHANE, H. G. The school and individual differences. In N. B. Henry (Ed.), *Individualizing instruction.* New York: Yearbook of the National Society for the Study of Education, 1962, Part I, Chap. 3.

SHAPLIN, J. T. Team teaching. *Sat. Rev.,* 1961, *44,* 54–55, 70.

————, and OLDS, H. F., JR. (Eds.) *Team teaching.* New York: Harper and Row, 1964.

SIMCHES, G., and BOHN, R. J. Issues in curriculum: Research and responsibility. *Ment. Retard.,* 1963, *1,* 84–87.

SMITH, L. L., and STROUD, J. B. *Effects of a comprehensive opportunity pro-*

gram on the development of educable mentally retarded children. Iowa City: University of Iowa, 1960.

Sparks, H. L., and Blackman, L. S. *What is special about special education* revisited: *The mentally retarded. Except. Child.*, 1965, *31*, 242–247.

Stanford Institute for Communication Research. *Educational television: The next ten years.* Stanford, Calif.: Author, 1962.

Stanton, Jeannette, R., and Cassidy, Viola N. Effectiveness of special classes for educable mentally retarded. *Ment. Retard.*, 1964, *2*, 8–13.

Steigman, M. J., and Johnson, G. O. Forum: Paradox in special education? *Except. Child.*, 1964, *31*, 67–70.

Stoddard, G. D. The dual progress plan. *Sch. Soc.*, 1958, *86*, 351–352.

Strauss, A. A., and Kephart, N. C. *Psychopathology and education of the brain-injured child.* Vol. 2. Progress in theory and clinic. New York: Grune and Stratton, 1955.

Syden, M. Preparation for work: An aspect of the secondary school's curriculum for mentally retarded youth. *Except. Child.*, 1962, *28*, 325–332.

Taylor, H., and Olsen, Katherine. Team teaching with trainable retarded children. *Except. Child.*, 1964, *30*, 304–309.

Terman, L. M., and Merrill, Maude A. *Stanford-Binet Intelligence Scale: Manual for the third revision, Form L-M.* Boston: Houghton-Mifflin, 1960.

Thorsell, Marguerite. Organizing experience units for educable mentally retarded. *Except. Child.*, 1961, *28*, 177–186.

Thurstone, L. L. The mental age concept. *Psychol, Rev.*, 1926, *33*, 267–278.

Thurstone, Thelma G. *An evaluation of educating mentally handicapped children in special classes and in regular classes.* Grambling, La.: Grambling College, 1960.

Tisdall, W. J. A follow-up study of trainable mentally handicapped children in Illinois. *Amer. J. ment. Defic.*, 1960, *65*, 11–16.

———. Productive thinking in retarded children. *Except. Child.*, 1962, *29*, 36–41.

———, and Moss, J. W. A total program for the severely mentally retarded. *Except. Child.*, 1962, *28*, 357–362.

Travelstead, C. R. Problems in the education of handicapped children in sparsely settled areas. *Except. Child.*, 1960, *27*, 52–55.

Trump, J. L. *Images of the future—Guide to better schools.* Washington, D.C.: National Association of Secondary School Principals, 1958.

———. *Focus on change—Guide to better schools.* Chicago: Rand McNally, 1961.

Vernon, P. E. Intelligence and attainment test. New York: Philosophical Library, 1961.

Voelker, P. H., and Mullen, Frances A. Organization, administration, supervision of special education. *Rev. educ. Res.*, 1963, *33*, 5–19.

Vontress, C. E. Our demoralizing slum schools. *Phi Delta Kappan*, 1963, *45*, 77–81.

Wallace, Helen M., and Starr, Helen. School services for mentally retarded children in urban areas. *Amer. J. ment. Defic.*, 1960, *64*, 679–688.

Wallin, J. E. W. *Education of mentally handicapped children.* New York: Harper and Row, 1955.

Warburton, F. W. Educational psychology. *Annu. Rev. Psychol.*, 1962, *13*, 317–414.

Wechsler, D. Cognative, conative and non-intellectual intelligence. *Amer. Psychologist*, 1950, *5*, 78–83.

WHEELER, L. R. A comparative study of the intelligence of East Tennessee mountain children. *J. educ. Psychol.,* 1942, *33,* 321–334.

WILHELMS, F. T. The curriculum and individual differences. In N. B. Henry (Ed.), *Individualizing instruction.* New York: Yearbook of the National Society for the Study of Education, 1962, Part I, Chap. 4.

WILLIAMS, H. M., and WALLIN, J. E. W. *Education of the severely retarded child.* Washington, D.C.: U.S. Government Printing Office, 1959.

WINDLE, C. Prognosis of mental subnormals: A critical review of research. *Amer. J. ment. Defic., Monogr. Suppl.,* 1962, *66* (2).

WOLINSKY, GLORIA F. Interdisciplinary action in special education. *Except. Child.,* 1961, *28,* 151–158.

WRIGHTSTONE, J. W. *A comparison of educational outcomes under single track and two track plans for educable mentally retarded children.* New York: New York City Board of Education, 1959.

The Characteristics, Selections, and Training of Institution Personnel[1] 12

EARL C. BUTTERFIELD

THOSE familiar with institutions for the retarded have seen the wonders and the horrors their employes can work upon their residents. Having seen these things, they may have asked themselves how to make certain that an institution's employes would be of sufficient quality to provide the best possible care and training for its retarded residents.

Some might object that it is not an institution's employes but the services they render that, when inadequate, result in patients' suffering. To some extent, this is true. But when a physician administers a fatal drug, we do not blame the drug; we blame the physician, because services cannot be divorced from the server. This is particularly true when the service being offered is not well understood, as in the case of an institution, which is, in effect, a substitute home. Who can say what acts constitute those of a good parent or parent-substitute? The best one can do when attempting to provide a home-like environment is to secure high-quality personnel to administer it.

At least two trends that have proceeded outside of institutions for the retarded have contributed to the growing concern over the quality of institution personnel in general and the attendant in particular (Bensberg, Barnett, and Hurder, 1964; Cleland, 1962; Shafter, 1960; Shafter, Chandler, and Coe, 1957). In the last few years, authorities in the field have become increasingly aware of the problems of the retarded and increasingly desirous of coping with those problems. Accompanying

these trends has been the realization that mental retardation is such a complex problem that many persons besides highly trained professionals will have to be involved if any substantial solution to the problem is to be reached (Bensberg, Barnett, and Hurder, 1964). Workers in the field of psychiatry also have recognized that the entire institution environment is part of a mentally disturbed patient's treatment (e.g., Belknap, 1956; Parloff, 1960). This emphasis undoubtedly has influenced authors concerned with mental retardation (e.g., Cleland, 1964).

Perhaps the easiest way to group an institution's many types of employes is by job description. Institutional employes can be classified as physicians, psychologists, teachers, social workers, attendants, etc. All of these different kinds of employes should be as capable and competent as possible. However, the literature on institution employes gives scant indication that this is so. Much has been written about the quality of attendants, but one seldom finds questions raised about the quality of professional or administrative personnel. Are our institutional physicians, psychologists, social workers, teachers, and superintendents so adequate? Probably not (Pleydell, 1950). The reason for the disproportionate concern about attendants seems obvious: The professional or the administrator is usually the one who writes about institutional personnel and one seldom finds kings burning their own castles. But more important, attendants constitute a majority of all institution employes (Bensberg, Barnett, and Hurder, 1964). They are the main executors of an institution's program (Cleland, 1964;

1. This paper was prepared while the author was being supported by United States Public Health Service Grant MH-06809.

Taylor, 1964) and have more contact with patients than any other employe group (Fleming, 1962). The qualifications for being a competent attendant are less clear than are those for almost any other institution role (Taylor, 1964). Turnover is greater among the attendant population than among any other group of institution employes (Fleming, 1962). The cost of replacing an attendant is a substantial drain upon the financial and time resources of the institution (Cleland, 1964; Vaccaro, 1952). The attendant exercises a profound, if poorly understood, effect upon the policies of an institution (Cleland, 1964; Scheff, 1961). For reasons such as these, the present chapter follows tradition and considers mainly the selection and training of attendants rather than other groups of institution employes.

AN INSTITUTIONAL ATTENDANT

DUTIES

Recognizing that a discrepancy often exists between the prescribed duties and actual functions of any occupational group (Taylor, 1964), we may consider attendants' duties apart from their actual performance. Attendants are charged with the kinds of care to retardates that would be provided by parents if the institutionalized retardate were residing at home. This means that attendants must provide a safe and sanitary place in which to live. They must feed, bathe, and dress the retardate. They must see that he receives medications, exercises a sufficient amount, and goes to receive any other kinds of care, training, and treatment he may require. Attendants are often charged with providing recreation and with training patients in a variety of self-help and simple occupational skills. They must discipline the patient, although they seldom are authorized to punish patients physically (Barnett, 1964d). They should teach him self-control and other desirable personal attributes. They are often expected to minister to patients' special physical and psychological needs. In short, an attendant should be, "first of all, a good parent substitute. However, in addition, he is expected to serve individuals with special needs, and therefore should be part nurse, part physical therapist, part psy-

chologist, and part educator" (Bensberg, Barnett, and Hurder, 1964). In the face of this bewildering and impossibly wide array of duties, one might reasonably ask: what do attendants actually do?

ACTUAL PERFORMANCE

Little systematic investigation of attendant performance has been reported. Some authors have reported developing, with the assistance of attendants themselves, detailed descriptions of attendants' actual performance (e.g., Porter, 1961; Schmidt and Cohen, 1955). The results of these efforts have not been described in detail nor have they provided information about the relative frequency of various attendant functions. Many authors have called for detailed observational analyses and descriptions of attendant functions (e.g., Tarjan, Shotwell, and Dingman, 1955, 1956). Most of these observational studies were executed in psychiatric settings that served adult patients only, and most have reported their results in a more sensation-seeking, value-laden fashion than in a systematic, descriptive fashion (e.g., Belknap, 1956; Greenblatt, 1955; Wells, Greenblatt, and Hyde, 1956). Of the three direct observational studies of attendants, the results of one are unavailable for publication (Headrick, 1964; Bensberg, Barnett, and Hurder, 1964), and the results of another are largely evaluative rather than descriptive (Fleming, 1962). The results of the remaining study (Oudenne, 1963) shed a little light on the question of attendants' actual performance.

Oudenne had a number of observers record patient-related activities of attendants who were caring for severely retarded children. By averaging four days (24 hours a day) of observations, he found that the direct care per patient per day amounted to 132 minutes of attendant time. This time estimate included attending to the personal needs of patients, toileting, bathing and dressing, feeding, bundling dirty linen and clothes, and bed making. It did not include any recreational or instructional activities. Oudenne estimated that just meeting these basic needs would require 44 attendants per 100 patients, or a ratio of one employe to every 2.3 patients. Pero (1949) found an employe-to-patient ratio of 1 to 12 in 74 state institutions in this country.

Barnett (1964) reported that there was one attendant per 4.74 patients in the 35 institutions in the southeastern United States. One wonders how all of the work in institutions is being done! Is it being done by patients (Cleland, 1964; Kaplan, 1961)? More observational studies of this type are necessary.

DESIRABLE TRAITS

A good attendant cannot be characterized in terms of acts and duties alone. Because of the complexities and uncertainties of the attendant's role, one must consider the personal characteristics of attendants as well. Edgett (1951) provides a detailed list of idealized characteristics to which the interested reader might refer. Barnett (1964c) has compiled a list of desirable characteristics of attendants drawn up by a large number of attendant supervisors. We will limit ourselves to the observation that any evaluation of desirable attendant characteristics must be made in terms of the goals of the institution in which the attendant is to serve. To appreciate the complexities involved in defining goals and desirable attendant characteristics, the reader might consider whether the treatment goal of an institution for the retarded should be fostering emotional growth or teaching skills necessary for non-institutional residence (Shafter, 1960). Attempting to translate the following statements of goals into sets of desirable attendant characteristics also should indicate the magnitude of the problem:

So we [institution personnel] finally come to realize that our main job . . . is to effect what I like to term, "The Rehabilitation of the Ego." We have the task of replacing failure with success. . . . We are supplying a new world, created just for the mentally retarded. A world in which his errors are largely overlooked, and his tiniest accomplishment is rewarded and praised. (Dayton, 1963)

The primary needs of ambulatory mentally deficient patients are concentrated around the training and preparation for the future. Life . . . must be presented to the patients in the most realistic fashion. Patients must learn to know right from wrong, to accept the consequences of their actions, to accept authority, and to realize their own limitations. (Rettig, 1956a)

No single set of desirable attendant characteristics can be laid down so long as such basic disagreements exist as those reflected in the quotations above. Given this state of affairs, each institution must decide for itself what its goals are to be and to translate them into statements of desirable attendant characteristics.

ATTENDANT CHARACTERISTICS

Perhaps more observers agree about what attendants are actually like than agree about what they should be like. Some evaluative judgments about attendants are best regarded as prejudices and unfortunate, unconstructive expressions of dissatisfaction with the attendant. Some are general, unsystematic observations about attendants as a group that are probably quite correct and that seem to further our understanding of attendants. And some contain systematically collected descriptive data and evaluative statements about attendants.

Extreme Opinions about Attendants. Extremely positive and negative beliefs about attendants do exist. One need only go to a large institution for the retarded and talk to a variety of people in order to hear them expressed. While expressions of extreme opinions seldom find their way into print, there are some examples in the literature of attitudes toward the attendant that reflect the type of emotional reaction with which administrators must deal if they are to attract, keep, and train quality attendant personnel. Consider the following quotation from Porter (1961):

The attendant counselors [attendants] give each resident as much individual attention as possible, get all residents up each day unless they are ill, see that there are opportunities for play, and ingeniously devise and arrange equipment to stimulate responses and to capitalize on the slightest interest of the severely retarded children and adults in their care. They lend their support not only to the services of the medical specialists, but also to those of the dentist, the physical therapist, the school teacher, the psychologist, the dietician, the recreation workers and the chaplains. All this would not be possible if there were objections, either conscious or unconscious, on the part of the personnel.

With all due deference to Porter, I suggest that this quote reflects less accurately the state of personnel in the institution he is describing than it does the state of his aspirations for them. Until all members of an institution's staff are willing to acknowledge that personnel problems exist—and personnel problems always do in an institution—little headway can be made in attacking those problems.

Extreme attitudes about attendants more often are negative in character. Consider the following:

Every institution has its "old timers," who may be the backbone of the program, but of whom it may be said they never forgot anything and never learned anything. Such workers, whatever their strength and sensitivity may be, cannot be expected to move into and with an expanding, professionally centered program (Scher, 1956).

It is all too frequent to find that even some of the best institutional workers treat the very retarded as they might a favorite dog, with affection, certainty, but without a truly human relationship (Scher, 1956).

Professionals believe attendants are overly concerned with such therapeutic activities as the cleanliness of the ward and the maintenance of discipline; also that attendants are inflexible, and not receptive to patient-care methods recommended by professionals (Fleming, 1962).

Attitudes of this type must be modified if attendants are to receive beneficial guidance and co-operation from other institution staff members.

Some persons hold closely related opinions about the position of attendant, as opposed to the person filling the position, which also need to be considered in any attempt to understand the role of the attendant in an institution. Some of these opinions are apparent in the following quotations:

The fact of the matter is that the job of house parent [attendant] is perhaps inherently and unchangeably difficult and unattractive to most people (Scher, 1956).

The role of the attendant is an only partially professional area (Scher, 1956).

A related possibility . . . is that the working conditions of the attendant are such that distressed and extreme reactions toward residents are altogether reasonable (Fleming, 1962).

Informal Observations Regarding Attendants. A number of informal observations about attendants and their position have contributed substantially to an understanding of them. Attendants are not an occupational group in the sense that nurses or the various professional disciplines are groups. They come from vastly different educational and occupational backgrounds (Taylor, 1964). Another way to say this is to note that:

Every institution seems to be staffed by a heterogeneous mixture. There usually is a group of "old timers." . . . There are young students who are seeking a temporary situation. . . . In isolated communities there is usually a group of local residents who become house parents as they might have become factory hands if the local industry had been a mill instead of an institution (Scher, 1956).

Attendants are at the end of the delegation process, and yet they are given relatively little authority (Cleland, 1964). Frequently, they are not even allowed to make discipline decisions independently (Barnett, 1964d). A related point is that the attendant has less status in the institution than an employee in any other occupational role within the institution (Cleland, 1964; Cleland and Peck, 1959; Kahne, 1959; Taylor, 1964).

Descriptions of Attendant Characteristics. Attendants come to their positions from a variety of occupational backgrounds. "An examination of previous work experience of applicants for the attendant position reveals that they have been farmers, factory workers, housewives, retired armed services personnel, and others with diverse backgrounds" (Taylor, 1964). The vast majority have had no relevant experience before becoming an attendant (Parker, 1951). They have, on the average, less than a twelfth-grade education (Barnett, 1964a; Butterfield, Barnett, and Bensberg, in press; Parker, 1961; Parnicky and Ziegler, 1964). Many have less than an eighth-grade education (Parker, 1951). Depending upon the location of the institution, a majority come from a rural or small-town background (Barnett, 1964a; Parker, 1951). They are, on the average, in the lower portion of the normal range of tested intelligence (Barnett, 1964a). They have a more marked interest in employment that provides services to people than does the general population (Vaccaro, 1952). The turnover rate among attendants is high and occurs mainly in the first few months after employment (Kline, 1950; McIntire, 1954; Tarjan, Shotwell, and Dingman, 1955).

Attitudes and Opinions of Attendants. Only one study has been directed at exploring the attitudes and opinions of attendants for the purpose of gaining a better understanding of them. Parker (1951) found that 37 per cent of attendants in the institution he surveyed were satisfied with their salary while 50 per cent cited low salary as the thing they disliked most about their job. The starting salary of this institution was less than $2,000 per year. Women were more satisfied than men with their salaries, and those men who were satisfied had lower levels of education and were older. A frank 17 per cent of the attendants acknowledged that they took the position of attendant because it was the first position that became available to them, while 66 per cent said they took the job of attendant because they were interested in that type of work. Parker found that 56 per cent of the attendants either would not or were uncertain as to whether they would send a retarded child of their own to an institution similar to the one in which they were working. Fully 35 per cent of the attendants favored euthanasia or mercy killing for some of the residents in their charge. This percentage was highest among the more well-educated attendants and among those who acknowledged that they found the patients personally irritating. A rather large number of attendants reported that they found the patients irritating rather than in need of love.

Parker's study makes it clear that salaries will have to be raised at this institution if young, well-educated males are to be attracted to the position of attendant. Furthermore, some attendant attitudes exist in this institution that some professionals would regard as undesirable. Of course, Parker's data were collected at just one institution, and their generality is open to question.

Differences in Viewpoint of Attendants and Other Institution Personnel. A number of rather well-executed studies have shown quite clearly that attendants and other groups of institution employes differ in their perceptions of the role of an attendant. Shotwell, Dingman, and Tarjan (1960) constructed 30 statements describing "a mode of thinking or acting generally recognized as desirable in a psychiatric technician [attendant]. Half of these statements related directly to patients and half related to other aspects of the job." They had 40 attendants, 20 attendant supervisors, and 27 professional personnel at one institution

rate these statements as to their importance. They found that professional personnel placed significantly higher value on the following items than did the attendants or their supervisors: (1) being friendly to patients; (2) calling charges' (supervising attendants') attention to patients whom the technician (attendant) thinks are working too hard; (3) initiating new ward activities for the pleasure and comfort of the patients; (4) liking to be with patients, and (5) playing simple games with the handicapped patients. The attendants and their supervisors placed significantly more value on the following items: (1) being neat and clean in personal appearance; (2) being on time; (3) keeping busy at making the ward neat and clean, and (4) thoroughly understanding that the charge is boss of the ward. These differences suggest that the professional staff placed heavier emphasis on the patient and his care while the attendants and their supervisors placed heavier emphasis upon non-patient related activities.

Shotwell, Dingman, and Tarjan suggest that these differences between attendants and their supervisors on the one hand and professional personnel on the other, might be "more apparent than real." By this they probably meant that the attendants and professionals were responding to different kinds of pressures; that the attendants would regard the patient-centered activities as being every bit as important as did the professionals if it were not for some very realistic demands that are made upon attendants by their supervisors and the patients. I would not de-emphasize so much the importance of these differences between attendants and professionals. Whether the reasons are understandable or not, attendants and professionals did differ in their estimate of important attendant activities. Regardless of whose judgments are more "realistic," the differences apparently exist and would have to be overcome to affect an institutional program that was mutually agreeable to attendants and professional personnel. This is all the more true since similar investigations in different institutions have revealed very similar differences between attendants and professional staff members (Fleming, 1962; Hamister, 1955; Rettig, 1956b).

Rettig (1956b) carried his analysis of the differences between professionals and attendant supervisors further than did Shotwell,

Dingman, and Tarjan (1960). Rettig composed a number of two-choice items describing specific situations between attendants and patients and had a variety of institutional employes indicate which response they thought the attendant should make. Rettig found a fairly large number of items on which psychologists and attendant supervisors chose different attendant responses as being desirable. After discussing the reasons for different choices separately with psychologists and attendant supervisors, Rettig wrote: "Probably the most significant finding consists in the fact that the training and interest of the psychologist is focused upon the indiivdual patient, while the interests and necessary dealing of the supervisors (and attendants as well) are focused upon large groups of patients." This group focus of the attendant and his supervisors is well-conveyed in the following statements made by attendants:

Well, if you tell one to do something and he does not do it and he gets away with it, none of them will want to do anything. We have to insist that they do what we ask them. . . . Very often they are willing to do it when one insists.

Because if we gave to one of them we would have to give to any number of people and we have over a hundred. . . . We can't possibly give to one without giving to another, and they resent partiality. That is one thing they notice more than anything is partiality (Rettig, 1956b).

Clearly, the attendant feels very real pressures to deal with the patients as groups rather than individuals, whereas psychologists feel that the attendant should deal with individuals. This is the kind of difference that needs to be attacked by some sort of in-service training if an institution is to develop a program that represents the best compromise which its employees can find.

Other important areas of disagreement were revealed by Rettig's study. Attendants and their supervisors classified patients' behavior as either right or wrong. Psychologists were more inclined to stress the relativity of judgments of right and wrong and to indicate that patient and situational circumstances had to be considered. Sometimes a psychologist would say that an act was neither right nor wrong. Similarly, psychologists tended to regard rules and regulations as flexible, whereas attendants and their supervisors regarded them as iron-clad.

Psychologists and attendants differed considerably in the sophistication of their judgments about the causes of various "problem behaviors."

Fleming (1962) has shown quite convincingly that the discrepancies between judgments of appropriate or effective attendant behaviors toward patients exist not only between psychologists and attendants. He found that a superintendent and a psychiatrist differed as much between themselves in judgments of recorded incidents of attendant-patient behavior as did attendant supervisors and either the psychiatrist or the superintendent. He found in the institution he studied that all three—attendant supervisor, psychiatrist, and superintendent—agreed considerably less than half of the time in their judgments of the effectiveness of attendant-patient interactions.

Attendants as Seen by the Patients. Hamister (1955), working in a psychiatric setting, discovered that patients' judgments of attendants differed systematically from those of staff members. Hamister did not describe the differences between these judgments, but his study does indicate that patients can be a source of information about institution personnel and their functions.

I have been unable to find any attempt published of retarded patients' evaluations of their attendants. A study by Patterson (1962) suggests that this could be a fruitful approach to furthering our understanding of the attendant. Patterson had retarded patients rate their work supervisors as "much liked," "liked," "disliked," and "much disliked." He found that, with a few notable exceptions, work supervisors were rated similarly by different patients. He also found that work supervisors' knowledge of mental retardation, educational level, and length of service were unrelated to whether they were judged by the patients as being liked or disliked. From his first hand, informal experience with the work supervisors, Patterson suggested that:

The only feature that seemed to stand out was that the most popular supervisors could be categorized as patient, indulgent and generally paternalistic or maternalistic as the case might be. They seemed to meet the needs of the institutionalized retardates for affection and kindness.

Patterson also noted that the most popular supervisors seemed to be less concerned with work productivity. While one may question whether work supervisors should be chosen on the basis of popularity with patients, further exploration of the views of patients about institution personnel seems desirable.

REQUIREMENTS OF A PROGRAM OF ATTENDANT SELECTION

Essentially three things are involved in the development of selection criteria for higher quality attendants. First, one must have some practical applicant assessment procedures that may be used as predictors of subsequent performance as an attendant. This assessment (predictor variable) may be any one of a number of things ranging from knowledge of educational level attained, marital status and employment history to intellectual, personality or attitude test results. Second, one must have some reliable and valid criterion of attendant performance to differentiate between attendants of high quality and attendants of low quality. This criterion could be length of employment, supervisors' ratings of performance, improvement in patients cared for, etc. The third essential for developing an effective selection program is some integrated conception of what a good attendant is, what characteristics are likely to make an untried person a good attendant, and why these characteristics make an attendant good. Some would argue that this guiding conception is not absolutely essential to the development of an effective attendant selection program and that all one needs is some predictor variable that is significantly related to the criterion variable of attendant performance. However, the following discussions will make it clear that attempts to relate predictor variables to criteria of attendant performance have not been successful unless they were guided by theoretical considerations.

Before going on to describe attempts to develop predictor variables for the selection of attendants in institutions for the mentally retarded, let us consider some of the difficulties involved in this kind of study. Limitations or criticisms of selection studies may be grouped according to the three requirements of an effective selection program—predictor variables, criterion variables, and the guiding conception of how these two are related.

PREDICTOR VARIABLES

The predictor variables used in any selection study must be relevant to the criterion being predicted and they must be reasonably exhaustive of the class of relevant predictors. Relevance can be determined either by informed judgment or by predictive ability. A predictor may be regarded as relevant because it fits the investigator's conception of what should contribute to being either a good or a poor attendant, or its relevance may be determined by whether it actually predicts the criteria of goodness employed in a study. Judgment probably provides the best basis for determining the relevance of a predictor because serious questions have arisen about the adequacy of existing criteria of attendant performance. If a predictor is studied as if it were the only relevant predictor, it is not likely to be found to be an efficient predictor of any criterion of attendant performance, even if it is highly relevant to that performance, because the contribution of other relevant predictors will not have been controlled or assessed. Studies that use only one predictor variable are suspect from the outset.

When predictor variables are secured is also important. If experience as an attendant affects a person's performance on the predictor variables, then an applicant must be tested before he has such experience to make certain that the predictor variables will be of assistance in the screening of prospective employes. This obviously presents no problem when one is concerned with predictor variables such as educational background and employment history, but it would have considerable relevance to those studies that attempt to evaluate personality and attitude measures as predictors of attendant competence.

CRITERION VARIABLES

The minimum standard of acceptability of any criterion of attendant performance is that it can be assessed reliably. In practice, this means that those in charge will agree that any one attendant should receive a score or a rating of X on that criterion. The reliability for some criteria is beyond question—length of tenure and absenteeism, for instance. For other criteria (e.g., supervisors' ratings of attendant performance), the question of reliability becomes intertwined inextricably with the question of their validity.

We have seen in a previous section that ratings of attendants vary systematically with the professional background of the rater. This reflects the fact that the standards that a rater uses are largely inexplicit. Investigators are not able to specify precisely what they mean when they ask a rater to classify attendants as "good" or "poor." A rater's conception of what makes a good and poor attendant varies with his values, which result, in part, from his educational and experiential background. Consequently, whether two raters will agree that a given attendant is "good" or "poor" depends upon the similarity of the raters' values.

When a criterion variable depends upon largely inexplicit factors such as the raters' values, its reliability is hard to determine. The commonly employed practice of showing that a small group of raters may agree is too simple a solution. Agreement among a small number of raters is possible without their specifying objectively what they are rating; but until one is able to instruct a sizable number of raters so that they will all agree reasonably well about the ratings to be assigned to attendants, one cannot contend that a criterion is sufficiently reliable to be generally useful.

While a criterion must be reliable to be of any practical value, a more important requirement of a criterion is that it be valid (i.e., measure what the investigator intends it to measure). Many authorities question the validity of criteria that have been used in selection studies. Perhaps the best way to discuss these questions is to consider separately the two most frequently used criteria of attendant quality.

Length of Tenure. A commonly employed criterion of attendant performance is the length of time a person remains an attendant. Persons who remain employed for a short period of time are compared with those who remain a longer period of time. Sometimes a distinction is made between those employes who leave voluntarily and those who are discharged.

Cleland and Peck (1959) clarified the assumptions of using tenure as an index of attendant quality when they said: "(1) the best attendant is of little value to the institution if he leaves after only a short period of service; and (2) some correlation between satisfactory service and tenure is inevitable." The first assumption makes it quite clear that relatively long tenure is a necessary condition of effectiveness as an attendant, but is not so clear on the question of whether long tenure is a sufficient condition to being an effective attendant. The second assumption suggests that long tenure is to some degree a sufficient index of attendant quality. At precisely this point, the questionable validity of the tenure index is most apparent. The fact is that a variety of factors besides high quality as an attendant affect length of tenure. Cleland and Peck's own research and their analysis of institutional pressures upon attendants suggest that the kind of attendant who adjusts well to institutional pressures may not be the most desirable person to care for children. Briefly, authoritarianism and rigidity favor longer tenure. (These findings are discussed in greater detail in a later section.) Findings by Butterfield, Barnett, and Bensberg (in press) indicate that the economic circumstance of the community in which an institution is located affects turnover or tenure in the attendant population. Tenure clearly is not a simple index of attendant quality. Unless the contribution of other factors is controlled, then tenure is a questionable index of attendant quality.

A less crucial question has been raised by Taylor (1964), who pointed out that an investigator never knows which attendants are going to leave in the near future. Comparing attendants who have already left to those who remain amounts to comparing a group who have left with a mixed group, some of whom will leave and some of whom will stay. From a practical viewpoint, this fact might be regarded as unimportant. If the investigator is willing to say that all he wants to do is to distinguish those attendants who remain employed for less than a given period of time from those who remain longer, then he might ignore the fact that some of the attendants who stayed longer than his arbitrary time interval would be leaving later. Taylor points out that this practical approach ignores the possibility that people who leave after different lengths of employment do so for different reasons or are different kinds of people. Therefore, both the "leavers" and the "stayers" may actually be heterogeneous groups. In order to predict tenure adequately, evaluators may have to group attendants more finely according to their length of tenure rather than according to some single arbitrary length of time set by the investigator.

Ratings of Attendants. A rating of attendants' performance has been the most frequently employed criterion in selection studies. Usually the ratings have been provided by attendant supervisors. The great appeal of this criterion is that it appears to be the most nearly ideal index of attendant quality, but this appearance is largely illusory.

Almost all investigators agree that ratings are not a satisfactory criterion of attendant quality. Nearly all of the difficulties with ratings stem from the fact that the behavior to be rated is not explicitly defined—the same source of difficulties with the reliability of ratings. The issues regarding validity are somewhat different; that is, if an investigator is not certain about the bases that his raters use in evaluating attendants, he cannot adequately judge the validity of those ratings. This crucial issue has been pointed out by Shotwell, Dingman, and Tarjan (1960), who indicated that when an investigator decides to employ ratings as a criterion, he conceives of ratings made in terms of his conception of a good attendant. He selects predictor variables that should be related to his conception. He then relies upon other persons, usually attendant supervisors, to make his ratings. We know that attendant supervisors have a different conception of adequate attendant performance than professional personnel have. Investigators are almost invariably professional persons. The upshot of this is that selection studies are designed to predict ratings that are conceived in one way but are executed with ratings made in another way.

Another aspect of the problem was pointed up by Parloff (1960), who attempted to investigate the effects of instituting different treatment philosophies in a mental hospital. He employed two criteria of change in treatment philosophy. He had psychiatrists judge changes from first-hand experience with the attendants and also employed a sophisticated questionnaire technique to evaluate change in philosophy. He found that one of his psychiatrists reported that the attendants on his ward had gradually changed their philosophy of

patient care. His questionnaire showed conclusively that what really had happened was that the psychiatrist's philosophy had changed so that it was more similar to that of the attendants, whose own philosophy remained unchanged. Similarly, Tarjan, Showell, and Dingman (1956) showed that "a group of supervisors' ratings on the same individual did not remain constant even over a short period of time." The point of these examples is that, for an investigator to have confidence in the validity of his ratings, he must be able to make their bases clear and objective enough that he is certain that the ratings are not biased by the rater. This condition has not been met in past studies of attendant selection and training.

The basic problem with ratings is that attendant behavior is so complex that a single gross rating cannot reflect it with sufficient validity for any meaningful prediction or selection to occur. More analytic indices of attendant behavior are needed. I pointed out earlier that there were no detailed descriptions of what attendants actually did; this problem drastically hampers the selection studies that we will consider momentarily.

GUIDING CONCEPTION OF ATTENDANT QUALITY

In an area of investigation as complex as that of predicting attendant performance, an investigator must work from some guiding conception of attendant performance and the factors that influence it. Deciding that attendant personality affects attendant performance, measuring personality, and securing performance ratings is not enough. One must consider what personality dimensions affect attendant performance, in what ways, and why. He must consider what variables besides personality affect performance. He must, in short, be extremely thoughtful about the difficulties involved in this area of investigation.

ATTENDANT SELECTION INVESTIGATIONS

Studies of attendant selection will be grouped according to the predictor variables they employed.

Opinions differ widely about whether personality variables should predict attendant quality. Consider the following quotations:

It is generally recognized that personality characteristics rather than academic skills account for the success or failure of the psychiatric technician [attendant] (Cattell and Shotwell, 1954).

Presumably, success of prediction would be greatly enhanced if appropriate measures of relevant personality variables . . . could be devised (Cliff, Newman and Howell, 1959).

The variance due to personality may account for only a small part of [attendant] behavior, while variance due to working environment may account for much more of the behavior (Taylor, 1964).

In the face of such disagreement, a person has two alternatives. He may look at the empirical evidence to see whether personality does affect attendant performance or he may consider on rational grounds the arguments for and against the proposition that personality affects attendant performance. We shall do both.

A number of investigations have attempted to relate personality measures to attendant tenure. Butterfield and Warren (1962) compared the Minnesota Multiphasic Personality Inventory (MMPI) scores of three groups of attendants who were hired at Oregon Fairview Home. The groups were those who (1) had been hired and subsequently discharged during their first year of employment, (2) had resigned during their first year of employment, and (3) had remained employed throughout the first year after they were hired. The MMPI scores had been secured prior to the hiring of the attendants and had been employed in an unvalidated fashion as partial criterion for hiring (Horner, 1954). Butterfield and Warren found no personality scales or pattern of scales that differentiated the three groups reliably. While some isolated scores did differentiate an initial three groupings of attendants, these same scores were not predictive when cross-validation samples of three other similar groups were compared. This study illustrates the need to cross-validate differences between groups of attendants before concluding that any personality variable is an effective predictor. This point is also illustrated in studies by Tarjan, Shotwell, and Dingman (1955, 1956) and Cuadra and Reed (1957). These authors constructed personality-type items specifically for the purpose of predicting attendant tenure and performance ratings, and they found that some items were predictive in some samples of attendants, but not in other samples. The interpretation is that when a large number of comparisons are made between groups, some will differentiate the groups by chance alone. When an attempt is made to differentiate similar groups with the same items, the items will not be effective. For reasons such as this, findings by Kline (1950), Cattell and Shotwell (1954), Barron and Donahue (1951), and Vaccaro (1952) are of little value. None of these investigators attempted to cross-validate the few differences they found between attendants of different lengths of tenure.

One study by Tarjan, Shotwell, and Dingman (1956) illustrates another important point to be considered in selection studies. Their investigation was unique in employing attendants from a number of institutions. They found that those few personality items that differeniated short- and long-tenure groups in one institution did not do so in others. (None of their differentiations proved reliable.) This emphasizes the need to consider carefully the factors that contribute to attendant tenure and performance that may be peculiar to a given institution.

A number of studies have differentiated attendants who had different lengths of tenure and who were rated as being differentially adequate. The similarities in these studies are impressive. Two of these studies differ from those previously considered in that they employed detailed rationales for their selection of predictor variables. The fact that none of them reports a cross-validation is less crucial to their interpretation. The idea here is a simple one and illustrates the power of employing a guiding conception of attendant behavior in selection research. When an investigator is able to specify in advance what kinds of personality measures should differentiate what kind of attendant groups, then a cross-validation is less necessary in order to be fairly certain that his results, if in agreement with his expectations, are reliable. If an investigator does more than just guess that personality should make a difference in attendant performance and if he specifies in advance what that difference should be and why, then we may relax somewhat our demand for cross-validation.

Melbin (1961) has pointed out two possible reasons why personality might be related to attendant performance or tenure. One is that some types of attendants might be irresponsible and, consequently, not remain in any employment for very long. Another reason is that the demands placed upon attendants by an institution may be more tolerable to some personality types than to others. Cleland and Peck (1959) took this latter reason as their primary premise. They began by analyzing informally but convincingly the characteristics of the institution in which they were working:

The state school can best be summarized in the phrase "cultural island." The state school in its societal role has remained relatively stable through time. . . . The hierarchy of command was definite and the analogy to a typical patriarchal family easy to perceive. . . . In the institutional hierarchy, the attendant was seen to comprise the functional level, the "workers" by whom all decisions of the higher levels of staff must eventually be administered. . . . The formal organization chart revealed that the attendants occupied the lowest rung of the ladder in the area of direct services to the patient. (Cleland and Peck, 1959).

This descripion of the attendant's role is quite consistent with those of writers mentioned earlier in this chapter.

From this analysis, Cleland and Peck asked themselves what kind of person was likely to stay in the position of attendant for a relatively long time and concluded it would be a person with an "authoritarian" personality. From a conception of authoritarianism posited by Fromm and elaborated by Adorno, they predicted that the long-tenure attendant should differ from the short tenure attendant in the following ways:

1. The long-tenure attendants would manifest a significantly higher degree of authoritarianism, as measured by the California F Scale, than would those attendants with six months or less of service.
2. The long-tenure attendants would reflect a significantly more positive rural orientation than would the short-tenure attendants and a significantly larger proportion of the long-tenure attendants would be of rural origin.

3. The long-tenure attendants would reflect significantly greater acceptance of the standards and the authority of their parents than the short-tenure group (Cleland and Peck, 1959)

In order to test these predictions, Cleland and Peck secured California F Scales and structured interview data from a group of attendants who had been employed for ten years or more and a group whose employment had been voluntarily terminated less than six months after they were hired as attendants. They found, as predicted, that the stayers had significantly higher F scores, came more often from a rural background, expressed considerably more desire for a rural life, and regarded their parents as expected. Consider the following description from Cleland and Peck (1959):

Beginning with the childhood perceptions, there were marked differences between the stayer and leaver. The stayer group unanimously indicated unquestioning obedience to a stern, aloof, somewhat domineering father. The father's dominance, even when it was recognized as having been used to thwart expressions of individuality on the part of the subject, was upheld on grounds of "he knew best" and other expressions of dependency on the father's superior judgment.

The stayers saw the mother's role as being completely overshadowed by that of the father. In the few instances in which the mother was mentioned, the tendency was to emphasize her weakness—"she was always sickly" . . .

The stayers placed strong emphasis upon responsibility. An early exposure to responsibility was noted in almost every stayer's interview. Either through parental demands or through circumstances such as the death of a parent, the stayers were forced to assume responsibility very early in life.

Examination of the leavers' data revealed a striking contrast in the perception of childhood and parents. The frequency with which the leavers' mothers figure as the dominant family member was much greater than in the stayer group. . . .

Parental standards, values, and authority were questioned, negated, or completely rejected by a great proportion of the leaver group. . . .

There was little to indicate that the leavers were exposed to early responsibility or work. . . .

The stayer group emerged as a rather passive-compliant individual whose characteristic mode of adjustment was one of pronounced dependency —either on parental figures or on parental substitutes.

There are several shortcomings in the Cleland and Peck study. They collected their data only after their subjects had worked as attendants. The stayer group was significantly older and had been hired earlier. The analysis of much of the data was largely descriptive and illustrative rather than statistical. Still, the results are convincingly consistent with their expectations and do correspond to the observations of others (e.g., Rettig, 1956b).

Butterfield and Warren (1963) took as their point of departure the thesis that personality would be related to short tenure because persons who were irresponsible or had other undesirable characteristics would not be employed long. In order to test this notion, they administered selected portions of the MMPI to prospective employes who were then hired on the basis of an interview and without knowledge of the MMPI results. The hiring interviewer attempted to base his decision upon the poise of the applicant and no attempt was made to verify the applicant's statements to the interviewer or the information provided on a standard job application form.

Five predictions were tested in this study. It was predicted that (a) dishonest persons (those with high MMPI *L* scale scores) and (b) defensive persons (those with high MMPI *K* scale scores) would have been able to hide poor work histories and undesirable characteristics from the hiring interviewer and that as those undesirable characteristics became apparent to their supervisors these persons would be discharged. It was also predicted that (c) persons with socially irresponsible tendencies (persons with high MMPI *Pd* scale scores) would be fired more frequently than more socially responsible people. It was expected, for example, that the high *Pd* would probably be irregular in his attendance, more likely to drink on the job, etc. It was also believed that (d) persons who were very active and inclined to assume responsibilities which did not really belong to them (persons high on the *MA* scale of the MMPI) would have conflicts with their supervisors and would consequently be more likely to be fired. Finally, it was predicted that (e) the greater number of these characteristics which any attendant possessed, the more likely he was to be discharged (Butterfield and Warren, 1963).

These predictions were tested by comparing the relevant MMPI scale scores of those employes who were discharged in the first six months after their employment as attendants with those who remained as attendants for more than six months. It was found that all four MMPI scales differentiated the two groups in the expected fashion, although results from one of the scales did not quite attain an acceptable level of statistical significance. "These results indicate that it is possible, given an understanding of the hiring and firing procedures of an institution, to predict, on a rational rather than a strictly empirical basis, which attendants will probably be fired and which ones will probably be retained as employes" (Butterfield and Warren, 1963). The Cleland and Peck and the Butterfield and Warren studies illustrate the advantage of working from a set of specific expectations and of attending quite closely to the nature of the criterion of attendant performance employed and the institution in which the study is being done.

Rettig (1956b) has provided a good example of the development of a potentially useful selection instrument. He began with the premise that a good attendant was one who demonstrated social responsibility in the "entire area of interaction between attendants and patients." Feeling that interactions in which attendants manifested warmth toward the patient rather than authoritarianism were more socially responsible, he devised a number of questionnaire-type items that were intended to assess these two dimensions of attendant-patient interactions. He had supervisors rate attendants as socially responsible, making it clear to the raters that he was concerned only with attendants' interactions with patients and not with other attendants or their supervisors. This structuring of the reference point of the behavior to be rated is a definite strength in Rettig's procedure. He found a group of attendants whom supervisors agreed were responsible in their interactions with patients and a group whom supervisors agreed were not responsible. He administered his items to the attendants and found thirteen that differentiated socially responsible from socially irresponsible attendants. He then rewrote the items in an effort to assess the same kinds of content and readministered them to the same groups of attendants. The items still differentiated the two groups. He then administered these thirteen items to the supervisors who had done the rating. His assumption was that the supervisors, who had judged his criterion of social responsibility, should respond in a more socially responsible fashion. They did so on seven of his items. Rettig has subsequently begun administering these seven items to all prospective attendant employes. When attendants are hired, their responses to these items are not considered. In the future, Rettig will be able to determine whether the items he has thus selected are predictive of socially responsible attendant behavior. This is an unusually good example of how an investigator might proceed in an effort to develop meaningful selection criteria for the hiring of attendants. Beyond that, Rettig's findings are of considerable interest because they relate closely to the findings of Cleland and Peck (1959):

An inspection of the significantly differentiating questions and their choices seemed to reveal that both tendencies, that of warmth, kindness, permissiveness and laxity as well as that of authoritativeness and definiteness of action appeared in the socially responsible attendant. . . .

The theoretical justification of this stronger second [authoritative] tendency may lie, again, in the needs of the patients. It is based on the assumption that the primary needs of ambulatory mentally deficient patients are concentrated around the training and preparation for the future. Life, according to this philosophy, must be presented to the patients in the most realistic fashion. Patients must learn to know right from wrong, to accept the consequences of their actions, to accept authority, and to realize their own limitations.

This statement of philosophy is what one might expect from the stayers in Cleland and Peck's study. Rettig's supervisors probably are similar to Cleland and Peck's stayers. Surely the supervisors have relatively long tenure. The view of the "successful" attendant as a socially responsible, passive, but somewhat authoritarian person thus emerges from the three attendant selection studies that have employed a theoretical orientation. In this regard, it is interesting to note the description that Tarjan, Shotwell, and Dingman (1955) gave of the successful attendant:

An analysis of the answers which the successful technician made pointed to a rather consistent personality pattern. It was that of a quiet, somewhat withdrawn, at times shy individual with conservative attitudes, a high degree of conformity and an inclination to accept the opinion of others. He was a person who attended strictly to business, had few outside interests and was satisfied with his job and work status. He was likely to have held previous jobs in other fields but definitely preferred work in a hospital and was

ready to accept personal inconveniences required by the job.

It cannot be emphasized too strongly that this conception of the successful attendant probably emerges because of the nature of the attendant's position and may not be the most desirable kind of personality for attendants to possess.

In a provocative article strongly recommended for the reader who is intimately concerned with attendant selection and training, Melbin (1961) reports the results of an investigation in which he established rather convincingly that attendants' unauthorized absences from work were preceded by either work-shift or days-off reassignments. In the same study he showed that both voluntary and involuntary terminations of employment occurred most frequently after a gradually increasing record of unauthorized absenteeism.

He concluded that "high absenteeism (lateness and absence) appears to be an earlier sign, and turnover (quitting and being fired) the dying stage of a long and lively process of leaving." Melbin went on to speculate about how attendant personality, in interaction with institution practices such as work-shift and days-off reassignment, might contribute to this "leaving" process. He suggested that an aide with strong affiliative needs would be more likely to suffer from a ward transfer (i.e., leaving patients with whom he had a relationship) than would an individual not so concerned with personal relationships. The practice of reassignment might, therefore, result in the elimination of attendants who had affiliative needs and the retention of attendants who were, perhaps, more oriented toward authority. Melbin suggested that as an alternative to actually leaving, the attendant with strong affiliative needs might respond to pressures created by practices such as rotating shift assigments by avoiding an emotional investment in the patients for whom he cared. Melbin also suggested that these various kinds of withdrawal reactions would be stronger in institutions that stress to their attendants the importance of providing emotional support to their patients. Hypothetical processes such as these could very well be operating in the differential selection of attendants of longer tenure and might account in part for the findings of such studies as Cleland and Peck

(1959) and Tarjan, Shotwell, and Dingman (1955).

Those studies that have attempted to cross-validate empirically derived personality differences between attendants who differ in tenure or performance ratings, indicate that differences that have been discovered do not appear on a second trial.. For that reason, empirically based studies that have not been based upon predictions about different kinds of attendants appear to be of little or no value. Those few studies that have made explicit predictions in advance from knowledge of the institution being studied and from theoretical conceptions of personality have yielded encouraging and similar results that suggest that attendant personality is related to attendant performance.

STUDIES EMPLOYING INTELLECTUAL MEASURES AS PREDICTORS

There is essentially no evidence that intellectual level of attendants affects their tenure or their performance even though several authors have investigated this possibility (Cliff, Newman, and Howell, 1959; Hadley and Proctor, 1940; Love, 1955; Tarjan, Shotwell, and Dingman, 1955). Still, largely because of the inadequacies in criterion measures employed in these studies, I would concur with Tarjan, Shotwell, and Dingman that "to underestimate the importance of intelligence for a psychiatric technician [attendant] in the present state of our knowledge . . . would be unwarranted." A finding that supports this judgment is reported by Barnett (1964b). He found that attendants who scored low on a test of information about retardation were more often nominated by their supervisors as poor attendants than were attendants who scored high on this test. Barnett also reported that scores on his test were related to intelligence test scores and grade completed in school.

OTHER PREDICTORS OF TENURE AND TURNOVER

I have suggested that any attempt to predict attendant tenure or quality must take many factors into account. The studies reviewed above were concerned mainly with personality variables and to a lesser extent

with intellectual abilities of attendants. Except on a theoretical level (e.g., Melbin, 1961), no studies have concerned themselves with situational variables in the institution. For example, one finds no investigations of the effects of different kinds of ward assignments upon tenure or attendant reactions even though one commonly hears attendant supervisors contend that some attendants definitely prefer working with certain kinds of patients. Nor can one find studies of the effects of different levels of employe health or family circumstances, even though superintendents contend that these are two of the most frequent reasons attendants give for terminating employment (McIntire, 1954). One study does relate community and institution characteristics to attendant turnover (Butterfield, Barnett, and Bensberg, in press).

Butterfield, Barnett, and Bensberg sent questionnaires to the superintendents of 26 institutions for the mentally retarded in the southeastern United States. From the responses to these questionnaires, sixteen objective items of information were selected for study. Of those sixteen characteristics, the ones that are relevant to the present discussion are:

1. Total nonattendant personnel turnover rate

$$\frac{\text{Number of nonattendant replacements}}{\text{Average nonattendant work force}} \times 100$$

2. Total attendant personnel turnover rate
3. Minimum attendant salary
4. Maximum attendant salary
5. Hours per week worked by attendants
6. Number of residents in institution

By correlational and factor analytic statistical procedures, the investigators found that attendant and nonattendant personnel turnover rate were unrelated to minimum attendant salary, maximum attendant salary, hours per week worked by attendants, and number of residents in the institution. Since these latter measures contribute significantly to what are generally termed working conditions and were closely related to one another, these results apparently show that objective working conditions do not influence attendant turnover rate. The question immediately arises, what does influence attendant turnover and, by implication, average attendant turnover?

In order to explore this question, information was secured from the United States Bureau of the Census (1962) about the counties in which each institution was located. The following items of information were secured for each county:

1. Per cent of labor force employed
2. Median income of all wage earners
3. Median grade attained by all adults
4. Population per square mile
5. Per cent of land in farms
6. Population increase or decrease from 1950 to 1960

These items of information were then correlated with a composite index of attendant and nonattendant personnel turnover rate. Roughly half of the variation in turnover rate in the 26 institutions could be accounted for by the factors (1) per cent of labor force unemployed and (2) population increase or decrease from 1950 to 1960. The greater the unemployment rate and the faster the growth of the communities surrounding the institution, the less the turnover rate. A composite index of the several indices of attendant working conditions was unrelated to any of the community factors studied. Working conditions in the institutions were not related systematically to the surrounding community and population factors that were studied. Comparison of the median family incomes of each of the counties surrounding the institutions with the minimum and maximum attendant salaries showed that in every instance the beginning salary paid to attendants and in 19 of the 26 instances the maximum salary paid to attendants was less than the median family income. In a majority of the institutions, the discrepancy between *maximum* attendant salary and median family income was more than $1,000.

These findings have marked implications for the study of factors that affect turnover rate, tenure, and attendant quality. They suggest that one of the major determinants of attendant turnover is the character of the economic climate in which an institution is located. This will undoubtedly continue to be true until attendant salaries are more competitive with those available to the type of person who works as an attendant. Until and unless investigators of attendant quality consider the effects of such variables as this, they will be unable to account for more than half of all turnover rate. Another way to say this is that

attendant characteristics such as personality and intelligence cannot now account for more than half of the turnover rate in institutions in general, although there may be particular institutions (those whose salaries are more competitive) in which factors such as these are more influential. Another implication of these findings is that while institution salaries and working conditions remain as they now stand, the intangible aspects of job satisfaction and their interaction with such characteristics as personality probably determine the remainder of the variation in turnover rate. This indicates that much more attention needs to be given to understanding how the attendant views his job, what factors in the institution besides salary and hours affect him, etc., if we are to reduce the high turnover rate among the attendant employes in institutions for the mentally retarded. (The annual turnover in the 26 institutions studied by Butterfield, Barnett, and Bensberg ranged from 10 to 54 per cent.)

OVERVIEW OF THE FACTORS AFFECTING ATTENDANT QUALITY AND TURNOVER

A persistent theme of this chapter has been that in order to gain a fuller understanding of the factors that affect attendant quality and turnover, one must work from a comprehensive conception of what is now known and what is likely to affect these factors. Without a comprehensive overview, one is seldom able to interpret the data he secures about any one factor that affects attendant quality and turnover. Research into factors that affect attendant quality is commendable and essential, but the researcher must recognize that he is studying extremely complex and poorly comprehended phenomena that require the continual use of judgment and intuition.

The size and quality of the pool of applicants from which attendants may be hired is affected by the economic condition of the community in which the hiring institution is located, the image or reputation of the hiring institution, the vigor of the institution's recruitment program, and the institution's minimal requirements for the position of attendant. The greater the unemployment rate and the less the discrepancy between attendant salaries and those of other positions that attendant applicants might secure, the larger and the higher the general quality of this pool will be. The better the reputation of the institution as a place to work, the more and better applicants the institution will receive. Reputation is probably affected by salary scale and other objective indices of working conditions. Less tangible factors such as the general quality of the existing staff of employes, practices regarding shift and work assignment changes, etc., also are important. An institution with a high rate of employe turnover probably gains a reputation as an undesirable place to work and as a result experiences difficulties in recruiting sufficient quality applicants. The institution that "beats the bushes" by doing such things as providing temporary work experiences for high school students, offering a "bounty" to present employes for referring job applicants, etc., probably has a greater applicant pool. The higher the minimum requirements for the attendant position, the smaller the applicant pool is likely to be.

The character of the attendants hired depends upon the characteristics of the applicant pool and the selection procedures employed by the institution. The characteristics of the persons in the applicant pool are probably the main determinants of the characteristics of attendants hired at the present time, since the selection procedures currently in use are minimal and bear questionable relation to the actual requirements of the position of attendant.

The character of the attendants who stay with an institution depends upon the characteristics of the attendants hired, the relationship between the characteristics of the attendants hired and the demands of the position of attendant, and the relationship between the rewards, financial and other, of being an attendant and the rewards of other positions available to the kind of person employed as an attendant. If generally unreliable and irresponsible people are hired as attendants, the hiring institution may expect a relatively high turnover or a relatively low level of attendant functioning. The literature gives some indications that generally unreliable people can be effectively screened out of the applicant pool by means of simple personality tests. Simple pre-hiring procedures such as securing letters

of reference from previous employers could also be effective in this regard.

Much less sound information is available for predicting how an attendant will respond to the demands of the attendant position. The demands of the attendant position have not been adequately explored. Such things as changes in work-shift and days off; relationships between supervisors and employes; the attitudes of various professional staff members; the characteristics of in-service training programs; trouble-shooting practices by supervisors and personnel officers; demands of various kinds of patients; attendant involvement in program planning; work evaluation procedures, etc., are all likely areas of investigation. The question must also be asked how attendants with various characteristics respond to variation in each of these factors. Further exploration of attendant characteristics is urgently needed both before and after hiring. The actual functions of attendants need to be investigated and analyzed in considerable detail. The person who would understand and predict attendant quality and turnover needs to be sensitive to changes in the economic circumstances in the community surrounding the institution with which he is concerned. Such things as seasonal demands for a large labor force, introduction of new employers into the community, etc., need to be comprehended.

Many details are missing from this general view of the attendant position. However, it does indicate many of the major factors that affect the questions of attendant turnover and quality, clearly suggesting that the factors influencing the character of the attendant staff are not independent. The working conditions, both tangible and intangible, affect not only those employes presently employed but also affect the kinds of persons who will be seeking employment in an institution. For reasons such as these, in addition to the very important task of providing the best possible care to the retarded patients in an institution, in-service training is coming to be regarded as more and more important in institutions for the retarded. The rationale for this is that attendant quality can be raised, patient care improved, and attendant turnover reduced by means of adequate in-service training programs.

THE INCREASED INTEREST IN IN-SERVICE TRAINING

In 1949, Pero sent a questionnaire to all state institutions for the mentally retarded in the United States, and 31 of the 74 that replied said they had some type of in-service training program. In 1957, Shafter, Chandler, and Coe sent a similar questionnaire to 93 state institutions for the mentally retarded. Of the 55 that replied, 30 reported having some type of in-service training program. In 1964, Parnicky and Ziegler surveyed 131 state institutions for the retarded. Of the 108 who responded, 102 reported some type of in-service training program. Barnett (1964d) reported that 23 of 35 state institutions in the southeastern United States had in-service training programs. The increased proportion of respondents to the surveys and the increasing percentage of those responding who reported having in-service training indicates that increased attention has been given to training attendants.

Another particularly dramatic indication of the increased interest in in-service training is the creation by the Southern Regional Education Board (SREB), which serves sixteen southeastern states, in co-operation with the federal government, in a special project for the purpose of facilitating training of attendants in state institutions for the retarded. The aims of the SREB project have been described by Bensberg, Barnett, and Hurder (1964) as:

1. Determination of knowledge and skills required of the attendant if he is to be effective in providing care and training for the residents in his care.
2. Determination of how to best teach this information and these skills.
3. Providing an opportunity for additional learning experiences for those co-ordinating training of attendants.
4. Evaluating the effectiveness and content of training procedures used with attendants.

To meet these goals, SREB has financed systematic visits by institution personnel involved in in-service training in other institutions; conducted surveys, field trials and research studies; developed information and attitude scales for use with attendants; published a newsletter for the dissemination of relevant information; maintained a file of information for use by interested persons, etc.

These kinds of services are badly needed. The idea of doing this on a regional basis is novel and, at least in the opinion of those involved, very useful.

CHARACTERISTICS OF EXISTING IN-SERVICE TRAINING PROGRAMS

While more and more institutions have shown an interest in in-service training, the character of the training varies widely from institution to institution. Some offer training mainly as orientation for new employes, some as training for older employes or supervisors, anl some do both (Parnicky and Ziegler, 1964). In some institutions the programs are compulsory, in others they are not (Barnett, 1964d; Parnicky and Ziegler, 1964). The incentives offered to attendants range from none, through the granting of certificates, to making pay increases and promotions contingent upon successful completion of the program (Parnicky and Ziegler, 1964). Some require that the attendant participate on his own time without any remuneration, and others train on "institution time" or give compensatory time off (Parnicky and Ziegler, 1964). Some train only attendants while others train all institution employes (Shafter, Chandler, and Coe, 1957).

Very few institutions have personnel assigned exclusively to the job of in-service training. In some institutions the superintendent is responsible, but in most a committee of various department heads or nurses conduct the training courses (Parnicky and Ziegler, 1964). Though most institutions use the lecture method to some extent, most also employ some kind of "on-the-job" training (Barnett, 1964d; Shafter, Chandler, and Coe, 1957). Many have formalized their instruction to the point of having manuals and handbooks, though the adequacy of these has been questioned by several authors (Parnicky and Ziegler, 1964; Scher, 1956; Stevens, 1963). Instruction most frequently includes history and objectives of the institution, and duties and responsibilities of the administration, individual employes, and various institution departments. Instruction in specific child handling and nursing techniques is also offered, but less commonly (Shafter, Chandler, and Coe, 1957). The only available estimate of the cost of in-service training—$117 per employe—comes from Columbus State School, where 60 hours of classroom instruction are given by a variety of regular institution employes (Harrison, 1963). The $117 figure may underestimate the cost to the typical institution, since Barnett (1964d) reports that the median length of training programs in the Southeast is 100 hours. Vaccaro estimated that in 1952 it cost psychiatric institutions an average of about $300 to replace an employe.

The reasons given for initiating in-service training vary from institution to institution and include such items as the following: (1) to decrease personnel turnover; (2) to decrease personnel problems arising out of misunderstandings of their and the institution's goals; (3) to improve the reputation of the institution as a place to work; and (4) to improve level of patient care (Stevens, 1963). Morris, Nellis, and Stromberg (1959) probably described many of the factors that induce institutions to institute in-service training when they said:

If you take some individuals from an older order and blend them with some from a new, if you take members of several different specialized backgrounds, with their average share of professional jealousies and other neurotic transferences, if you put them in a job which makes very heavy demands upon their time, and if you compound all that with a fair degree of misunderstanding about administrative policies and lines of communication—then you have the ingredients of a difficult situation.

Another factor cited as demonstrating the need for in-service training is the increased demands being made upon attendants because of the shift downward in mental level of patients in many institutions. This downward shift has resulted in a shortage of competent patient-workers (Kaplan, 1961).

The reasons given by those institutions that do not have in-service training programs center on economic considerations. Thus, lack of personnel to do the training, lack of time of available personnel, and lack of facilities are the commonly cited reasons (Barnett, 1964c; Shafter, Chandler, and Coe, 1957). A related and somewhat paradoxical reason offered by some is the existence of too high a turnover rate to make it practical to train new employes (Shafter, Chandler, and Coe, 1957).

Another paradoxical reason was indicated by Kline and Eaton (1952), who reported that they "have known institutions that make a deliberate effort to keep from their employes a knowledge of what they should be doing, on the theory that they would become dissatisfied with the inadequacies of the status quo."

INVESTIGATIONS OF THE EFFECTIVENESS OF IN-SERVICE TRAINING

A host of researchable questions arise from a consideration of the differences between existing in-service training programs and the reasons given for having or not having such programs, and few of these questions have been adequately investigated. A large segment of the available literature on in-service training merely describes and extolls existing programs at specific institutions (Daly, 1963; Edgett, 1947; Farrel and Forsley, 1956; Fox, 1950; Graves, 1958; Harrison, 1963; Lash and Otness, 1949; Morris, Nellis, and Stromberg, 1959; Roselle, 1950). While this literature serves to illustrate the variety of approaches available to those who would provide in-service training to attendants, it does not begin to answer many of the questions about in-service training. We will now consider a few experimental studies of in-service training.

Barnett (1964d) has reported the results of a series of lectures to attendants that were intended to increase their knowledge of retardation and to change their attitudes toward retarded persons. Extensive information and attitude inventories were constructed and then administered both before and after the lecture series. Two different groups of attendants were given the lecture series, and both groups showed significant increases in knowledge about retardation and the care of retarded patients as well as favorable changes in attitudes. The tests showed that their initial level of knowledge was related to the intellectual level of the attendants as was their subsequent knowledge about retardation. The change or increase in information was not related to intellectual level. Attendants benefited equally from the training regardless of their intellectual level. A question that this research does not answer is to what degree did the changes that were reflected in attendant information and attitudes reflect themselves in their performance on the ward with the patients. Perhaps the attendants merely learned what the instructor wanted them to say and said it, but did not change their job performance. That this is a very real possibility is indicated in a study conducted by Parloff (1960) in which he showed that attendants knew that an instructor was attempting to modify their manner of dealing with patients but they still did not change nor did they agree that a change was desirable.

In order to compare the effects of three different training procedures, McDowell (1963) developed a series of situations with which attendants are frequently required to cope. In one group these situations were discussed with an eye to improving attendants' handling of them. In another group, attendants acted out (role-played) various kinds of responses to the situations. In a third group attendants both discussed and role-played the situations. A fourth group had no experience with the situations through either discussion or role-playing. The first three groups met for five hours, one hour on each of five occasions. Before the five hours of training, all groups indicated how they would respond to a number of different situations that might occur between attendants and patients. These same situations were rated after the training. McDowell found that all groups, including the ones who had neither role-playing nor discussion experience, changed in a positive direction their reports of how they would respond to the situations. When he tested another group of attendants from another institution, he found no such change. His interpretation of these findings was that those attendants who had had training talked to their fellow attendants about it and this communication influenced the responses of those who had not had training. His findings also indicated no differential effectiveness between the role-playing, discussion, and role-playing and discussion groups. Again it must be asked whether the changes found indicate any change in attendants' performance; the effects that McDowell found were quite slight. Nevertheless, one provocative implication of

McDowell's findings is that all attendants need not be given in-service training. So long as some are trained, they may, in turn, train their fellow attendants.

Quay, Bartlett, Wrightsman, and Catron (in press) compared three quite different methods of attendant training—lectures by an expert, group discussion, and a booklet—each tested on a different group. A fourth group was given none of these procedures. The lecture method was most effective in changing attitudes as measured by one attitude scale. The booklet method was next most effective, but it did not produce results that attained statistical significance. The discussion method produced no differences from the group that received no special training. Quay, Bartlett, Wrightsman, and Catron employed a second attitude scale that revealed no differences between any of the groups, suggesting that the results found with the first scale reflected the fact that attendants had learned how the different instructors wanted them to answer but had not actually changed their attitudes. Unlike McDowell (1963), Quay, Bartlett, Wrightsman, and Catron did not find that nontrained attendants changed in their attitudes. Perhaps role-playing procedures such as those used by McDowell lead to more discussion of what transpired in training classes than did the methods employed by Quay, Bartlett, Wrightsman, and Catron. And perhaps some institutions do not have sufficient communication between attendants for the "lessons" learned by some of them to be transmitted to others.

The results of these three studies (Barnett, 1964d; McDowell, 1963; Quay, Bartlett, Wrightsman, and Catron, in press) are encouraging. They suggest that attendant information and attitudes can be changed. Similar results have been reported by A. Thorne and R. Fox (personal communications). However, none of these studies attempted to assess the effects of training procedures upon attendant performance or turnover. Influencing responses on an attitude inventory is one thing; changing attendant behavior is another.

Both Parloff (1960) and Scheff (1961) attempted to influence attendants' behavior toward patients in a psychiatric hospital. Both found that they were completely unable to affect attendants' attitudes and behavior.

Parloff describes his experiences as follows:

From the Messianic tone of some articles, it may quite reasonably be assumed that practically any desired ward atmosphere can readily be invoked and reproduced. After participating in efforts over a period of two years to establish a variety of predetermined ward atmospheres, I have reason to be somewhat less sanguine. . . . Obviously, . . . some administrators have managed somehow to create distinctive therapeutic ward philosophies. What may be equally obvious is the fact that they must possess gifts and talents which may be less common than the ward milieu literature might lead one to believe.

What Parloff does not say is that there is considerable question that any administrator has been able through any procedures to produce changes in existing ward atmospheres (i.e., attendant behavior).

OBSTACLES IN THE WAY OF EFFECTIVE
IN-SERVICE TRAINING

While one may raise serious questions about the training techniques employed by Parloff and Scheff, the implication may be drawn from the discrepancy between their findings and those of Barnett (1964d), McDowell (1963), and Quay, Bartlett, Wrightsman, and Catron (in press) that the reason these latter authors found significant changes as a result of in-service training was that they failed to assess the most relevant variable (attendant behavior) and they did not try to affect the most pressing problems that face the in-service trainer.

Scheff (1961) has provided an excellent discussion of the problems encountered in one effort to modify attendant attitudes and behavior. His discussion and that of Parloff (1960) clearly indicate that there can be and perhaps usually is organized resistance to attempts to change attendant behavior. One incident described by Scheff shows why one might conclude that the behavior patterns and emotions that need to be changed by in-service training in some institutions might not be changed by lecture, no matter how expert:

[As a part of their effort to change ward behavior and attitudes of attendants, "Therapeutic Community" meetings were held.] The meeting was part of the series of demonstrations of the Therapeutic Community. A period had been left for questions, with the superintendent in charge. Initially, staff members were slow to raise questions, but after the early minutes had passed, questions came rapidly. The rejection of the [training] pro-

gram soon became evident from the character of the questions. Toward the end of the hour, the meeting nearly broke up when one staff member asked if it were true that the administration condoned intimate contacts between male and female patients. The superintendent answered that the administration did not condone improper behavior, but the phrasing of his answer was not direct enough to satisfy his audience. In what was virtually a demonstration, the audience jeered and hooted the superintendent.

This is undoubtedly an extreme example. However, it points out the problems that must inevitably arise when a group of professional personnel or administrators attempt to impress their values and ways of doing things upon attendants. These differences lie at the heart of a viable training program. The resistance that one should expect in attempting to impose a "dynamic and progressive" way of handling patients upon a group of attendants should be appreciated and should, perhaps, condition one's approach to in-service training.

Scheff has described the many faces that resistance to an in-service training program may take. Attendants may not give professional staff members information that is essential to economical treatment of patients. Attendants might encourage patients to engage in activities that disrupt the usual pattern of institution functioning. Attendants might be disobedient. They might tie up valuable staff meeting time with discussions of minor problems of patients.

The impression should not be given that the difficulties involved in in-service training all arise out of the perverse nature of attendants. We already have noted that professional staff members can create problems that are no less serious in the disruption of a training program. Professionals can be intolerant of problems with which attendants must cope. The turnover rate among professionals is frequently greater than that among attendants (Cleland, 1964), a situation that makes it very difficult to maintain continuity of treatment philosophy. Moreover, in-service training instructors can be poor teachers (Stevens, 1963). All of these things make it difficult to bring about adequate in-service training. Factors such as these have not been subjected to systematic research; perhaps the best one can do is to describe the experiences of others with problems of this kind.

"COMMON SENSE" CONSIDERATIONS THAT AFFECT IN-SERVICE TRAINING

Stevens (1963) has provided a thoughtful consideration of many of the problems involved in in-service training of the attendant. He suggests that "on the job" training such as that implied in the "buddy system" among attendants simply perpetuates the traditional attitudes and inadequate procedures. He points out that curriculum guides and materials for in-service training are largely nonexistent. He suggests that follow-up as well as orientation training is necessary. He indicates that not all competent professionals or supervisors are competent instructors. Each of these observations cries out for elucidation through systematic research.

CONCLUSIONS

Quay (1960) has pointed out a number of general questions about in-service training that need to be investigated. We need to find out whether any kind of training program is effective. Effectiveness must be carefully defined. Parloff (1960) has noted that the most statistically significant change in attendants' behavior is not adequate if that behavior still falls short of the minimum goals of the administrator. Attention needs to be given to what kinds of training methods are most effective for solving what kinds of problems. Some methods are much more economical than others and some are more well-suited to solving some kinds of in-service needs than are others. Training attendants in the best way to make beds, clean wards, change diapers, etc., might be best done with a combination of lecture and practical demonstration. Such an approach is unlikely to change basic disagreements about attitudes toward patients, handling discipline problems, etc. Attention also needs to be directed at what kinds of attendants benefit most from what kinds of teaching methods. Perhaps some attendants learn more from a lecture course while others learn more from individual supervision on the job. The other large area of necessary investigation concerns the question of what kinds of instructors are most effective. Instructors may very well be most effective depending on the methods, the pupils, or the topics discussed.

REFERENCES

BARNETT, C. D. Attendant Training Newsletter, 1964, *4.* (a)

————. *General evaluation activities.* Atlanta: Southern Regional Education Board, 1964. (b)

————. *Regional survey of attendant supervisors: their characteristics and role in attendant training.* Atlanta: Southern Regional Education Board, 1964. (c)

————. *Behavioral management of the institutionalized mentally retarded— a survey.* Atlanta: Southern Regional Education Board, 1964. (d)

BARRON, E. M., and DONAHUE, H. H. Psychiatric aide selection through psychological examination. *Amer. J. Psychiat.,* 1951, *107,* 859–865.

BELKNAP, I. *Human problems of a state mental hospital.* New York: McGraw-Hill, 1956.

BENSBERG, G. J., BARNETT, C. D., and HURDER, W. P. Training of attendant personnel in residential facilities for the mentally retarded. *Ment. Retardation,* 1964, *3,* 144–151.

BUTTERFIELD, E. C., BARNETT, C., and BENSBERG, G. Objective characteristics of institutions for the mentally retarded: Implications for attendant turnover rate. *Amer. J. ment. Defic.,* in press.

————, and WARREN, SUE A. The use of the MMPI in the selection of hospital aides. *J. appl. Psychol.,* 1962, *46,* 34–40.

————, and ————. Prediction of attendant tenure. *J. appl. Psychol.,* 1963, *47,* 101–103.

CATTELL, R. S., and SHOTWELL, A. M. Personality profiles of more successful and less successful psychiatric technicians. *Amer. J. ment. Defic.*, 1954, *58*, 496–499.

CLELAND, C. C. Selection and training of attendants: A review of research. *Amer. J. ment. Defic.*, 1962, 76, 205.

———. Natural versus systematic selection of attendants: Intrainstitutional administrative problems. Paper delivered at American Association on Mental Deficiency convention, 1964.

———, and PECK, R. F. Psychological determinants of tenure in institutional personnel. *Amer. J. ment. Defic.*, 1959, *64*, 876–883.

CLIFF, N., NEWMAN, S. H., and HOWELL, M. A. Selection of subprofessional hospital care personnel. *J. appl. Psychol.*, 1959, *43*, 42–46.

CUADRA, C. A., and REED, C. F. Prediction of psychiatric aide performance. *J. appl. Psychol.*, 1957, *41*, 195–197.

DALY, W. C. Some keys to training personnel in a residential school. *Ment. Retardation*, 1963, *1*, 97–99, 125–127.

DAYTON, N. The real goal in the education and training of the mentally retarded in residential schools. *Ment. Retardation*, 1963, *1*, 137.

EDGETT, C. D. Attendant training in schools for the mental deficient. *Amer. J. ment. Defic.*, 1947, *53*, 153–161.

———. Characteristics of desirable employees. *Amer. J. ment. Defic.*, 1951, *56*, 290–294.

FARRELL, M. J., and FORSLEY, E. Enhancing patients' adjustments by means of group sessions with attendants. *Amer. J. ment. Defic.*. 1956, *60*, 603–607.

FLEMING, J. W. The critical incident technique as an aid to in-service training. *Amer. J. ment. Defic.*, 1962, *67*, 41–52.

FOX, W. W. Suggestive training programs for employee training. *Amer. J. Ment. Defic.*, 1950, *55*, 179–186.

GOLDBERG, N., and HYDE, R. W. Role-playing in psychiatric training. *J. soc. Psychol.*, 1954, *39*, 63–75.

GRAVES, W. S. The psychological development of the mentally retarded child: a training course for attendants. *Amer. J. ment. Defic.*, 1958, *62*, 912–915.

GREENBLATT, M., YORK, R., and BROWN, ESTHER. *From custodial to therapeutic care in mental hospitals.* New York: Russell Sage Foundation, 1955.

HADLEY, R. V., and PROCTOR, A. Relationship between mental age and efficiency of ward attendants in a mental hospital. *Amer. J. ment Defic.*, 1940, *45*, 243–264.

HAMISTER, R. C. An investigation of patient and staff opinions concerning the effectiveness of neuropsychiatric hospital staff members. *J. soc. Psychol.*, 1955, *41*, 115–137.

HARRISON, J. H. Discussion of the article on in-service training. *Ment. Retardation*, 1963, *1*, 16–17.

HEADRICK, MARY. Ward observations at Gracewood, Ga. Unpublished manuscript, George Peabody College, Nashville, 1964.

HORNER, J. E. Selection of employees. *Amer. J. ment. Defic.*, 1954, *58*, 390–396.

KAHNE, M. C. Bureaucratic structure and impersonal experience in mental hospitals. *Psychiat. J. Stud. interper. Processes*, 1959, *22*, 363–375.

KAPLAN, S. The growing importance of the trainable in an institutional setting. *Amer. J. ment Defic.*, 1961, *66*, 393–398.

KLINE, N. S. Characteristics and screening of unsatisfactory psychiatric attendants and attendant applicants. *Amer. J. Psychiat.*, 1950, *106*, 573–586.

————, and EATON, F. L. Indoctrination procedures for personnel. *Amer. J. ment. Defic.*, 1952, *56*, 547–550.

LASH, F. M., and OTNESS, R. H. An experiment in-service orientation lectures series for employees in a state school. *Amer. J. ment. Defic.*, 1949, *54*, 172–177.

LOVE, JEAN O. Educational background and job adjustment of subprofessional hospital care personnel. *Amer. J. Psychiat.*, 1955, *112*, 186–189.

MCDOWELL, F. E. *Role playing and discussion as training methods for changing role-definitions of attendants for institutionalized mental retardates.* Unpublished doctoral dissertation, George Peabody College, Nashville, 1963.

MCINTIRE, J. T. Causes of turnover in personnel. *Amer. J. ment. Defic.*, 1954, *58*, 375.

MELBIN, M. Organization practice and individual behavior: Absenteeism among psychiatric aides. *Amer. Sociological Rev.*, 1961, *26*, 14–23.

MORRIS, C. C., II, NELLIS, BARBARA, and STROMBERG, C. E. The development of an interdisciplinary psychotherapeutic program in an institution for the mentally retarded. *Amer. J. ment. Defic.*, 1959, *63*, 605.

OUDENNE, W. Development of a cottage staffing ratio: A result of a practicum method of training for administrative positions. *Ment. Retardation*, 1963, *1*, 371–374.

PARKER, G. O. Attendant nurses for the mentally deficient—some evidence. *Amer. J. ment. Defic.*, 1951, *55*, 326–336.

PARLOFF, M. B. The impact of ward-milieu philosophies on nursing-role concepts. *Psychiat.*, 1960, *23*, 141.

PARNICKY, J. J., and ZIEGLER, R. C. Attendant training—a national survey. *Ment. Retardation*, 1964, *2*, 76–82.

PATTERSON, R. G. Coordinates of "popularity" of institutional work supervisors. *Amer. J. ment. Defic.*, 1962, *67*, 29.

PLEYDELL, A. Training for institutional administration. *Amer. J. ment. Defic.*, 1950, *55*, 183–186.

PERO, J. F. Policies in the operation of an institution for the mentally deficient as they are influenced by its location. *Amer. J. ment. Defic.*, 1949, *54*, 166–171.

PORTER, R. M. Administrative planning in a new institution. *Amer. J. ment. Defic.*, 1961, *65*, 708–712.

QUAY, L. C. Problems in the evaluation of attendant-employee training programs. *Amer. J. ment Defic.*, 1960, *65*, 322–325.

————, BARTLETT, C. J., WRIGHTSMAN, L. S., JR., and CATRON, D. Attitude change in attendant employees. *J. soc. Psychol.*, in press.

RETTIG, S. An exploratory study of social responsibility in attendant employees. *Amer. J. ment. Defic.*, 1956, *60*, 446–450. (a)

————. An investigation of behavior potentials of psychologists and supervisors toward the institutionalized patient. *Amer. J. ment. Defic.*, 1956, *60*, 714–720. (b)

ROSELLE, E. N. The need for employee training. *Amer. J. ment. Defic.*, 1950, *55*, 187–190.

SCHEFF, T. J. Control over policy by attendants in a mental hospital. *J. Hlth. Hum. Behav.*, 1961, *2*, 93–105.

SCHER, B. Professional supervision of house staff in work with the retarded child. *Amer. J. ment. Defic.*, 1956, *60*, 696–702.

SCHMIDT, D. P., and COHEN, D. The selection of psychiatric aides: I. Critical requirements of the job. *Amer. J. Psychiat.*, 1955, *112*. 451–456.

SHAFTER, A. J. A philosophy of institutional administration. *Amer. J. ment. Defic.*, 1960, *65*, 313.

———, CHANDLER, C. S., and COE, R. M. Survey of orientation and training courses in institutions for mental defectives. *Amer. J. ment. Defic.,* 1957, *62,* 225–231.

SHOTWELL, A. M., DINGMAN, F., and TARJAN, G. Need for improved criteria in evaluating job performance of state hospital employees. *Amer. J. ment. Defic.,* 1960, *65,* 208–213.

STEVENS, H. A. The administrator looks at in-service training. *Ment. Retardation,* 1963, *1,* 13–15, 54–55.

TARJAN, G., SHOTWELL, A. M., and DINGMAN, H. F. A screening test for psychiatric technicians: A preliminary report on five years experience with the work assignment aid. *Amer. J. ment. Defic.,* 1955, *59,* 388–394.

———, ———, and ———. A screening test for psychiatric technicians: Continuation report on the work assignment aid, validation studies at various hospitals. *Amer. J. ment. Defic.,* 1956, *60,* 458–462.

TAYLOR, H. G. Attendants: Assessment and application. *Ment. Retardation,* 1964, *2,* 83–88.

U.S. Bureau of the Census. *County and city data book, 1962.* (A statistical abstract supplement.) Washington D.C.: U.S. Government Printing Office, 1962.

VACCARO, J. J. Judging the adequacy of psychiatric aides. *Hospital Management,* 1952, *46.*

WELLS, F. L., GREENBLATT, M., and HYDE, R. W. As the psychiatric aide sees his work and problems. *Genet. Psychol. Monogr.,* 1956, *53,* 51.

Counseling the Parents of the Retarded[1] 13

WOLF WOLFENSBERGER

THE field of counseling parents of the retarded has many unusual features. Hundreds of publications have dealt with the problem, the vast majority of these reporting personal experience, opinion, or speculation. Despite the many testable hypotheses that have been advanced or that can be derived from these publications, only a small number of experimental studies have been conducted. Among these, I found very few that satisfy the following criteria of most good experimental work: translation of a problem into a well-defined question or hypothesis; sampling that is at least partly appropriate to the problem; adequate controls; quantitative treatment of the results; use of reliable and valid measurement; description of the experiment so as to permit at least approximate replication by others, and sufficient consideration of the sampling restrictions in generalizing the findings.

In compiling the material for this chapter, I found that much of the work on the family of the retarded in general was highly relevant even though it may not have been conducted with parent counseling in mind. Much that has been written on the effects of handicapped, "defective" and especially cerebral palsied children upon the family seemed equally relevant. Although I was tempted to include all of this material, I had to rather arbitrarily exclude some of it so as not to make the chapter excessively broad and long.

In scanning the early literature on retardation, one is struck by the fact that very little

mention was made of parents, of their feelings and sensibilities, or of the impact of the diagnosis upon them. In the mid-1940s through the early 1950s, a trickle of armchair papers began to discuss the relevant parent dynamics, to be followed by almost a flood of such papers in the more recent past. Observations made by intelligent, sensitive, and astute observers can occasionally be as valid as, and more profound than, information collected by controlled and empirical methods, and scarcity of experimental work does not ipso facto mean that we do not possess valuable information. This particularly would appear to be the case if observers displayed a high degree of agreement with each other. On the other hand, the recurrence of almost verbatim quotes seems to indicate that later writers in this field did not arrive at their insights independently. In reviewing the literature, I was often struck by well-phrased insights and statements, only to find later that these were apparently copied from earlier writers without citing the source. Roith (1963) reports the same impression. This leads one to wonder about the validity of the proffered insights, and the possibility that later writers only perpetuated cliches uttered by the pioneers. This suspicion is by no means allayed by the scarcity of quite feasible studies or by the tendency of some researchers to omit relatively simple controls from studies that might otherwise have been highly significant.

Another curious thing is that the parents discussed in the literature are rarely representative of parents of the retarded in general. Instead, they often tend to be: (1) mothers, (2) of middle- and upper-class status, (3) white, (4) consumers of outpatient

1. The preparation of this chapter was supported by NIH Grant No. HD-00370 from the National Institute of Child Health and Human Development.

diagnostic clinic services, and (5) parents of young and low-functioning retardates. Nevertheless, generalizations are only too readily drawn about "parents of the retarded." As an illustration, I heard one retardation worker state that he no longer believed that cultural-familial retardation was the most prevalent kind. After all, he said, he had seen many hundreds of families at a clinic, and only a small handful could be classified as cultural-familial. As it happened, this individual worked in a setting where only young children are handled. Those youngsters who later make up the educable classes scarcely are ever seen there unless they are multiply handicapped because, generally, they are not retarded enough to be identified at an early age.

Failure to include fathers in research, over-reliance on maternal information, and an assumption that such maternal information is valid, particularly regarding the father, are very common. "Reading the scientific literature in this field, a student unfamiliar with our culture might easily get the impression that fathers play no part in the rearing of our children" (Ross, 1964, p. 27).

In organizing this chapter, I felt that many publications were relevant to a number of topics to be covered. A clear separation of topics would have led to some redundancy in recapitulation of the same material. Therefore, I decided to follow a loose temporal sequence in describing the development of a family with a retarded child and to sacrifice some tightness of organization for the sake of space economy.

THE IMPACT OF A RETARDED CHILD UPON THE INDIVIDUAL PARENT

INITIAL REACTION

Many writers who comment upon parents' initial reactions to learning that their child is retarded are actually only referring to a minority among parents. The parents who have provided the "case material" for many writers were disproportionately middle- and upper-class parents of lower functioning children, and this has probably introduced some bias. In only a very small number of children can the diagnosis be made at birth. In most cases, diagnosis is made at school age, and

when mild retardation is suspected by the parents of such children, awareness of its existence usually grows gradually and does not have the sudden impact as often implied in the literature. Even in the case of lower functioning children, the diagnosis usually arises out of the observation of retarded development. More often than not, formal diagnosis only confirms the parents' suspicions, and while the act of confirmation may be abrupt and sudden, the suspicion or even knowledge of retardation may have been present for months or years.

An almost infinite variety of initial or early reactions have been described or mentioned in the literature, e.g., alarm, ambivalence, anger, anguish, anxiety, avoidance, bewilderment, bitterness, catastrophic reaction, confusion, death wishes, denial, depression, despair, disappointment, disbelief, dissociation, embarrassment, envy, fear, financial worries, frustration, grief, guilt, helplessness, hopelessness, identification, immobility, impulses to destroy the child, lethargy, mourning, over-identification, pain, projection, puzzlement, regret, rejection, remorse, self-blame, self-pity, shame, shock, sorrow, suicidal impulses, trauma, etc. The list is neither exhaustive of reactions that have been described nor of those conceivably possible. While some authors emphasize one or a few reactions as predominant, others recognize the diversity of reactions both within and between people. For example, Dalton and Epstein (1963) point out that parents may concurrently be "depressed about their disappointment, guilty about their responsibility and ambivalence, angry about the narcissistic injury done to them, and anxious about the child's future."

By far the most prevalent parental reaction that is mentioned by a large number of writers is guilt. While Roith (1963) is probably correct in pointing out that no matter what a parent does, some professional is apt to attribute it to guilt, a number of good reasons can be offered why guilt may be a prevalent phenomenon. A parent may feel guilty because he notices that his anger and hostility is directed toward the child and that he feels impulses to reject and perhaps destroy the child. One of the most prominent sources of guilt has been seen in the parent's puzzled reaction of "Why did it happen to me?" and his review of all possible causes. Thus, poor prenatal care and practices may be remembered. Husbands may feel they treated their wife inconsiderately. Parents may wonder if they provided adequate care during the child's infancy, or they may accuse themselves for not preventing the many little accidents that had nothing to do with the retardation, for not calling a physician when the child had a fever, or other probably inconsequential events.

Often the child is viewed as a punishment sent by God for some transgression of the past. Kramm (1963) found that 12 per cent of parents of mongoloids saw the retardation as resulting from a direct act of God, even though mongolism is much more circumscribed and understood than most types of retardation. Because of the close connection between sexuality and reproduction, many parents are said to harbor often unconscious or difficult-to-elicit feelings that their sexual sins provoked divine punishment. Thus, Boles (1959) found that parents of cerebral palsied children had much higher guilt, as assessed by a fairly objective scale, regarding premarital sexual relationships and marriage outside one's religion. Not only do some parents see a connection between the retarded child and pre- and extra-marital transgression, but unusual intra-marital sex practices and intercourse late in pregnancy are felt to give rise to this conflict. The counselor must be sensitive to many possibilities. e.g., that of Catholic parents having engaged in contraceptive practices, etc. It must be kept in mind that it is not the nature of an act which arouses guilt but the parents' construction of it.

Guilt also has been said to arise when an unwanted child turns out to be retarded, particularly if unsuccessful attempts at abortion had been made. This latter conflict may well be more prevalent than assumed and has been mentioned by Bryant and Hirschberg (1961), Hastings (1948), Reed (1963), Stang (1957), Walker (1949), Waterman (1948), and Wortis (1965). Waterman described it as a "common" experience, and 3 per cent of Wortis' clinic population admitted to abortion attempts.

Guilt can also be very real where parents harbor homicidal impulses toward the child, as was documented by Bice (Boles, 1959) and Kramm (1963). Smith (1952) saw the theme of the death wish emerge in a majority of interviews with parents of younger and more severely retarded children and thought

that this wish could be identified even when it was well disguised.

Alford (1955) felt that parents undergo repeated destruction of their recurrent hopes and that this process finally results in anger. The anger, in turn, was then seen to produce guilt feelings. Cohen (1962) reasoned that parental anger was the same as that occasionally experienced by most people toward those they love, but because of the handicapped condition of the child the normally experienced guilt may be intensified. In other words, she viewed guilt more as an exaggerated product of normal interpersonal relations than specific to the occurrence of retardation itself. Baum (1962) suggested that guilt should be viewed as overdetermined and as a result of the high levels of anxiety and anger only natural to parents, as well as a multiplicity of other factors.

The writers in the field generally imply that parental guilt is usually without a reality basis and leads to maladaptive and nonadaptive behavior. For example, parents may spend large sums of money for medical care and attempt to place the child outside the home in order to shift responsibility to others (Begab, 1956). Schild (1964) reasoned that alleviation of guilt must precede successful counseling. However, such views can only be considered assumptive. In the first place, where guilt has a reality basis, as in cases where retardation probably did result from abortion attempts, one must consider the moral question: should the parent feel guilty? In analogy, should one, if possible, remove all feelings of guilt from a drunken driver who has caused an accident? In what cases may it be socially desirable for a person to be ridden by a nagging conscience? Second, even assuming that guilt had little basis in reality, when is it maladaptive, and when either adaptive or irrelevant? Perhaps a bit of guilt may go a long way in motivating a parent to provide the extra attention, effort, and even love a retarded child may need. Perhaps it may prevent premature institutional placement, thus serving for the welfare of the child, society, and perhaps even the family, and instead of being alleviated, some parents may need to be helped to a realistic and manageable dose of it.

Because of the many possible dynamisms that can engender guilt, one can reasonably conclude that an appreciable number of parents do experience such feelings, that these feelings are likely to be intense in many instances, and that they are likely to occur not only during an initial reaction but also over the long run. While the construct of guilt seems thus a very important one, it is also one that has produced remarkably little research. The construct can be manipulated with ease in verbalization and conceptualization but has proven difficult to anchor to an independent, quantifiable and reproducible measurement. An attempt has been made by Boles (1959), but, until more intensively studied, the construct and the conceptualizations built upon it will retain the flavor of speculation.

In more recent years, writers seem to have become a bit more skeptical regarding the universality of guilt and the importance assigned to it, and instead have given more prominence to other reactions. McDonald (1962) has pointed out that, during history-taking, parents may be asked questions regarding prior attempts at diagnosis or treatment, or follow-up on previous recommendations, and may, especially if interviewing is not very skillful, read accusatory implications into the questions. They may then display guilt and this situational guilt might be mistaken for a more basic type. Patterson (1956), a parent representative, believes that "regret" is a better term, especially regret for the occasional negative behavior a parent may display toward a retarded child.

Ambivalence is another one of the more readily understood reactions a parent may undergo. On one hand, a handicap in a child is almost certain to make for disappointment, grief, frustration, and anger in a parent who will occasionally have these feelings even about a normal child. On the other hand, the impulse to love and protect the young is deeply rooted in human values, and probably instincts. Logically, ambivalence should be stronger in parents of handicapped than non-handicapped children, but ambivalence has been rarely mentioned in the literature, even though it may be easier to quantify and to research than guilt. According to Schild (1964), ambivalence is a never completely resolved conflict and is stirred up again by each new crisis. This ambivalence is seen to be sustained by the fact that no rational way can be found to blame the child. While many writers interpret parental overprotection to be a result of underlying rejection of the child, Roos (1963) considers it more meaningful to view it as a manifestation of ambivalence. This is a refinement in conceptualization worthy of some consideration.

Frustration was seen as a principle reaction by Peck and Stephens (1960) and Grebler (1952). Grebler saw frustration as a result of social and aesthetic stigmata, lack of services, financial demands, slow maturation, efforts in upholding limits, and the feeling that "the stream of the generation is stopped" (Buck, 1950) and that the parent will not live on in the child beyond death. Grebler studied eleven cases in an educational clinic, and, using Rosenzweig's frustration-aggression model, she concluded that: (1) extra-punitive parents reject the child, (2) impunitive ones accept, and (3) intropunitive ones are ambivalent. While this constituted one of the earliest efforts in this area to derive a prediction from a psychological theory and then to test the prediction empirically, the study suffered too much from insufficient sampling and inadequate quantitative treatment to be considered more than suggestive. The reasoning, however, is noteworthy, and the study deserves more sophisticated replication.

According to Zuk (1962), parents' reactions fall into three major categories: disappointment, anger, and guilt. One of the causes of guilt is seen as denial and inward-turning of anger. Peck and Stephens (1960) discern two main reactions, namely disappointment and frustration. Schild (1964) offers an interesting line of reasoning. In conditions such as delinquency and emotional disturbance, the parent can place a good portion of blame on the child. In retardation, there is no rational way whereby this externalization can be accomplished. Thus, alleviation of guilt becomes less likely and resistance to help remains high. The more the guilt, the higher the resistance. This hypothesis would be an attractive one to test. Similarly, Zuk (1962) sees the great parental search for the cause of the retardation as an attempt to shift anger and guilt. Other writers feel that in cases where retardation is due to a clear-cut postnatal agent such as meningitis, parental guilt is lower (Holt, 1958a).

Graliker, Parmelee, and Koch (1959) interviewed parents in 67 families who had obtained diagnostic services in a clinic. They found: (1) 48 per cent of the parents showed guilt, shame, embarrassment, and frank rejection as a result of the diagnosis (not necessarily the recognition) of retardation; (2) 33 per cent expressed concern about the financial cost of retardation and why it happened to them, and (3) 30 per cent worried about the reactions of friends, relatives, and the other children. Even after a presumably complete diagnostic study, rejection of the diagnosis was judged to have occurred in a third of the families. Focusing upon other handicaps was believed to serve as the main crutch in such rejection.

A relatively novel view was introduced by Beddie and Osmond (1955), who likened the institutionalization of a retarded child to a child loss that engenders grief. Quoting Lindmann's maxim, they propose that "grief work" must accompany any loss and, if not accomplished at the time of the loss, it will have to be done later. Institutionalization is a death without the proper rites. Parents have no socially constituted and approved way to express mourning, which may thus be delayed and prolonged. For instance, a mongoloid baby who had been placed in an institution at birth was visited for the first time by his parents, who were surprised and delighted to find a sweet child instead of the expected monster. When the baby died shortly thereafter, the parents stated that they would never have forgiven themselves if they had not come to see him. They took him home and buried him with the proper rites and decorum. Failure to perform such a "rite of passage" is seen as psychologically damaging and leading to subsequent psychiatric disturbances. In societies where children are denied full membership or participation, various rituals and ceremonies exist to support those who suffer from this condition and to express social approval to them.

The "grief motif" was taken up by Thurston (1960a), who administered a sentence completion test to parents of institutionalized cerebral palsied residents. Besides guilt and helplessness, grief was mentioned as one of the main initial reactions by the parents. Even the passage of years had apparently done little to ameliorate this condition. Shortly thereafter, Solnit and Stark (1961), placing the birth of a defective child into a psychoanalytic framework, asserted that such a birth is perceived by the parent as an "object-loss," i.e., the loss of the expected healthy child at a time of regression, great stress, and physiological and psychological depletion. The parents may grieve, the course of this grief depending upon the abruptness of the loss, the nature of the preparation for the event, and the meaning of the lost "object" to the survivor. Parental defenses are necessary against feelings of guilt, depression, and narcissistic injury; and two extreme reactions may occur. In one, guilt leads to unremitting and exclusive dedication to the welfare of the retarded child; in the other, parents feel manifest intolerance of the defect and an almost irresistable impulse to deny their relationship to the child. If parents are poorly handled or receive inadequate follow-up counseling, they may become fixated between recognition and denial. A state of chronic mourning may result.

The idea that the intense and often chronic emotionality of some parents may be understood as an outcome of grief and mourning has since become widely accepted and elaborated (Baum, 1962; Cohen, 1962; Dalton and Epstein, 1963; Goodman, 1964; Olshansky, 1962; Owens, 1964; Roos, 1963; Tisza, 1962). Roos (1963) went so far as to assert that if feelings of depression are absent in a parent his defenses may be quite atypical and even pathological. Another version of the grief motif was advanced by Olshansky (1962). He proposed that most parents who have a retarded child suffer from a pervasive psychological reaction identified as chronic sorrow, particularly if the child is more severely impaired. Our culture, especially the Anglo-Saxon tradition, requires that this sorrow be concealed, and professional workers may thus mistake it as a pathological symptom. "The helping professions have somewhat belabored the tendency of the parent to deny the reality of his child's mental deficiency. Few workers have reported what is probably a more frequent occurrence, the parent's tendency to deny his chronic sorrow. This tendency is often reinforced by the professional helper's habit of viewing chronic sorrow as a neurotic manifestation rather than as a natural and understandable response to a tragic fact. All the parental reactions reported in the literature, such as guilt, shame, and anger, may well be intertwined with chronic sorrow." Similarly, Roos (1963) wrote: "The drama of experiencing retardation in one's child may precipitate serious existential conflicts. Concern with religion, the meaning of life, the tragedy of death, the inescapability of aloneness, and the relative insignificance and helplessness of man may preoccupy the parents. Although these concerns are less obvious than other reactions, their significance should not be underestimated."

In this regard, Olshansky and Roos have joined a small but growing group of workers who are exhorting their fellow professionals to take less of a traditional psychiatric clinic view of parents of the retarded. Cohen (1962) cautions not to mistake the parents' realistic initial grief reaction as inability to accept the handicap, and Dalton and Epstein (1963) point out that attempts to deny retardation may really be a defense against depression. Michaels and Schucman (1962) even propose that the feelings of worthlessness resulting from having created a defective child may, especially in already self-depreciating individuals, lead to suicidal fantasies or even actual suicide. However, this is a hypothesis for which there is, to my knowledge, no empirical support.

Only a few writers concern themselves with types of retardation that are of relatively sudden but late onset, or of early onset but insidious manifestation because of the mildness of the retardation. Heilman (1950) was one of the first to point out that the problems of parents of the mildly retarded were different than those of the severely retarded or physically handicapped. Dalton and Epstein (1963) offer a good discussion of the dynamics of parents whose child is mildly retarded. This condition renders itself much more to wishful thinking, and particularly the label "slow learner" may lead to "catching-up fantasies." Retardation may be construed in terms of speech impairment and the attainment of various developmental milestones may lead to repeated denials. Parents may also be apt to be deluded by the islands of relative strength that can be encountered in many retardates. Waterman (1948) sees parents of the mildly retarded as the ones most obsessed with scholastic achievement and the mental retardation handbook of the American Medical Association (1965) advances that family crisis may be more pronounced if the retardate is diagnosed on entering school rather than at birth.

According to one clinical lore, parents of the severely retarded are supposed to have an easier adjustment to make because the condition is more obvious. Thus, Teska (1947) thinks that concomitant physical handicaps make mental handicaps more acceptable to parents. Miller (1958) sees parents of the severely handicapped not only as more accepting but also more appreciative of the child's progress. Denhoff (1960) states that uncertainty of the future has the greatest impact upon maternal-child relationship. He then goes so far as to say that this explains why some mothers of the severely handicapped are "free and easy," while those of the mildly handicapped worry "for months." In contrast, Auerbach (1961) thought that parents of the severely handicapped, especially if the parents are older, displayed more depression of mood, and Cain and Levine (1961), in a very complex analysis of questionnaire data, found that mothers were more adaptable to children of higher ability levels, at least while the children were young. Cook (1963), in an experimental study, found that regardless of their nature, mild handicaps were more likely to elicit parental rejection, severe ones overprotection. Barber (1963) and Teitel (1958) encountered more negative attitudes in mothers of the mildly retarded, but this may have been because of other confounded variables.

The description of early impact has been based mostly upon subjective experiential impressions of workers in the field and upon relatively unstructured retrospective self-reporting by parents. The validity and adequacy of both approaches can be questioned in principle.[2] Furthermore, even if valid information

2. There are a number of difficulties with questionnaire and interview approaches to parental feelings. On a structured questionnaire, the parent may tend to answer only what is asked and other feelings he may be aware of may thus not be recorded. With less structured interview material problems in classifying or interpreting responses increase. Thus, Graliker, Parmelee, and Koch (1959) categorized a statement such as "I try to love her more now that I know she is retarded" as rejection. Such scoring appears to be very debatable. With both techniques one must remember that conflicts are likely to be and have been so strong, needs so urgent, and repression so likely that any verbal statement of parents regarding past and present feelings cannot easily and forever be accepted at the manifest level.

could come from these methods, one cannot expect all parents to undergo the same reactions as some writers seem to think. Not only personal differences seem important, but social, class, educational, and religious ones as well. Also, the fact that articles on parents of the more severely retarded are numerically and proportionately vastly over-represented should give rise to caution.

One task ahead is to determine if some parents fall rather clearly into well-describable reaction patterns and whether parents with these different patterns will benefit from management techniques distinctly appropriate to that reaction.

THE CONTINUITY OF PARENTAL REACTION

The initial impact of a retarded child can be severe and profound; parental coping can be unsuccessful or incomplete; and repeated crises may arise. Many parents may thus suffer from rather chronic conditions of what might unelegantly but parsimoniously be described as poor mental health. Some of the mechanisms by which this might come about have already been indicated.

After counseling groups of parents of retarded children, Auerbach (1961) found that these parents displayed much more intense feelings than parents of normal children. This appeared to be so even in cases where a number of years had passed since the child was identified as retarded. Parents seemed to have an inexhaustible need for catharsis, and hostility was so high that ordinary group leaders could not handle it. Klausner (1961) compared a group of parents who belonged to the parent movement and who had kept their retarded children at home with an unaffiliated group who had institutionalized their children. While no control data were collected, both groups were judged to be impulsive and emotionally unstable, the parent group members being slightly better adjusted.

Kramm (1963), in an intensive interview study of 50 families with mongoloid children, was told by some parents that their initial reaction had failed to dissipate after as much as five years. In 16 per cent of the cases, the parents felt too emotional to even discuss the child with each other. Regarding the latter point, the possibility of cultural difference exists. Tizard and Grad (1961) found very

few similar instances among British parents, although 23 per cent of this sample was unwilling or unable to discuss plans for the future with the interviewers. Thurston (1960a, 1963) administered the Thurston Sentence Completion Test (Thurston, 1959) to one or both parents of apparently retarded institutionalized cerebral palsied individuals. Again, passage of as much as fifteen years had done little to dissipate the initial reactions of helplessness, grief, and guilt. Emotional disturbance and unhappiness was much in evidence, and 21 per cent of the parents felt too distressed to discuss the condition with outsiders.

In a rather thorough and social-class-controlled study, Holt (1958a), found that many parents were unable to overcome their earlier feelings of frustration and disappointment. Generally, this long-range conflict was more likely to be encountered in the upper-class families than in those of lower status.

Harris and Schechtman (1959) found that parents of retardates at a day care center had a very high number of atypical and deviant MMPI profiles. Of 111 parents, only 5 per cent fell within half a standard deviation about the means on all scales, while 36 per cent deviated by two or more standard deviations on at least one scale.

A number of writers see parental conflicts as evolving from crisis situations. Farber (1960a) has hypothesized two types of crises reactions. The "tragic crisis" resembles bereavement as expectancies for life careers are demolished. This crisis is usually precipitated at the time of diagnosis, especially so in high socio-economic groups, and may continue thereafter. It may lead to symptoms and complaints of "nervousness." The "role organization crisis" occurs when the parents are unable to cope with the child over a long period of time and is more common in lower classes. This reaction is likely to lead to complaints about poor physical health, especially from the mother. Farber confirmed the relationship between symptomatic complaint and social class, but without benefit of a control group.

I would like to offer a bit of my own crisis theorizing, which will subsume some of the foregoing thinking and can be the source of a number of testable hypotheses. I propose that parents may be undergoing three types of crises, some parents experiencing all of these, others one or none. The crises may occur simultaneously, but they will tend to correlate to some degree with the age of the child. Conceivably, some of the crises can be of rather long-term nature.

The first crisis is most likely to occur when the diagnosis of retardation is presented to an unsuspecting parent as, for example, at the birth of a mongoloid baby. As has been pointed out in the literature, even a normal birth tends to be an occasion for stress, regression, uncertainty, emotionality, and vulnerability. The parents are in a very high state of expectancy and look forward not only to the birth of a normal child but a perfect one (Solnit and Stark, 1961). They are filled with ready notions as to race, sex, appearance, and future occupation, marital status, and other attributes of the expected child. The arrival of any baby that markedly upsets these expectancies will induce a "novelty shock," and may precipitate a "novelty shock crisis." Let us imagine that the faithful and presumably caucasoid wife of a presumably caucasoid husband gave birth to a negroid baby; or that the physician walks into the mother's room after recovery and announces: "Your baby has purple horns;" or "Your baby weighed 30 pounds," or "Your baby is four feet long." Let us go one step further, and imagine the physician announcing: "Your child suffers from the Caucasian Reversal condition and should be institutionalized immediately, without your seeing it!" Would it not be likely that the parents would be anguished by conflicts and might well relinquish the baby without seeing it even though they might be devoid of any knowledge of the nature of the condition? Yet this is exactly what often happens in retardation. At a point of great vulnerability, an unexpected event disorganizes the parents' adjustment as when they are told that their baby is "a mongolian idiot." The parents realize that the event is rare and that their expectancies have to be radically revised, but they know virtually nothing about what the realistic expectancies now are. The crucial element here is not retardation at all; it is the demolition of expectancies.

A number of cases in the literature exemplify the novelty shock crisis. McDonald (1962) relates the story of a man who was told that his newborn baby had a cleft palate. He walked the streets for a night, a day, and the night following in a state of dumbfounded agitation—wondering what a cleft palate was.

In another instance (Kramm, 1963), a parent was very upset after being told his child was mongoloid. Enlisting the help of a relative and a dictionary, the parent decided that the child was something that had to do with being a mongrel, like a mongrel dog. Kozier (1957) cites one case of parents who, when told their child was a mongoloid and should be institutionalized, reacted very strongly, refused to see him, and rejected him. Later on they stated that they actually had no idea what mongolism was and asked for literature about it. Schipper (1959) studied a series of 43 consecutive mongoloids seen at a clinic. He found that catastrophic reactions were much more prevalent if diagnosis was made at birth than if it was made later. Solnit and Stark (1961) point out that usually some discrepancy exists between the expected and "real" infant, but that this discrepancy can become traumatic if it is too great. Thus, the birth of a defective child can have the same effects as the unexpected birth of a premature child, or of twins, or of the death of a longed-for healthy child. Murray (1959) stresses that initial nonacceptance may be caused by a lack of familiarity with the term "mental retardation," and the fact that many parents have never knowingly seen a retarded child.

The second crisis can be described as a "value crisis." Retardation and its manifestations are unacceptable to many persons for a number of reasons. Often the parents' reaction is to a construct in their own minds rather than to an objective state. The mere idea that a son may not even have the potential to become a professional man or a successful merchant may be excessively painful to a parent. Even an alternate possibility that the youngster may become a self-supporting, honest citizen who does unskilled or semi-skilled work may be unacceptable. Fear of social and abhorrence of physical stigmata, censure by in-laws, feelings of guilt or failure, and other essentially subjectively determined anguish may contribute to the value crisis.

The value crisis is seen as leading to various degrees of emotional rejection of the retardate. In mild instances, this may be manifested by ambivalence and overprotection. In its severest form, it usually leads to institutional placement and complete denial of the retardate's existence. Unlike the other two crises, the value crisis is more likely to last a lifetime, and may coincide with any of the others.

The value crisis is rather well exemplified in the writings of such parents as Abraham (1958) and Frank (1952). In these two instances, retarded children were born to families of academicians who apparently placed great value on achievement and education. Parental reaction was as much or more to the diagnosis of retardation than to the underlying condition, and this can be viewed as one of the hallmarks of a value crisis. Giannini and Goodman (1963) found that some parents who were quite capable of caring for their child at home found themselves blocked from doing so by inner pressures or external influences, some of these being class-correlated. Olshansky and Schonfield (1964) found that parents with more education, fewer children, and better houses and maternal health were the ones most likely to institutionalize children in the first year of life. They concluded that such parents may respond more to an abstraction of mental retardation than to any experience. In contrast, the Hutterites (Eaton and Weil, 1955), whose social-religious structure values even the retardate, have no such conflict about keeping the child at home.

The third crisis is the "reality crisis." Forces external to and only partially controllable by the parents result in situations that make it impossible, exceedingly difficult, or inadvisable for the retardate to remain integrated into the family or the community. Thus, the physical demands made by a hyperactive child in a family with several young children may not be able to be met by the mother, and unless effective community help is forthcoming, the situational demands may overwhelm her. Sexual behavior on the part of a young adult retardate may be judged either as dangerous to others or unacceptable to the community. While this may sometimes be more of a value crisis as far as the community is concerned, the social pressures may constitute a reality crisis to the family. Death of a spouse is a very straightforward reality crisis, especially for a surviving father. The reality crisis rarely occurs at birth unless the baby requires unusual amounts or types of medical care, as perhaps in cases of spina bifida.

If one is able to conceptualize the type of crisis a family experiences, one can more easily identify the treatments most likely to be effective. Parents in novelty shock need primarily information and support; those in the value crisis need prolonged counseling or personal therapy; those in a reality crisis require practical, down-to-earth help such as training in home management, baby sitting, day care, sheltered workshops, and perhaps some forms of residential placement.

The various crises and the long-range adjustment problems of parents are found documented in their own writings. Even parents who have made commendable contributions to the field of retardation may display various degrees of long-lasting conflict, in some instances of major proportions. The reader who refers to books and articles by Abraham (1958), Buck (1950), Frank (1952), Gant (1957), Junker (1964), Logan (1962), Rogers (1953), and Stout (1959) will find that a number of these parents were victims of their own attitudes toward retardation rather than to extraordinary external and situational demands.

Most of the data on long-range adjustment of parents is impressionistic, and, if experimental, poorly controlled. Nevertheless, there is a considerable amount of consensus and agreement with a reasonable rationale. If this rationale is a valid one, one should not find it too difficult to design more well-controlled experiments that would demonstrate abnormally high emotionality and conflicts in parents who have lived some years with the problem of mental retardation. However, matching families who have a retarded child with those whose children are not retarded is necessary. Thus, when professional workers in the field see signs of parental disturbance, they should ascertain to what degree the distribution of such conflicts and disturbances exceeds that already known to be very high in the general population.

THE IMPACT OF A RETARDED CHILD UPON THE FAMILY UNIT

So far the focus has been upon the emotional reactions and adjustments of individual parents. In this section, the more global and long-term effects of a retarded child upon the family unit will be discussed.

Again, let us trace the work on this topic historically. Aldrich (1947) rather categorically viewed a mongoloid baby as one who would totally wear down the mother and drew a very pessimistic picture of the effects upon the family. Natt (1954) described the birth of a retardate as a "catastrophe," adding, "it can truly be stated that there is nothing that can have a greater effect on the entire family and its welfare than a mentally retarded child."

One of the earlier representatives of another view is Hastings (1948), who held that poor family adjustment is not caused by a retarded child but is merely symptomatic of already existing or latent marital and family problems. Cohen (1962) also indicated that marital dissatisfaction may be displaced onto the child rather than be caused by it. Michaels and Schucman (1962) rather pessimistically stated that, "Unfortunately, constructive mutual support between the parents is, in our experience, relatively rare." Instead, they felt that mutual antagonisms were much more likely to be aggravated.

A series of studies conducted in Britain and Australia seemed to bear out the more pessimistic thinkers. Schonell and Watts (1956) studied 50 Australian families of school-age retardates with IQs below 55. The effects upon the family were severe and could be roughly categorized as economic, social, and emotional. Many families had incurred great expenses, mostly for medical treatment that might ameliorate the child's condition. The most desperate need voiced by the mothers was for day care or baby-sitting service that would permit them to get away once in awhile.

Holt (1958a) thoroughly interviewed 201 families of "ascertained" lower functioning retardates of age five or above in Britain. His was one of the very few studies in which careful consideration was given to the social-class distribution of the families. Holt took pains to show that he had the same class distribution in his sample as did the city where the study was conducted. He found that a severely retarded child placed great physical demands upon the family and that the general impact was hard and severe. In higher classes, neighbors tended to be more helpful, but they avoided direct contact with the retarded child. Lower classes seemed to make a better adjustment, but, in the limited (i.e., very low class, marginal, or retarded) family, retardation was

found to be only one of many problems and thus to be of relatively less significance. Significant emotional disturbance in the siblings could occur, but was found only in about 12 per cent of families. In the main, siblings reflected parental feelings, whatever these were. One of the hardship factors encountered was lack of living space, and some of the family problems were felt to be a direct consequence thereof. The author concluded with the observation that the retarded child often brought something of value to the family. These families, he felt, often gained in a spiritual and philosophic way, achieving new understanding of more ultimate values and the deeper meaning of life.

One of the most extensive studies of the effects of a retardate upon the family (Tizard and Grad, 1961; Tizard, 1964) focused on 150 London families who lived with a lower functioning retardate, and 100 families with a retardate in an institution. While sampling was not as representative as that of Holt, it was much more representative than that of most studies, and, except for a restriction on parental age, the community group was felt to be representative of London retardates of that severity level. Families with the child at home were found to have more problems than those who institutionalized their children and half of all placements were a result of management problems. While the strain due to anxiety, social isolation and management problems could be great, one of the main effects of retardation was a sharp lowering of what might be described as the general standard of living, similar to findings of Schonell and Watts (1956). Similar to Holt (1958a), living space was a big problem. A large percentage of parents had physical or mental health problems. Tizard (1964, p. 48) concluded that "families that care for a mentally subnormal member at home are undoubtedly heavily penalized, despite help given by welfare services." "The remarkable thing is that so many of these families still wish to care for their handicapped children at home" (Tizard, 1964, p. 49).

However, not all the evidence from the British Commonwealth is unanimous. Evans (1954) conducted intensive home interviews with families of a series of 224 mongoloids seen at a London clinic. He found that the families generally functioned well and that few were unhappy. About half of the problems were of a practical nature, the other half psychological, and additional services might have reduced the incidence or severity of both.

Studies in the United States generally paint a more favorable picture than most Commonwealth studies, and the difference in style and standard of living may perhaps be a factor. Schipper (1959) studied a series of 43 families of mongoloid children seen at a clinic. Here, too, a retarded child could wreck the adjustment of those families already plagued by serious financial problems, but two-thirds of the families, in spite of anxiety, adjusted well. Kramm (1963) found that the first six to ten years with a mongoloid child were the most tumultuous ones, but that family adjustment improved thereafter. Indeed, many parents seemed to have undergone a cognitive dissonance resolution process: 76 per cent of them contended that the retarded child had been good for them, and more parents reported that the experience with the retardate had strengthened rather than weakened their marriage except during the initial period. Caldwell and Guze (1960) attempted to set up controls for a number of historical and socio-economic factors in studying families of institutional and community retardates. They concluded that keeping the child at home did not affect the adjustment of mothers or siblings, but their samples were so small and the matching so questionable as to seriously limit the interpretation. A number of group differences existed that, even though mostly non-significant statistically could well have combined to introduce a very definite bias.

A series of publications (Downey, 1963; Farber, 1959, 1960a, 1960b, 1963; Farber, Jenne, and Toigo, 1960) resulted from a project directed by Farber studying the impact of a retarded child on the family. Since these studies overlap considerably, they will be discussed mostly as a unit. The data for these publications were derived by intensive investigation of several hundred families in the metropolitan area of Chicago in 1955 and 1956, and a number of the studies resulted from the same or overlapping sampling. Because of their complexity, the findings cannot be adequately summarized here, and some aspects are discussed elsewhere in this chapter. Retarded boys seemed to be more disruptive than girls, particularly in lower-class families and with increasing age. Family interaction with the mother's mother seemed beneficial, with the father's mother detrimental. Those families with any consistent marital strategy functioned better than those with an inconsistent one. Initial impact was greater on the father, long-range impact greater on the mother. Long-range impact seemed also directly related to initial impact. Fathers identified more with a male child, with no difference for mothers. Willingness to institutionalize was higher in fathers of upper and mothers of lower classes, and in upper classes increased with size of sibship.

The Farber studies occupy a significant place in the development of the field because they are coherent and constitute one of the earliest attempts to introduce sociological theorizing into the design of retardation experimentation. However, because of its historical significance, reviewers of this research have tended to de-emphasize some of its shortcomings:

1. The families sampled were not representative of families of the retarded in general as they either belonged to parent associations or had a child in, or on a waiting list for, an institution. The sample not only tended to be white and of higher education, income, and social class than the source population but was further restricted by an appreciable number of both fortuitous and experimenter-determined factors.

2. While attempting to isolate treatment effects, treatment cells were sometimes progressively split until comparisons were based on very small and unequal, in addition to nonrepresentative, numbers of individuals.

3. Sibling behavior was inferred mostly from maternal reports, subject to maternal perceptions and distortions.

4. Some of the data are, if closely examined, not based on well-quantified and validated measurements. Some of the ratings used were arrived at "intuitively" and described in a fashion that would not render them easily replicable by other investigators.

5. Variables that could only be properly evaluated prospectively were investigated retrospectively.

6. In order to establish that certain variables were relevant to a family because a child was retarded, control groups would have been needed.

The shortcomings of the Farber studies are similar to those encountered in much of the work in this field, and, aside from their historical significance, they must be considered suggestive and a source of good testable hypotheses.

All but one of the studies of the families of retarded children suffer from a major inadequacy—lack of controls. The one controlled study was poorly controlled. Authors have demonstrated abundantly that a large number of families in general have problems in individual and marital adjustment, child rearing, sibling rivalry, and various other spheres. Until families of the retarded are carefully matched with other families, and the two groups compared, we shall not be certain what the qualitative and quantitative long-range effects of a retarded child are. For instance, the finding that placement leads to a higher standard of living for the family is irrelevant *per se*. Placement of a normal child might have the same effect. The very variability of findings between studies of families with retardation underlines the need for controls.

THE ADJUSTMENT OF THE SIBLINGS OF THE RETARDED

The main reason for this section is that parents are sometimes counseled that keeping the retarded child at home will be harmful to the siblings. Unfortunately, studies of the siblings of the retarded have also been poorly controlled, and the findings on adjustment and maladjustment of siblings of the retarded can only be viewed as suggestive until equivalent families with nonretarded children are studied with the same methods and instruments.

Holt (1958a) found that 12 per cent of his families reported significant emotional disturbance among the normal children. In the literature, one sees this quoted both as a high figure and as "only" 12 per cent (the difficulty in interpreting the figure without controlled data is apparent). In lower-class families, siblings were expected to help with the chores, the girls playing more of an auxiliary mother role. Farber (1959, 1960b) found that if a normal girl interacted frequently with a retarded sibling, she tended to get along poorly with her mother, but the findings for boys were inconclusive. He also found that

normal sisters made a better adjustment if the retardate was institutionalized than if the latter lived at home, while the reverse was found for brothers. Farber interpreted this to mean that placement freed sisters from many responsibilities but resulted in more restrictive supervision of brothers. However, the data on the children's adjustment were derived from interviews with the mothers and not from any direct assessment of the children themselves.

In contrast, Graliker, Fishler, and Koch (1962) interviewed 21 teen-age siblings of retarded children directly and concluded that the presence of a young retarded child in the home did not seem to have an adverse effect upon the teen-agers. This seemed to be particularly the case where early parent guidance had helped the family to maintain its equilibrium. Strauss (1963) tested siblings 10 to 16 years old directly, asking them to rank the importance of 10 hypothetical life goals, but, here too, the mothers served as informants on the frequency of the interaction between the sibling and the retarded child. Apparently, sustained interaction with a retarded sibling came to be regarded as a duty and resulted in an internalization of life goals calling for dedication and sacrifice. This is perhaps the only study that can be cited in support of Tudor's (1959) contention that keeping the retarded child at home provides excellent character training for the siblings, instilling them with social consciousness and responsibility at an early age. The lack of a control group in Strauss' study is unfortunate, since high interaction between nonretarded siblings conceivably might have correlated with similar values.

Jolly (1953) points out that families may be urged to institutionalize and, since openings in public facilities are often not available, private placement may be sought. This, in turn, can be financially so demanding on a family that the siblings, far from benefiting, are actually disadvantaged.

Rosen (1955), interviewing mothers, did not find any unusual problems with the siblings as a result of the presence of the retarded child. Schipper (1959) reported that siblings of 43 mongoloids seen at a clinic were well adjusted, and that, where problems existed, most of them appeared to be caused by other factors. This aspect of the study was subjective and impressionistic.

Although the study by Caldwell and Guze (1960) suffered from a number of shortcomings, it needs to be considered here. A sibling of each of 32 retarded children, half of these living at home and half in an institution, was interviewed, as were "the parents" (i.e., the mothers). A number of scales were also administered. The siblings appeared to be as well adjusted as the mothers and notably mirrored the maternal values. The authors concluded that the retarded child had no detrimental effects on the siblings.

Another issue occasionally raised is that children may undergo shame and embarrassment while attempting to explain their retarded sibling to others. Barsch (1961a) had parents fill in checklists of common labels that might be applied to retardates in attempts to be explanatory to others, and also had the parents describe the normal children's explaining and labeling habits. The parents did not feel that their children had any significant problems in explaining. The youngsters apparently tended to both imitate the parents and to be more likely to profess ignorance as to the condition.

To summarize, no strong evidence has been presented that siblings of the retarded are either better or worse adjusted than comparable children in general. What evidence there is mildly supports the view that youngsters will make an adequate adjustment to a retarded sibling and that they are apt to reflect the parental values and conflicts. Thus, if problems exist, they may be of the parents' making, and planning may be more effective if directed at them instead of being rationalized around the siblings' benefit.

PARENTAL DYNAMICS

Parental dynamics are, of course, discussed in many different contexts in the literature. Some contributions devote themselves completely to this topic, but quite frequently dynamics are discussed in connection with topics such as initial impact, group and individual counseling, etc. In order to save space, this section will serve as a miscellany of contributions on dynamics that are not more appropriately placed with one of the other sections. Again, most of the contributions are based on experience, impression, and theory, only a few being experimental.

SPECIFICITY OF PARENTAL DYNAMICS

One issue occasionally encountered is whether the dynamics of parents of handicapped children in general are very similar or alike, or whether there are dynamics specific to a particular handicap. Coughlin (1941) implies that parental attitudes toward handicapped children are basically the same as those toward all children, except that the disability elicits feelings that otherwise would be less prominent and repressed. Cohen (1962) also sees little differentiation between handicaps.

An intermediate position is assumed by McDonald (1962) and Ross (1964) who see much similarity but some specificity. Klebanoff (1959) administered the PARI (a parental attitude scale) to mothers of schizophrenic, normal, and brain-injured or retarded children. The mothers of the schizophrenic and of the brain-injured or retarded children were more possessive than the mothers of normal children. On the other hand, the mothers of brain-injured or retarded children showed more pathological attitudes than mothers of the schizophrenics—a finding that may be surprising to some people. The study would thus support the idea of some specificity as well as some generality.

The notion of specificity is supported by three other writers. Heilman (1950) saw the parent of the mildly retarded in a particular dilemma. The child may be socially retarded so that he is identifiable as handicapped, but, unlike many of the physically disabled, may not be able to compensate, thus eliciting a more specific set of attitudes. Fredericks (1957) administered some attitude scales to mothers of retarded, orthopedically handicapped, and normal children, the groups being matched for socio-economic level. While she found no differences between the normal and the orthopedic group, the mothers of the retarded scored significantly higher on scales that apparently indicate a repressive and domineering element. Cook (1963) gave the PARI to mothers of blind, deaf, mongoloid, and cerebral palsied or "organic" children. The mothers of the mongoloid and cerebral palsied groups tended to be punitive, those of the deaf overindulgent, and those of the blind overprotective. Mothers of mongoloid, cerebral palsied, and blind children were strongly authoritarian in child-rearing attitudes. Degree as well as type of handicap seemed important as mild handicaps were associated more with rejection, severe ones with overprotection.

More experimental work has been done on this issue than on most others covered in this chapter. The evidence indicates that parental attitudes may vary to some degree with type of handicap, but that some handicap groups may share certain dynamics. Also, severity of functional impairment, which may be somewhat confounded with type of handicap, may be important and may underlie some of the differences found. Cook's suggestion appears fruitful and worthy of follow-up.

DIFFERENCES BETWEEN MATERNAL AND PATERNAL DYNAMICS

One of the controversial questions in the literature is whether fathers and mothers have different abilities to accept or manage the problem of mental retardation. Judging from an experience in group orientation to a clinic, Anderson (1962) decided that fathers accept the diagnosis more readily and take more initiative in describing details of the child's behavior. Hersh (1961), also on an impressionistic basis, hypothesized that the mother is more threatened than the father, that she is more likely to develop an isolated or martyr role, and that she is more likely to act as if she had been insulted by life. Fathers are seen as more remote and objective, and less involved and expressive. In cases where they do appear very guilty, they seem to be warmer and nearer the maternal role than usual. They are more apt to turn their hurt into regression because of their inability to tolerate strong feelings. Fathers who have not worked through their own separation from their own fathers seem to have a particular problem with a retarded child. The less well-established a man is as a husband and father, the more traumatic will be the impact of a retarded child. Solnit and Stark (1961) made a similar point regarding the mothers, pointing out how childbirth can sensitize feminity conflicts arising out of a woman's relationship with her mother.

A number of writers see matters differently. Stang (1957) contends that the father is more likely to view the retardate as a danger to his social status, while the overprotective and possessive mother may be more threatened by progress and growth in the child. Yates and Lederer (1961), also speaking from short-term group-therapy experience, see fathers as having more difficulty in accepting the diagnosis, but find them more intellectualized and less personal than mothers. Begab (1963) concurred, and Oberman (1963) also viewed the fathers as less accepting of the diagnosis.

All of the above contributions were based upon experience and impressions. Four studies offer evidence derived from more formal or experimental approaches. Scott (1960) conducted an intensive study of 30 families of the retarded and found only a few differences in parental behavior, these being in amount of contact, emotionality, and affection. None of these may have been related to the condition of retardation as no control group was studied. Capobianco and Knox (1964) obtained parents' estimates of their child's mental level, finding that fathers were more realistic, but that mothers overestimated only slightly. Unfortunately, similar studies by Ewert and Green (1957), Schulman and Stern (1959), and Zuk (1959a) did not include enough fathers to clarify this matter further. Kurtz (1965) included many fathers but only obtained a joint judgment from each couple. Tizard and Grad (1961) found that fathers had more mental health problems than mothers, but then the authors' informants were usually mothers.

Two other studies indicate that the relationship between parental sex and attitudes towards mental retardation may be very complex. Kramm (1963), in an intensive interview study of 50 families, found that other family characteristics may affect parental differences. Thus, fathers in large families reacted more favorably than those in small families, and parental age, education and religion were of some importance but were also somewhat confounded with parental sex. Cain and Levine (1961) studied both children and parents, the children being enrolled in a program for trainables. This study illustrates one of the difficulties of research that attempts to present more definitive answers. While bad studies may suffer the penalty of scorn and rejection from fellow workers in the field, studies that attempt to avoid previous errors and take into account the multi-factorial nature of certain phenomena may become so involved as to be penalized with an almost irresolvable complexity of findings. In this study, a very commendable attempt was made to trace the source of the correlations between parent characteristics and parental behavior *vis-à-vis* mental retardation. By the time the children's etiology, age, severity level, and progress in the program was considered, along with each parent's adaptability to retardation, age, sex, education, income, occupation, and interaction with the child of the same or opposite sex, and by the time adaptability was subdivided into elements of flexibility, empathy, and motivation, the result was a work that might awe the reader but bewilder him as well. The findings, too complex to be reviewed here in detail, may indicate that a mother's adaptability is more related to the child's ability (high being more accepted), and a father's adaptability to the child's sex (boys being more acceptable) and to whether the diagnosis is mongolism or not. The findings also seemed to give some support to Stang's (1957) hypothesis that fathers are more sensitive to the possible social stigma of having a retarded child.

The evidence on differences between fathers' and mothers' attitudes is inconclusive. The more complex studies seem to indicate that parental sex differences, if demonstrated, would be rather meaningless. On the other hand, adequate study of potentially significant higher order relationships and interactions will require the use of large samples, broad sampling of adequate continua of characteristics, and more sophisticated statistical designs.

PARENTAL ABILITY TO ASSESS THE CHILD

Occasionally, parents are quite aware of the backwardness of their child, will describe this backwardness accurately, and will give a fairly correct mental age estimate. However, they may not be able to reconcile themselves to labels that have a strong emotional connotation. Such examples were documented by McDonald (1962), and Barsch (1961a) found that parents were more comfortable using the term "brain injury" than "mental retardation" or similar labels. Some workers may have noticed that certain parents appear to feel that the term "brain injury," or, in some

circles, even "autism," lends a degree of status. I once knew a local parent association where the parents of the presumably brain-injured made a very clear distinction between themselves and those members who children were, in their opinion, retarded because of undifferentiated and possibly genetic factors.

In the helping relationship, the professional often is only too apt to insist that the parent surrender himself to the professional's terminology. Actually, one of the main considerations that should be of importance is whether or not the child receives appropriate handling and management. Parents who understand the condition fairly well but balk at terms have come a long way and should not be alienated in a fashion that may produce regression to a lower level of conflict resolution.

A whole series of studies tends to indicate that parents do not distort their perception of the child's ability as much as professionals have been inclined to assume. Rheingold (1945) was one of the first to notice that when parents were asked to estimate the mental or developmental age of their child—rather than to give his IQ or label him—they would usually come very close to his assessed level. This impression was also confirmed by Rosen (1955) and Sheimo (1951) from clinical experience, although the latter felt that parental behavior toward the child might not be consistent with this parental knowledge. Ewert and Green (1957) provided the first empirical test, converting mothers' estimates of their child's mental age level to IQs. They found that 63 per cent came within 15 IQ points and that the following factors had no effect on estimates: (1) multiple handicaps, (2) child's functioning level or sex, (3) father's or mother's socio-economic level, and (4) previous psychological tests. The mother's educational level was significant. Schulman and Stern (1959) assigned the same task to mothers and a few fathers and relatives of 50 retarded children. In only four instances did the derived IQ exceed the test IQ by more than 20 points. The correlation was .67.

Boles (1959), in his study of mothers of cerebral palsied children, found that maternal judgment agreed well with professional judgment not only on intelligence, but also on emotional maturity and behavior problems. Distortion, if one wants to call it that, occurred on estimates of future functioning.

Here, mothers believed that their child might someday be self-supporting when such chances appeared to be very slim.

Capobianco and Knox (1964) reported a previous study by Johnson and Capobianco where parents were asked to fill in items from the Stanford-Binet the way they thought their child would respond. Again parents were, on the average, only four points higher than the child's performance. Capobianco and Knox repeated this feature of the study and found that fathers, as a group, estimated within one point while mothers overestimated by an average of about seven points. However, variability was appreciable, especially so in fathers who tended to over- or underestimate more often. Capobianco and Knox also derived the hypothesis from Farber's work that family integration might correlate with parental ability to estimate the child's mental level realistically. However, their study did not bear this out. One of the suggestions offered by the authors was that perhaps the study of families of normal children or of different types of retarded children would be relevant as the hypothesis still appeared to have good theoretical basis.

Kurtz (1965) had parents make a joint estimate of their child's level, and also obtained estimates from examining pediatricians and speech and hearing personnel. The correlations with a psychological test was .74 for parents, .79 for the speech and hearing people, and .86 for the pediatricians. Additional evidence for parental realism in perceiving the child's retardation comes from studies by Deno, Henze, Krantz, and Barklind (1965) and Roith (1963).

There are two negative studies. Zuk (1959a) compared mothers' Vineland estimate with the IQ of retardates with and without multiple handicaps. He found that the SQs were much higher than the IQs in the multi-handicapped but less so in the other group, attributing this to "autistic distortion" of the "parents" (i.e., the mothers). However, the two groups differed in age; the Vineland SQs were not transformed to standard scores as they have to be in order to compare different age groups (Wolfensberger, 1962), and the developmental measures were derived from different tests, including less reliable infant scales. In another attempt to assess parental realism, Stoddard (1959) conducted two-hour interviews with parents of four classes of trainable children.

Teacher ratings of ability and achievement of the children were correlated with interviewers' assessment of parents' awareness and acceptance of the child's disability. No significant correlations were obtained between parental attitudes and the childrens' achievement, but the techniques used in this study left much to be desired.

Writers such as Capobianco and Knox (1964) have speculated about the type of parent who might be unrealistic in an estimate of the child's ability. One fruitful approach yet to be tried might be to identify parents who grossly over- or underestimate ability, and then to explore communalities within and differences between these extreme groups. Also, it may be useful to draw a distinction between parental ability to recognize the existence of retardation and ability to utilize an emotionally charged diagnostic label or to predict the future realistically.

MISCELLANEOUS DYNAMIC ASPECTS

Parenthood, it has been pointed out (Gramm, 1951; Stoddard, 1959) is a very primitive area of human functioning. Few such functions are associated with as many anxieties, defenses, distortions, and misconceptions. Parenthood is also often very selfish and many parent-centered needs may be satisfied under the guise of child welfare. One of the basic maxims in parent management is that some parents will only be satisfied if they get from their children what they want from such a relationship (Denhoff, 1960). Parents do not feel free to love their child unconditionally, and often love is contingent upon the child's measuring up to his age mates (Mead, 1942; Stone, 1948).

A retarded child can deprive parents of the sense of certainty, however unrealistic, that they might have felt with a normal child in regard to the future (Denhoff, 1960). On the other hand, the situation may also give them another kind of certainty, one of woes, trials and misery, unto their death or that of the child, so that they may look upon either as a welcome solution (Olshansky, 1962). Smith (1952) perceives a death wish in almost all parents of young lower functioning children.

A retarded baby may make parents feel inadequate even in ordinarily very routine baby care. A sickly infant may induce great anxiety and insecurity by fretting and never seeming placated (Denhoff, 1960). On the other hand, a lost sense of worth may be recaptured by overmothering (Stang, 1957; Stone, 1948). This may be one of the reasons why overprotective and authoritarian child rearing attitudes have been reported in mothers of the handicapped by Dingman, Eyman, and Windle (1963), Fredericks (1957), and Klebanoff (1959). Klausner (1961) found that mothers with a retarded child had more dominant and directive attitudes if the child was at home than if it was in the institution. It stands to reason that the child at home is more likely to elicit these attitudes, although, of course, such mothers may also be less inclined to institutionalize. Boles (1959), in a very well-controlled study, found mothers of cerebral palsied and mostly retarded children to be highly overprotective. Cook (1963), as mentioned previously, found overprotection to be a function of degree of impairment, to some extent independent of type of handicap. However, some of the above studies did not adequately control for certain important variables such as education, socioeconomic status, etc.

Many writers construe overprotection as an indicator of underlying rejection. Roos (1963) prefers to interpret it in terms of ambivalence. Once again, professionals may have been apt to overinterpret the significance of strong protectiveness in parents and to fall back upon their psychiatric ancestry. Overprotectiveness toward the handicapped young is even encountered among animals, and sometimes leads to prolongation of the ordinary upbringing period. In humans a handicapped child, by virtue of its prolonged dependency demands, may elicit dominant child-rearing attitudes almost by necessity. High protectiveness may thus be an adaptive and desirable dynamic in the parent, especially the mother, rather than a pathogenic one. This dynamic, of course, though adaptive for survival of the young, may not be beneficial in all aspects. Thus, Blodgett (1958) hypothesizes a vicious "circular dependency." The only way parents can take care of the long-term infantile dependency needs of a child who grows up ever so slowly is by forcing themselves to a belief that they enjoy it. Otherwise, their frustration may become unbearable. In the process of convincing themselves of their enjoyment, they become dependent on the child's need. In

such, as well as other cases, the child's physical and mental growth may become a threat to the parent (Stang, 1957) and result in yet further efforts at infantalization (Mandelbaum and Wheeler, 1960). Very close identification is sometimes viewed as a similar dynamic (e.g., Dalton and Epstein, 1963), usually one which results in lower accessibility to help (Mandelbaum and Wheeler, 1960; Stone, 1948).

One of the more unhealthy parental reactions is the one that sees the retarded child as willfully producing its defectiveness as an attack upon the parents (Mandelbaum and Wheeler, 1960). Kanner (1952) tells of encountering parents who could not forgive the child for not fulfilling their expectations. He felt that these parents were venting their disappointment on their child by holding him personally responsible for what they regarded as a betrayal of their ambitions. Their retarded child might be confronted with a continual onslaught of parental hostility that might be open and undisguised.

Mandelbaum and Wheeler (1960) contend that parents with marked feelings of inadequacy and low esteem commonly see their feelings of rejection as the cause of the child's damage. This self-blame may become a powerful force against realistic planning since it concerns itself with the past instead of the present or the future. On the other hand, parents may also externalize their hostility and, in an attempt to maintain feelings of adequacy, display a high level of antagonism (Teska, 1947). In any case, wherever parental defenses are rigid, Cummings and Stock (1962) forsee a poor prognosis.

Michaels and Schucman (1962) believe that the conflict between intellectual knowledge and belief on one hand, and emotional attitudes and desires on the other, can lead to dissociative processes. Levy (1952), taking a more environmental view, thinks that many of the emotional problems encountered within families may be caused by a lack of services with subsequent feelings of hopelessness. Investigators might find it interesting to check whether the sense of hopelessness might not be one of the causes of the "chronic sorrow" described by others. This could be tested by comparing equated groups of unselected parents whose children have been receiving various degrees of services.

A number of authors indicate that a retarded child may have a deep unconscious meaning to a parent that may only come to awareness in depth psychotherapy (Olshansky, 1962). This meaning may, again, satisfy pre-existing neurotic needs of the parent (Mahoney, 1958). The child may be seen as a symbol of past transgressions, of the end of generations of a name, of a divine intent or mission, of failure in reproduction or child rearing, etc. A parent may symbolically re-enact with the retarded child the relationship with his or her own parents (Cohen, 1962; Hersh, 1961; Solnit and Stark, 1961), or may view the child as a symbol of underlying failure of a marriage (Goodman, 1964). These and other possible interpretations are further elaborated by Mandelbaum and Wheeler (1960), Ross (1964, p. 57 ff.), Stone (1948), and particularly Ryckman and Henderson (1965).

According to Adams (1960), irrational or far-fetched explanations for the retardation may reflect an attempt to defend against the unconscious and fantasy implications of the condition. Adams considers it ill-advised to destroy belief in somewhat forced explanations unles the counselor is capable of working through the implications of a more realistic understanding of the etiology.

Surprisingly little has been said, and virtually nothing done, regarding mental retardation in the first-born or only child as compared with families where the retardate is younger or has younger siblings. Entirely different parental dynamics are operant during the first creation of a child than in later ones. Many of the conscious and unconscious parental hopes, expectations, and meanings are realized, satisfied, or extinguished with the first-born. Thus, the later birth of a retardate may be much less traumatic. Furthermore, considerable difference in dynamics can be expected in those families who can compensate the birth of a retarded first-born by having subsequent children in comparison with those who, for some reason or other, are deprived of this possibility. I was able to find only two authors who gave explicit consideration to this problem (Kanner, 1962; Kramm, 1963). Some findings relevant to the issue are that first-born retardates seem to be institutionalized more readily (Graliker, Koch, and Henderson, 1965; Kramm, 1963) and that

discontent was highest in those families where the retardate was the first-born (Kramm, 1963).

Greenberg (1950) speculated about the significance of social changes in parental coping with a handicapped child. In former days when families tended to be larger, a parent might have found it easier to displace his hopes and investments onto the other children. A handicapped child today is also more likely to constitute a threat to a modern mother's career aspirations and to be resented on this account alone.

Some writers (e.g., Mahoney, 1958; Mandelbaum and Wheeler, 1960; Peck and Stephens, 1960) propose that parental dynamics are only accentuated versions of those dynamics and latent or overt adjustment problems that would have existed in a person or marriage anyway. Further interesting and detailed discussion of parent dynamics can be found in Baum (1962) and in Group for the Advancement of Psychiatry (1963).

PARENTAL COPING MECHANISMS

STAGES IN ADJUSTMENT

A number of writers believe that if parents ever learn to adjust to the impact of a retarded child, they do so in orderly and predictable stages. Six authors identify three stages of parental growth, two define four, one specifies five, and another describes six steps.

One of the earlier writers about parents (Stone, 1948), scanning case files of a clinic, felt that parental adjustment could be defined in terms of the degree of awareness of the retardation. Those with considerable awareness state that the child is retarded, recognize the limitations of treatment, and request information about suitable training or placement. Those with partial awareness describe the symptoms and inquire about causes. They hope for improvement, are afraid that treatment may not succeed, and question their own ability to cope with the problem. Those with minimal awareness refuse to recognize that certain behavior is abnormal, blame causes other than retardation, and believe that treatment will produce a normal child. Kanner (1953) similarly perceived three levels of adjustment that essentially depend upon the parent's degree of acknowledgment of reality. On one level, the parents display complete inability to face reality, on another they try to disguise reality and envelop it in artificial explanations. On the third level, the parents maturely face up to the actuality of the child's retardation.

Boyd (1951), a parent himself, has defined perhaps the most quoted developmental milestones of parents in an article that has been republished as a pamphlet by the National Association for Retarded Children. In the initial stage, a parent engages in self-pity, asking the perennial "Why did it happen to me?" Concern here is predominantly with oneself and one's own feelings. In the second stage, the parent emerges from a narcissistic self-concern to a concern for the child and his condition. In the third stage, this concern broadens yet further to include the spouse and others and is manifested by considerations of what to do for them instead of what they may do for oneself. Many parents may become arrested at an early stage, probably only a minority attaining the highest level.

Blodgett (1958) also seems to see parents in counseling to develop in three stages. First, parents accept the disability; secondly, they make long-range plans; and thirdly, they work on their feelings and attitudes. Thurston (1963) echoes these hypotheses, but if there really are orderly stages of parental coping, one wonders if the stages proposed by Blodgett and Thurston should not be totally or partially reversed. Conceivably, emotional "work" has to come first, planning next, and true acceptance, if there is such a thing, only at last. Many parents who never seem to reach an understanding or acceptance of the condition nevertheless seem capable of providing good management.

The mental retardation handbook of the American Medical Association (1965) describes three other stages of parental development: initial emotional disorganization, gradual reintegration, and mature adaptation. However, the third stage may not be achieved by all parents.

Grays (1963) and Koegler (1963) view parental development in four stages. Grays defines parental growth in stages from guilt and shame, to knowledge and understanding, to acceptance, and to help for the child so that he may reach the fullest potential. Koegler specifies shock, disbelief, fear and frustration, and intelligent inquiry.

Rosen (1955) concluded that parental growth proceeds in five stages: (1) awareness of the problem, (2) recognition of its nature, (3) a search for the cause, (4) a search for a solution, and (5) acceptance of the problem, which may never be attained fully. Rosen's distinction between awareness, recognition and acceptance is appealing and might be utilized more than it has in the past. Hay (1951) saw parents as progressing in stages of bewilderment, suspicion, shock, protest, education, and finally acceptance. He made a distinction between acceptance and resignation and considered ability to talk freely and without embarrassment as an indication of acceptance.

THE SIGNIFICANCE OF PARENTAL ACCEPTANCE

A good deal has been written about parental "acceptance" of retardation or the retarded child. This concept has three difficulties. Firstly, it is not usually defined (for an exception, see Gallagher, 1956). Secondly, when defined, it may be defined very poorly and not in a fashion that is meaningfully researchable. Thirdly, it has not been shown adequately just what the relationship between implied acceptance and parental behavior is. The second point is exemplified by the aforementioned debatable method of assessing acceptance and rejection employed by Graliker, Parmelee, and Koch (1959) and by Zuk (1959b). The latter rated level of parental acceptance by judging on three criteria of interview behavior: display of anxiety or hostility in the presence of the child, display of minimal defensiveness about the child's limitations, and neither obvious rejection nor fostering of overdependence. However, later (Zuk, Miller, Bartram, and Kling, 1961) such judgments were not found to be very reliable.

According to Adams (1960), initial rejection of a retarded child may undergo a subtle change in that the baby is physically accepted, but its defectiveness is denied. At the same time, the parents will manifest an overcompensating love that will sustain the denial. Adams has coined a very apt term for such a love, calling it "hard and hostile." In cases such as these, Adams sees no limit to the parental capacity for self-deception and memory distortion.

Professionals have been very ready to accuse parents of rejecting their handicapped child but have been very fuzzy in their terminology. For example, Kanner (1953) and Stoddard (1959) virtually equate parental awareness of the child's disability with acceptance thereof—a conceptual jump that does not appear justifiable. "The helping professions have somewhat belabored the tendency of the parent to deny the reality of his child's mental deficiency. Few workers have reported what is probably a more frequent occurrence, the parent's tendency to deny his chronic sorrow. This tendency is often reinforced by the professional helper's habit of viewing chronic sorrow as a neurotic manifestation rather than a natural and understandable response to a tragic fact" (Olshansky, 1962). He also inquires just what it is the professional wants of the parent when he asks him to accept mental retardation. Does it, perhaps, mean that he should see it through the eyes of the professional?

Michaels and Schucman (1962) do not even see denial as pathological, pointing out its integrative and adaptive features. According to Hersh (1961), not every parent should be expected to accept the handicap as this might destroy parental adjustment. "The pervasive or life-long character of certain forms of retardation is an unending burden to many parents that few can carry unaided" (Begab, 1964). Hope may be necessary for certain people overcome by adversity, and such hope can sometimes only be held if retardation is denied (American Medical Asociation, 1965). Parental regression, a form of denial of the obvious, may actually help a parent to adjust to a very terrible reality (Olshansky, 1962). Cummings and Stock (1962) describe one kind of nonacceptance of retardation as consisting of "rescue fantasies" of a magical nature, such as sudden "cures," etc., but according to Michaels and Schucman (1962), if parents believe in magical cures, their ability to continue functioning may depend on such fantasies. Therapy may break down at the point where this belief is dispelled too abruptly before a more realistic kind of hope can be offered and accepted. Thus, premature emphasis on reality can lead to hopelessness and chronic depression.

Simply by coming to an agency, the parents have indicated that they are confused, puzzled, and alarmed, and that they want some clarification (Blodgett, 1958). Rejection of a diagnosis of retardation at that point should be interpreted not so much as a rejection of the interpretation as an indication of a slow acceptance.

Just what will be lost, Olshansky (1962) asks, if parents delay being able to admit the fact of retardation for a few years? After all, he suggests, they have a lifetime ahead of them, and both the child and the parent may actually make a better adjustment by this delayed admission. Hastings (1960) also agrees that the child's welfare may be better served if the parents do not know early about the retardation. Thus, the child may be able to create a place for himself in the family which otherwise may not have been possible.

Sheimo (1951) and others have pointed out that the advent of a retarded child can induce a high drive state in the parents that can be channeled and utilized in a constructive fashion. Mandelbaum and Wheeler (1960) even concede that diagnosis shopping may be an indicator of strength rather than pathology, reflecting a rebelliousness which could be adaptive.

Murray (1959), who often presents the parent's viewpoint, feels that parental nonacceptance only reflects societal values. Once retardation is better accepted and understood in the population at large, it will also become more acceptable to parents. Bower (1957) points to the importance of the prevailing cultural values in America as determiners of parental reactions to retardation, as when social worth is equated with intellectual prowess (Kelman, 1953). Zuk (1962) perceives the inconsistencies of these values as one of the sources of parental conflict. Finally, Dybwad (1964) reminds workers in the field that what was once considered unrealistic striving for treatment, and neurotic nonacceptance, is now increasingly recognized as feasible expectations.

The belief that expressed parental awareness or acceptance of retardation is crucial in the management of the child is one of the sacred cows that mental retardation has probably inherited from the traditional psychiatric emphasis on "insight." I am not aware of any studies that indicate that the child suffers emotionally or intellectually from parents' lack of verbally expressed insight. To the contrary, the scanty evidence that is available indicates little relationship between parental verbalization and child rearing behavior in general (e.g., Ross, 1964). One could even go one step further and hypothesize that as a group, children of parents who come late and slowly to a verbal awareness will receive the social treatment more beneficial to them than those early recognized as retarded by their parents. The crucial point made here is that whatever the reality, authoritative pronouncements are not yet warranted, and the questions raised by some of the above writers should be carefully considered. Otherwise, counselors may base their views and attitudes upon stereotyped cliches instead of thought, and convention instead of conviction. Perhaps the view of Adamson, Ohrenstein, Lake, and Hersh (1964) will prevail—that the entire issue of parental acceptance is a "wasted and overstated one."

THE ROLE OF RELIGION IN PARENTAL ADJUSTMENT

A healthy controversy has arisen as to the role of religion, specifically Catholicism, in parental adjustment. Zuk (1959b) obtained subjective ratings of parental acceptance of a retarded child and found it highest in Catholic and lowest in Jewish mothers. In fact, the Jewish mothers in his sample were rated as totally nonaccepting. He proposed that certain elements of the Catholic faith accounted for the greater acceptance. Among these might be the absolution of guilt, real or imagined, that a Catholic can obtain in the confessional. Protestant and Jewish doctrine was seen as neither equally explicit or absolving. On the other hand, Jews were seen as placing particularly high value on intellect. Religious outlook in general may also be important, and a parallel was drawn between the Catholic and Hutterite viewpoints (Zuk, 1959b; Zuk, Miller, Bartram, and Kling, 1961). Among Hutterites, retardates are not institutionalized (Eaton and Weil, 1955), but are integrated and appropriately cared for. In a further study, Zuk, Miller, Bartram, and Kling (1961) sent mail questionnaires about attitudes and religious practices to mothers of retarded children seen at a clinic. Catholics again were found to be more accepting, though only slightly so. However, the study suffered from several weaknesses, e.g., agreement between professionally rated and questionnaire acceptance was nonsignificant, ratings were obtained at different times for different subjects, and the religious groups differed greatly on many potentially relevant variables. Kramm (1963) felt that Catholic parents reacted more favorably toward a retarded child than non-Catholics, and Stone and Parnicky (1965) reported Catholic parents to be less likely to institutionalize. However, both studies also confounded Catholicism somewhat with other factors, such as age, social class, degree of acculturation, etc. That Catholicism may be confounded with social-class factors was confirmed in Klebanoff's (1959) work. Farber (1959, 1960b) also found some evidence that Catholic families were better able to cope with a retarded child and, in some instances, were less willing to institutionalize. However, as discussed elsewhere, these studies suffered from certain limitations.

In contrast to the above studies, Leichman (1960) as quoted by Zuk (1962), reported no difference in verbalized acceptance between Catholic and Protestant mothers of retarded children. Saenger (1957) found that institutionalization was lowest among Italian and highest among Jewish groups. This had been widely interpreted to mean that Catholics may institutionalize less readily than non-Catholics, but in a later and probably better-controlled study, Saenger (1960) discovered that the earlier conclusions were not substantiated.

There is no doubt that the role of religion in parental dynamics and management must be recognized (Stubblefield, 1965). The hypothesis that religious values, outlooks, institutions, and rituals may make retardation more acceptable and bearable to some religious groups than others is a reasonable and attractive one. However, the evidence is grossly insufficient. Studies would have to be very careful to take into account a number of family characteristics and socio-economic variables. Otherwise, Catholicism and social class may be confounded, just as Robbins

(1948) found that retardation in the family can correlate with indices of social class such as parental income, occupation, education, size and type of habitat, home ownership, etc.

PARENT-PROFESSIONAL RELATIONSHIPS

The story of the handling of parents of the retarded by professionals is a very sad one. While many unfortunate episodes have been the result of ill-advised but well-meaning management, others have been due to callousness and outright malpractice. Stern (1951), one of the first parents to tell her story in the popular press, indicated that perhaps every parent was misinformed and misdirected at least once by a professional. Even though some parents may be inclined to distort or exaggerate, the literature is so replete with reprehensible examples that the reality of the situation can scarcely be denied.

One of the first parents to take his case before a professional audience was Reilly (1942) who recounted the story, repeated so often, of how parents were told on a routine basis by state institution officials to forget their child, never visit, and to have other children instead. Thorne and Andrews (1946), though justified in disapproving of parents who abandoned their children to the state exemplified the administration viewpoint in chiding parents for behavior aimed at improving residents' rights in the institution, or for attempts to retain guardianship privileges over their child. Wardell (1947) also exemplified earlier writers who saw counseling as serving mostly the eventual process of institutionalization. Sampson (1947) was one of the first professionals who, in effect, proposed that it was time to be nice to parents.

A wide range of bad practices in family management, mostly on the part of physicians, is documented or denounced by Ambrosina (1960), Denhoff (1960), Jensen (1950), Kopek (1964), Kramm (1963), Kugel and Reque (1961), McDonald (1962), Patterson (in Martmer, 1959), Roith (1963), Rosen (1955), Schumacher (1946), Sheimo (1951), Solnit and Stark (1961), Wolf and Lourie (1953), Zwerling (1954), and many others. A number of these studies will be discussed in more detail.

Zwerling (1954), reporting on 85 letters he received from members of parent associations, recorded a wide range of practices the parents said they had encountered. This is the article in which a physician was first quoted as advising parents that "retardates make nice pets around the house," a phrase that has become a much-repeated classic in the field. Instances of hasty and casual diagnosis and many other regrettable experiences viewed with bitterness by the parents were reported. The author also related one extreme of what he described as "maudlin sentimentality" when a physician told a mother with tears streaming down his cheeks that her baby was mongoloid. Zwerling made a strong plea for physicians to develop appropriate knowledge and skills in the field of retardation as they will continue to be the first contact of most families. He thus not only questioned their attitudes and practices based thereon, but also their competencies. Hastings (1960) stated that she could only confirm Zwerling's findings. She pointed out that in hardly any hospitals is someone trained in counseling, such as the hospital social worker, called in when a retarded child is born: "The anxieties, guilt, and disappointment that go with the statement 'your child is retarded' are seldom handled by the physician who has delivered the baby." Jensen (1950) specifically singled out three common errors in medical practice: delay in defining the problem, false encouragement of parents, and too much direct advice or urging on matters such as institutionalization. Sheimo (1951) admonished physicians to recognize and respect the parents' right to decide their own destinies.

Waskowitz (1959) interviewed 80 per cent of the members of a parent group regarding their experience with diagnosis and feedback. Only 25 per cent of these parents were satisfied with their professional contacts. Extreme examples of poor handling included one case where a physician told a parent over the phone that the child was a "mongolian idiot." Koch, Graliker, Sands, and Parmelee (1959) questioned parents of 105 infants regarding their satisfaction with previous medical care and reported that 47 per cent were satisfied with pediatricians, 55 per cent with their general practitioners, and 77 per cent with obstetricians. The main complaints were abruptness, overly hurried handling of the case, lack of interest, and hesitancy to communicate. Thurston (1960a) pointed out that the parent may be beset with poor advice and poor handling by a large number of persons, of whom the physician is only one. He felt that most relationships between parents and others are not amenable to modification, but that the one between the parent and the physician is one that could be improved. "The only truly adequate decisions are those that have been arrived at by the parents after a thorough appraisal of the entire situation and all its complex ramifications."

Tizard and Grad (1961) divided families into three groups according to the way in which they had been informed of the diagnosis: 14 per cent, apparently very poorly handled; 41 per cent, some unsatisfactory features, and 45 per cent, apparently satisfactory or not ascertainable. In 80 cases of mongolism, 62 sets of parents were apparently either never told of the condition, or only well after the diagnosis had been made. In more than 10 per cent of the cases, the parents were uninformed until the child was of school age. In one case, a physician demonstrated a child to students as an idiot in the presence of the mother who had been told nothing. In another case, the mother heard the physician say, amid peals of laughter among the attending professionals and students, that the child had "the belly of a porpoise, the legs of a greyhound and the brains of an imbecile." Tizard and Grad concluded, "One cannot rate or assess the pain that a clumsily handled interview can cause the parents of a mentally subnormal child" (p. 99). In a study by Kugel and Reque (1961), between 20 and 30 per cent of parents of both home-reared and institutionalized mongoloids regarded the physician's explanation of the diagnosis as poor. Logan (1962), a mother, told a typical story of abrupt handling. She said that the possibility of retardation in her child was discounted by pediatricians even after walking was greatly delayed and after the onset of convulsions. She made a strong plea for increased use of the public health nurse or similar personnel who might relate more effectively to parents.

A study by Kramm (1963) reported some of the more objectionable examples of medical management. She spent an average of eight hours with each of 50 families with a mongoloid child and found that 62 per cent of parents either had been told their child was normal or had been told nothing, yet over a third of the physicians contacted later admitted that they knew—a state of affairs that might be considered malpractical. Two-thirds of the parents felt that they had been handled harshly.

Thurston (1963) found that only 4 per cent of parents understood the nature and cause of their child's handicap, and even after as much as 15 years, including years of institutionalization, many were very disturbed and unhappy. He concluded that the parent-physician relationship was at the core of much of this and suggested, in so many words, that physicians handle the medical aspects and leave the counseling to those trained for it. Ehlers (1962), who interviewed families in their homes, felt that parents were more likely to remember how the physician told them the facts than what the facts were. The public health nurse was viewed as one of the most helpful, acceptable and non-threatening professionals.

The studies by Hung and Haritos (1961) and Kugel and Reque (1961) indicated that a serious discrepancy may exist between the perceptions of parents and physicians. Hung and Haritos sent mail questionnaires to 35 pediatricians in Washington, D.C. The vast majority of respondents informed the parents while still in the hospital, and most of them denied ever having met nonacceptance of the diagnosis, although only three reported using what might be called counseling. In contrast to the Hung and Haritos study, Kugel and Reque (1961) found, in a mail survey of parents' experience, that 40 per cent of parents who kept their child at home reported that they had rejected the diagnosis at first as opposed to 30 per cent of those who institutionalized their children. Between 20 to 30 per cent of both groups regarded the physician's explanation as poor, dissatisfaction being highest among those who kept the child.

Olshansky, Johnson, and Sternfeld (1964), Olshansky and Kettell (1963), Olshansky, Schonfield, and Sternfeld (1962), and Olshansky and Sternfeld (1962) reported an extensive project in which medical interns, residents, general practitioners, pediatricians, and obstetricians were interviewed by means of a structured questionnaire regarding their attitude toward retardation and institutionalization. The results were little short of shocking, especially if one considers that the studies were conducted in 1960 and 1961, and that the interviewees worked in or near an outstanding medical center. All groups had had surprisingly little contact with cases that they had recognized as retarded, but frequency of contact was not found to be related to attitudes. In all groups, terms such as "monsters" and "vegetables" were readily encountered. Of pediatricians and obstetricians, only a very small number (17 per cent and 14 per cent, respectively) thought that the decision to institutionalize was up to the parents, instead viewing it as their responsibility. Immediate institutionalization was considered appropriate by 8 per cent of the interns and residents, 11 per cent of the obstetricians, 17 per cent of the pediatricians and 40 per cent of the general practitioners. Mongolism was frequently equated with total unchanging helplessness. Rather amazingly, 67 per cent of pediatricians thought that their most important service to parents was counseling, but the authors felt that few had integrated their views into an organized perspective that might guide them in their day-to-day relationship with parents. Of the general practitioners, 48 per cent denied ever having heard of the local mental retardation clinic, and only 14 per cent could give basic identifying data regarding its location, sponsorship, or services. This clinic, part of the local health department, had functioned for more than three years prior to the survey, had mailed more than six communications to each physician, and had "innumerable" newspaper releases published! Younger physicians showed considerably more sophistication than their more experienced elders, but even among them, 25 per cent had had no lectures in retardation in medical school, and only 30 per cent could name a single authority in the field. These studies, being empirical rather than impressionistic, make parental reports of poor management sound very plausible and likely.

The medical profession apparently is carrying the brunt of parental hostility, distrust, and blame. It should, however, be noted that to some degree this may be an historical accident, and that hostility is not directed at physicians alone (e.g., Blatt, 1957; Murray, 1959; Nadal, 1961). Roos (1963) points out that a parent's attack upon a counselor may only be a manifestation of generalized anger and hostility that happens to be focused upon

him. Traditionally, the physician has been the first, and also the most frequent, contact of the family, and has been the one who has been cast in the role of case-manager and diagnostician. Other professionals who might have shared the same attitudes may have been "lucky" in being less involved with retardation, thus drawing less criticism. On the other hand, quite possibly medical practitioners have tended to be less sensitive to the emotional element in cases of retardation and have lacked the training to give the wise counsel that is necessary. Thus, Rosen (1955) found that mothers tended to be more satisfied with a psychological than a physical-medical interpretation, while special educators were preferred over physicians in a study by Costello (1963). This may well be accounted for by the more thorough training behaviorally oriented professionals have usually had in counseling. An extreme example of a hyper-medical approach to family management is illustrated by Drayer and Schlesinger (1960) where the family is "presented" at the end of a case conference, and where feedback may take place on the spot. It is humorous to read the comment that "in some instances the non-medical problems loom large." The informing interview may be conducted by a number of different individuals, and apparently the entire findings and recommendations formulated at the case conference are thrown at the family. Other extreme medical-psychiatric views are exemplified by Michaels and Schucman (1962) and Goshen (1963) who apparently view parents as "patients" and their need as one for psychotherapy.

A number of writers have concerned themselves with the reasons for the physician's apparent difficulties in retardation management. Kurtz (1964) proposes that the management of a retardate presents a very frustrating demand upon the physician, who tends to be action-oriented, but who feels powerless *vis-à-vis* retardation. In order to purge himself of his feelings of inadequacy, he either can concentrate on the less relevant medical aspects (e.g., vision and hearing) or can rid himself of the embarrassing case by referring the patient up the line of specialists and perhaps eventually the institution. The American Medical Association handbook (1965) makes the point that the physician may, deep down, harbor the hope that the retarded client will go to somebody else. I would add that he may translate his discomfort into such overt behavior as to impel parents to take the problem away and never come back. Zuk (1962) feels that physicians often mishandle the parents because they, as bearer of the news, feel that they participated in the creation of the defect. Giannini and Goodman (1963) and Goodman (1964) suggest that a retarded child symbolizes failure to the physician, and by recommending placement he rids himself of a threatening presence.

The American Medical Association (1965) has published a mental retardation handbook for the "primary physician." This handbook, growing out of a conference sponsored by the association, seems to constitute an attempt to advance the primary physician as an effective force in mental retardation management. It exalts the role that the physician can and should play in such management, and even views him as the one who should be charged with the responsibility of devising, with the family, the entire life plan of the retardate. While the handbook has much to offer, it is curiously weak in defining the optimal relationship between the primary physician and mental retardation specialty clinics and agencies. In fact, it has very little to say about the many specialty clinics now in existence. At no point does the handbook seem to advocate that the specialty agencies should be viewed as the chief referral and management centers by the practitioner. Also, its advocacy of competency upgrading for the physician is limited to such weak statements as "the physician may find it valuable to inaugurate a self-education program to increase his own competence and confidence" (p. 207). The difficulty of getting physicians to become interested in competency upgrading in mental retardation is recognized: "Any educational effort faces the built-in resistance of many physicians, both because of their pessimistic attitude toward the disease [sic] in general and because of the personal feelings of anxiety and guilt such patients may arouse" (p. 218). The handbook upholds an almost idealized standard of involvement with the retarded child and his family which, if generally adopted by physicians, should indeed mark a most satisfying improvement in parent-physician relationships. "As a significant member of the community, the physician in his steadfast interest certifies the child's continuing value and diminishes parental feelings of isolation and failure. The physician helps keep hope alive" (p. 207).

Other problems that beset professionals in general who are involved in parent counseling work are discussed in the section on counselor qualifications. Regardless of the question of professional differences in management, the time is past when parents could be mishandled without repercussions. I believe that if private medical practitioners fail to adapt their attitudes and practices in regard to retardation, parent organizations, public opinion, and policy-making bodies will see to it that other professionals or structures will replace them in the management of retardation. Indeed, the swift expansion of subsidized, public, and government-supported clinics is probably, in part, a manifestation of such a trend.

THE PARENT AND THE CLINIC

In Children's Bureau-supported mental retardation clinics, more than 25,000 retarded children and their families were evaluated between 1956 and 1960 (Rubinstein, 1962). In 1960 alone, almost 11,000 children were seen in 38 states with such clinics, and 75 per cent of these children were under 9 years old. Further vast increases in clinic services for the retarded seem inevitable.

A number of studies have concerned themselves with parental satisfaction with clinic services. Theoretically, the complex nature of retardation calls for the diagnostic skills of a number of disciplines, and therefore the team or interdisciplinary approach is supposed to be preferable to that of any individual practitioner. Although this is a view now almost held sacred in the field, the clinic approach does have certain built-in problems (Bakwin, 1956; Wolfensberger, 1965a, 1965b; Woloshin and Williams, 1964).

The first rather primitive clinic follow-up (Collie, 1943) found that most parents were dissatisfied and had gone shopping elsewhere. A second study (Galibof, 1951, as summarized by Weingold and Hormuth, 1953) indicated, more than anything, that members of parent groups were more accepting of their child and expressed better satisfaction than nonmembers. More recently, Kaplan and Hingeley (1958) mailed questionnaires to families seen at an institution out-patient clinic. The parents reported that the findings and recommendations were of value to them, but in a significant proportion of instances did not follow the recommendations. Over 20 per cent did not indicate a clearer understanding of their child. Another study is reported by Caldwell, Manley, and Nissan (1961) and Caldwell, Manley, and Seelye (1961). Again, a mail questionnaire was used, but the return was a very poor 30 per cent and is difficult to interpret. The only result worthwhile considering is that satisfaction correlated with frequency of clinic contact.

A good 84 per cent return at a Children's Bureau-sponsored demonstration clinic was obtained by Barclay, Goulet, Holtgrewe, and Sharp (1962), and their results were interesting. Length of waiting was inversely related to satisfaction, and two or more months' delay was considered partially or wholly unsatisfactory. While the staff had not become aware of this during the evaluation, parents had expected more detailed discussion regarding need for institutional care. Also, parents desired more instruction on home training and self-help skills and explanation of the child's capabilities. In spite of the fact that 73 per cent of parents declared themselves satisfied, 21 per cent of these had obtained another evaluation elsewhere. (With parents of older children, or a later follow-up, this might have been much higher.) The major conclusion from this study is that verbally expressed satisfaction does not imply cessation of shopping, and that clinic personnel should be sensitive to what parents expect of them.

A 60 per cent return of a mail survey of 313 cases seen at another demonstration and pilot evaluation project (McIntire and Kiekhaeker, 1963) showed a high satisfaction with the examination but a significant dissatisfaction with the amount and type of feedback. Eighteen per cent felt their questions were not answered, and 71 per cent would have appreciated reading materials. Moreover, 66 per cent had suggestions for improving the clinic, mostly in connection with practical help to parents. One very significant finding was that in this clinic, which only saw children below 6 years of age, parental dissatisfaction was higher the older the child was. One might infer that parents of young children may be put off by being given the more traditional

diagnostic feedback, but once the parents have lived with the problem a few years, they may want more practical answers and services.

Four tentative conclusions may, perhaps, be drawn from clinic satisfaction studies:

1. Stated parental satisfaction is now higher than it used to be.

2. Satisfaction seems to be higher with the diagnostic evaluation than the guidance and counseling function. This should not be surprising as clinics have tended to emphasize the diagnostic aspects, have often referred parents to nonexisting services, and have done their best not to get involved in services and long-range management themselves.

3. Despite their shortcomings, clinics seem to have the edge over independent practitioners, primarily because they have more experience and are oriented to the problem. One wonders if, indeed, an ordinary private practitioner can compete in competency with specialty clinics, and whether past experience does not indicate that such clinics should relieve the practitioners of an apparently unhappy yoke. However, many clinics, in order to serve a socially useful function, will have to orient themselves more to services other than diagnosis.

4. As data reviewed here as well as later in the chapter indicate, verbally expressed satisfaction is an inadequate measure of parental gain. It seems appropriate to call for a moratorium on such satisfaction studies unless they include objective measures of parental diagnosis-shopping, knowledge of or attitudes toward retardation, child rearing practices, etc. An attempt in this direction was made by Costello (1963) who developed a measure of parents' attitudes toward the counseling they have received.

COUNSELOR QUALIFICATIONS

A professional must be very conscious of the fact that his intervention may have the profoundest effect, perhaps for their lifetime, not only upon clients but also their entire family groups. Unless he approaches his task with awe and the willingness to be most cautious and circumspect with his counsel, he is not ready to work with parents of the retarded, if, indeed, in any kind of helping relationship. Social workers, clinical psychologists and physicians are sometimes heard to assert that any member of their profession is qualified to render counseling to parents of the retarded. Common sense and the foregoing review clearly indicate that this is not so. Desirable counselor qualifications have already been implied by the work discussed, but additional comments seem in order.

The Group for the Advancement of Psychiatry (1963) and the American Medical Association (1965) echo numerous medical writers who propose that the medical practitioner can and should assume a major role in the management of the retarded child. However, Wishik (1957; also in Martmer, 1959) presents a creed of 25 points to which physicians would have to adhere in order to prevent the kind of mismanagement documented in the literature. Thurston (1963) suggests that the physician should confine himself to the medical aspects and leave counseling to those trained for it. He specifically feels that psychologists have much to offer in this area, that they have "much firepower," but are "out of range." A British report (Paediatric Society, 1962) sets forth the principle that regardless of who counsels the parents, he must be exceedingly well informed about all the facets of the situation, but Beck (1962a) states rather flatly that counseling should not be attempted by anyone not trained for it.

Commenting on the frequent failure of physicians to handle the human factor adequately when a mother gives birth to a retarded child, Goodman (1964) recommends that the hospital social worker intervene actively if the physician seems unable to perform the necessary casework function. Ehlers (1964), working in a community clinic, concluded that physicians, in order to play an effective role in family management, would need specialized training such as seminars, lectures, and reading. A somewhat ambivalent role is displayed by Oberman (1963). He gives a very good appraisal of what has happened between the parent and the medical profession, but then goes on to urge a strong role for the pediatrician and general practitioner in the management of retardation problems and families. "Through his knowledge of the home atmosphere he can anticipate problems that may arise and can give the parents many practical suggestions for managing the child." This is an assertion that, in light of past experience, can only be accepted if supported by fresh evidence.

I suggest that a counselor's professional affiliation is irrelevant. Possession of a medical or any other degree neither qualifies nor disqualifies a person from counseling and managing parents. Instead, the following criteria are proposed as relevant: (1) knowledge of the broader medical, social, educational, habilitational, behavioral, etc. aspects of retardation; (2) knowledge of resources in the broadest sense (i.e., agencies, services, long-range local prospects, reading materials, "gadgets" useful in home management, etc.); (3) competency, acquired through training, in counseling principles and techniques in general; (4) experience in the applied-clinical area of retardation; (5) freedom from stereotypes about retardation; (6) possession of genuinely positive attitudes toward retardation, the handicapped, and their parents; (7) an orientation to the current community centered management approach; (8) a sensitivity to the reality needs of the family; (9) willingness to go beyond traditional approaches to help parents, even at the cost of personal convenience; and (10) great patience.

In addition to finding a very high degree of parental dissatisfaction with professional contacts, Waskowitz (1959) also discovered that when mothers were asked how they would have liked to be handled, they responded with a great variety of suggestions. This would tend to indicate that considerable individualization is required from the counselor, and that his skill will be taxed in determining how and at what rate counseling should be conducted.

I believe that three counselor-centered obstacles have barred the way for effective work with parents. One of these is a certain prevalent psychiatric orientation that views parents as "patients" and that sees the source of their problems as residing within them. Workers of this persuasion then translate those measures they have applied traditionally, though often equally unsuccessfully, in psychiatric settings to retardation services. Parents' reaction to retardation is described in the terms of abnormal psychology, their need is seen to be in the area of therapy, and involvement in their situational dilemma is studiously avoided. Indeed, the verbal-theoretical and office-centered nature of psychiatric training and practice would render many such workers incompetent to render other needed services even if they wished to do so.

Secondly, many professionals, overtly or covertly, are subject to deep-seated attitudes toward defect and retardation that are basically no different than those often held by the parents themselves or by the community at large (Mandelbaum and Wheeler, 1960). Even well-trained professional workers may hold unconscious or conscious antipathy toward the retarded and their problems (Bindman and Klebanoff, 1959). Such professionals may wrap themselves in a defense of nondirective, redirective, and reflective techniques, obscure vocabulary (Gallagher, 1956), or any other methods that will maximize their distance to the problem while yet allowing to view themselves as involved. According to Ross (1964), professionals who have their anxieties aroused when confronted by defect may be inclined to rationalize that some other professional will assume the major counseling role. However, often the other one is also uncomfortable, and, in the end, the parent may get help from no one. The Group for Advancement of Psychiatry (1963) points out that the physician is in danger of overidentifying himself with the parents and then trying to impose his solution upon them. Spock (1961) has experienced and expressed well the conflict a physician may undergo, and other professionals, too, must search their innermost feelings before they can handle the parents competently.

Thirdly, many individuals who counsel parents, even if free of detrimental attitudes and backgrounds, have had little training or experience in mental retardation or even in normal child development. They feel inadequate in managing practical problems and therefore restrict counseling to often stereotyped discussions of parental feelings.

INDIVIDUAL AND JOINT COUNSELING OF PARENTS

A distinct historical trend can be traced in the literature and can also be observed in the practice of the field. At one time, parental counseling was viewed as taking place primarily within the context of a single interview

consequent to the evaluation of the child. The parents were told the facts as the diagnostician, the counselor, or the team saw them, then told to accept these facts, and sent on their way. If the parents felt that they needed repeated feedback, this need was apt to be viewed as somewhat extraordinary or even neurotic, and repeated sessions as being in the line of psychotherapy—something many diagnostic clinics were unwilling to provide (Wolfensberger, 1965a, 1965b).

However, professionals increasingly have become aware that hardly anyone can digest in one session all the facts and implications of a diagnosis of retardation in their child. Indeed, in the ordinary parent, the emotional "work" that follows such a diagnosis needs extended time and requires repeated regurgitation and recapitulation. Also, professionals have become more sensitive to the realistic situational demands retardation places on parents, and gradually more practical help and tuition is being provided for them.

Collie (1943), as mentioned, conducted perhaps the first clinic follow-up of parents of the retarded and found that most parents were dissatisfied, regardless of their intelligence or socio-economic status. Apparently, very few had received adequate interpretation. Rheingold (1945), in a very enlightened article well ahead of her time, discussed feedback counseling in terms of a single session. Only occasionally, if parental anxiety seemed high, were several interviews considered advisable. Jensen (1950), also in an otherwise very sophisticated discussion, likewise saw parent counseling as a one-shot situation. Bakwin (1956), in an article peculiarly progressive as well as traditional, stated rather naively that those parents who already know or suspect the diagnosis are easy to handle and may need only simple confirmation.

In contrast, numerous writers have recognized the parents' need for more intensive and repeated contacts. Schumacher (1945), though one of the first to write about parent counseling, recommended that parents be seen repeatedly. Sheimo (1951) pointed out that diagnosis and recommendations are neither sufficient, nor, perhaps, what the parents are really seeking. What they may be asking for in ostensibly presenting the child for diagnosis is resolution of their own conflicts. Sarason (1952) observed that many parents, even after seeing numerous specialists, were amazingly ill-informed. He stated that he knew that in some cases this was because of inadequate feedback.

Zwerling (1954), who solicited letters from parents, found that one of their major concerns was lack of adequate feedback counseling and a need for referral to parent groups and to appropriate reading matter. Weingold (1954) felt that parents could easily obtain diagnosis, but not intelligent prognosis or help in planning the future. This, of course, depends upon the nature of the feedback. The World Health Organization (1954) report emphasized: "It need hardly be added that more than one discussion may be necessary, since the parents cannot be expected to understand and face the full consequences of matters of such strong emotional significance after a single interview" (p. 15), and added that therapeutic discussion may have to be continued sporadically over the years (p. 16). Kanner (1962, but reprinted from a 1956 article) stated that "no examination and no plan of treatment can be regarded as complete without a meaningful explanation to the parents and a consideration of their curiosities and emotional involvements." Blodgett (1957), Ownby (1964), and Richards (1964) expressed preference for repeated sessions in feedback counseling, and Kelman (1957) was among the first to emphasize that even interpretation and supportive or reassuring counseling is not sufficient unless accompanied by practical, tutorial assistance and guidance in home management and daily care of the child. Harris and Schechtman (1959), after failing to find changes in knowledge and attitudes of parents exposed to various educational techniques, concluded that, despite the repeated contacts that were offered, parents needed yet more as well as a greater variety. Beck (1959) pointed out that extensive follow-up is sometimes more important than intensive one.

Murray (1959) was one of the first to advocate the concept of lifelong counseling. As a child develops, new problems and crises arise, each calling for further counseling. Thus, Hastings (1960) sees seven crisis points at which the diagnosis may be made or where counseling may become necessary again even though the retardation is recognized: (1) birth, (2) developmental delay, (3) school entrance, (4) adolescence, (5) vocational planning, (6) death of a parent, and (7) institutional placement. In the mental retardation handbook of the American Medical Association (1965), 12 crisis periods are identified: (1) the first family suspicion of retardation, (2) final diagnosis, (3) school entrance, (4) rejection by peers, (5) sibling relationships, (6) acute illness, (7) general family crises, including moving, succeeding pregnancies, etc., (8) sexual problems at puberty, (9) vocational adjustment, (10) marriage, (11) decision on placement, and (12) separation following placement.

The mental retardation handbook of the American Medical Association (1965) warns the physician against haste in diagnosis and refers to retardation as an "atypical crisis." Most other crises in medicine require prompt diagnosis and action, and the physician may be inclined to apply this customary approach to retardation instead of giving it the deliberate attention it requires. DiMichael (HEW, 1961) feels that parent counseling should not only be provided for specific problems or crises, but should even be provided in a preventive fashion and should be sustained for years. Gardner and Nisonger (1962) also emphasized the need for long-term guidance.

A number of writers stress the point that the diagnostic process must not have a casual (Solnit and Stark, 1961), hurried (Koch, Graliker, Sands, and Parmelee, 1959; McDonald, 1962), or incomplete (Bakwin, 1956) flavor. If it does, parents may reject the diagnosis and shop elsewhere, may lose faith in the helping professions, or may become fixated in a stage of unresolved conflict (Solnit and Stark, 1961). A business-like "delivery" (Bryant and Hirschberg, 1961) and lack of follow-up in general (Solnit and Stark, 1961) were also blamed as causes of shopping. Indeed, Yates and Lederer (1961) suggested that diagnosis take place in repeated sessions, and I heartily endorse this view. I have seen too many instances in which diagnosis and feedback counseling were offered on the basis of information gathered in an artificially limited time instead of after all potentially important data had been obtained. Some have argued that a poor diagnostic workup is better than none, but one could very easily argue the converse—that poor diagnosis is often worse than none.

Graliker, Parmelee, and Koch (1959) found in their parental reaction survey that most parents are so overwhelmed by their reaction to the diagnosis that they cannot give proper attention to planning for the future. The authors recommend that the initial focus of feedback counseling be on etiology, diagnosis, and parental feelings, and only later upon prognosis and planning. Mild experimental support for this implied notion of repeated contact comes from Caldwell, Manley, and Seelye (1961) While their study suffers from several shortcomings, they did find that a larger number of clinic contacts correlated with higher degrees of parental satisfaction.

As time has passed and experience has accumulated, professional judgments have become stronger. Hersh (1961) stated emphatically thae one-shot feedbacks are of little value and called for periodic follow-up over two to three years. Llewellyn (1962) decided that parental acceptance can never be accomplished in one interview, or even a few. Parents have to go through a developmental process, much like children, and the length of this process depends on many factors. Among these may be the age of the child, as parents of young children were seen as less capable of handling long-range predictions. Olshansky (1962) felt that no matter how effective the counseling is, many parents need to talk on many occasions. Parents in a state of chronic sorrow, especially, may need years before they can muster enough strength to live with the recognition of retardation. Baroff (1963) emphasized that the intense emotional involvements of the parent precluded attitude change in a single conference. Schild (1964), reviewing a series of cases, concluded that parents need time to take in the extent of their problem and have to work out their solutions step by step. They need not only crisis help, but continued contact as well. The latter is to be educationally focused on practical problems and is considered crucial.

Dybwad (1964) has discerned a trend away from the traditional emphasis on the diagnostic process and diagnostic feedback counseling. He feels that the diagnosis has been of limited value in answering questions about the child's future—a conclusion reached 19 years earlier, and apparently uniquely so, by Rheingold (1945). Parents, Dybwad asserts, were told too often "what happened" instead of "what can be done for the child."

Evidence that many parents cannot digest diagnostic feedback without repeated contact is beginning to accumulate. Drake and Ober (1963) compared hospital records with parental reports about having or not having been informed of their child's possible retardation. The results indicated that 87 sets of parents of 132 children who turned out to be retarded, or 66 per cent, denied having been told about the possible retardation, contrary to the records. Possibly, the records were in error, and the physicians repressed telling the parents. Also, the parents may have been told, but in a poor fashion. A casual and not atypical statement that the child "may be a bit slow but may grow out of it" may not have registered upon the parents at that time. Appell, Williams, and Fishell (1964) found that before a group counseling sequence, 52 per cent of the parents admitted having been told of the retardation by a physician. After two years and 60 sessions, 71 per cent admitted the same. Schild (1964), conducting a group experience for parents of phenylketonuric children, observed that the participants had to go over the same questions of fact in session after session in order to assimilate the information adequately. Studies such as these suggest a need for experiments comparing the effect of different amounts or types of feedback upon parents' retention and interpretation of the facts.

A study of the antecedents to parental diagnosis shopping might help to determine to what degree it is affected by feedback and counseling variables. One problem would be to assess the amount of shopping, which is more difficult than it sounds. Parents are sometimes reluctant to give this information. They may feel that a clinic may refuse to see them if it knew, or that it would obtain the previous reports and that the evaluation would no longer be an independent, unbiased one. Evasiveness in the history-gathering phase was viewed by Michaels and Schucman (1962) to be caused by irrational fears of becoming tainted. Accuracy of information, they feel, may sometimes have to be sacrificed in the interest of preserving psychological integration. Finally, some parents seem to forget or repress previous contacts, especially if they were numerous and if they took place some time ago. In one clinic (Haskell, Woodcock, Streeter, Morton, Smith, and Ervin, 1961), even in the age group below five years, 9 per cent of cases were found to have had diagnostic evaluations elsewhere. The lifetime number of redundant diagnostic contacts is probably much higher, and on the increase.

THE CHALLENGE OF COUNSELING PARENTS

"The challenge that the retarded offer to the professional caseworker is most profound both in terms of the complex community planning involved, as well as in the rich possibilities it offers in rendering needed individual services to the parents and siblings" (Kelman, 1957).

"Counseling with parents at the time of first knowledge of their having a retarded child is a strenuous, arduous, and exacting task. It is a task that is not always done too well" (Jensen, 1958).

"Whenever parents are given an opportunity to express themselves, they invariably air their emotional involvements in the form of questions, utterances of guilt, open and sometimes impatient rebellion against destiny, stories of frantic search for causes, pathetic accounts of matrimonial dissensions about the child's condition, regret about the course that has been taken so far, anxious appraisals of the child's future, and tearful pleas for reassurance. It takes a considerable amount of cold, hard-boiled, pseudo-professorial detachment to turn a deaf ear on the anxieties, self-incriminations, and concerns about past, present, and future contained in such remarks. We have learned to distinguish between abrupt, brutal frankness and a sympathetic statement of fact, between a dictatorial, take-it-or-leave-it kind of recommendation and the sort of presentation which would appeal to parents as the most constructive and helpful procedure, best suited under the existing circumstance" (Kanner, 1953).

Those who counsel parents of the retarded have a high obligation to develop and maintain their competencies. Four texts that are highly useful in parent counseling are Egg (1964), Kirk, Karnes, and Kirk (1955), McDonald (1962), and Ross (1964). Kanner (1953) provides one of the better of the earlier discussions of parental counseling, reviewing a number of the specific questions frequently asked by parents. Hung and Haritos (1961) compiled a list of 26 questions characteristically asked by parents of mongoloid children. Articles by Rheingold (1945)

and Roos (1963) are also very noteworthy, and Boggs (in Martmer, 1959) discusses a number of points counselors can review with parents. One of the best discussions of the interpretive interview is found in Sarason (1959, pp. 331–346).

Those in a learning or teaching role may wish to make reference to instructive case materials. A gold mine of case material is to be found in McDonald (1962). A very extensive discussion of a single case of retardation with multiple handicaps is given by Ross (1964), and other probably worthwhile or typical single cases are found in Beck (1962) and Mahoney (1958). Stone (1959) and White (1959) both discuss the same case in depth. Schipper (1959) and Kramm (1963) give mongoloid case material, and Jolly (1953) exemplifies a premature institutionalization of a mongoloid infant. Zwerling (1954) cites examples of initial impact reactions. Waskowitz (1959) gives two cases from her interview study. The close relationship between parental and child behavior is illustrated by three cases in Heilman (1950). Miscellaneous material is found in Kanner (1953) and in Tizard and Grad (1961).

THE DO'S AND DON'TS OF PARENT COUNSELING

The cornerstone of counseling parents of retarded children is competency in counseling in general. This chapter cannot recapitulate the principles of counseling. The only specifics to be covered will be those that are of particular significance to our topic or that need special emphasis. The points below have been collated from various writers, from my experience, and from certain considerations that appear to have face validity.

1. The counselor *must* be honest with himself and the parent. "Deception, no matter for what motive, is deplorable" (Kanner, 1962).

2. The counselor should not see a parent until he has prepared himself for the interview. This is particularly important in feedback interviews, which are often given in a haphazard, disorganized fashion.

3. Feedback or more didactive guidance should not be initiated until all the relevant available facts are at hand.

4. The counselor should go out of his way to involve both parents during the initial

phase (intake) of a diagnostic evaluation (e.g., Mandelbaum and Wheeler, 1960) and during the more important feedback sessions. Failure to include both parents, particularly the father, can lead to distortions and to marital friction later on and may end in disregard for the findings. It can also place an unfair burden of responsibility and decision-making on one parent, especially when placement is considered. The non-involved parent can dissociate himself too easily from the consequences. According to Schild (1964), joint counseling can serve the unique function of alleviating the personal guilt in each parent by focusing on the mutuality of feelings and responsibility.

5. The rendering of the diagnosis should constitute a new beginning and not the end of professional involvement. The professional should offer repeated discussion opportunities to the parent as an integral part of the diagnostic service, and he should do everything possible to see to it that the parents receive whatever other kind of help and service they need. Without such follow-up, diagnosis is usually meaningless, and sometimes more for the professional's than the parent's benefit and profit.

6. Particular care should be taken if the evaluation is the first major one and the diagnosis of retardation has not definitely been made before. Beck (1959) points out that this time is a particularly sensitive one during which parents must be handled very carefully. If they are not, rigid defenses may develop that may be very difficult to dispel later on.

7. The parents should be given some written feedback to which they can refer repeatedly. This may reduce chances of distorting or misunderstanding the findings and provides an opportunity to do more working-through between discussion sessions.

8. Agencies should make every effort to preserve the continuity of relationship between one main contact person and the parents. Some agencies have multiple contact persons, one for intake, one during the evaluation, one for feedback, and yet others during follow-up contacts. There should not be more than two, if that many, and only one main long-term counselor should be present at or, at worst, fully informed of, the content of any other contacts. Multiple counseling—where anybody may tell the parents results or give advice—is deplorable, in my opinion.

9. Outdated, ambiguous or unpleasant terminology should be avoided.

10. The younger the child, the more cautious should be the prognostication. Particular care should be taken not to stereotype the prognosis of clinical types of retardation, as atypical cases with intelligence above the usual and even retarded range have been documented. Roos (1963) suggests that the counselor give probability estimates for his predictions and that he explain the likely future functioning of the child in positive terms instead of using language that emphasizes what the child will not be able to do. Incorrect prognoses can jeopardize the parents' faith in all professional practice and lead to nonacceptance of the retardation (Weir and Kelley, 1963).

A particular problem arises on how to inform parents if diagnosis is made at birth. Werkman, Washington, and Oberman (1961) propose that the old approach of gradual information may no longer be appropriate with the medically sophisticated American parent. This, however, does not imply that informing need to be precipitate. Beck (1962a) asks that mothers not be informed of a retarded birth in the delivery room or before the father has gotten to the hospital.

I propose the following rule of thumb. If a child is stigmatized to a degree likely to be quite obvious to the parents, they should be prepared gently and in a fashion which, in no way, is intended or likely to lead to their rejection of the baby. This should be done in the presence of both parents, and then the baby should be introduced. Someone trained in counseling should participate in this procedure. If the baby is not very stigmatized, as in many cases of mongolism or in possible brain injury, it should be introduced with the explanation that the physician is concerned about its health and condition, and will want to examine it further, perhaps in consultation with other physicians. It may then be best to offer a more definite diagnosis or explanation some days after the baby has been taken home. The act of taking a baby home may have a profound meaning to parents, many of whom do not seem to accept their parenthood until the baby has actually passed into their physical possession. Acceptance of a handicapped baby may be more likely if the diagnosis or the problem is communicated after such possession has taken place. In discussing the condition, institutional placement need not be brought up at all as a well baby is just as helpless as a handicapped one. One of the few justifications for placing a baby at birth is in cases that require very close medical attention, but this attention may be less accessible in some institutions than in some homes.

Following below, a miscellany of insights and advice will be reviewed. Some parents may have personal problems warranting psychotherapy and may use the retarded child as a means for establishing contact with a helping agency (Mandelbaum and Wheeler, 1960). The counselor should realize, however, that some parents will be beyond help, for various reasons (Hersh, 1961; Rheingold, 1945). One such reason, according to Esty (1957), may be the parents' unconscious need for punishment. Mahoney (1958) hypothesizes that the greater the shift of symptomatic behavior in a parent from previous external defenses, the less can counseling be realistically oriented toward the needs of the child, and the more the parent will need intensive treatment. In other words, the more the child is actually a crutch to the parent, the less is his retardation the primary problem.

On the other hand, Beck (1962b) advances the possibility that parents of the retarded may be easier to counsel than individuals with personal conflicts. She thinks that the press of reality demands may reduce the amount of negative transference that parents may develop toward the counselor. The belief that the majority of parents of retarded children are in need of some kind of professional help is held by Michaels and Schucman (1962). While they draw a very pessimistic picture regarding parental acceptance and marital integration in the face of mental retardation, they state that, in time, most parents can make constructive use of therapeutic assistance. However, Beck (1959) and Cohen (1962) feel that parents can only accept help from those workers who empathize with their experience, and tend to reject the painful information that comes from a seemingly uninterested or unfeeling source. Parental reaction toward the professional may be a cry of pain and a plea for patience while the parent tries to handle his hurt.

Blodgett (1957) believes that understanding of the present condition of the child will have to precede the parent's ability to think about the future. Sometimes the possibility of re-evaluating the child later on can be made part of the feedback understanding and can be exploited during counseling. Font (1951) provides a discussion, with some good examples, of the use of psychological test interpretation as a tool in the parent counseling process.

Rheingold (1945) has suggested an interpretive approach to parents that is temporally the reverse of that used by many people in the field. She has found it more advisable to begin by reviewing the parental concern and feelings for coming for consultation. She would then proceed to a review of the history, and only later cover topics such as diagnosis, etiology, treatment, and future functioning. She has also recommended that the counselor overlook temporary lapses to earlier states of self-delusion in the parent's development.

Beck (1962a) cautions professionals that even casual remarks may have considerable impact upon parents and that offhand opinions or advice should be carefully avoided. McDonald (1962) also warns against casual comments about the child or the family in front of members of the family unless made within the context of counseling. Otherwise, distortion may result.

Bryant and Hirschberg (1961) offer eight pointers for physicians that are also applicable to other professionals: (1) allow sufficient time for the examination; (2) show objectivity as well as kindness toward parents and child; (3) be sympathetic without being patronizing; (4) accord proper dignity and respect to child and parents; (5) show support without taking over in an authoritarian fashion; (6) allow parents sufficient time to raise questions, absorb findings, and work at their decisions; (7) allow them to mobilize their strength for their own mature decision; and (8) be prepared for parents who postpone action on any recommendations made to them. The authors also suggest that if the physician does not feel that he can align himself with the parents, cannot deal objectively with the problem, is not interested in the demanding work of parent counseling, or is already overburdened, he should tactfully refer them elsewhere. This, they point out, is good practice of medicine.

Concern about the long-term supervision and guidance of the mentally retarded is growing. Many feel that some interested person should concern himself with the welfare of a retardate who is devoid of or abandoned by his family—particularly the older retardate whose family may be deceased. Many also feel that viewing the state as the guardian of such individuals is inadequate and that retardates should enjoy the benefits of a highly involved patron. Agencies that consider themselves as providing a specialty service in mental retardation should be up-to-date with these trends and its legal implications. Some relevant material will be found in the President's Panel Task Force on Law (1963), Begab and Goldberg (1962), and Ober (1963). When counseling parents regarding long-range prospects, particularly in the case of older parents, guardianship problems can be explored at the same time as legacy planning is considered (see the next section on guided reading for parents).

In long-range counseling, especially when the child is very young, counselors need to keep in mind the changing patterns of services. Thus, counseling should not be based on today's service resources, but on an extrapolation to those services likely to be developed under the impetus of recent thinking and legislation. Parents of a newborn mongoloid, for example, may hold considerable optimism that trainable classes will greatly increase by the early 1970s. They may have even more reason to believe that such a youngster will find sheltered employment when he reaches young adulthood.

The parents' often overriding need for practical help is increasingly being recognized by professionals. Weingold (1952) pointed out that "very frequently even so elementary a thing as toilet training may mean a difference to the parents between courage and despair." Kelman (1953) emphasized the need to train the parents to train the child and called for more practical guidance for parents: "The best parental attitudes can never substitute for pedagogical training, sheltered workshops, recreational centers, or medical care and treatment." Beck (1962b), using case material, illustrated the need to integrate personal counseling, feeling management, and handling of the parents' reality problems. Olshansky

(1962) called attention to the very real need of the mother to get away from the situation and the necessity for practical services such as babysitting. Leichman (1962) found that parents felt as much need for management counseling for themselves as they did for educational tutoring for the child. On the other hand, only few parents expressed the need for counseling that emphasized mostly parental emotions rather than management problems. Weingold (1954) defined five functions of a mental retardation clinic: (1) to make a prognosis, (2) to help parents in the child's training, (3) to experiment with therapy, (4) to render direct services such as speech therapy, etc., and (5) to get existing agencies to provide more services to retardates. As a parent, he was more concerned with treatment and outcome than with diagnosis.

An interesting research question is whether parents whose child received a meaningful referral after a diagnostic evaluation are more responsive to parent counseling than parents whose child's evaluation ended, as it does only too frequently, in no service assignment or a fruitless cross-referral between agencies.

READINGS FOR PARENTS

One of the least-exploited options in parent counseling appears to be guided reading. Such reading can provide the solid factual information about retardation that professionals increasingly feel to be important for parents (e.g., Bhatia, 1964; Schucman, 1963). Furthermore, readings can acquaint parents with experiences of other families who have handled the problem of retardation adaptively. Finally, guided reading can be a means of satisfying the growing counseling need while conserving the limited manpower resources.

However, counselors may actually alienate parents from reading in this area by recommending material which is trite, uninformative, perhaps inappropriate, and quite often not up with facts or current attitudes. Alternatively, an omnibus reading list that does not guide the parent to what is most appropriate for his specific needs is also not useful and may lead to waste of money if the titles are not available to the parent for loan or inspection. A number of titles appear very popular with counselors and are found on numerous reading lists. These tend to be the earlier writings, some by illustrious parents, which played a historic role in bringing retardation to respectability. However, as useful as these books once were, some of their contents is quite objectionable today.

I have read and compared more than 100 titles which either were written for parents of the retarded or might be useful for them, though not specifically written for this purpose. Authors of this material include agencies, parents, and professionals; the items cover facts, fiction, and experiences.

The best broad, most factually accurate, and most attitudinally up-to-date introductory text I would recommend as suitable for parents is by Begab (1963), although it was written for a different audience. For more sophisticated parents, I recommend the President's Panel Report (1962) as a supplement. For general coverage of a wide range of problems a parent faces, Egg (1964) and Kirk, Karnes, and Kirk (1955) are highly suitable. These are also excellent texts on home training and management, as is Dittman (1959). Bare, Boettke, and Waggoner (1962) have compiled a most ingenious booklet on clothing, dressing self-help, and dressing instruction applicable to retardates.

Various worthwhile materials and activities of a recreational, craft, or sense-training nature are described by Alpha Chi Omega (1960), Avery and Higgins (1962), Carlson and Ginglend (1961), Dixon State School Parents' Association (undated), and Dorward (1960). Battin and Haug (1964) and Molloy (1961) are highly recommended for those parents desirous of structuring a home environment optimal to the speech and language development of the retarded child. Seizures, a frequent concomitant handicap to retardation, are well discussed for lay readers by Livingston (1963). A number of good texts are available for cerebral palsy, and Phelps, Hopkins, and Cousins (1958) can be recommended. A very good booklet on problems of the teen-age and young adult retardate is NARC (1959), though it is now apparently out of print. Parents who are wrestling with the decision to institutionalize are likely to find guidance in Kirk, Karnes, and Kirk (1955), Kramm (1963), Stevens

(1963), and Stout (1959). Legacy planning will be facilitated by NARC (1960; 1961) and AHRC (1960). Parent leaders or parents who are also professionals may find the study of parent groups by Katz (1961) of interest.

I can recommend only a few books written by parents: Murray (1956), one of the best; Hood (1957); Neal (1962); and Stout (1959). Two good, and in some respects similar, stories written by sisters of the retarded (Berg, 1960; Lee, 1961 [3]) present a striking contrast to a number of parents who have written because they were, apparently, propelled by guilt or an unresolved search for meaning. One very readable fiction story (Mann, 1963) is based on the movie, *A Child Is Waiting*. Magee (1964) has fictionalized a story about a mongoloid child and his teen-age sister. Parents can be guided to this book and to a pamphlet by AHRC (undated) as a means of teaching their other children facts about and positive attitudes toward retardation.

Those of any Christian persuasion who are searching for a deeper meaning or understanding of retardation may find solace in Petersen (1952), while, of the various books with a Catholic orientation, I find only Breitenbeck (1958) somewhat recommendable. A good therapeutic text for resolution of emotional and interpersonal conflicts about retardation is McDonald (1962).

Several other titles are good and commendable, but the topics they cover may be covered as extensively and as well or better in one or a combination of the other sources listed. For example, most of the contents of the rather good paperbacks by Chamberlain and Moss (undated), Mental Health Division (1962), and Minnesota Department of Welfare (1945) are subsumed by Kirk, Karnes, and Kirk (1955) and Egg (1964).

I suggest that much more care and emphasis be placed on parental self-education via reading, and that every retardation clinic operate a high quality reading and browsing display, assisting parents in borrowing and ordering or buying material appropriate to their need. Public lending libraries can sometimes

---

3. Berg and Lee exemplify the "golden-hearted" sisters who, according to Adams (1960), have been described by Repond. These are the sisters who become the angel of the home and little mothers to the handicapped child.

be persuaded to order appropriate texts or to act as a convenient repository for donated books. Parent associations will probably find this a more practical and useful arrangement than operating their own suitcase libraries.

GROUP COUNSELING

In an attempt to trace the material written on group counseling of parents of the retarded, I came across about 35 articles I had planned to include in a more intensive review. Most of these articles constituted primary material, i.e., they related direct experience with parent groups. However, there was so much contradiction, speculation, subjectivism, and conceptual and terminological confusion, and only two controlled experimental outcome studies, that it was decided to omit a detailed review. Instead, an attempt will be made to identify issues, summarize impressions, and selectively highlight some contributions that appear to contain more noteworthy elements.

When group counseling first came into vogue, its advocates emphasized the efficiency of handling several clients at once. Now they often argue that group counseling can make a unique contribution by utilizing group processes, whether numerically efficient or not. Thus, many writers propose that parental attitudes about retardation are, in good part, the result of cultural and community, and thus also group, pressure. The World Health Organization (1954) report states that since many parental feelings such as shame are socially determined, association with other parents may be of more benefit than individual guidance or psychotherapy from professionals. Goodman (1964) sees a unique advantage in the group process as it counteracts the parents' tendency to cut themselves off from the stream of conventional life. Similar arguments in favor of a unique group process benefit are advanced by Giannini and Goodman (1963), Goodman and Rothman (1961), and Weingold and Hormuth (1953).

While much has been written on group counseling, great confusion and contradiction exists regarding terminology, methods, and goals. The terms readily encountered include group therapy, group counseling, group education, parent group training, parent group information, parent education, parent seminar,

and education counseling (Dybwad, 1964). It is not always possible to infer the group methods used from the label applied.

In terms of emphasis and conceptualization, groups fall along a broad continuum. At one end is a traditional psychiatric approach that sees parents in need of therapy. Relatively little concern is expressed for parent-child relationship, and perhaps not at all with the parents' situational problems. Parents' questions regarding such practical problems are avoided and may even be considered resistance (e.g., Cummings and Stock, 1962). While there are exceptions (Yates and Lederer, 1961), the group tends to meet over long periods, even years, but sometimes only once or twice a month. On the other end of the continuum, the approach is primarily educational and didactic. Parents are taught facts about mental retardation; home management techniques, such as feeding, toilet training, discipline, etc.; community resources; state legislative issues; research trends, and similar subjects. Occasionally, parents may discuss their feelings and attitudes as well as personal and parent-child problems, but this is usually considered tangential, unnecessary, or perhaps even undesirable. Groups tend to meet approximately six to twelve times, usually on a weekly basis. On the middle of the continuum are groups that tend to focus on the parent-child relationship and that may be oriented either toward the more therapeutic or the more didactic side. Attitudes toward mental retardation and the other children are explored and the parents are helped to realize how their own personality and behavior will affect the behavior of a retarded child as well as that of the other children. The number of sessions may vary from as few as approximately eight to several dozen.

Because of the historical confusion of terms, in group, and perhaps in individual counseling as well, it may be useful to apply labels such as level I, II, or III counseling to correspond to the more didactic approach, the parent-child centered counseling, and more personal therapy, respectively. Occasionally, a group will stretch across several levels. Presentation of some didactic content may be combined with a therapeutic emphasis on parental feelings (Ambrosina, 1960), or a mixed didactic-level II counseling approach may be continued at length and be eventually restructured as level III therapy (e.g., Roche, 1964; Sternlicht and Alston, 1964).

Few in the field of group counseling agree on definitions, rationalizations or structures of the groups. Studies that I reviewed differed as to the size of the group, the length and frequency of sessions, and the number of sessions, which varied from as few as three to as many as 60. Not only did the studies disagree on rationale, but many also suffered from a lack of adequate rationalization why one particular approach, method, or parent selection was chosen rather than another. In a number of studies (Ambrosina, 1960; Auerbach, 1961; Bitter, 1963; Harris and Schechtman, 1959) it appeared that the group leaders lacked various degrees of training and preparation for their task. One can only wonder in how many other situations that may have been the case. One also gets the impression that in some instances someone casually decided, "Let's have a group of parents, what do you say?" Most of the studies seem to be one-shot affairs and display little interest in bringing about a systematic long-range improvement in group techniques with parents of the retarded or in adding to the meager body of empirical facts.

Undoubtedly, many parents have a different perception of group counseling benefits than many group workers do. The parents, as is apparent over and over (e.g., Blatt, 1957; Cummings and Stock, 1962; Harris and Schechtman, 1959; Nadal, 1961), want counsel on child management and facts about retardation. The professionals often prefer to give them therapy. This points out the need for clarification of goals and better selection of parents for different types of groups. Adhering rigidly to a feeling-oriented therapy is absurd when a parent is overwhelmed by the situational demands of three infants in diapers, a hyperactive child, or a nonambulatory, incontinent adult retardate.

Many authors seem to be very unsure of what to expect from group counseling or how to structure the group if they do know. If they do know and have a well-defined structure, they may select a parent sample inconsistent with the goal and structure. For example, Yates and Lederer (1961) conducted groups that fell far on the therapeutic side of the group counseling continuum. The groups were conducted non-directively and all factual questions were redirected to the other group members. The authors noted that couples tended to agree with each other at first but that they grew apart in opinion toward the end. Two inconsistencies are reflected in this study. Firstly, only three sessions were held, yet the structure was one that encouraged parents to open up and leave themselves vulnerable. On wonders what happened after the couples discovered, with the help of the "therapy," that they really lacked the agreement about the child that they thought they had, an illusion that might have been essential to their marriage. Second, the groups were selected for homogeneity of diagnosis (mongolism). This appears very relevant if the authors had been ready to handle the issues specific to such a group, but by refusing to focus the group or answer reasonable questions, the advantage of such grouping seems much diminished.

Similarly, Cummings and Stock (1962) describe a longer (ten to twelve sessions) group therapy sequence, emphasis also being upon parental emotions rather than practical aspects. The authors imply that mothers who seek practical solutions to some of their problems are "externalizers" and therefore poor prospects for group therapy. "Such preoccupations typically make for a variety of resistances." Apparently the authors propose that if a mother with three children in diapers insistently asks those whom she considers experts for pointers on toilet training, she must be "resisting." If she had discussed her feelings and attitudes about elimination and perhaps feces in general, she presumably might have been viewed as a good client.

In contrast, Daniels (1962) has described an approach which, whether effective or not, reflects careful rationalization. Meetings were held weekly for eight to ten weeks, about 1.5 hours each, and with both spouses if at all possible. Groups were as large as 20 and emphasis was on facts, although expression of feelings was also encouraged. Daniels stated that the leader for such a group must understand both his subject matter and group methods. He must know normal child development, parent-child relations, behavior dynamics, resources, etc. Catharsis alone was not felt to be of enough benefit to parents. Apparently a method was selected consistent with the goal, the group leader was qualified to apply the method, and the participants were included on the basis of their need for this rather than some other type of experience.

Blatt (1957) has pointed to the need to make a clear distinction between therapy, counseling, and education (levels III, II, and I), and I would add that once this distinction is made, it should be recognized that the structure of these groups must be different and that some parents may be unfit for one, but well suited for another type of group. A similar plea for clarification of goals and rationales has been issued by Dybwad (1964).

From a review of parent group studies, a few other themes emerge rather repeatedly. Parental catharsis seems to be very necessary; sometimes the first few sessions of a group may be completely taken up by it (Auerbach, 1961; Cummings and Stock, 1962). The parents are often viewed as being problem-ridden, anxious and maladjusted, sometimes even to a higher degree than parents of other problem children (Ambrosina, 1960; Auerbach, 1961; Cummings and Stock, 1962; Harris and Schechtman, 1959; Nadal, 1961). Nadal (1961) assumes that having a retarded child ipso facto impairs a parent's role performance and competence. A number of workers observe a high degree of hostility in the parents, particularly toward professionals (Blatt, 1957; Gordon and Ullman, 1956; Nadal, 1961). In one instance, this level of hostility was so high as to become almost unmanageable by the apparently inexperienced group leader. Fathers are under-represented in the groups, as they are in most studies in retardation (Ambrosina, 1960; Barsch, 1961; Blatt, 1957; Giannini and Goodman, 1963). To some degree this may be because of a failure to make group attendance more convenient. Giannini and Goodman (1963) point out that an agency should be prepared to hold groups at night or on Saturday in order to make it easier for fathers. Group attendance generally was reported to be rather erratic, especially if scheduled during the daytime (e.g., Institute for Retarded Children of the Shield of David, 1962). In some cases, a high absenteeism and drop-out rate was noted (Ambrosina, 1960; Bitter, 1963; Blatt, 1957; Cummings and Stock, 1962). Again, agencies sensitive to the reality problems of parents may be able to make their services more readily available by

such measures as applied by Weingold and Hormuth (1953). They provided group baby-sitting, a very sensible but rather rare gesture. Some workers recognized that the particular group experience they offered was not sufficient for some parents and proposed that additional help might be necessary concurrently or subsequently (Cummings and Stock, 1962; Nadal, 1961).

Rankin (1957) gave a rather detailed analysis of the group process from a group therapeutic viewpoint. In contrast to other studies, those persons who continued in the group were seen as having the more serious adjustment problems. The greatest advances were seen in the overprotective mothers who were helped considerably by the insights given them by other group mothers. Appell, Williams, and Fishell (1964) administered the Thurston Sentence Completion Test at the beginning and the end of their study. Although this test is of dubious quantifiability, it indicated that more mothers admitted after the counseling than before that they had been told of their children's retardation by a physician.

Various authors have made observations or suggestions that appear sufficiently noteworthy to be highlighted. Goodman and Rothman (1961) felt that group methods are most potent at a time of vulnerability and impact. Two such times were identified as being at the end of a clinic evaluation and at the onset of adolescence. Cummings and Stock (1962) described a number of "core problems" that were encountered in almost every case and tended to become topics of discussion: (1) struggle with personally unacceptable feelings of hostility toward the child, (2) decisions about institutionalization, (3) disappointment, loss, and sense of bereavement about the child not being able to fulfill his life the way the parents wished, (4) narcissistic hurt about having produced a damaged child and perception of the child as reflecting parental inadequacies and imperfections, (5) guilt about parental responsibility for the condition, and (6) feelings of desertion and abandonment in the parent. Coleman (1953) also listed a number of topics that often recurred in group discussions.

Barsch (1961b) observed a definite development of a long-term group in five stages:

(1) information seeking, (2) sharing, (3) emphasis on feelings, (4) generalization of gains to dynamics of child development and parental relationship to the other children as well, and (5) maturity and integration of the child into the family, with effective handling of the problem. In these groups fees were charged, and there were 30 to 36 sessions.

Blatt (1957) recommends that parents be grouped according to intelligence, and Ambrosina (1960) urges no fewer than twelve to fifteen sessions with an attendance of no less than twelve to fifteen parents. This is in contrast to Yates and Lederer (1961) who recommend a maximum of four couples.

Primarily educational groups or even classes have been described by Babitz (1961), Daniels (1962), Popp, Ingram, and Jordan (1954), and Weingold and Hormuth (1953), and have also been conducted by me. The content of such courses might include the following: (1) causes of retardation, including certain genetic aspects; (2) the diagnostic process; (3) treatments, both preventive and secondary, and ranging from biochemistry to habilitation; (4) the effects of a retarded child on the family; (5) home management with emphasis upon habit training, behavior and discipline, sexual behavior, etc.; (6) speech and language; (7) seizures; (8) normal child development and its relevance to retardation; (9) the retarded child's feelings and needs; (10) interpretation of retardation to relatives, friends, and neighbors; (11) a review of retardation facilities in the area, perhaps with visits; (12) a review of relevant national and state laws, from taxes to sterilization; (13) a review and display of appropriate reading materials; (14) legacy planning; (15) historical trends in retardation, both of the past and the present, with a discussion of the President's Panel Report; and (16) research trends in mental retardation. I have found Begab (1963) to be the best and least expensive (45 cents) text for such groups and also have recommended the President's Panel (1962) Report as a supplementary text although not all parents can use it meaningfully.

Weingold and Hormuth (1953) offered education to relatively homogeneous groups of parents of pre-school mongoloids and young adult retardates in a recreation program. They reported occasionally dramatic improvements in child management as well as in the behavior of the young adults. This may have been a result of focusing a well-rationalized method upon a homogeneous group.

Groups have also been used in situations where efficiency was as much an issue as the benefits of group dynamics. Thus, Anderson (1962) used group orientation of parents to a clinic both to expedite services, reduce the likelihood of broken appointments, and facilitate later parent acceptance of the feedback. Similarly, Goodman and Rothman (1961) have also been successful in reducing inappropriate referrals to a clinic by conducting a group intake for screening purposes. Probstein and Kusuda (1962) described a very sensible daylong group and workshop program for parents before their child's admission to an institution.

Dybwad (1964) points out that parent groups have usually been conducted for parents whose children were lower functioning and were often also physically impaired. If group leaders are trained for this type of parent, quite a problem could arise when one attempts to move toward more socially, economically, and otherwise deprived groups. Here, not only the child is likely to be different but, of course, the parent as well. Begab (1963) points out that limited parents are not usually accessible by the ordinary group methods.

A very good discussion of group techniques is offered by Begab (1963) who makes a distinction between types of groupings and different structures optimal for them. McDonald (1962) also contains much good material.

I could find only four studies that subjected the group counseling process to satisfactorily quantified experimentation; two of these were uncontrolled and another statistically inadequate. A number of other studies might very well have been experimental in nature with only modest additional efforts. Harris and Schechtman (1959) assigned parents of children in a day care center randomly to three treatment groups: a didactic lecture series, a group discussion with a group worker, and informal interaction with a day care director. The treatments were administered in ten "doses" over 20 weeks. A group of parents on the waiting list served as controls, and the three treatments were replicated at a second day care center. The following measures were obtained at the beginning and the end of the experiment: (1) a mental retardation knowledge and information test, (2) a number of attitude tests toward children and child rearing, (3) an interview in five attitude areas, and (4) observation of mother-child interaction in an experimental situation. No gains were noted in any group on any measure, nor any differences between any groups. As if this were not startling enough, all groups expressed satisfaction with the treatments they received. The parents in the lecture group were very satisfied, those in the informal contact group were somewhat less satisfied, and those in the discussion group were the least satisfied. The most satisfied of all, however, were the controls. Also, the parents in the lecture group reported that their greatest gain was in the area of facts, those in the discussion group reported largest gains in the realm of feelings and attitudes.

The authors considered a number of explanations why the quantitative measures failed to show any changes. They felt that perhaps the measures were inadequate, that subject attrition and erratic atendance may have been contributory, or that the parents may have been already well informed. The quality of the presentations and the nature of the personnel involved was considered. Also, the possibility was raised that the parents may have been too disturbed to profit from such experience. On the MMPI, a standardized personality test, a large number of parents showed marked deviations from the norms, and those with healthier profiles did, indeed, gain a bit more than the others. Quite possibly, a combination rather than any single factor may have accounted for the results.

Fliegler and Hebeler (1960) investigated the efficacy of four types of group counseling structures upon adjustment and attitudes of parents of retarded children. The experimental variable was the distribution of counseling rather than the amount thereof. One group of parents received all their counseling in one massive dose over a weekend, in another group it was spread out over six months, and two groups received intermediate type treatments. The control group received no counseling but was tested on the same instruments as the experimental groups. Unfortunately, the results of this rather massive experimental study are virtually uninterpretable. Firstly, the counseling variable was poorly described. Secondly, some of the experimental groups were very small, one having only eight members. Thirdly, some of the groups differed significantly before the experimental treatment, and these initial differences were unlikely to be controlled statistically. Fourthly, and most importantly, the results were only subjected to those statistics for which the computer was programmed. Groups were compared before and after counseling, but the crucial hypothesis of an interaction between any experimental and the control group was never tested. This test would have required a statistic that compared differences between differences, such as perhaps a Lindquist Type I design. Instead, the results demonstrated that the experimental groups showed a significant increase on a number of measures, while the control group usually did not. However, the control group did increase sufficiently on some measures to reach the $P = .10$ level. It is therefore doubtful that some of the reported improvements in the experimental groups would have exceeded the changes in the control group to a significant degree.

The authors concluded that the massed counseling groups seemed to gain primarily in specific areas of attitudes, particularly attitudes toward retardation, while the distributed counseling groups appeared to make more gains in more generalized areas and outlooks. However, perhaps one of the most noteworthy findings was that parents of normal children had a much higher test-retest reliability on a scale of attitudes toward mental retardation than did parents of retarded children. Even though the authors confounded knowledge of retardation with attitudes toward it in this scale, the finding is a very provocative one and may imply that parents of retarded children have so many conflicts that they are ordinarily incapable of a stable possession of facts about or set of attitudes toward mental retardation. This possibility, which implies a potential use of parental consistency on an attitude scale as a criterion measure of parental conflict, needs to be explored further.

Bitter (1963) conducted a study that, while uncontrolled, was experimental. Parents with trainable children in two public school classes were given retardation knowledge tests, the PARI, a semantic differential, and the Child

Character Trait Questionnaire. These measures were given before and after a series of seven group discussions. Meetings were held once a month and the topics, mostly of a practical nature, were selected by the parents. The leaders were untrained and inexperienced. There was a significant loss on the fact test, no change on two of three PARI dimensions, and only some improvement on attitudes toward two out of the ten concepts important in mental retardation.

In another study (Institute for Retarded Children of the Shield of David, 1962), some instruments were administered to parents at the beginning and the end of a multiple-treatment sequence that included a parent group experience. However, the design was such as to preclude the isolation of the group effect.

Two conclusions can be drawn from these studies. First, verbalized parental satisfaction with any kind of treatment may be an inadequate measure of parental growth and studies which have used such verbal expressions as a criterion are herewith suspect. Second, all the subjective professional reports of parental change in group counseling are suspect. Uncontrolled and unquantified group studies can no longer be considered acceptable research, if indeed they ever were.

Even if a parental test behavior had been modified in these studies, Brim (1957) has pointed out that one would still need to demonstrate that such change transfers to the parent's actual handling of the child. Serious and well-controlled experimental work of a programmatic nature is overdue.

THE PROBLEM OF INSTITUTIONAL PLACEMENT

One question that often confronts counselors is the appropriateness of institutional placement. The question may have to be discussed even in cases where such placement is unlikely to occur but where parents may have deep-seated concerns about the child's future. Even in situations where the retardate probably will live with his family during his life expectancy, parents will, appropriately, ask themselves just what might happen in case they should be disabled or die prematurely. During the years of the "genetic scare," segregation of retardates, while it never proved

feasible, was considered the appropriate and desirable course of action. The resulting institutional mentality has been very strong until recently and, although showing signs of rapid weakening, is still readily discerned among many professionals. Editorial policy and writers' reticence to defend publicly an attitude considered archaic by the advanced elements in the field may account for the fact that the "pro-institutional" views are now rarely seen in print, but traditional thinking has by no means died out. While the professional literature does not give an adequate picture by itself of the prevalent professional attitudes, the direction of the historical trends can be traced.

Representative of the traditional view is a paper by Aldrich (1947). When the physician attending at birth recognizes the baby as mongoloid, the baby is withheld from the mother under the pretext that it is weak. In the meantime, the physician marshals the father and other relatives, instructing them that the baby should be institutionalized immediately. After father and relatives have agreed to this, the mother is then told about the baby and informed of the decision which was made without her having been consulted. All this is done because a mongoloid child is seen as having a destructive impact upon the family, because the mother is considered incapable of making a sensible decision, and because the child is presumably much better off and happier in an institution. This model for "instant institutionalization" (Grant, 1965) and for handling parents of mongoloid children is offered as an example of good preventive medicine.

In 1953, a director of a private school sent a letter to the editor of the Journal of Pediatrics, complaining about the poor management of families with retarded children by pediatricians. Their attitude toward early institutionalization was especially criticized. The editor took issue with the writer and solicited opinions from members of the editorial board (Veeder, 1953). Their response showed that while some members of the board did hold more progressive views, others indeed favored early institutionalization of children identified while still young, such as mongoloids.

Kozier (1957) states that children who are "hopeless" or have severe "inoperable" brain defects will need institutionalization. This is typical of earlier writings in that institutionalization is recommended on the basis of labeling instead of careful consideration of family dynamics, family and community resources, and other criteria.

The most recent statement of the traditional view is found in Reed (1963). After making reference to "the drooling idiot" and "the common, garden variety of moron family," he states: "Very frequently it will be the duty of the physician to convince the parents that the child would be better off in the state school than at home and to help with the procedures necessary to have the child admitted to the public institution. Even though the building may be old and crowded and the food scorned by Duncan Hines, the child will find himself among his equals and will be able to compete with them, whereas in the home community he will always be either overprotected or cruelly rejected from social contacts." He goes on to contend that the child probably will not miss his parents after two weeks' absence and that this is fortunate.

A number of writers have documented the prevalence of the traditional view and its effects upon the family. Zwerling (1954) solicited accounts of personal experiences from members of a parent organization. In their letters to him, a number of parents blamed some of their most bitter feelings on the way they had been advised to institutionalize. Often, they stated, the advice had been utterly inappropriate in terms of finances, distances, etc. Similarly, Waskowitz (1959) also found from parent interviews that placement advice was often given with little knowledge of the family or the alternative resources available. Both authors expressed regrets about these practices.

The parents who participated in the group sessions reported by Gordon and Ullman (1956) stated rather commonly that they were subjected to various pressures to institutionalize. Koch, Graliker, Sands, and Parmelee (1959) studied the degrees of satisfaction with the medical care that parents had received, using a sample of 105 parents with retarded infants less than 1 year old. Obstetricians and pediatricians were reported to have recommended immediate institutionalization in 50 per cent of cases, obstetricians being a bit more eager to place than pediatricians. The

Olshansky (1962–1963) studies, of relevance here, have already been mentioned. In a symposium on mongolism (Werkman, Washington, and Oberman, 1961) it was estimated that 80 per cent of pediatricans recommend institutionalization at birth. Very recently (Kugel, Fedge, Trembath, and Hein, 1964), parents of institutionalized mongoloids were interviewed to determine their reason for placement. The majority said it was because they were told to do so, mostly by physicians, and for reasons considered insufficient by the authors. Where physicians had advised, placement usually occurred in the first year. Professional advice was also reported to be very influential in the placement decision of the parents studied by Andrew, Kime, Stehman, and Jaslow (1965) and by Stone and Parnicky (1965). Those who sought placement had been advised 2 to 1 to do so while parents who kept their retarded child at home had been counseled 3 to 1 against placement. Counsel for placement was reported to have been given particularly by pediatricians. However, here as in other studies, the data had been collected retrospectively and may, of course, have been subject to parental distortion.

Of Kramm's (1963) 50 families with mongoloid children, 44 had been advised to institutionalize when first told of the condition, and 31 of these had been urged to do so immediately. In most cases, the parents felt that this had intensified their shock and conflict. Graliker, Koch, and Henderson (1965) found that, in 50 to 68 per cent of those families who at one time had been advised to institutionalize their retarded child, parents developed emotional problems severe enough to require professional help.

Farrell (1956) cites a since oft-quoted example where parents institutionalized their newborn mongoloid child on medical urging. When they encountered a similar child in someone else's home, leading a well-adjusted life and in no way resembling the monster depicted to them, they were severely shocked and their subsequent life was filled with bitterness and resentment toward the responsible physician. One can also surmise that their confidence in the medical or related professions as a whole may have been severely shaken.

Baroff (1962) tells about one couple who

had been exposed to various advice to institutionalize and who were very startled when they were asked about their own feelings. They had never considered that their own feelings should weigh more heavily in this decision than the opinion of the experts, and instead had felt guilty about failing to comply with some of the professional advice.

Saenger (1957) found that advice to institutionalize came most often from psychiatrists, secondly from pediatricians, and only thirdly from family friends. He (1960) felt that many social workers and physicians had somewhat exaggerated notions as to the services available to the retarded in a state institution. As a result, they tended to favor institutionalization. Medical personnel associated with hospitals and clinics especially were responsible for the greatest number of recommendations to institutionalize, and physicians seemed to be more ready to recommend institutionalization than social workers. As Smith (1952) has pointed out, agencies where placement is "oversold" run the risk of losing the confidence of the parents. Saenger concluded that many parents who were subjected to strong influences to institutionalize were, at the same time, not informed of the existence of alternate mental retardation services, nor encouraged to use services of which they may have been aware. In consequence, they may have been instilled with a feeling of helplessness and hopelessness that they would not have experienced if properly counseled. He also discovered that very few parents had actually visited the institution before their child's commitment. Kamins (1963) found that few parents were acquainted with their institutionalized child's daily routine. I strongly urge that no child be ordinarily admitted until the parents have not only visited the institution, but have been given an opportunity to become aware of the living conditions under which their child is likely to reside after admission.

The resistance of some physicians to enlightenment regarding institutionalization may spring from certain irrational conflicts of their own, as discussed in a previous section, and the "unqualified dictum" so often issued by the physician may be a sign of his own discomfiture. In addition, most physicians know little about the field of mental retardation or mongolism. They do not recognize the guilt and struggle in parents who have seemingly rejected their child completely, and are not aware of community resources (Giannini and Goodman, 1963; Goodman, 1964).

A conservative approach to placement is proposed by a number of writers. Sheimo (1951) points out that advice to parents to institutionalize may intensify, rather than solve, the parental conflict since a deep-seated ambivalence about accepting or rejecting the child may be sensitized, and placement may be perceived as a "forbidden impulse." Sheimo also states that the physician must recognize and respect the parents' right to decide their own destinies. Esty (1957) also feels that institutionalization of the child at birth may aggravate rather than diminish the conflict in the parents. Goodman (1964) sees the decision to institutionalize as potentially "emotionally self-destructive" for the parent. Recommendations for immediate placement usually reflect misunderstanding about the precision of the prognosis, parental attitudes and values, and the physician's own reaction (Solnit and Stark, 1961).

In a very influential and much quoted article, Jolly (1953) emphasized that it is dangerous and premature to advise placement as long as the parents view such a step as "putting the child away." Jolly also felt it inappropriate to argue that placement should be effected before parents become attached to the child. After all, the mother has probably been attached to the child for nine months already, and detachment is much more likely to occur as parents live with the child and become convinced of its differentness and need for special care in an experiential instead of verbal fashion. Also, to urge placement where no public beds exist is often unrealistic. It may lead to private placement, and far from being beneficial to the family it may be disruptive because of the financial sacrifices it may entail.

The World Health Organization (1954) report denounced what was considered a "growing practice" of very early institutionalization and failure to take the retarded neonate home from the hospital. This kind of decision was seen as constituting "a real hazard to the mental health of the family unit" (p. 17).

Beddie and Osmond (1955) warned physicians against making recommendations involving decisions contrary to social mores. A physician's decision in favor of placement has social, ethical, and moral implications, but no thought at all is often given to the consequences for the mother, the baby, or society. As indicated in a previous section, if placement does take place, the lack of socially instituted "passage rites" denies the parents a proper mourning ritual and may lead to chronic conflict. Since placement deprives parents not only of the baby, but also of a proper opportunity to mourn, it may be even more detrimental to parents than infant death. The authors conclude that since the mores do not permit rejection of an infant, a physician who advises placement sets himself up against these mores, with consequences of which he is usually unaware.

Esty (1957), Slobody and Scanlan (1959), Tudor (1959), and Yannet (1957) reinforce some of the points expressed above. Yannet (1957) argues against the views espoused by Aldrich and for the ones advanced by Jolly. He states that "it is difficult to rationalize successfully the withdrawal from what must be one of the strongest instinctual demands of parents—the care of the young," a statement repeated by Tudor (1959). Tudor also echoes Yannet's point that the physician should not even become involved in the placement decision except in a mildly advisory capacity, pointing to the complicated intrafamilial relationships that contribute to such a decision. Generally, Tudor favors keeping the child at home, believing this to provide excellent character training for the siblings. Slobody and Scanlan (1959) believe that it is a fallacy to assume that a retarded child who is out of sight is also out of the mind of parents, and they assert that early placement can have forseeable and disastrous consequences for both child and family.

The Group for the Advancement of Psychiatry (1959), in a special report on retardation, takes the rather bold position that "accepted psychiatric principles do not support the separation of any child from his family if the only purpose is to make an educational program available for him." Giannini and Goodman (1963) also take a strong stand: "We can state categorically that most mongoloid infants should be cared for at home. . . . Many parents who appear to have been able to emotionally disassociate themselves from their child by placing him at

birth carry with them conscious or unconscious feelings of guilt and self-recrimination."

The Saenger (1960) study yielded a number of interesting insights. It revealed that in New York City the foreign-born were much more likely to keep their child at home than native-born Americans. However, groups most desperately in need of services, such as Puerto Ricans and Negroes, were much less likely to receive them than Jewish and Protestant groups. Those families who institutionalized had many more family difficulties than those who kept their child at home. This points to the importance of prospective and controlled studies, insofar as the institutionalizing families still had much poorer adjustment and more handicaps even after the child was no longer in the home. Another finding was that family cohesion may be a more important variable in a family's tendency to keep the child at home than even family adequacy. At least, this seemed to be the case with the higher functioning retardates, though less so with the lower functioning ones. In his previous study, Saenger (1957) had found that the attitudes of parents might be as important in the decision to institutionalize as the actual behavior of the child. Numerous other studies have concerned themselves with the question as to what differentiates parents who place their retarded child in the institution or on its waiting list from those who do not. While such studies can be very suggestive, most of them have failed to control crucial variables, and their findings must be viewed with caution.

THE PLACEMENT DECISION: A SUGGESTED ORIENTATION FOR COUNSELORS

Attitudes toward institutionalization vary even between professional workers fully engaged in retardation and possessed of positive feelings toward their work. The issue is one that seems to be particularly capable of being beclouded by emotionality and personalized, subjective views.

An attempt will be made here to conceptualize some of the issues involved in the separation decision, and to arrive at some principles and guidelines that may be applied in individual cases. While these guidelines will have some arbitrariness, an attempt will be made to anchor them to two foundations: the

Judaeo-Christian morality as largely expressed in our socio-cultural values, and the body of knowledge and experience in human management generally and retardation specifically. To some degree, this knowledge is reflected in the President's Panel Report (1962) and by writers such as Kirk, Karnes, and Kirk (1955) and Stevens (1963).

Some basic principles which probably may be drawn from these foundations are:

1. An individual's worth and the degree of his humanity is not to be measured primarily by his intellectual endowment, worldly achievement, or number of handicaps.

2. By its very nature, the procreative contract imposes responsibilities and hardship. Even extraordinary demands may still be within a range of hardship that parents should expect to tolerate as part of parenthood. Parents should not be viewed as possessing a right to "shop" for acceptable infants, divesting themselves of "seconds" at will. Appropriateness of placement into public care is, ultimately, a decision to be made by society, not by an individual parent.

3. The parents should be expected to bear as much hardship on account of a retarded child as they would have been able or willing to bear for a nonretarded child.

4. If a decision is to be made that has detrimental effects upon the retardate and beneficial effects upon others, then the retardate's loss must be more than only equally offset by the others' gain.

5. If a family seems capable or potentially willing to integrate the retardate into the home, they should be given all possible help and services so as to make their success more likely.

6. Removing a retardate from home is more justified when family hardship is likely to be prolonged than short. This implies, for example, that removal is less justified when the retardate's life expectancy is short, or when services are being developed which may reduce hardships considerably in the future.

7. The justification for removing a retardate from home increases with the number of individuals suffering hardship from his presence.

8. Consideration of the retardate's physical welfare cannot be viewed as categorically preempting considerations of his emotional well-being. For instance, a child may be happy at home, but may be accident-prone or lack a certain optimal level of medical attention even to the point of definitely lowering his life expectancy. This situation should not be viewed as categorically less desirable than one where the child may enjoy better health and a higher life expectancy, but will live in a state of emotional deprivation and unhappiness.

In applying more specific rules to individual cases, four dimensions must be explored.

1. Is the crisis that precipitates the separation question a novelty shock, value, or reality crisis? As previously discussed, this conceptualization should aid in determining the necessary services.

2. Do conditions indicate removal of the retardate from the home or placement in an institution? As the range of services increases, the answer to this question will imply different courses of action.

3. Whose welfare is more immediately at stake? Is it the retardate's, the family's, or society's? Is the retardate to be protected from the family, from society, or from himself? Is the family or society to be protected from the retardate?

4. Do the circumstances of the case call for a judgment on whether separation is justified, indicated, or strongly indicated?

I propose that the two foundations, eight principles and four considerations above will yield 14 guidelines on which many workers in the field may be able to agree:

1. A diagnostic label (such as mongolism, hydrocephaly, etc.), by itself, is entirely insufficient in evaluating separation need.

2. Separation at birth is unjustified unless there are other reasons than the mere fact diagnosis occurred then. Separation would only be justified if factors are operant that would have justified separation at another time as well.

3. Multiple handicaps, *per se,* should not be sufficient cause for separation unless they are demonstrated to lead to conditions constituting sufficient grounds otherwise.

4. Aesthetic handicaps should not be sufficient reason for separation unless they are irreparable and have been shown to cause unallayable and severe anguish in the family.

5. Embarrassment to a sibling in a courtship phase should not, by itself, be sufficient cause for separation, especially not if sibling counseling has not been attempted.

6. Removal is not justified because a mar-

riage is threatened, unless the chances are good that removal will, in fact, reduce threat of dissolution and unless the family has other children.

7. Placement away from home for educational purposes is only justified if the education will likely result in appreciable, rather than slight, improvement and the detrimental effects of removal upon the retardate do not cancel or even outweigh the beneficial ones derived from placement.

8. Removal is justified if a very high likelihood exists that in the near future the home cannot or will no longer provide minimal physical and emotional care, as in cases of parental terminal illness or death, mental illness, etc.

9. Removal is justified if the family does not suffer therefrom and the retardate benefits while losing nothing. For example, relatively young grandparents may be willing to raise the retardate so that no one loses and everyone gains.

10. Removal from home is indicated if the retardate is exposed to unmitigably subliminal physical or emotional care and if the alternate placement is likely to be an improvement.

11. Appropriate placement is indicated to prevent the retardate's certain death or appreciable injury.

12. Removal may be indicated where the emotional welfare of other family members is threatened, if removal does result in improvement of the other member(s), and if such improvement is substantial enough to clearly outweigh disadvantages to the retardate.

13. Removal is strongly indicated where the physical welfare of other family members is clearly threatened and where other measures are ineffective or unavailable.

14. Placement is strongly indicated if the retardate is a demonstrated—not merely suspected—menace to society and if other feasible measures have failed.

Occasionally, one encounters "pure" cases fitting rather clear-cut paradigms, as in numbers, 1, 2, or 5 above. In many instances, however, the factors are complex and many facets, probabilities, and alternatives must be weighed. This, however, does not mean that one should abdicate one's responsibility to identify the principles and values underlying our actions, or that every case should be handled *ad hoc* as if no broad guidelines could ever be constructed and considered.

I believe that by conceptualizing, categorizing, and objectifying the factors that argue for and against a separation, removal, or placement judgment, counselors will be able to increase their skills, and retardate, family and society will, in the long run, be served better.

THE RELATIONSHIP BETWEEN THE PARENT AND THE INSTITUTION

The National Association for Retarded Children (1963) found that even in one of the most painful periods of parents' lives (i.e. the child's institutionalization), they may have to manage without much-needed counseling. One-third of institutions in the survey did not provide any orientation for parents and apparently made little if any effort to involve them in any long-range planning of the child's future.

Dittman (1962) and Smith (1952) concerned themselves with the parental dynamics and the type of counseling relevant at the time of placement. Begab (1955) described a number of pre-commitment services and their advantages, but today such services might well be performed by a good diagnostic clinic instead of an institution. Kamins (1963) documented the lack, and Mason (1963) stressed the importance, of good communication between parents and institutions. The latter recommended interpretation and counseling in conjunction with an evaluation, visits to the institution, and home visits. He suggested that the institution work with parent groups, facilitate mail from the children to parents, vacationing with the family, and special family meetings at holidays. Barber (1956) proposed that institutions maintain a liaison committee with parents and conduct periodic roundtable conferences with them. He also suggested that the institution offer education to the parents, maintain good radio, TV and press publicity, send out monthly newsletters, provide speakers, conduct tours and clinics, maintain a good level of personal contacts and counseling, invite outside speakers and specialists, and open its doors for open house and holiday events.

Because of the great selection that precedes placement, the institution is likely to receive many children without parents, with disturbed and highly conflicted parents, or with parents who have low interest in their child. Thorne and Andrews (1946) found that during a five-year period, 25 per cent of a sample of institution residents never received a gift, 45 per cent received gifts but no visits, 8 per cent visits but no gifts, and only 22 per cent received both. Visits declined with age (averaging 2.50 per year between the ages of 5 to 9, and .07 between the ages of 45 to 49) and length of stay (4-13 the first year, 0-4 after the fourth year). One of the studies of the Farber project (Downey, 1963) found that parental interest in the institutionalized child was lower if the child was placed young by educated parents in the early stages of the life cycle. There were other significant variables, but they were highly confounded, and degree of retardation was apparently not extricated from age at placement. Maintenance of family ties after placement is probably strongly determined by cultural values. In Britain, Stanley (1963) found that contact was often maintained for as long as 50 years regardless of the level of the resident's retardation.

Parents are quite justified in demanding the maintenance of high standards and the application of enlightened management techniques from the institution. Robbins (1957) spells out some of the basic demands that a parent would make upon the institution. These include care for the physical well-being and medical and dental health of the child, adequate education and training, provision for his happiness and emotional welfare, and close ties with the parents. On the other hand, the institution is justified in placing certain demands upon the parent. Farrell (1957) identified the following expectations: (1) preparation of the child for the institution, (2) complete and honest information about the child's habits and behavior patterns, (3) continuity of relationship with the child, (4) consideration for the institution's rules and regulations, (5) honesty in communications to the child in the institution and informing the child of family plans and changes, (6) presentation of family news to the child in a constructive and least upsetting fashion, (7) discussions of problems with the social worker, particularly if they might upset the child, (8) joining the parent organization of the institution, (9) interpretation of the institution to the community. Dittman (1962), among her suggestions for parents, proposes that they offer volunteer services to the institution where their child resides. This, of course, may be difficult to do in institutions that specifically refuse the volunteer services of parents of residents.

SELECTED PROBLEMS IN FAMILY MANAGEMENT

COUNSELING PARENTS OF MONGOLOID CHILDREN

The counseling of parents of mongoloid children deserves special attention. Such children, with a few exceptions, can be identified at birth and constitute the largest single group of retardates who are easily and early identifiable. The condition has been so extensively described in the medical literature that failure at least to suspect its presence in an affected baby borders on malpractice in most instances. Also, professionals, especially physicians, have in the past treated this condition in a questionable and stereotyped manner, as documented in countless narratives in the literature and as noted over and over in my experience. Only too often, parents have been reported to have been handled in the manner advocated by Aldrich (1947) and detailed in a preceding section. Poor examples of handling parents of mongoloids are also documented by Farrell (1956) and Kramm (1963); Beddie and Osmond (1955) reported one case where the mongoloid baby was withheld from the mother virtually by force.

Mongolism can elicit a stereotyped reaction from physicians, as apparent in the letter exchange initiated by Veeder (1953). Kugel and Reque (1961) found that, in 55 cases of mongolism, the advice to keep the child at home was seldom given by the physician, in contrast to the counsel to place. The ratio was more favorable in the Hung and Haritos (1961) study of pediatricians, consistent with the findings of the Olshansky surveys. Hormuth (1953) pointed out that the label "mongoloid" can blind a professional and make him forget that he is still dealing primarily with a child. He feels that many problems that do arise, even in the home, stem from prejudices rather than anything else. The finding that about half of all children placed during the first year of life in two Massachusetts state institutions were mongoloid (Olshansky and Schonfield, 1964) probably reflects the categorical response of some professionals to a diagnostic label.

Kirman (1953) drew attention to some physicians' reluctance to offer even ordinary and routine medical care to mongoloids, whose treatment they consider a waste of time. Tizard and Grad (1961) found that the parents of mongoloid children in their sample felt that they detected a distinct difference in the medical treatment the mongoloid child received as compared to that of the siblings. I also have been told by parents of mongoloid children how they were rebuffed by physicians, and in one instance the physician reportedly stated that he did not want to handle the child any longer unless the parents instituted placement proceedings.

Kirman (1953) considers routine placement advice as "unsound in every way," pointing out the potential damage to the mental health of parents and siblings, especially if the mongoloid's existence becomes the unspeakable secret of the family. He suggests that parents be advised to treat the mongoloid child as being half his age and that, if they are capable of doing this, everyone will fare better. Evans and Carter (1954), Kramm (1963), and Schipper (1959) found that many families can adjust very adequately to a mongoloid child.

Handelman (1961) suggests that in cases where a newborn child appears to be mongoloid, consultation should be arranged. I would add that if feasible, this consultation be obtained at a retardation specialty clinic to which the parents can then return in later years.

One highly relevant issue in the question of placement of mongoloid children is their relative development at home or in the institution. The pro-institutional rationale often includes arguments that placed mongoloids are happier and would not develop to any appreciable extent at home anyway. McNeill (1955) compared institutional- and home-reared mongoloids on a number of intelligence and motor tests. The home group was superior on almost all measures except motor development. Quaytman (1953) and Schipper (1959) compiled data regarding certain developmental milestones of home-reared mongoloids and found virtually identical mean ages for onset of sitting (12 months), walking (24-25 months), words (30-34 months) and toilet training (41-42 months). In terms of developmental quotient, the rank order of least retardation to most is sitting, walking, toilet

training, and talking. Only slightly slower development of home mongoloids was reported by Kramm (1963).

Centerwall and Centerwall (1960) conducted the first of the better controlled studies and found some rather drastic differences in an early- and a late-placed group. They confirmed Quaytman and Schipper by finding that 44 per cent of the home mongoloids walked at 24 months, while none in the institution group did at that age. The home group was seven points higher in IQ and eight in SQ at age 7. Birch and Belmont (1961), without providing additional evidence, pointed out some possible weaknesses in the Centerwall study, especially possible selection factors. They contended that statistical differences may not be meaningful, a criticism that is rather odd considering that a difference of seven IQ points from a very early age—if growth rate thereafter remained constant—will make for a mental age difference of over one year at maturity. In a further letter exchange on this controversy (Hersher, 1962), the Centerwalls repudiated this criticism.

Additional evidence was provided by Kugel and Reque (1961) who found home mongoloids much more advanced than institution-reared ones, 40 per cent of whom did not even walk by age 6. Though a retrospective study, placement in the first year of life would have tended to reduce selection factors. Shotwell and Shipe (1964) compared two institutionalized groups of mongoloids, one previously having been reared at home, the other in private residential centers. By age 3 to 3.5, the home-reared group exceeded the other one by 11 IQ and 16 SQ points. After state institution placement, the scores of both groups declined. However, in a three-year follow-up (Shipe and Shotwell, 1965), the home-reared children were still significantly superior on IQ and SQ scores. Stedman and Eichhorn (1964), sensitive to the Centerwall vs. Birch and Belmont controversy, presented perhaps the best controlled study to date. A wide range of motor and muscle, social and intellectual measures were used, and the home-reared group was found superior on almost all of these, even though not all reached statistical significance. The IQ difference was 15 points. Tizard (1964), summarizing the Brooklands study, reported that mongoloids were, in fact, even more adversely affected by placement as regards their development of verbal intelligence than non-mongoloids. However, selection was perhaps less well controlled in this experiment.

One can conclude from the experimental work that although at least one more experiment that is prospective rather than retrospective and that would minimize selection should and can be done, the evidence is nevertheless sufficient for one important conclusion: the average home-reared mongoloid can be expected to walk, talk somewhat, and be partially toilet trained by age 4. At that age, he will already be more advanced than many people picture him to be even at maturity.

THE LIMITED PARENT

A good deal of lore exists to the effect that lower-class families are more accepting of a retarded child. Saenger (1957) found, on an impressionistic basis, that embarrassment about having a retarded child was somewhat more frequent among the more educated groups. Later (Saenger, 1960), shame and guilt was judged to be much higher in the Protestant and Jewish, and lowest in the Puerto Rican group. Holt (1958b), in his thorough study of randomly selected families, concluded that acceptance of the retarded child seemed to be poorest in the upper-class families, and Ehlers (1962) found the blue-collar class more tolerant of deviancy. In the experience of Walker (1949) and Michaels and Schucman (1962), the low intellectual groups appeared to accept retardation more readily, and in Kramm's (1963) sample, parents with less education seemed to be able to adjust better to a mongoloid child than did parents with more education. Giannini and Goodman (1963) felt, from their experience in a New York clinic, that families with less status concern seemed to be far less traumatized by mental retardation. Olshansky and Schonfield (1964) found a high relationship between early placement and a number of indices of parental socio-economic status. The study by Ewert and Green (1957) indicated that maternal level of education may be an important factor as mothers with more education were better judges of the child's ability level.

On the other hand, Zuk (1959b) ruled out a number of socio-economic factors as differentiating between accepting and nonaccepting mothers. It may be recalled, however, that his acceptance ratings left much to be desired. Barber (1963) reported lower-class mothers to be more stigmatized by a retarded child than higher-status mothers. Begab (1963) felt that retardation may be less tolerable among boys than girls in the lower classes as the former are looked upon as future breadwinners.

Regarding institutionalization, opinions are more divided. Saenger (1960) found that low economic groups had a higher institutionalization rate than higher ones but that the nature of the antecedents to institutionalization varied greatly. In lower-class families, community problems led to placement while problems within the family were more readily tolerated than in the upper classes. Shotwell and Shipe (1964) encountered a slightly higher socio-economic level among parents who placed their mongoloid child early than among those who placed later. Sabagh, Dingman, Tarjan, and Wright (1959) studied social-class distribution of retardates admitted to a state institution in California for the 1948 to 1952 period, but selection and control problems complicate interpretation of this study. Tizard and Grad (1961), in a more controlled study, found no social class difference between parents of institutional and community retardates. The trend, however, was for more placements from the middle class. Graliker, Koch, and Henderson (1965) also failed to find socio-economic differences between parents who kept or placed their child in the first year. Actually, application for placement is a much better variable to study than placement itself as the former is more reflective of family, and the latter of selection, factors.

Begab (1964) is one of the few authors who points out that counseling with parents from the lower socio-economic groups may involve entirely different sets of dynamics. By the time children from these groups come to the attention of agencies, the child's retardation may be one of the less important of the multiple problems disrupting the family life. This type of family, particularly, needs help with homemaking and other practical problems. He (1963) makes the important point that the least intelligent parents are often the most inadequate, but that the most intelligent ones are not necessarily the best adjusted.

Farber (1960a), it will be recalled, hypothesized and confirmed a class difference in maternal long-range adjustment patterns to a severely retarded child. Garfield and Helper (1962) performed a well-conceived study in which two groups of mothers of normal children of contrasting socio-economic status were compared with a group of mothers of retarded children. Socio-economic status apparently was more related to expressed attitudes on the PARI than retardation in the child.

The controversy over class differences reflects some of the recurrent confusions in the field. The question of differences in acceptance will not be settled until acceptance is defined more clearly. Institutional placement also cannot be viewed as an index of rejection or tolerance until selection, population factors, and degree of severity are controlled or considered. Possibly, mildly retarded individuals are more readily integrated into the family in the lower socio-economic classes. Firstly, their parents may not value achievement as much as bread-winning capacity. Secondly, they may not even recognize mild retardation, not only because of its insidious expression, but also because of limited parental intelligence. However, an entirely different situation may exist if the child suffers from what Kanner has called "absolute" retardation, in which case dynamics similar to the ones hypothesized by Farber may come into play. I suspect that isolated cases of extreme rejection resulting from value crises in the upper classes have been overgeneralized because of their spectacular quality. So far, the experimental evidence is only suggestive and far from conclusive.

Regarding counseling, there can be little doubt even on an *a priori* basis that counselors will have to make great adjustments with limited parents. That such families are not accessible to verbal contact should not be considered established, but it is quite likely that the type of verbal contact professionals employ with their middle-class clients may be inadequate, or that verbal contact of any quality by itself is insufficient.

MISCELLANEOUS PARENT GUIDANCE APPROACHES

Chamberlain (1963), Goodman (1964), and Ownby (1964) advocate that the clinic reach out aggressively for the parent in need by making home counseling available. Such counseling is considered to be specifically use-ful in breaking up self-destructive patterns of withdrawal and isolation, or in maximizing treatment susceptibility during a family's sensitive phase. Lipsett (1964) describes a volunteer service that provides trained workers who will go into the homes of hard-pressed mothers and help out with day-to-day problems. This service, first originated by a parent group, was later carried on by official agencies. In New Jersey, home services to parents were found to be cheaper than institutional care, and consequently a program was initiated in which parents who had applied for placement were visited and instructed on home management (Yepsen and Cianci, 1946; Cianci, 1947, 1948, 1951, 1955, 1956). The home visitors were educationally trained and the resultant increase in parental management efficiency decreased the demand for placement. Kugel, Fedge, Trembath, and Hein (1964), as many before them, wondered why families, at the point of placement, are not offered financial assistance to keep the child. The state would save money; the parents might be able to purchase whatever services, space, or gadgetry it takes to lighten the daily burden; and the child would probably be better off. Giliberty and Porter (1954) described another home visiting program which supplemented a group project. The home visitors were called teacher-counselors and utilized both therapeutic and didactic methods.

Ehlers (1962, 1964), working in a clinic that had mostly lower-class clients, found that the public health nurse was able to offer one of the most appreciated and nonthreatening services of the clinic. The social caseworker, on the other hand, was viewed more as a question-asker than a help-giver. A public health nurse, if properly oriented and prepared, can play a most significant role in parent guidance, both in a traditional role or in adjunct to a retardation clinic. Relevant materials regarding her potential contribution and activities, especially in home education, are contained in bibliographies distributed by NARC and by the U.S. Children's Bureau. The booklet by McDermott (1960) is specifically worth mentioning.

A very creative, sensitive, and provocative visiting program (The Pine School Project) into the homes of limited families was documented by Parrons (1960) and Triplett (1965).

A social worker, a public health nurse, and a home economist visited such families who might already have a number of children in institutions. The project staff worked diligently to build trust and confidence, and then initiated group meetings and taught the mothers skills in sewing, cleaning, cooking, planning diets, etc. Modest but highly gratifying changes in the entire home atmosphere were observed. This type of project is most noteworthy and deserves consideration for emulation.

Standifer (1964) described a program in which "pilot parents" with a child at an institution assisted other parents with application procedures, setting up car pools for visiting, interpreting the institution program, etc. Conceivably, this paradigm could be translated to other situations, such as diagnostic clinics, and might not only save but even be more effective than some professional contacts. This type of service must be viewed as quite different from the benefits of association with formal parent groups, which are often so business-oriented and occupied with association affairs that they preclude adequate exchange of feelings, experiences, and counsel.

Blodgett (1958) proposes that parents can learn by observing agency staff interacting with their child. The staff can display tolerance, acceptance, and affection for the child in a manner and within a structure that permits parents to observe. Realistic expectations and demands may be made and the child's behavior repertoire demonstrated. Parents may then be able to carry some of this back to the home.

Mulligan (1941) felt that many parents saw themselves acquitted of all further educational responsibility once they had been able to place their child in a special education program, and he pointed to the importance of impressing upon the parents that school learning and activities may have to be supplemented or supported in the home. Ruzicka (1958) discussed the parent counseling role of the school psychologist, and Disner (1956) indicated how the teacher can help parents in subtle ways. For example, she can, in reporting to them, emphasize the social and personality progress of the child so that parents gain perspective regarding their importance. She can help them to appreciate the small increments of progress and to compare the child's progress with his previous status instead of with that of age peers.

The most effective service for parents is probably the one that offers the most options and alternatives, and, to be effective with certain parents, a combination of methods may need to be applied (Justison, 1958).

FAMILY GUIDANCE

More and more, workers in the field are recognizing that the family and the retarded child form such a close unit that, on the one hand, help for one member may also help the others, but that sometimes help for one can be ineffective if the others are not helped as well. In many ways, a vicious and maladaptive circle of interaction can be developed between a parent and a child. Thus, even small perceived defects in an infant can result in the parent's withdrawal of emotional involvement or expectation for normal growth. This, in turn, may lead to interference with the developmental progression of the child that otherwise would have taken place in the medium of a healthy parent-child relationship. The resultant developmental retardation may thus provide corroborative evidence to the parent, reinforcing his fears and apprehensions and leading to further maladaptive circularity. Thus, Kramm (1963) thought that those parents who displayed the most conflict and pity for themselves found the child most difficult to control and the other siblings antagonistic. Heilman (1950) illustrated the close interrelationship between parent and child behavior by means of three cases.

Positive intervention may not only break up a maladaptive circularity, but may even institute a beneficial cycle. Thus, French, Levbarg, and Michal-Smith (1953) documented a case in which a home management method was worked out with the mother, resulting in dramatic improvements in the intelligence and behavior of the child and, concomitantly, in parental adjustment. Kelman (1953) thought that children of parents involved in self-help situations gained more from their own programs and, conversely, Blatt (1957) had the impression that many children were not profiting from a day school program because the parents failed to come to grips with their own feelings and attitudes.

Beck (1959) thought that the child's progress depends in good part upon the parent's attitudes, pointing out (1962a) that services to the child may not be enough. Services must be used constructively, and this may require working with the parents. Scher (1955) saw it as inevitable that help to the child required helping the parent. Scott (1960), studying 30 families very intensively, found that the mother's behavior had a direct effect on both the retarded child and the normal siblings. Denhoff (1960) felt that a child may suffer if parents hold poor attitudes. Schonell and Rorke (1960) conducted intensive interviews with 50 families whose child had attended a special training center. Although no control group was used, the parents reported not only great improvement in the child's behavior in a number of spheres, but also in their own attitudes and perceptions of the problem even after as little as six months. Such work is relevant to all attempts to ameliorate the parents' problems primarily by psychotherapy instead of the provision of services that meet the situational demands.

Doll (1953) originated the term "cluster approach," meaning that disposition should depend upon the evaluation of the entire family situation. Similarly, McDonald (1962) suggested that a treatment program, in order to be effective, should view the entire family as a unit instead of treating only the child. Unfortunately, one rarely encounters practical suggestions on how to use relatives such as grandparents or siblings of the retarded in the family guidance process. Conceivably, teen-age siblings, if of average or higher intelligence, might become a valuable adjunct in planning and managing the parents (e.g., Beck, 1962a). They may be able to act as checks on parental distortions of fact and might contribute otherwise to family harmony by being counseled regarding their retarded sibling's condition. O'Neill (1965) and Schreiber and Feeley (1965) are among the few who concerned themselves with sibling counseling. Grandparents are sometimes tangentially mentioned in the literature and are usually depicted as playing an unconstructive role. Schumacher (1945) recommended using grandparents constructively, but, with the observed loss of family cohesion in the last decades, this may be less feasible today.

GENETIC COUNSELING [4]

A retarded child can be viewed as representative of failure in a very primitive area of human functioning—procreation (Stoddard, 1959). "There is nothing rational about parenthood. It is primitive and emotional" (Gramm, 1951). If parenthood were rational, mental health workers and child specialists would probably have either no children or the best adjusted ones. The birth of a retarded child can trigger off not only intrapersonal conflicts, but all kinds of intrafamilial hostilities and suspicions (Tips, Smith, Perkins, Bergman, and Meyer, 1963). Parents seeking a cause frequently search for presumably genetic antecedents both in their own kinship and that of the spouse, and their deep-seated concern with heredity may be stronger than is often recognized.

While some parental conflicts are associated with uncertainty about the cause of retardation (Fried, 1955), once a condition is identified as hereditary, a new set of conflicts may arise. Thus, the perceived implication of a family taint is very painful to some people. Boles (1959) makes reference to Perlstein's work, which indicated that one of the principal causes of conflict between parents of a cerebral palsied child was the belief that the affliction was evidence of such a taint. This belief led to accusations, many of them unverbalized, between the parents, thus causing disharmony and destructive self-blame, particularly in the mother. Boggs (1952) has indicated that deep down a parent may associate the idea of a genetic defect with the potential need for sterilization of either the parent, the child, or both. If true, this could be very threatening not only because of the possible loss of reproduction potential, but also because of the unconscious association often made between sterilization and castration.

A number of studies have reported that the retarded child has tended to be disproportionately often either the youngest or the only child (Kramm, 1963; Mandelbaum and Wheeler, 1960; Rosen, 1955; Schonnel and

4. I wish to acknowledge the helpful comments of Dr. James Eisen, head of the Human Genetic Laboratories at the Nebraska Psychiatric Institute, University of Nebraska College of Medicine.

Watts, 1956; Tips and Lynch, 1962; Tips, Smith, Perkins, Bergman, and Meyer, 1963; Tizard and Grad, 1961).[5] For example, of Kramm's 50 families, 24 per cent of those still of apparent childbearing ability actively avoided pregnancy, another 30 per cent delayed it. Holt (1958b) studied the influence of a retarded child upon family limitation and found that of 160 families with apparent childbearing capability, 63 per cent did not want any more children even though in only 7 per cent of the cases would it have been the last planned or desired child. Comparing recalled intentions with actual fertility, Holt found that some of the families who had ostensibly wanted no more children did, in fact, have more, but not as many as one might expect actuarially. Only 24 per cent of the families definitely wanted more children, and, in these cases, the mother tended to be young and the retardate a first-born. Severity level of the child did not seem to be related to parental desire for other children. Tizard and Grad (1961) found that while 49 per cent of parents were worried about the prospect of additional children, 27 per cent avoided further offspring, 8 per cent tried unsuccessfully to do so and 14 per cent had others in spite of their worry.

After controlling for a number of factors, Tips and Lynch (1962) and Tips, Smith, Perkins, Bergman, and Meyer (1963) confirmed that a retarded child not only brought about reduction or cessation of reproduction in the parents but also among the kindred females. They felt that this was as much emotional as intentional, presumably reflecting the female relatives' fear of also bearing a retarded child. Rosen (1955), on the other hand, felt, and Kramm (1963) showed, that the cessation of reproduction can be quite intentional. Again, controlled studies are clearly needed in which young parents who desire further offspring and do nothing to prevent it are compared to equivalent parents whose previous child was not retarded.

Some writers contend that the birth of a retarded child sometimes also propels parents to try to have another baby sooner so as to heal their wounds, restore their self-concepts, or give a companion to the retardate (e.g., Mandelbaum and Wheeler, 1960; Reed, 1963;

5. Thompson (1964) found the retardate most likely to be the oldest or only child.

Tizard and Grad, 1961). While this is quite plausible, little evidence supports this hypothesis, and what evidence there is (e.g., Tizard and Grad, 1961) indicates that the number of such parents may be very small.

At one time, the number of cases of retardation in which the genetic mechanism was known was insignificant. With the breakthrough in chromosomal studies, this picture has changed somewhat. A growing number of agencies and individuals perform chromosome studies, and someone will have to counsel the parents regarding the findings. This presents a problem: those who understand genetics may have no training in counseling and may be naive about parental dynamics; on the other hand, those who are skilled in counseling may not be adequately versed in genetics.

While the number of cases in which a specific genetic mechanism can be either identified or ruled out is still relatively modest, it is nevertheless substantial enough to be given careful consideration. So far, however, little has been done or written about genetic counseling of parents of the retarded, and what little there is leaves much to be desired. Some information is offered by Reed (1963), Tips and Lynch (1962), and Tips, Smith, Perkins, Bergman, and Meyer (1963). Sections or chapters on genetic counseling or prognostication that discuss conditions associated with retardation have been written by Clarke (1962), Roberts (1963), Shaw (1963), and the American Medical Association (1965). However, they and a few other scattered articles on genetic counseling concern themselves almost exclusively with genetic diagnosis and probability derivations. For example, Roberts (1963, p. 253) states: "What the patients need are the chances." The orientation reflected in these discussions is quite medical, and very little consideration is given to the emotional aspects of genetic counseling.

On the other hand, what counseling parents receive from those not versed in genetic aspects can be scientifically unsound. Hung and Haritos (1961), in questioning 35 pediatricians in Washington, D.C., found that the majority freely advised parents of mongoloids regarding future children despite the fact that no chromosomal studies were available to them. Only one pediatrician referred the parents to a genetic clinic. Baroff (1962) quoted sources which indicated that parents are often not in-formed of the hereditary nature of disorders, even those genetically as well understood as phenylketonuria. Tizard and Grad (1961) also found a parent who had been told that the chances of a second child having PKU was 1 in a 1000. The true chances being 1 in 4, the next child they had was affected. In several other instances of tuberous sclerosis, Rh in-compatibility and amaurotic conditions the genetic factors were apparently not explained to the parents.

While Tips, Meyer, and Perkins (1962) state that genetic counseling should be an in-tegral part of the over-all management of the family, they describe a service in which all other counseling seems to revolve around the genetic aspect. Even if parents place great verbal emphasis upon this aspect, chances are that it is only one element in a very complex constellation of problems. Some genetic coun-selors seem to feel that the matter is very sim-ple and straightforward. After collecting the necessary case history material and conducting the relevant tests, the parents are presented with the scientific aspects of the situation. For example, from one of the most extensive treat-ises on the subject (Reed, 1963), one gains the definite impression that a rational exposition and explanation is supposed to be capable of dispelling deep-seated and irrational attitudes and fears about reproduction, defect in the off-spring, and tendencies to be ashamed or cast blame upon the spouse or oneself. In one ex-ample cited, a father thought that his mon-goloid child was a result of his earlier habit of masturbation. When informed that in his case, it was really due to hereditary factors, the father supposedly was able to free himself of his feelings of guilt. The possibility that he may have acquired an even more profound guilt or conflict instead was not mentioned. Thus, Saenger (1957) and Schild (1964) found, although on a judgmental and impres-sionistic basis, that guilt feelings occurred more frequently among those parents who thought or knew that hereditary causes ac-counted for the mental retardation condition, while Anderson (1963) indicated that parents may even view a genetic defect in their child as payment for sins of their own parents.

Most parental counseling will concern itself eventually with the genetic question. Kanner (1953) points out that parents of a retarded child are almost invariably plagued by the question whether to have another child. The parents virtually always wait for an opportu-nity to present this problem to the professional who counsels them. They may, in fact, seek someone who will take the responsibility in this decision and whom they can later blame if something goes wrong. One may thus ask whether genetic counseling should ever be viewed as a separate area or a type of coun-seling which should be conducted apart from the more general counseling context. I propose that it should not. Parent management is al-ready too fragmented as it is. Before parents come to a specialty clinic, they are likely to have been exposed to sundry diagnostic and advice-giving experiences. At the specialty clinic, they are processed by a series of other professionals who contribute to the diagnosis, and chances are that even their major contacts within the clinic change from intake to feed-back counseling. It seems ill-advised to add to this array of contacts yet another who may only see the parents a few times, but who may give them information and counsel that may be of the most profound importance to them and that touches upon a primitive and irra-tional area of functioning. Many diagnostic centers, of course, do not value or even offer prolonged counseling, and there is no counsel-ing continuity or relationship to violate in such situations. The same holds true for agen-cies in which every major member of the diag-nostic teams tells the parents his version of the elephant.

One of the two feasible ways to handle ge-netic counseling is for the geneticist to inter-pret his findings to the parents in the presence of the regular counselor. To maximize the con-tinuity cues of the counseling process, this should probably be done in the regular coun-selor's office. In this fashion, the regular coun-selor knows exactly what was said, how it was said, and how to handle the material in later sessions. The parents will know that the regu-lar counselor will carry the burden of casework and that the geneticist's presence is only short-term and his contribution primarily one of diagnosis and risk assignment.

The second method is for the counselor to acquaint himself sufficiently with genetics to be able, on hand of the geneticist's report, to conduct the genetic interpretation himself. This is a much more feasible procedure than for the geneticist to acquire counseling skills and making himself available for broader counseling.

Parents who have had a retarded child and who seek counsel regarding future children should be sensitized to the possibility of having another retardate. The literature indicates that parents are often told that lightning never strikes twice, an irrelevant simile aptly described as revolting by Roberts (1963). By chance alone, even if no genetic mechanisms were involved, some people will have more than one retarded child. The counselor who is confronted with the unlucky parents to whom he previously gave bland probability figures will have to carry a heavy burden. To Kanner's (1962) statement that parents should not have other children if they cannot free themselves from the expectation of disaster, I would add that they should also be prepared to accept another retardation if it does occur. Parents in general are not properly prepared for this, but should be helped to be the second time.

A distressing story of parental conflict is contained in the autobiography of a mother (Junker, 1964). After giving birth to several normal children, and two who were retarded for apparently different reasons, she desired and brought about another pregnancy. Then, however, she was seized by morbid expectations and obtained an abortion. Occurrences like these might be greatly reduced by proper genetic counseling. Indeed, according to Reed (1963) and Roberts (1963), genetic counseling will have the general effect of resulting in more children than parents otherwise would have had since chances tend to be better than many parents assumed. However, the possibility exists that the next baby born after the retardate may be viewed as a symbol of rejection of the retardate, especially in those parents who feel that love and care is needed to compensate the child for his handicap (Mandelbaum and Wheeler, 1960).

A genetic counselor should have a deep respect for the sensitivities, attitudes, values, and reactions of the client. He should present the facts, but be exceedingly careful not to impose his own judgments. While many seem to agree on this, others without thorough training in counseling may easily be seduced into authoritarianism. Such authoritarianism is most likely to emerge when the genetically oriented professional deals with cases with well-known mechanisms and a high likelihood of defective offspring.

Stang (1957) takes the view that a middle-aged mother of a mongoloid child should be definitely dissuaded from having additional children. This attitude reflects a poor understanding of the role of parental counseling. Such counseling should try to get at the mother's feelings and motives, and should help clarify these in her mind. If she still desires another child after having profited as much from counseling as she can, the decision is not, under any presently existing circumstances, to be the counselor's.

Reed (1958) sets forth the three basic questions a parent may ask about genetics: Does the child's condition have a genetic basis? What are the chances of having another retarded child in subsequent pregnancies? What are the chances of the normal children having retarded offspring? To these, in the light of the work by Tips and Lynch (1962) and Tips, Smith, Perkins, Bergman, and Meyer (1963), might be added: What are the genetic implications for an affected parents' blood relatives?

One issue that occasionally arises in genetic counseling deserves some consideration. It is possible that one parent only may be a carrier of a disorder which afflicts the child (e.g., in one of the translocations found in mongolism). When the parents are told which of them is the carrier, the affected individual may develop a profound sense of conflict and guilt, and the other spouse may be given a channel for blame and hostility. Even in sound marriages, the moment is likely to come when the unaffected spouse will point out who is "at fault" for the retarded child. Though spoken in anger, such a barb may leave profound scars on the other spouse's psyche. I propose that the family data be examined to determine if any purpose is served by overtly identifying the carrier parent. Possibly, because of the kinship constellation and the age, sex, and childbearing stage of the relatives, the condition is without relevance to them. In such cases, I propose that the mechanism of the disorder be explained to the parents without identifying which of the two is the carrier. If the retardate has siblings, they should, if possible, be examined to determine whether they are carriers. If they are or may be carriers, the importance of their coming in for counseling as they become marriageable should be emphasized. In other words, the only justification for identifying the carrier parent, if there is only one, is seen in cases where this would serve a useful and distinct purpose. On the other hand, Roberts (1963) recommends telling parents who are both carriers that they contributed equally to the condition. Also, in conditions that are of unknown mechanism or in which a recessive gene may be operant, he advises that the equal probability, if any, be stressed. In this fashion, one-sided taints and blame may be minimized.

THE ROLE OF RELIGION IN COUNSELING

The most basic values of many people are mediated to them by religion. Religion provides them with a rationale for living and an emotional as well as intellectual framework wherein to explain events. Particularly during times of distress, individuals tend to seek solace and support in religion even if they were otherwise not particular devout.

"The drama of experiencing retardation in one's child may precipitate serious existential conflicts. Concern with religion, the meaning of life, the tragedy of death, the inescapability of aloneness, and the relative insignificance and helplessness of man may preoccupy the parents. Although, these concerns are less obvious than other reactions, their significance should not be underestimated" (Roos, 1963). Holt (1958a) and Stubblefield (1965) also feel that the advent of a retarded child is likely to impel the parents to seek answers to the more profound questions regarding the meaning of human existence, and that they may turn to religion for answers. Murray (1959) points out that one of the six problems faced by parents but often ignored by professionals concerns the theological conflict that the parents may undergo.

Parents may ascribe the child's retardation to a direct act of God. This is probably consistent with man's tendency to seek a nonnatural explanation for any events that he cannot explain or that appear unreasonable or painful to him. Kramm (1963) found that as many as 21 per cent of parents of mongoloid children ascribed the condition to a divine act. Boles (1959) found parents of handicapped, as well as nonhandicapped, children quite ready to see the hand of God in the advent of a handicapped child. Waterman (1948) inter-

preted the martyr complex in parents as occasionally due to a religious construction of the cause of retardation.

Of the parents in Kramm's (1963) sample, 41 per cent found religion of the greatest help. Therefore, one would have assumed that clergymen play a major role in the counseling and referral of parents, but this does not seem to be the case. Ehlers (1962) found that mothers did not approach the clergy in appreciable numbers. In an as yet unpublished study of several hundred families seen at the mental retardation evaluation clinic at the Nebraska Psychiatric Institute, only 7 per cent had taken their problem to their minister.

Spiritual and religious counseling is desirable in many instances, as affirmed by several writers. Bakwin (1956) and the American Medical Association (1965) suggest that physicians may find it helpful to call upon religious counselors in cases of retardation. Wilkins (1956) points out that retardation is, like death, an event of major impact, and, as in other crises, religious counseling can be very powerful. Dybwad (1964, p. 77) believes that for some parents religious counseling may be the best counseling. Parental self-reports (Zwerling, 1954) have underlined the importance of religion in the adjustment process, and Holt (1958a) reached a similar conclusion in his survey of family adjustment. Boyd (1951) sees religion as of major importance in gaining the third stage of parental growth, while Michaels and Schucman (1962) view it as both a constructive force in realistic and practical action, as well as an obstacle. That the latter can be the case was further observed by Blatt (1957) who noted that parents caught up in religiosity responded poorly to group therapy and tended to drop out.

THE PARENT SPEAKS

Weingold (1952), a parent and a leader in the parent movement, tells how he received very poor reception from professionals in his work for the movement. At first, parents were not even taken seriously by the professionals in retardation. When they were, they encountered suspicion and hostility. "We were accused of selling 'blue sky' when all we insisted on was that all is not darkness or penumberous region."

Levy (1952) inquired at a number of professional agencies as to their attitudes toward parent groups. He found them rather hesitant in encouraging such groups and a number of reasons were given: (1) the groups' tendency to emphasize the differentness of the children; (2) their preoccupation with the pathological; (3) domination by disturbed members, leading to disturbance in other parents; (4) passing on of misinformation; (5) fear of development of pressure groups; (6) unconventional methods of fund raising; and (7) danger of their establishing their own services which would be of poor quality due to a lack of professional leadership.

As in the field of mental health, and probably even more so, a good deal of the impetus for program development, and much leadership, has come from parents and laymen. Progress was often not only not supported, but even opposed, by workers in the field. There can be little doubt that since 1950, the most progressive, militant, and probably effective force in retardation has been the parent, particularly as represented by NARC. Increasingly, professionals are beginning to realize that the supposedly unrealistic and unfeasible dreams of yesterday's parent are today's realities (Dybwad, 1964). The parent's voice has sometimes been shrill and discordant, but often it has also been the prophet's voice. Workers in the field owe the parent a great debt and a great apology. Counselors are advised to familiarize themselves with the parent movement, join local associations, and discard their occasionally condescending and patronizing, if not actually hostile, stance. The parent should be considered a member of the clinical team (Greenberg, 1950), and should not have to plead in vain for "people who understand the problem of retardation and what it means" (Baldini, 1962). Counselors should remember that association with fellow parents was, for a long time, the only or major source for solace, therapy, and hope (e.g., Lund, 1958). Sarason (1952) states that parents "by virtue of becoming a group, have done more for their own happiness and stability than the professional or specialist have ever done for them." Many services developed at first as private parent endeavors and, while service develop-

ment is now proceeding rapidly, many localities in this country still remain where the only services, if any, are those provided by parents.

Two pointers from parents to professionals may be in order here. Murray (1959) defines six problem areas faced by the parent but sometimes ignored by the professional: (1) the acceptance of the fact of retardation; (2) the consequent financial burden and similar reality implications; (3) the emotional tension in the parents, particularly those engendered by partial nonacceptance; (4) the theological conflict; (5) the need to distinguish between long-term versus short-term decision making; and (6) inept, inaccurate, and ill-timed professional advice. Another parent (Patterson, 1956) gives the following advice to professionals: (1) give honest feedback as early as possible; (2) always see both parents; (3) use up-to-date terminology and down-to-earth language; (4) let the parents make their own decisions, and help them to see that it is their problem and their decision; (5) help them to understand the problem, and recommend reading materials; (6) know your resources; (7) never put parents on the defensive; (8) remember parents are just ordinary people; (9) remember the difference between parents and professionals, and that each can make a unique contribution; and (10) remember the importance of a professional attitude. Professionals may also profit by Patterson's (in Martmer, 1959) lucid review of the parental role and problems.

CONCLUSIONS

Research needs have been amply indicated in the above sections. The main areas of consideration for counselors in the field are these:

1. Traditional practices of parent management should be subject to speculation, manipulation, and experimentation until empirically demonstrated effective.

2. Parent counselors need to think out very carefully the rationales that underlie or are implied by their practices.

3. Professionals working with parents need to possess positive attitudes toward handicap, competency in counseling, and a very thorough knowledge of retardation, including laws, services, and resources.

4. The parent has been grossly misjudged, misunderstood, and mishandled by professionals as a group.

5. Counselors need to give increased consideration to the reality problems with which parents are confronted, and insist less upon a therapy-oriented approach.

6. Diagnosis must be more intimately related to case management.

7. One-shot or very short-term counseling may well be a waste of time, or even harmful in some cases. The field will have to reorient itself to long-term, perhaps life-long, guidance of parents.

REFERENCES

ABRAHAM, W. *Barbara: A prologue.* New York: Holt, Rinehart, 1958.

ADAMS, MARGARET (Ed.). *The mentally subnormal: The social casework approach.* New York: W. S. Heinemann, 1960.

ADAMSON, W. C., OHRENSTEIN, DOROTHY F., LAKE, DOLORES, and HERSH, A. Separation used to help parents promote growth of their retarded child. *Soc. Wk.,* 1964, *9* (4), 60–67.

ALDRICH, A. Preventive medicine and mongolism. *Amer. J. ment. Defic.,* 1947, *52,* 127–129.

ALFORD, A. F. Mental health despite mental retardation. *Lancet,* 1955, *1,* 1233–1235.

Alpha Chi Omega. *Toy book.* Indianapolis: National Headquarters, 1960.

AMBROSINA, S. A project in group education with parents of retarded children. In Family Service Association of America, *Casework papers.* New York: Author, 1960, 95–104.

American Medical Association. Mental retardation: A handbook for the primary physician. JAMA, 1965, *191,* 183–232.

ANDERSON, ALICE V. Orienting parents to a clinic for the retarded. *Children,* 1962, *9,* 178–182.

ANDERSON, I. F. Genetic prognosis. *S. Afr. Med. J.,* 1963, *37,* 205–208.

ANDREW, GWEN, KIME, W. L., STEHMAN, V. A., and JASLOW, R. I. Parental contacts along the route to institutional commitment of retarded children. *Amer. J. ment. Defic.,* 1965, *70,* 399–407.

APPELL, M. J., WILLIAMS, C. M., and FISHELL, K. N. Changes in attitudes of parents of retarded children effected through group counseling. *Amer. J. ment. Defic.,* 1964, *68,* 807–812.

Association for the Help of Retarded Children. *A lawyer's guide: Wills and trusts for parents of retarded children.* New York: Author, 1960.

————. *It's tough . . . to live with your retarded brother or sister.* New York: Author, undated.

AUERBACH, ALINE B. Group education for parents of the handicapped. *Children,* 1961, *8,* 135–140.

AVERY, MARIE L., and HIGGINS, ALICE. *Help your child learn how to learn.* Englewood Cliffs, N. J.: Prentice-Hall, 1962.

BABITZ, M. *Parent education—curriculums, methods and material.* Sacramento, California: State Department of Education, 1961, 69–73.

BAKWIN, H. Psychologic aspects of pediatrics. Informing the parents of the mentally retarded child. *J. Pediat.,* 1956, *49,* 486–498.

BALDINI, J. T. Importance of professional standards as viewed by a parent and his organization. *Except. Children,* 1962, *28,* 507–508.

BARBER, B. A study of the attitudes of mothers of mentally retarded children as influenced by socioeconomic status. Unpublished doctoral dissertation, University of Southern California, 1963.

Barber, T. M. Better parent education means more effective public relations. *Amer. J. ment. Defic.,* 1956, *60,* 627–632.

Barclay, A., Goulet, L. R., Holtgrewe, M. M., and Sharp, A. R. Parental evaluation of clinical services for retarded children. *Amer. J. ment. Defic.,* 1962, *67,* 232–237.

Bare, Clari, Boettke, Eleanor, and Waggoner, Neva. *Self-help clothing for handicapped children.* Chicago: National Society for Crippled Children and Adults, 1962.

Baroff, G. S. Mental retardation: A family problem. In The Training School, *Conference on psychological problems in the habilitation of the mentally retarded.* Vineland, N.J.: Author, 1962, 85–90.

———. Some parent-teacher problems in mental retardation. *Train. Sch. Bull.,* 1963, *60,* 38–42.

Barsch, R. H. Explanations offered by parents and siblings of brain-damaged children. *Except. Children,* 1961, *27,* 286–291.(a)

———. Counseling the parent of the brain-damaged child. *J. Rehabilit.,* 1961, *27,* May-June, 26–27, 40–42. (b)

Battin, R. R., and Haug, C. O. *Speech and language delay: a home training program.* Springfield, Ill.: Charles C Thomas, 1964.

Baum, Marian H. Some dynamic factors affecting family adjustment to the handicapped child. *Except. Children,* 1962, *28,* 387–392.

Beck, Helen. Counseling parents of retarded children. *Children,* 1959, *6,* 225–230.

———. Parent counseling in mental retardation In The Training School, *Conference on psychological problems in the habilitation of the mentally retarded.* Vineland, N.J.: Author, 1962, 69–76. (a)

———. Casework with parents of mentally retarded children. *Amer. J. Orthopsychiat.,* 1962, *32,* 870–877. (b)

Beddie, A., and Osmond, H. Mothers, mongols and mores. *Canad. Med. Ass. J.,* 1955, *73,* 167–170.

Begab, M. J. Precommitment services in a training school for mental defec-- tives. *Amer. J. ment. Defic.,* 1955, *59,* 690–697.

———. Factors in counseling parents of retarded children. *Amer. J. ment. Defic.,* 1956, *60,* 515–524.

———. *The mentally retarded child: A guide to services of social agencies.* Washington, D.C.: U.S. Government Printing Office, 1963.

———. Counseling parents of retarded children. *Canada's ment. Hlth.* 1964, *12* (3), 2–5.

———, and Goldberg, Harriet. Guardianship for the mentally retarded. *Children,* 1962, *9,* 21–25.

Berg, Margaret Arbore. *Wednesday's child.* Philadelphia: Muhlenberg, 1960.

Bhatia, B. D. Education and guidance of parents of the mentally retarded. *J. Rehabilit. Asia,* 1964, *5* (2), 14–16.

Bice, H. V. Group counseling with parents of the cerebral palsied. In *Psychological problems in cerebral palsy: A symposium.* Chicago: National Society for Crippled Children and Adults, 1952.

Bindman, A. J., and Klebanoff, L. B. Nursery center program for preschool mentally retarded children. *Amer. J. ment. Defic.,* 1959, *64,* 561–573.

Birch, H. G., and Belmont, Lillian. The problem of comparing home rearing versus foster-home rearing in defective children. *Pediatrics,* 1961, *28,* 956–961.

Bitter, J. A. Attitude change by parents of trainable mentally retarded children as a result of group discussion. *Except. Children,* 1963, *30,* 173–177.

BLATT, A. Group therapy with parents of severely retarded children: A Preliminary report. *Group Psychother.*, 1957, *10*, 133–140.

BLODGETT, HARRIET E. Counseling parents of mentally retarded children. *Minnesota Med.*, 1957, *40*, 721–722, 730.

——. Helping parents in the community setting. In *Woods School Proceedings*, Langhorne, Pa., 1958.

BOGGS, ELIZABETH M. Relations of parent groups and professional persons in community situations. *Amer. J. ment. Defic.*, 1952, *57*, 109–115.

BOLES, G. Personality factors in mothers of cerebral palsied children. *Genet. Psychol. Monogr.*, 1959, *59*, 159–218.

BOWER, E. M. Cultural values and the retarded child. *Ment. Hygiene*, 1957, *41*, 201–206.

BOYD, D. The three stages in the growth of a parent of a mentally retarded child. *Amer. J. ment. Defic.*, 1951, *55*, 608–611.

BREITENBECK, G. *For parents of retarded children*. Liguori, Mo.: Liguorian Pamphlets, 1958.

BRIM, O. G., JR. Evaluating the effect of parent education. *Marriage Fam. Living*, 1957, *19*, 54–60.

BRYANT, K. N., and HIRSCHBERG, J. C. Helping the parents of a retarded child. *Amer. J. Dis. Children*, 1961, *102*, 52–66.

BUCK, PEARL S. *The child who never grew*. New York: John Day, 1950.

CAIN, L. F., and LEVINE, S. A study of the effects of community and institutional school classes for trainable mentally retarded children. San Francisco State College, U.S. Office of Education, Dept. of Health Education, and Welfare, Contract #SAE 8257., 1961.

CALDWELL, BETTYE M., and GUZE, S. B. A study of the adjustment of parents and siblings of institutionalized and non-institutionalized retarded children. *Amer. J. ment. Defic.*, 1960, *64*, 845–861.

——, MANLEY, E. J., and NISSAN, Y. Reactions of community agencies and parents to services provided in a clinic for retarded children. *Amer. J. ment. Defic.*, 1961, *65*, 582–589.

——, ——, and SEELYE, BARBARA J. Factors associated with parental reaction to a clinic for retarded children. *Amer. J. ment. Defic.*, 1961, *65*, 590–594.

CAPOBIANCO, R. J., and KNOX, S. IQ estimates and the index of marital integration. *Amer. J. ment. Defic.*, 1964, *68*, 718–721.

CARLSON, BERNICE W., and GINGLEND, D. R. *Play activities for the retarded child*. New York: Abingdon Press, 1961.

CENTERWALL, S. A., and CENTERWALL, W. R. A study of children with mongolism reared in the home compared to those reared away from home. *Pediatrics*, 1960, *25*, 678–685.

CHAMBERLAIN, E. R. Maximizing treatment susceptibility during the diagnostic process. *Slow Learning Child*, 1963, *10*, 32–37.

CHAMBERLAIN, NAOMI, and MOSS, DOROTHY. *The three R's for the retarded (repetition, relaxation, and routine): A program for training the retarded child at home*. New York: National Association for Retarded Children, undated.

CIANCI, V. Home supervision of the mental deficient. *Amer. J. ment. Defic.*, 1947, *51*, 519–524.

——. A program for the home training of the mentally retarded. *Train. Sch. Bull.*, 1948, *45*, 63–68.

——. Home training for retarded children in New Jersey. *Train. Sch. Bull.*, 1951, *48*, 131–139.

————. Home training for the mentally retarded child. *Children*, 1955, *2*, 99–104.

————. Home training. *Amer. J. ment. Defic.*, 1956, *60*, 622–626.

CLARKE, C. A. *Genetics for the clinician*. Philadelphia: F. A. Davis, 1962.

COHEN, PAULINE C. The impact of the handicapped child on the family. *Soc. Casewk.*, 1962, *43*, 137–142.

COLEMAN, J. C. Group therapy with parents of mentally deficient children. *Amer. J. ment. Defic.*, 1953, *57*, 700–704.

COLLIE, M. Parents' reactions to diagnosis of mental retardation in their children. *Smith Coll. Stud. soc. Wk.*, 1943, *14*, 243–244.

COOK, J. J. Dimensional analysis of child-rearing attitudes of parents of handicapped children. *Amer. J. ment. Defic.*, 1963, *68*, 354–361.

COSTELLO, PATRICE M. The attitudes of parents of mentally retarded children toward the counseling they have received. Unpublished doctoral dissertation, Colorado State College, 1963.

COUGHLIN, ELLEN W. Parental attitudes toward handicapped children. *Children*, 1941, *6*, 41–45.

CUMMINGS, S. T., and STOCK, DOROTHY. Brief group therapy of mothers of retarded children outside of the specialty clinic setting. *Amer. J. ment. Defic.*, 1962, *66*, 739–748.

DALTON, JUANITA, and EPSTEIN, HELENE. Counseling parents of mildly retarded children. *Soc. Casewk.*, 1963, *44*, 523–530.

DANIELS, ADA M. Parent group education: Its meaning for parents of mentally retarded children. In The Training School, *Conference on psychological problems in the habilitation of the mentally retarded*. Vineland, N.J.: Author, 1962, 77–83.

DENHOFF, E. The impact of parents on the growth of exceptional children. *Except. Children*, 1960, *26*, 271–274.

DENO, EVELYN, HENZE, R., KRANTZ, G., and BARKLIND, K. *Retarded youth: their school-rehabilitation needs*. Minneapolis: Minneapolis Public Schools 1965.

DINGMAN, H. F., EYMAN, R. K., and WINDLE, C. D. An investigation of some child-rearing attitudes of mothers with retarded children. *Amer. J. ment. Defic.*, 1963, *67*, 899–908.

DISNER, EVELYN. Reporting to parents. *Amer. J. ment. Defic.*, 1956, *61*, 362–367.

DITTMAN, LAURA L. *The mentally retarded child at home: A manual for parents*. Washington, D.C.: U.S. Dept. of Health, Education, and Welfare, Children's Bureau Publication, No. 374, 1959.

————. The family of the child is an institution. *Amer J. ment. Defic.*, 1962, *66*, 759–765.

Dixon State School. *One hundred twenty-five low cost—no cost projects for home, school and hospital*. Dixon, Ill.: Author, undated.

DOLL, E. A. Counseling parents of severely mentally retarded children. *J. clin. Psychol.*, 1953, *9*, 114–117.

DORWARD, BARBARA. *Teaching aids and toys for handicapped children*. Washington: Council for Exceptional Children, 1960.

DOWNEY, K. J. Parental interest in the institutionalized, severely mentally retarded child. *Soc. Probl.*, 1963, *11*, 186–193.

DRAKE, M. E., and OBER, GRACE. Parental medical histories of mental retardates as compared and evaluated against newborn and hospitalization records. *Amer. J. ment. Defic.*, 1963, *67*, 688–690.

DRAYER, C., and SCHLESINGER, ELFRIEDE. The informing interview. *Amer. J. ment. Defic.*, 1960, *65*, 363–370.

DYBWAD, G. Group approaches and working with parents of the retarded: An overview. In *Challenges in mental retardation*. New York: Columbia University Press, 1964, 41–52.

EATON, J. W., and WEIL, R. J. *Culture and mental disorders: A comparative study of the Hutterites and other populations*. Glencoe, Ill.: Free Press, 1955.

EGG, MARIA. *When a child is different: A basic guide for parents and friends of mentally retarded children, giving practical suggestions on their education and training*. New York: John Day, 1964.

EHLERS, W. H. The moderately and severely retarded child: Maternal perceptions of retardation and subsequent seeking and using services rendered by a community agency. Doctoral Dissertation. Brandeis University, 1962.

————. The moderately and severely retarded child: Maternal perceptions of retardation and subsequent seeking and using services rendered by a community agency. *Amer. J. ment. Defic.*, 1964, *68*, 660–668.

ESTY, G. W. Emotional problems presented by handicapped children and their families. *Pa. Med. J.*, 1957, *60*, 721–727.

•EVANS, KATHLEEN, and CARTER, C. O. Care and disposal of mongolian defectives. *Lancet*, 1954, *2*, 960–963.

EWERT, JOSEPHINE C., and GREEN, M. W. Conditions associated with the mother's estimate of the ability of her retarded child. *Amer. J. ment. Defic.*, 1957, *62*, 521–533.

FARBER, B. Effects of a severely mentally retarded child on family integration. *Monogr. Soc. Res. Child Devlpm.*, 1959, *24*, No. 2.

————. Perceptions of crisis and related variables and the impact of a retarded child on the mother. *J. Hlth. hum. Behav.*, 1960, *1*, 108–118. (a)

————. Family organization in crisis: Maintenance of integration in families with a severely mentally retarded child. *Monogr. Soc. Res. Chld. Devlpm.*, 1960, *25*, No. 1. (b)

————. Interaction with retarded siblings and life goals of children. *Marriage and Fam. Living*, 1963, *25*, 96–98.

————, JENNE, W., and TOIGO, R. Family crisis and the decision to institutionalize the retarded child. *CEC Res. Monogr.*, 1960, No. 1.

FARRELL, M. The adverse effects of early institutionalization of mentally subnormal children. *Amer. J. Dis. Children*, 1956, *91*, 278–281.

————. What the institution expects of parents. *Amer. J. ment. Defic.*, 1957, *61*, 675–678.

FLIEGLER, L. A., and HEBELER, J. *A study of the structure of attitudes of parents of educable mentally retarded children and a study of a change in attitude structure*. U.S. Office of Education, Cooperative Research Project, Contract No. 018, SAW-7408, 1960.

FONT, MARION M. Parental reactions to psychologic measurement. *Amer. J. ment. Defic.* 1951, *56*, 48–51.

FRANK, J. P. *My son's story*. New York: Alfred A. Knopf, 1952.

FREDERICKS, MARILEE U. A comparative study of expressed parent attitudes: mothers of mentally retarded and orthopedically handicapped vs. mothers of non-handicapped children. Unpublished doctoral dissertation, University of Oregon, 1957.

FRENCH, ANNE C., LEVBARG, M., and MICHAL-SMITH, H. Parent counseling as a means of improving the performance of a mentally retarded boy: A case study presentation: *Amer. J. ment. Defic.*, 1953, *58*, 13–20.

FRIED, ANTOINETTE. Report of four years of work at the Guidance Clinic for Retarded Children, Essex County, N.J. *Amer. J. ment. Defic.*, 1955, *60*, 83–89.

GALIBOF, Z. Parent attitudes towards the services of a clinic for retarded children. New York: Columbia University (New York School of Social Work), 1951.

GALLAGHER, J. Rejecting parents? *Except. Children,* 1956, *22,* 273–276; 294.

GANT, SOPHIA. *One of those: The progress of a mongoloid child.* New York: Pageant, 1957.

GARDNER, W. I., and NISONGER, H. W. A manual on program development in mental retardation: guidelines for planning, development and coordination of programs for the mentally retarded at state and local levels. *Amer. J. ment. Defic. Monogr. Suppl.,* 1962, *66* (Whole No. 4).

GARFIELD, S. L., and HELPER, M. M. Parental attitudes and socio-economic status. *J. clin. Psychol.,* 1962, *18,* 171–175.

GIANNINI, MARGARET J., and GOODMAN, L. Counseling families during the crisis reaction to mongolism. *Amer. J. ment. Defic.,* 1963, *67,* 740–747.

GILIBERTY, F. R., and PORTER, E. LOUISE. Beginning of a home training program. *Amer. J. ment. Defic.,* 1954, *59,* 149–151.

GOODMAN, L. Continuing treatment of parents with congenitally defective infants. *Soc. Wk.,* 1964, *9* (1), 92–97.

————, and ROTHMAN, R. The development of a group counseling program in a clinic for retarded children. *Amer. J. ment. Defic.,* 1961, *65,* 789–795.

GORDON, E. W., and ULLMAN, M. Reactions of parents to problems of mental retardation in children. *Amer. J. ment. Defic.,* 1956, *61,* 158–163.

GOSHEN, C. E. Mental retardation and neurotic maternal attitudes. *Arch. gen. Psychiat.,* 1963, *9,* 168–174.

GRALIKER, BETTY V., FISHLER, KAROL, and KOCH, R. Teenage reaction to a mentally retarded sibling. *Amer. J. ment. Defic.,* 1962, *66,* 838–843.

————, KOCH, R., and HENDERSON, R. A. The study of factors influencing placement of retarded children in a state residential institution. *Amer. J. ment. Defic.,* 1965, *69,* 553–559

————. PARMELEE, A. H., and KOCH, R. Attitude study of parents of mentally retarded children: II. Initial reactions and concerns of parents to a diagnosis of mental retardation. *Pediatrics,* 1959, *24,* 819–821.

GRAMM, EDITH P. Peter beautiful: The story of an enchanted child. *Amer. J. ment. Defic.,* 1951, *56,* 271–274.

GRANT, D. K. Out of the shadows. *Amer. J. Dis. Children,* 1965, *110,* 2–3.

GRAYS, CAROL. At the bedside: The pattern of acceptance in parents of the retarded child. *Tomorrow's Nurse,* 1963, *4* (3), 30–34.

GREBLER, ANNE MARIE. Parental attitudes toward mentally retarded children. *Amer. J. ment. Defic.,* 1952, *56,* 475–483.

GREENBERG, H. A. Problems of parents of handicapped children. *Except. Children,* 1950, *17,* 1–7; 23–24.

Group for the Advancement of Psychiatry. *Basic considerations in mental retardation: A preliminary report.* New York: Author, 1959.

————. *Mental retardation: Family crisis—the therapeutic role of the physician.* New York: Author, 1963.

HANDLEMAN, N. I. Counseling parents of the mongoloid child. *Pediat. Clin. N. Amer.,* 1961, *8,* 207–211.

HARRIS, D. B., and SCHECTMAN, AUDREY. *A study of the modification of parental attitudes toward an understanding of mentally retarded children.* Duluth: Institute of Child Development and Welfare, University of Minnesota, 1959.

HASKELL, ELIZABETH N., WOODCOCK, DOROTHY L., STREETER, HELEN S., MORTON, MARY C., SMITH, N. S., and ERVIN, E. N. The first three years of a clinic for mentally retarded pre-school children. *J. Maine Med. Assn.,* 1961, *52,* 47–53.

HASTINGS, D. Some psychiatric problems of mental deficiency. *Amer. J. ment. Defic.,* 1948, *52,* 260–262.

HASTINGS, MARGUERITE. The social worker's role in helping families of mentally retarded children meet crisis points. In A multidisciplinary approach to the diagnosis and treatment of mental retardation. *Johnstone Bull.,* 1960, *2,* 58–63.

HAY, W. Mental retardation problems in different age groups. *Amer. J. ment. Defic.,* 1951, *55,* 191–197.

HEBELER, JEAN RUTH. A factor analysis of an attitude scale toward retardation with a population of parents of educable mentally handicapped children. Unpublished doctoral dissertation. Syracuse University, 1960.

HEILMAN, ANN E. Parental adjustment to the dull handicapped child. *Amer. J. ment. Defic.,* 1950, *54,* 556–562.

HERSH, A. Case work with parents of retarded children. *Soc. Wk.,* 1961, *6,* 61–66.

HERSHER, L. Home care of mongoloid children. *Pediatrics,* 1962, *30,* 1007–1008.

HOLT, K. S. Home care of severely retarded children. *Pediatrics,* 1958, *22,* 744–755. (a)

———. The influence of a retarded child upon family limitations. *J. ment. Defic. Res.,* 1958, *2,* 28–34. (b)

HOOD, O. E. *Your child or mine: The brain injured child and his hope.* New York: Harper, 1957.

HUNG, W., and HARITOS, N. P. The mongoloid newborn: Problems faced by the pediatrician and family. *Clin. Proc. Child. Hosp. (Wash.),* 1961, *17,* 31–42.

HORMUTH, R. P. Home problems and family care of the mongoloid child. *Quart. Rev. Pediat.,* 1953, *8,* 274–280.

Institute for Retarded Children of the Shield of David. *Program for preschool trainable retardates and their parents.* New York: Author, 1962.

JENSEN, R. A. The clinical management of the mentally retarded child and the parents. *Amer. J. Psychiat,* 1950, *106,* 830–833.

———. Counseling with parents at time of first knowledge of retardation. In *Woods School Proceedings,* Langhorne, Pa., 1958.

JOLLY, D. H. When should the seriously retarded infant be institutionalized? *Amer. J. ment. Defic.,* 1953, *57,* 632–636.

JORDAN, T. E. *The mentally retarded.* Columbus, Ohio: Charles E. Merrill, 1961.

JUNKER, KARIN S. *The child in the glass ball.* New York: Abingdon Press, 1964.

JUSTISON, GERTRUDE G. Parents in programs for the severely retarded. *Except. Children,* 1958, *25,* 99–100.

KAMINS, P. The communication of information from a state training school to parents of institutionalized mentally retarded children. Unpublished doctoral dissertation, University of Denver, 1963.

KANNER, L. The emotional quandaries of exceptional children. In *Woods School Proceedings,* Langhorne, Pa., 1952.

———. Parents' feelings about retarded children. *Amer. J. ment. Defic.,* 1953, *57,* 375–383.

———. Parent counseling. In J. Rothstein, *Mental retardation: Reading and resources.* New York: Holt, Rinehart and Winston, 1962.

KAPLAN, M. M., and HINGELEY, HAZEL. A study of the out-patient clinic services for the mentally retarded at the Muscatatuck State School. *Amer. J. ment. Defic.*, 1958, *63*, 517–523.

KATZ, A. H. *Parents of the handicapped: Self-organized parents' and relatives' groups for treatment of ill and handicapped children.* Springfield, Ill.: Charles C Thomas, 1961.

KELMAN, H. R. Parent guidance in a clinic for mentally retarded children. *J. soc. Wk.*, 1953, *34*, 441–447.

———. Some problems in casework with parents of mentally retarded children. *Amer. J. ment. Defic.*, 1957, *61*, 595–598.

KIRK, S. A., KARNES, M. B., and KIRK, WINIFRED D. *You and your retarded child: a manual for parents of retarded children.* New York: Macmillan, 1955.

KIRMAN, B. H. Mongolism: diagnosis and management at home. *Med. World (London)*, 1953, *78*, 258–265.

KLAUSNER, M. The attitudes of mothers toward institutionalized and non-institutionalized retarded children. Unpublished doctoral dissertation. New York University, 1961.

KLEBANOFF, L. B. Parents of schizophrenic children. I: Parental attitudes of mothers of schizophrenic, brain-injured and retarded and normal children. *Amer. J. Orthopsychiat.*, 1959, *29*, 445–454.

KOCH, R., GRALIKER, BETTY V., SANDS, R., and PARMELEE, A. H. Attitude study of parents with mentally retarded children: I. Evaluation of parental satisfaction with medical care of a retarded child. *Pediatrics*, 1959, *23*, 582–584.

KOEGLER, S. J. The management of the retarded child in practice. *Canad. Med. Ass. J.*, 1963, *89*, 1009–1014.

KOPEK, PAULINE E. A group experience with parents of mongoloid children. In The Report of Educational Program for Nurses in Region III of the Children's Bureau on Mental Retardation, May 1964, Winston-Salem, N.C., 167–173.

KOZIER, ADA. Case work with parents of children born with severe brain defects. *Soc. Casewk.*, 1957, *38*, 183–189.

KRAMM, ELIZABETH R. *Families of mongoloid children.* Washington, D.C.: U.S. Government Printing Office, 1963.

KUGEL, R. B., FEDGE, A., TREMBATH, J., and HEIN, H. Analysis of reasons for institutionalizing children with mongolism. *J. Pediat.*, 1964, *64*, 68–74.

———, and REQUE, D. A comparison of mongoloid children. *J.A.M.A.*, 1961, *175*, 959–961.

KURTZ, R. A. Implications of recent sociological research in mental retardation. *Amer. J. ment. Defic.*, 1964, *69*, 16–20.

———. Comparative evaluations of suspected retardates. *Amer. J. Dis. Children*, 1965, *109*, 58–65.

LEE, CARVEL. *Tender tyrant.* Minneapolis: Augsburg, 1961.

LEICHMAN, N. S. Parent attitudes in rearing the mentally retarded child. Paper read at American Psychological Association, Chicago, September, 1960.

———. *Parent attitudes in rearing mentally retarded children.* Sacramento, Calif.: State Dept. of Education, 1962. (Coop. Res. Project No. OE175, Contract No. SAE7146).

LEVY, J. H. A study of parent groups for handicapped children. *Except. Children*, 1952, *19*, 19–26.

LIPSETT, RENEE. Home care for the retarded. *Canada's ment. Hlth.*, 1964, *12* (3), 6–9.

LIVINGSTON, S. *Living with epileptic seizures.* Springfield, Ill.: Charles C. Thomas, 1963.

LLEWELLYN, EVA. Counseling with parents of handicapped children. *J. Med. Ass. Alabama*, 1962, *31*, 329–332.

LOGAN, HARRIET. My child is mentally retarded. *Nurs. Outlook*, 1962, *10*, 445–448.

LUND, A. F. The role of parents in helping each other. In *Woods School Proceedings*, Langhorne, Pa., 1958.

MCDERMOTT, ITA K. *Public health nursing in the mental retardation program.* New York: National League for Nursing, 1960.

MCDONALD, E. T. *Understand those feelings.* Pittsburgh: Stanwix House, 1962.

MCINTIRE, MATILDA S., and KIEKHAEKER, T. C. Parental reaction to a clinic for the evaluation of the mentally retarded. *Nebr. Med. J.*, 1963, *48*, 69–73.

MCNEILL, W. D. D. Developmental patterns of mongoloid children: A study of certain aspects of their growth and development. *Dissert. Abstr.*, 1955, *15*, 86–87.

MAGEE, CATHERINE F. *One of the family: A novel for young people.* New York: David McKay, 1964.

MAHONEY, S. C. Observations concerning counseling with parents of mentally retarded children. *Amer. J. ment. Defic.*, 1958, *63*, 81–86.

MANDELBAUM, A., and WHEELER, MARY ELLA. The meaning of a defective child to parents. *Soc. Casewk.*, 1960, *41*, 360–367.

MANN, ABBY. *A child is waiting.* New York: Popular Library, 1963.

MANN, VERA D. A study of the attitudes of mothers of cerebral palsied children toward child adjustment. Unpublished doctoral dissertation. American University, 1957.

MARTMER, E. E. (Ed.). *The child with a handicap.* Springfield, Ill.: Charles C Thomas, 1959.

MASON, L. F. Developing and maintaining good parental relationships. *Amer. J. ment. Defic.*, 1953, *57*, 394–396.

MEAD, MARGARET. *And keep your powder dry.* New York: William Morrow, 1942.

Mental Health Division, Dept. of National Health and Welfare. *The backward child.* Ottawa: Queen's Printer and Controller of Stationery, 1962. (Cat. No. H57-462.)

MICHAELS, J., and SCHUCMAN, HELEN. Observations on the psychodynamics of parents of retarded children. *Amer. J. ment. Defic.*, 1962, *66*, 568–573.

MILLER, ELSA A. Cerebral palsied children and their parents: A study in parent-child relationships. *Except. Children*, 1958, *24*, 298–302, 305.

Minnesota Department of Welfare. *Teach me: A guide for parents and others who have the care of retarded children.* St. Paul, 1945.

MOLLOY, JULIA S. *Teaching the retarded child to talk: a guide for parents and teachers.* New York: John Day, 1961.

MULLIGAN, L. H. Responsibility of parents in rearing a mentally deficient child. *Ky. Sch. J.*, 1941, *20* (4), 18–20.

MURRAY, DOROTHY G. *This is Stevie's story.* Elgin, Ill.: Brethren, 1956.

MURRAY, M. A. Needs of parents of mentally retarded children. *Amer. J. ment. Defic.*, 1959, *63*, 1078–1088.

NADAL, R. M. A counseling program for parents of severely retarded preschool children. *Soc. Casewk.*, 1961, *42*, 78–83.

National Association for Retarded Children. *Now they are grown: Information for parents of teen-age and young adult trainable retarded children.* New York: Author, 1959.

————. *NARC group life insurance plan: Extra protection for your child if you're not there.* New York: Author, 1960.

————. *What will happen to my child? Some suggestions for parents who are concerned with providing lifetime protection for a retarded son or daughter.* New York: Author, 1961.

————. *A survey and study of state institutions for the mentally retarded in the United States.* New York: Author, 1963.

NATT, J. Mental retardation. *Gen. Pract.,* 1954, *9* (5), 57–60.

NEAL, ELIZABETH. *One of those children.* New York: Taplinger, 1962.

OBER, GRACE G. Some aspects of legal guardianship for the adult mentally retarded. *Amer. J. ment. Defic.,* 1963, *68,* 15–23.

OBERMAN, J. W. The physician and parents of the retarded child. *Children,* 1963, *10,* 109–113.

OLSHANSKY, S. Chronic sorrow: A response to having a mentally defective child. *Soc. Casewk.,* 1962, *43,* 191–194.

————, JOHNSON, GERTRUDE C., and STERNFELD, L. Attitudes of some GP's toward institutionalizing mentally retarded children. In *Institutionalizing mentally retarded children: Attitudes of some physicians.* Washington, D.C.: U.S. Government Printing Office, 1964.

————, and KETTELL, MARJORIE. Attitudes of some interns and first-year residents toward the institutionalization of mentally retarded children. *Train. Sch. Bull.,* 1963, *59,* 116–120.

————, and SCHONFIELD, J. Institutionalization of pre-school retardates. *Ment. Retard.,* 1964, *2,* 109–115.

————, ————, and STERNFELD, L. Attitudes of some obstetricians toward mental retardation. *Obstet. & Gynec.,* 1962, *19,* 133–136.
retardation. *Obstet. & Gynec.,* 1962, *19,* 133–136.

————, and STERNFELD, L. Attitudes of some pediatricians toward the institutionalization of mentally retarded children. *Train. Sch. Bull.,* 1962, *59,* 67–73.

O'NEILL, JANE. Siblings of the retarded: II. Individual counseling. *Children,* 1965, *12,* 226–229.

OWENS, CHARLOTTE. Parents' reactions to defective babies. *Amer. J. Nurs.,* 1964, *64,* (11), 83–86.

OWNBY, R. The interpretative conference with parents of the mentally retarded child. In The Report of Educational Program for Nurses in Region III of the Children's Bureau on Mental Retardation, May 1964, Winston-Salem, N.C., 80–94.

Paediatric Society of the Southeast Metropolitan Region. *The needs of mentally handicapped children.* London: Milbrook Press, 1962.

PARRONS, MABEL H. A home economist in service of families with mental retardation. *Children,* 1960, *7,* 184–189.

PATTERSON, LETHA L. Some pointers for professionals. *Children,* 1956, *3,* 13–17.

PECK, J. R., and STEPHENS, WILL BETH. A study of the relationship between the attitudes and behavior of parents and that of their mentally defective child. *Amer. J. ment. Defic.,* 1960, *64,* 839–844.

PETERSEN, S. D. *Retarded children: God's children.* Philadelphia: Westminster Press, 1952.

PHELPS, W. M., HOPKINS, T. W., and COUSINS, R. *The cerebral-palsied child: A guide for parents.* New York: Simon and Schuster, 1958.

POPP, C. E., INGRAM, VIVIEN, and JORDAN, P. H. Helping parents understand their mentally handicapped child. *Amer. J. ment. Defic.,* 1954, *58,* 530–534.

President's Panel on Mental Retardation. *A proposed program for national action to combat mental retardation.* Washington, D.C.: U.S. Government Printing Office, 1962.

————. *Report of the task force on law.* Washington, D.C.: U.S. Government Printing Office, 1963.

PROBSTEIN, I., and KUSUDA, P. Use of group techniques in the pre-admission process. *Amer. J. ment. Defic.,* 1962, *67,* 227–231.

QUAYTMAN, W. The psychological capacities of mongoloid children in a community clinic. *Quart. Rev. Pediat.,* 1953, *8,* 255–267.

RANKIN, J. E. A group therapy experiment with mothers of mentally deficient children. *Amer. J. ment. Defic.,* 1957, *62,* 49–55.

REED, S. C. Genetic counselling. In *Woods School Proceedings,* Langhorne, Pa., 1958.

————. *Counseling in medical genetics.* (2nd ed.) Philadelphia: W. B. Saunders, 1963.

REILLY, W. N. Let the parent live again. *Amer. J. ment. Defic.,* 1942, *46,* 409–413.

RHEINGOLD, HARRIET L. Interpreting mental retardation to parents. *J. consult. Psychol.,* 1945, *9,* 142–148.

RICHARDS, B. W. Mental subnormality in the general hospital. *J. ment. Subnorm.,* 1964, *10,* 19–22.

ROBBINS, J. E. The home and family background of Ottawa Public School children in relation to their IQ's. *Canad. J. Psychol.,* 1948, *2,* 35–41.

ROBBINS, MARGARETTA. What parents expect the institution to do for their children. *Amer. J. ment. Defic.,* 1957, *61,* 672–674.

ROBERTS, J. A. *An introduction to medical genetics.* London: Oxford University Press, 1963.

ROCHE, TRESSA. A study of the impact on child-family relationships of group counseling of mothers of mentally retarded children. In *Maintaining the integrity of the individual, the family, and the community: A nursing responsibility.* New York: American Nurses' Association, 1964, 31–38.

ROGERS, DALE E. *Angel unaware.* Westwood, N. J.: Fleming H. Revell, 1953.

ROITH, A. I. The myth of parental attitudes. *J. ment. Subnorm.,* 1963, *9,* 51–54.

ROOS, P. Psychological counseling with parents of retarded children. *Ment. Retard.,* 1963, *1,* 345–350.

ROSEN, L. Selected aspects in the development of the mother's understanding of her mentally retarded child. *Amer. J. ment. Defic.,* 1955, *59,* 522–528.

ROSS, A. V. *The exceptional child in the family.* New York: Grune and Stratton, 1964.

RUBINSTEIN, J. H. Role of the diagnostic clinic in the care of the mentally retarded child. *Amer. J. ment. Defic.,* 1962, *66,* 544–550.

RUZICKA, W. J. The proposed role for the school psychologist: Counseling parents of mentally retarded children. *Amer. J. ment. Defic.,* 1958, *62,* 897–904.

RYCKMAN, D. B., and HENDERSON, R. A. The meaning of a retarded child for his parents: A focus for counselors. *Ment. Retard.,* 1965, *3* (4), 4–7.

SABAGH, G., DINGMAN, H. F., TARJAN, G., and WRIGHT, S. W. Social class and ethnic status of patients admitted to a state hospital for the retarded. *Pacif. sociol. Rev.,* 1959, *2,* 76–80.

SAENGER, G. *The adjustment of severely retarded adults in the community.* Albany: New York State Interdepartmental Health Resources Board, 1957.

————. *Factors influencing the institutionalizing of mentally retarded individuals in New York City: A study of the effect of services, personal* characteristics, and family background on the decision to institutionalize. Albany: Interdepartmental Health Resources Board, 1960.

SAMPSON, A. H. Developing and maintaining good relations with parents of mentally deficient children. *Amer. J. ment. Defic.*, 1947, *52*, 187–194.

SARASON, S. B. The psychology of the exceptional child. In Woods Schools, *Helping parents understand the exceptional child.* (Proceedings, annual spring conference), Langhorne, Pa.: Author, 1952.

———. *Psychological problems in mental deficiency.* (3rd ed.) New York: Harper, 1959.

SCHER, B. Help to parents: An integral part of service to the retarded child. *Amer. J. ment. Defic.*, 1955, *60*, 169–175.

SCHILD, SYLVIA. Counseling with parents of retarded children living at home. *Soc. Wk.*, 1964, *9*, 86–91.

———. Parents of children with phenylketonuria. *Children*, 1964, *11*, 92–96.

SCHIPPER, MARTHA T. The child with mongolism in the home. *Pediatrics*, 1959, *24*, 132–144.

SCHONELL, F. J., and RORKE, MEG. A second survey of the effects of a subnormal child on the family unit. *Amer. J. ment. Defic.*, 1960, *64*, 862–868.

———, and WATTS, B. H. A first survey of the effects of a subnormal child on the family unit. *Amer. J. ment. Defic.*, 1956, *61*, 210–219.

SCHREIBER, M., and FEELEY, M. Siblings of the retarded: I. The guided group experience. *Children*, 1965, *12*, 221–225.

SCHUCMAN, HELEN. Further observations on the psychodynamics of parents of retarded children. *Train Sch. Bull.*, 1963, *60*, 70–74.

SCHULMAN, J. L., and STERN, SHEILA. Parents' estimate of the intelligence of retarded children. *Amer. J. ment. Defic.*, 1959, *63*, 696–698.

SCHUMACHER, H. C. Contribution of the child guidance clinic to the problem of mental deficiency. *Amer. J. ment. Defic.*, 1945, *50*, 277–283.

———. A program for dealing with mental deficiency in children up to six years of age. *Amer. J. ment. Defic.*, 1946, *51*, 52–56.

SCOTT, FRANCES A. The appraisal of behavior of thirty mentally retarded children, their parents, and siblings. *Dissert. Abstr.*, 1960, *20*, 4312.

SHAW, MARGERY W. Genetic counseling. In M. Fishbein (Ed.), *Birth Defects.* Philadelphia: J. B. Lippincott, 1963, 311–318.

SHEIMO, S. L. Problems in helping parents of mentally defective and handicapped children. *Amer. J. ment. Defic.*, 1951, *56*, 42–47.

SHIPE, DOROTHY, and SHOTWELL, ANNA M. Effect of out-of-home care on mongoloid children: A continuation study. *Amer. J. ment. Defic.*, 1965, *69*, 649–652.

SHOTWELL, A. M., and SHIPE, D. Effect of out-of-home care on the intellectual and social development of mongoloid children. *Amer. J. ment. Defic.*, 1964, *68*, 693–699.

SLOBODY, L., and SCANLAN, J. Consequences of early institutionalization. *Amer. J. ment. Defic.*, 1959, *63*, 971–974.

SMITH, E. Emotional factors as revealed in the intake process with parents of defective children. *Amer. J. ment. Defic.*, 1952, *56*, 806–811.

SOLNIT, A. J., and STARK, MARY H. Mourning and the birth of a defective child. *Psychoanal. Stud. Child.*, 1961, *16*, 523–537.

SPOCK, B. *On being a parent—of a handicapped child.* Chicago: National Society for Crippled Children and Adults, 1961.

STANDIFER, FRANCES R. Pilot parent program: Parents helping parents. *Ment. Retard.*, 1964, *2*, 304–307.

STANG, FANNY. Parent guidance and the mentally retarded child. *Publ. Hlth.* (*London*), 1957, *71,* 234–236, 220.

STANLEY, R. J. A social survey of a long-stay hospital population. *J. ment. Subnorm.,* 1963, *9,* 63–69.

STEDMAN, D. J., and EICHORN, DOROTHY H. A comparison of the growth and development of institutionalized and home-reared mongoloids during infancy and early childhood. *Amer. J. ment. Defic.,* 1964, *69,* 391–401.

STERN, EDITH M. Problems of organizing parents' groups. *Amer. J. ment. Defic.,* 1951, *56,* 11–17.

STERNLICHT, M., and ALSTON, T. Evolution in group work with parents of retarded children and adolescents. Paper read at AAMD convention, Kansas City, 1964.

STEVENS, H. A. (Ed.). *The mentally retarded: Guide lines for determining need for residential care.* Madison, Wis.: Dept. of Public Welfare, 1963.

STODDARD, HILDA M. The relation of parental attitudes and achievements of severely mentally retarded children. *Amer. J. ment. Defic.,* 1959, *63,* 575–598.

STONE, MARGUERITE M. Parental attitudes to retardation. *Amer. J. ment. Defic.,* 1948, *53,* 363–372.

STONE, NELLIE D. Clinical team treatment of a mentally retarded child and his parents. Casework with the mother. *Amer. J. ment. Defic.,* 1959, *63,* 707–712.

———, and PARNICKY, J. J. Factors associated with parental decision to institutionalize mongoloid children. *Train. Sch. Bull.,* 1965, *61,* 163–172.

STOUT, LUCILLE. *I reclaimed my child.* Philadelphia: Chilton, 1959.

STRAUSS, M. A. Interaction with retarded siblings and life goals of children. *Marriage Fam. Living,* 1963, *25,* 96–98.

STUBBLEFIELD, H. W. Religion, parents and mental retardation. *Ment. Retard.,* 1965, *3* (4), 8–11.

TEITEL, S. The relationships between maternal child rearing attitudes, atypical behavior among mentally retarded children to levels of severity of amentia. Unpublished doctoral dissertation, Adelphi College, 1958.

TESKA, P. T. Some problems in the adjustment of the mentally handicapped. *J. consult. Psychol.,* 1947, *11,* 276–280.

THOMPSON, JANE H. A social study of mental subnormality. Part II: A special study of 50 cases of severe subnormality. *J. ment. Subnorm.,* 1964, *10,* 42–48.

THORNE, F. C., and ANDREWS, JEAN S. Unworthy parental attitudes toward mental defectives. *Amer. J. ment. Defic.,* 1946, *50,* 411–418.

THURSTON, J. R. A procedure for evaluating parental attitudes toward the handicapped. *Amer. J. ment. Defic.,* 1959, *64,* 148–155.

———. Counseling the parents of the severely handicapped. *Except. Children,* 1960, *26,* 351–354. (a)

———. Attitudes and emotional reactions of parents of institutionalized cerebral palsied retarded patients. *Amer. J. ment. Defic.,* 1960, *65,* 227–235. (b)

———. Counseling the parents of mentally retarded children. *Train. Sch. Bull.,* 1963, *60,* 113–117.

TIPS, R. L., and LYNCH, H. T. The impact of genetic counseling upon the family milieu. *JAMA,* 1962, *184,* 183–186.

———, MEYER, D. L., and PERKINS, A. L. The dynamics of genetic counseling. *Eugen. Quart.,* 1962, *9,* 237–240.

———, SMITH, G. S., PERKINS, AUDREE L., BERGMAN, ELIZABETH, and

MEYER, D. L. Genetic counseling problems associated with Trisomy 21 Down's disorder. *Amer. J. ment. Defic.,* 1963, *68,* 334–339.

TISZA, VERONICA B. Management of the parents of the chronically ill child *Amer. J. Orthopsychiat.,* 1962, *32,* 53–59.

TIZARD, J. *Community services for the mentally handicapped.* London: Oxford University Press, 1964.

————, and GRAD, JACQUELINE. *The mentally handicapped and their families: A social survey.* London: Oxford University Press, 1961.

TRIPLETT, JUNE L. A women's club for deprived mothers. *Nurs. Outlook,* 1965, *13,* 33–35.

TUDOR, R. B. What to tell parents of a retarded child. *J. Lancet,* 1959, *79,* 196–198.

U.S. Department of Health, Education and Welfare. *Preparation of mentally retarded youth for gainful employment.* Washington, D. C.: U.S. Government Printing Office, 1961.

————. *Feeding mentally retarded children: a guide for nurses working with families who have mentally retarded children.* Washington, D. C.: U.S. Government Printing Office, 1964.

VEEDER, B. Early home care or institution for the retarded child. *J. Pediat.,* 1953, *42,* 396–400.

WALKER, GALE H. Some considerations of parental reactions to institutionalization of defective children. *Amer. J. ment. Defic.,* 1949, *54,* 108–114.

WARDELL, WINIFRED. Case work with parents of mentally deficient children. *Amer. J. ment. Defic.,* 1947, *52,* 91–97.

WASKOWITZ, CHARLOTTE H. The parents of retarded children speak for themselves. *J. Pediat.,* 1959, *54,* 319–329.

WATERMAN, J. H. Psychogenic factors in parental acceptance of feebleminded children. *Dis. nerv. Syst.,* 1948, *9,* 184–187.

WEINGOLD, J. T. Parents' groups and the problem of mental retardation. *Amer. J. ment. Defic,* 1952, *56,* 484–492.

————. Discussion of paper by Dr. Joseph Wortis, towards the establishment of special clinics for retarded children. *Amer. J. ment. Defic.,* 1954, *58,* 479–480.

————. Parents counseling other parents. *Child. Limited,* 1963, *12,* No. 1, 2.

————, and HORMUTH, R. P. Group guidance of parents of mentally retarded children. *J. clin. Psychol.,* 1953, *9,* 118–124.

WEIR, H. R., and KELLEY, FRANCES. Management of the retarded child under three years of age. *Pediat. Clin. N. Amer.,* 1963, *10* (1), 53–66.

WERKMAN, S. L., WASHINGTON, J. A., and OBERMAN, J. W. Symposium: The physician and mongolism. *Clin. Proc. Child. Hosp. (Washington),* 1961, *17,* 42–49.

WHITE, B. L. Clinical team treatment of a mentally retarded child and his parents: group counseling and play observation. *Amer. J. ment. Defic.,* 1959, *63,* 713–723.

WILKINS, W. L. Information and emotional release in counseling of parents of exceptional children (summary of address). *Nat. Cath. Educ. Ass. Bull.,* 1956, *53,* 336–338.

WISHIK, S. M. The pediatrician's responsibility to handicapped children: A credo. *Pa. Med. J.,* 1957, *60,* 377–379.

WOLF, S., and LOURIE, R. S. The impact of the mentally defective child on the family unit. *J. Pediat.,* 1953, *42,* 521–524.

WOLFENSBERGER, W. Age variations in Vineland SQ scores for the four levels of adaptive behavior of the 1959 AAMD behavioral classification. *Amer. J. ment. Defic.,* 1962, *67,* 452–454.

————. Embarrassments in the diagnostic process. *Ment. Retard.*, 1965, *3* (3), 29–31. (a)

————. Diagnosis diagnosed. *J. ment. Subnorm.*, 1965, *11*, 62–70. (b)

WOLOSHIN, A. A., and WILLIAMS, RUTH. New concepts in treating mental retardation. *Ment. Hosp.*, 1964, *15*, 425–427.

World Health Organization. *The mentally subnormal child.* Geneva: Author, 1954.

WORTIS, J. Prevention of mental retardation. *Amer. J. Orthopsychiat.*, 1965, *35*, 886–895.

YANNET, H. Mental deficiency. *Advances Pediat.*, 1957, *8*, 217–257.

YATES, MARY L., and LEDERER, RUTH. Small, short-term group meetings with parents of children with mongolism. *Amer. J. ment. Defic.*, 1961, *65*, 467–472.

YEPSEN, L. N., and CIANCI, V. Home training for mentally deficient children in New Jersey. *Train. Sch. Bull.*, 1946, *43*, 21–26.

ZUK, G. H. Autistic distortion in parents of retarded children. *J. consult. Psychol.*, 1959, *23*, 171–176. (a)

————. Religious factor and role of guilt in parental acceptance of the retarded child. *Amer. J. ment. Defic.*, 1959, *64*, 139–147. (b)

————. Cultural dilemma and spiritual crisis of the family with a handicapped child. *Except. Children*, 1962, *28*, 405–408.

————, MILLER, R. L., BARTRAM, J. B., and KLING, F. Maternal acceptance of retarded children: a questionnaire study of attitudes and religious background. *Child Develpm.*, 1961, *32*, 525–540.

ZWERLING, I. Initial counseling of parents with mentally retarded children. *J. Pediat.*, 1954, *44*, 469–479.

Index